# A Guide to Review
## *General Science*

Give your students a powerful overview of science in their world!

The list below is a brief guide to key features of *General Science*. Page references to the student's textbook provide examples of these features.

► **Comprehensive, up-to-date science coverage** (pages vi-xvii), with emphasis on physical science and earth/space science, provides students with information they can use and apply throughout their lives.

► A **captivating writing style** (pages, 5, 173, 401) and **lively graphics** (pages 28, 106, 350) ignite student interest and enhance science instruction.

► **Practical applications** and **everyday examples of scientific principles** help students relate scientific concepts to their lives (pages 49, 226, 610).

► **Effective learning strategies** promote development of critical-thinking and science process skills.
  - Reading Critically (page 399)
  - Thinking Critically (page 399)
  - Writing Critically (page 475)
  - Investigation (page 410)
  - Skill Activity (page 317)
  - Questions within the text (pages 10, 33, 253)

► **Continual attention to the latest advances in science and technology,** integrated throughout the text and highlighted in special sections, helps students understand their rapidly changing world (pages 31, 395, 476).

► **Engaging special features** capture student interest and explore real-life applications of science.
  - Activity (page 26, 288, 446)
  - Science Fact (page 51, 445, 550)
  - Career (pages 299, 323)
  - Computer Application (page 406)

► **Consistent review strategies** monitor and reinforce understanding of science.
  - Section Review (page 312)
  - Chapter Review (page 165)
  - Skill Reinforcement (page 347)
  - Research Ideas (page 85)

The extensive **Reference Section** (pages 632–678) provides valuable resources to facilitate learning.

**HBJ** Harcourt Brace Jovanovich, Inc.
School Department

# GENERAL SCIENCE

## Brings science down to earth!

**Comprehensive coverage of life, earth, and physical sciences!**

# **G**ENERAL SCIENCE ignites student interest through lively graphics, a captivating writing style, practical activities, and everyday examples of scientific principles.

What is science? *Science* is a method of obtaining knowledge—knowledge of what things are made of and of how things work. With this knowledge, people have developed technologies to take them to the moon and to take their machines even further. This unit discusses how people can use scientific knowledge to make informed decisions on how technology affects their lives.

A striking illustration of the unit theme sparks excitement for learning.

T2

Sample pages are reduced. Actual sizes are 8″ × 10″.

Written in an engaging style that makes students want to read and understand, *General Science* uses everyday examples to illustrate facts and concepts.

A **Chapter Outline** previews content to build early interest.

**Section Objectives** focus attention on important lesson concepts and set motivating goals for reading.

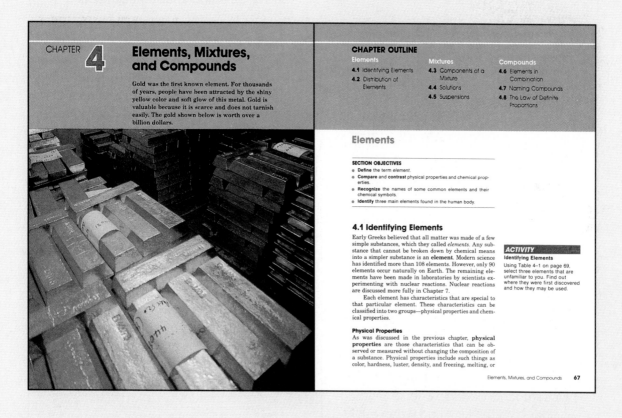

CHAPTER 4

## Elements, Mixtures, and Compounds

Gold was the first known element. For thousands of years, people have been attracted by the shiny yellow color and soft glow of this metal. Gold is valuable because it is scarce and does not tarnish easily. The gold shown below is worth over a billion dollars.

### CHAPTER OUTLINE

**Elements**

4.1 Identifying Elements
4.2 Distribution of Elements

**Mixtures**

4.3 Components of a Mixture
4.4 Solutions
4.5 Suspensions

**Compounds**

4.6 Elements in Combination
4.7 Naming Compounds
4.8 The Law of Definite Proportions

### Elements

#### SECTION OBJECTIVES

- **Define** the term *element*.
- **Compare** and **contrast** physical properties and chemical properties.
- **Recognize** the names of some common elements and their chemical symbols.
- **Identify** three main elements found in the human body.

#### 4.1 Identifying Elements

Early Greeks believed that all matter was made of a few simple substances, which they called *elements*. Any substance that cannot be broken down by chemical means into a simpler substance is an **element**. Modern science has identified more than 108 elements. However, only 90 elements occur naturally on Earth. The remaining elements have been made in laboratories by scientists experimenting with nuclear reactions. Nuclear reactions are discussed more fully in Chapter 7.

Each element has characteristics that are special to that particular element. These characteristics can be classified into two groups—physical properties and chemical properties.

#### Physical Properties

As was discussed in the previous chapter, **physical properties** are those characteristics that can be observed or measured without changing the composition of a substance. Physical properties include such things as color, hardness, luster, density, and freezing, melting, or

**ACTIVITY**

**Identifying Elements**
Using Table 4–1 on page 69, select three elements that are unfamiliar to you. Find out where they were first discovered and how they may be used.

Elements, Mixtures, and Compounds  **67**

Cross references throughout the program increase interest by emphasizing connections among the sciences.

To enhance learning, new science terms are boldfaced, phonetically respelled, and defined in context. In addition, the *Annotated Teacher's Edition* provides a complete list of new science terms at the beginning of each section.

# Effective learning strategies promote development of science process skills— and help students *learn to think.*

**Reading Critically** helps students analyze and understand chapter concepts.

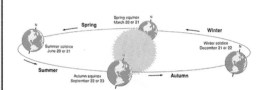

**Figure 15–10.** The earth's axis is tilted 23°28'. This tilt is one of the determining factors of the seasons. If the axis were perpendicular to the plane of the earth's orbit, there would be only one season.

When a hemisphere is tilted toward the sun, it is summer in that hemisphere. When a hemisphere is tilted away from the sun, it is winter in that hemisphere. When the two hemispheres are equally exposed to the sun, it is spring or fall.

The noonday sun is directly overhead at the latitude of 23°28'N during the northern summer solstice. The noonday sun is directly overhead at the latitude of 23°28'S during the southern summer solstice. These two latitudes are called, respectively, the **Tropic of Cancer** and the **Tropic of Capricorn.** The latitudes between the tropics of Cancer and Capricorn, including the equator, are called the *tropics.*

Figure 15–10 shows that north of latitude 66°32'N, there are 24 hours of daylight during the northern summer solstice. In this region, the sun never sets on that day. When the part of the earth north of latitude 66°32'N experiences 24 hours of daylight, the earth south of latitude 66°32'S has 24 hours of darkness. The latitudes of 66°32'N and 66°32' are called, respectively, the **Arctic Circle** and the **Antarctic Circle.** They are also called *polar circles.*

**READING CRITICALLY**
Why is the temperature at the equator higher than the temperature at the North Pole?

## Section Review

1. Describe two effects of the earth's rotation.
2. If it is 3 P.M. in New York City, what time is it in Denver?
3. Where in the Northern Hemisphere is the noonday sun directly overhead on the shortest day of the year?
4. THINKING CRITICALLY In order for a person in California to see the sun rise over the Pacific Ocean, how would the earth's rotation have to change?
5. THINKING CRITICALLY If the earth did not rotate, how long would a day be?

316    Chapter 15

A brief **Section Review** checks short-term learning. **Thinking Critically** requires students to draw conclusions about section content.

## Writing Critically

1. Compare and contrast the speed and abilities of supercomputers, mainframe computers, minicomputers, and microcomputers. Include in your comparisons some examples of what each type of computer is used for.
2. Many technological advances have made the development of the computer possible. Summarize these advances and the events

that led to them. Be sure to mention the names of the people responsible for these advances and the dates important scientific breakthroughs were made.
3. CHALLENGE Artificial intelligence is a very controversial issue. Make arguments for and against the use of this technology in computers.

## Skill Reinforcement

The Skill Activity on page 291 describes how to make a flowchart. Using the steps outlined in the activity, make a flowchart for the following problem. Imagine you are an editor. You have twenty-four weeks to edit a book that is 720 pages long. How many pages must you edit per

week in order to meet your deadline? (*Hint:* Work through the calculations yourself to make sure that what you would enter into the program is correct. Be sure to include a step in your program to check your calculations.)

## Research Ideas

1. Through the use of artificial walking technology, some people who are paralyzed below the waist have been able to walk again. Using computer-controlled electrical stimulation, Jerrold Petrofsky at Wright State University in Dayton, Ohio, has made great progress in enabling paralyzed people to walk again. Investigate Petrofsky's program and the progress he has made with paraplegics. Discuss other possible applications of his research in this area.
2. The next time you are in a shopping mall, notice the different ways in which computer technology is used. Make a list of all the

computers or computerized devices you find (not including those for sale in electronics or computer stores) and how they affect the way you shop.
3. CHALLENGE The idea of owning a personal household robot has fascinated people for years. What would you want your own robot to be able to do? What sources could you check to find out how to get a robot? If possible, contact a robot manufacturer to determine what kinds of robots or robotic devices they make and how much they cost. Discuss your findings with your classmates.

## For Further Reading

Baron, Naomi S. *Computer Languages: A Guide for the Perplexed.* New York: Doubleday, 1986. This book explains in simple English the basis for computer languages, what they are, how they evolved, and how they are still evolving.
Kassab, Vincent. *Apple IIe: BASIC Programming with Technical Applications.* Englewood Cliffs, NJ: Prentice-Hall, 1985. This book is a well-written guide for the beginning

programmer. Graphics sections are also included, as well as data base and inventory programs.
Schultzer, Daniel. *Artificial Intelligence: An Applications-oriented Approach.* New York: Van Nostrand Reinhold, 1987. This book discusses the ideas that make artificial intelligence possible and how they are being used with today's computer technology.

In the Chapter Review, **Writing Critically** helps students develop and strengthen higher-level thinking and writing skills. **Challenge** poses problems to stimulate thought and creativity.

A full-page **Investigation** in each chapter helps students develop laboratory skills as they learn science concepts. Step-by-step instructions and helpful illustrations clarify each investigation.

**Safety** symbols and boldfaced **Caution** statements are included—when necessary—to alert students to procedures that require special care.

Students discuss practical applications at the conclusion of each investigation.

## INVESTIGATION 8: Making a Blueprint

*How can you use a chemical reaction to make a blueprint?*

### PURPOSE
In this investigation you will make a blueprint. Blueprints can be used to show how a building is to be constructed. Blueprints are made by chemical reactions. This investigation shows that a chemical reaction using light can be used to record an image. Photography is another very common example of using a chemical reaction involving light to record an image.

### MATERIALS
2 beakers (100 or 250 mL)
4.0 g of potassium ferricyanide
5.0 g of iron(III) ammonium citrate
2 stirring rods
graduate (50 mL)
2 or 3 paper towels
1 piece notebook paper

### PROCEDURE
1. **CAUTION: Put on safety goggles, rubber gloves, and a laboratory apron.** Place the 4.0 g of potassium ferricyanide in a clean beaker. Add 25 mL of water. Stir gently until the potassium ferricyanide has dissolved. Set this beaker aside until step 3.
2. Place the 5.0 g of iron(III) ammonium citrate in another beaker. Add 25 mL of water. Stir gently until the iron(III) ammonium citrate has dissolved.
3. In a location away from direct lighting, such as in a closet or under a desk, add the solution made in step 2 to the solution made in step 1 above.
4. Using a paper towel, soak up some of the mixture made in step 3. Using the soaked paper towel as a brush, coat a piece of paper with the solution.
5. Place the coated piece of paper in a dark area, such as inside a desk drawer, until it is dry.
6. When the paper is dry, place the paper on a flat surface under the room lights. Place

one or more objects, such as coins or paper clips, on the paper. Leave the paper with the objects exposed to the light for about 5 minutes.
7. At the end of the 5 minutes, remove the objects from the paper. Wash the exposed paper with cool water to remove any left-over chemicals.
8. Wash your hands to remove any chemicals.
9. Set the paper aside to dry.

### RESULTS AND CONCLUSIONS
1. When the paper is dry, record your observations of the images produced. Attach your paper to your laboratory report.
2. How is the image on your blueprint helpful?
3. What is not shown by the image on your blueprint?
4. Why should you combine the two solutions in a location removed from direct light?

### APPLICATIONS
1. Why are blueprints sometimes used to show the construction plans of buildings?
2. What other techniques use chemicals and light to produce images?
3. Would it be possible to make an image of a glass object using the technique you just performed?

**164**   Chapter 8

**Skill Activity** develops and reinforces critical-thinking and process skills, such as interpreting data, inferring conclusions, reading for comprehension, making measurements, and using inductive and deductive reasoning.

## SKILL ACTIVITY    Reading for Comprehension

INTRODUCTION — Information is often presented by means of words and diagrams. Being able to use the two in combination is a skill that can help you more easily learn and remember certain information.

PROCEDURE —
1. Read the following information about ozone.
2. Study the diagrams shown below.

Ozone Buildup

Earth's Ozone Layer

Ozone Breakdown

Earth's Ozone Layer

CFC-11          CFC-12

Ozone is a form of oxygen that has three atoms in each molecule, compared with oxygen's two atoms in a molecule. It is constantly being built up and broken down in the atmosphere. The sharp odor of ozone can be noticed after a thunderstorm.

The process of building up and breaking down ozone plays almost like a computer game. Notice in the diagram how one "side" tries to destroy ozone and the other "side" tries to build it up. On one side, ultraviolet (UV) rays strike molecules of oxygen. The oxygen molecules break apart. Some of the stray oxygen atoms combine with others to form ozone.

The ozone molecules line up to form an ozone layer about 15 to 30 kilometers above the earth. This is a barrier that shields the earth from strong UV rays. The ozone layer protects living things on the earth by absorbing harmful UV rays.

On the other hand, the ozone layer is under constant attack by the chlorofluorocarbons, called CFC-11 and CFC-12. These are sent into the air by refrigerants in air conditioners and refrigerators. They are also present in insulation products.

UV rays break up CFC-11 and CFC-12 in the atmosphere and release chlorine atoms. These chlorine atoms react with other chemicals that cause the ozone to break down. Scientists fear that with a reduced ozone layer the earth may become a dangerous place for people to live.

APPLICATION —
1. Where does the energy needed to form ozone come from?
2. In what way is the ozone layer useful to living things on earth?
3. How could industry help to preserve the ozone layer?
4. What element in CFC-11 and CFC-12 is responsible for breaking down ozone?

The Atmosphere    **425**

Sample pages are reduced. Actual sizes are 8" × 10".

**T5**

# E
**ngaging special features** capture interest and help students understand the real-life applications of science.

---

on a string, the north pole of the magnet will point toward the earth's magnetic South Pole. The south pole of the magnet will point to the earth's magnetic north. Just as with negative and positive electric charges, like magnetic poles repel and unlike magnetic poles attract. In Figure 12–14, magnetic repulsion is being used to raise a train called a *MAGLEV* above the track. Instead of being supported by wheels, this train floats on a magnetic field, which reduces friction. The magnetic force is used to propel as well as to support the train.

**Magnetic Fields**

As you bring a compass near a magnet, the compass needle, which is also a magnet, will respond by moving. Depending on the location of the compass relative to the magnet, the compass needle will point in a definite direction. The compass needle lines up with the magnetic field. A magnet does not have to be touching something for its pull to be felt. A **magnetic field** is the area around a magnet in which the magnet is exerting a force. As you bring a compass near a magnet, the direction of the compass needle indicates the direction of the magnetic field at that point. How might a natural deposit of lodestone result in a person getting lost if he or she were using a compass?

A useful way to picture a magnetic field is by using *magnetic lines of force*. The magnetic fields of several different magnets can be mapped out by iron filings that line up along each magnet's lines of force. The lines of magnetic force are continuous; they do not begin at one pole and end at the opposite pole. The number of lines is greatest where the magnetic field is strongest.

### ACTIVITY
**Making a Magnet**
Align a steel nail parallel to the north-south direction. Using a hammer, tap the tip of the nail sharply a number of times. Now bring the nail near a compass or some iron filings. What happens? Why?

**Figure 12–14.** Shown here is an experimental magnetic levitation train (MAGLEV). This train has attained speeds of 640 km per hour.

### SCIENCE FACT
The world's largest magnet weighs 40 metric tons and is 65 m in diameter. It is used in a particle accelerator in a research laboratory outside of Moscow.

Electricity and Magnetism **253**

---

**Activity** provides a variety of hands-on and library experiences, as well as home activities. Students can perform many of these activities with a minimum of equipment, material, and teacher preparation.

**Science Fact** supplies fascinating information and little-known facts related to lesson topics.

---

The Neanderthals disappeared about 35,000 years ago. However, no one knows what caused their disappearance. At the time the Neanderthals disappeared, the Cro-Magnons (kroh MAG nuhnz) appeared. **Cro-Magnons** were the most direct ancestors of today's humans. They were intelligent people whose physical appearance was similar to ours. Cro-Magnons lived in large communities. They were accomplished in hunting and fishing. They also produced artwork such as cave paintings, stone carvings, and sculptures of bone and ivory.

### SCIENCE FACT
Cro-Magnons carved ivory fishhooks, among other tools. They carved the hooks with great care. In this way, they showed the desire and the ability to combine the necessary tools of survival with the human need to make the job pleasant.

**Section Review**

1. List two important hominid fossils and the scientists who discovered them.
2. Give three characteristics of Cro-Magnons.
3. Which early humans were the first to formally bury their dead and why is this fact important?
4. THINKING CRITICALLY Imagine that you are a paleontologist studying an ancient rock formation. You discover fossil bones that appear to be human. Among the bones you find charred remains of animals. What might you conclude about these early humans from their remains?

---

Questions throughout the text encourage students to think as they read.

Career explores a wide range of occupational opportunities in the sciences. Each feature includes a brief job description, training requirements, and an address for obtaining additional information.

---

### CAREER
**Animal Breeder**

**DESCRIPTION** An animal breeder breeds animals to help or change the animal's characteristics. For example, breeders have developed heavier beef cattle, cows that give more milk, and miniature pigs that can be used in laboratory experiments. Most animal breeders work for the federal and state governments and for colleges and universities.

**REQUIREMENTS** A student planning to be an animal breeder should take science and mathematics courses in high school. After graduation, the student needs to earn a bachelor's degree in agricultural science. Many positions in animal breeding are open only to applicants who have an advanced degree such as a master's or Ph.D.

**INFORMATION** Science and Education Higher Education Programs, U.S. Department of Agriculture, Administration Building, 14th Street and Independence Avenue S.W., Washington, DC 20250

Evolution and Natural Selection **539**

# Consistent review strategies monitor and reinforce understanding of science.

**Chapter Review** helps students confirm their understanding of content. Cross references facilitate location of key topics and science terms within the chapter.

A variety of questioning strategies—including modified true-false, completion, multiple choice, and essay—ensures effective review and reinforcement. Complete answers appear in the *Annotated Teacher's Edition*.

**Skill Reinforcement** reviews the process skill developed earlier in the chapter.

**Research Ideas** encourages extended investigation of scientific topics.

---

## CHAPTER 22 REVIEW

### Summary

1. Active continental margins have high, rocky coasts, while passive continental margins have low coastlines with broad beaches. **(22.1)**

2. The continental shelf is the land under water that forms a shelf along the edge of a continent. **(22.2)**

3. Deep-sea trenches trap sediment. The depth of oceans depends in part on the deep-sea trenches they contain. **(22.3)**

4. Salinity is the total amount of salts dissolved in a kilogram of sea water. **(22.4)**

5. The thermocline is a layer below the surface of the ocean through which temperature changes rapidly. **(22.4)**

6. Ocean currents are produced by wind or tides. **(22.5)**

7. A swell is a system of long waves traveling out of a storm center. **(22.6)**

8. Tides are produced by the gravitational attraction exerted on the earth by the moon and the sun. **(22.7)**

### Science Terms

On a separate sheet of paper, define each term in a sentence.

active continental margin (457)
continental shelf (459)
continental slope (459)
delta (458)
estuary (458)
neap tide (470)

ocean current (465)
oceanography (459)
passive continental margin (457)
rip current (467)
salinity (460)
sea wave (467)

spring tide (470)
swell (467)
thermocline (463)
tides (469)

### Modified True-False

On a separate sheet of paper, mark each true statement *TRUE* and each false statement *FALSE*. If false, change the underlined term to make the statement true.

1. Tsunamis are sea waves caused by earthquake motion on the sea floor.

2. Calcium chloride is the most abundant compound in sea water.

3. Active continental margins have high, rocky coastlines with intense wave action.

4. Surface sea ice is generally no thicker than 1 m.

5. Deep-sea sediment composed of clay and the shells of sea creatures is called red clay.

6. The thermocline is the layer between warm and cold water.

7. The transport of ocean water is called a tide.

8. In wave motion, the only thing that travels is the water.

9. The thickness of deep-sea sediment increases with distance from the crest of the mid-ocean ridge.

10. Winds transport 20 percent of the heat on Earth.
*(continues)*

The Oceans   **473**

---

### CHAPTER REVIEW

#### Multiple Choice

On a separate sheet of paper, write the letter of the term that best answers the question or completes the statement.

1. Two tidal crests circle the earth in
   a. 25 hours.       c. 24 hours,
   b. 23 hours,       50 minutes.
   50 minutes.        d. 24 hours.

2. Elements in sea water not found in fresh water are _____ and sodium.
   a. nitrogen        c. hydrogen
   b. oxygen          d. chlorine

3. Ocean areas where evaporation is low and the supply of fresh water is abundant have
   a. low salinity.       c. high salinity.
   b. average salinity.   d. no salinity.

4. The ocean functions as a temperature _____ for the entire globe.
   a. equalizer       c. releaser
   b. absorber        d. neutralizer

5. The freezing point of sea water is lower than that of
   a. brine.          c. chlorine.
   b. pure water.     d. mercury.

6. The layer between the warm water of the ocean surface and the colder water below is known as
   a. a delta.        c. a tsunami.
   b. ooze.           d. the thermocline.

7. The periodic motion of the sea surface is a
   a. current.        c. thermocline.
   b. tsunami.        d. wave.

8. One cause of _____ is the gravitational attraction the moon exerts on the earth.
   a. tides           c. waves
   b. tsunamis        d. currents

9. The spring tides are due to the alignment of the moon and
   a. the earth.      c. Mars.
   b. the sun.        d. Venus.

10. Neap tides occur when the moon and the sun are at _____ to each other as seen from Earth.
    a. 180°           c. 45°
    b. 60°            d. 90°

#### Completion

On a separate sheet of paper, complete each statement by supplying the correct term.

1. Shorelines are also known as _____ .

2. The study of the oceans is called _____ .

3. The _____ marks where the continental shelf drops off to the ocean floor.

4. Because the Pacific Ocean has many _____ , the floor of the Pacific is deeper than those of other oceans.

5. The total amount of salts dissolved in 1 kg of sea water is known as _____ .

6. When sea water freezes, the ice contains little or no _____ .

7. The movement of ocean water is a _____ .

8. The pressure of the atmosphere at s _____ is _____ .

9. A _____ consists of waves sever _____ dred meters in wavelength.

10. A _____ is a current of water flow along a channel perpendicular beach.

**474**   Chapter 22

---

### Writing Critically

1. How do different continental margins affect the appearance of the shorelines?

2. Describe how the amount of sediment and the depth of the oceans are affected by deep-sea trenches.

3. CHALLENGE Compare and contrast tsunamis, swells, and rip currents.

4. CHALLENGE Describe the special characteristics of sea water and explain how these characteristics determine the effects of sea water.

### Skill Reinforcement

The Skill Activity on page 464 describes how to interpret tables. Using the table in the activity, do the following problem.

If a diver is wearing an air tank holding 85 cubic feet of air and is breathing air at a rate of 2.4 cubic feet per minute at a depth of 99 feet, how long will the air last? Justify your answer.

### Research Ideas

1. Research the effect of plate tectonics on the appearance of a coastline.

2. Many communities along the Atlantic coast have constructed sea wall barriers to protect their beaches. In some cases the sea walls themselves have been washed away. Research the effect of sea walls on the shape of a coastline. Find out how effective sea walls are.

3. CHALLENGE Reseach and graph the height of daily tides on the shores of the Pacific coast and the Atlantic coast in the United States.

4. CHALLENGE Tsunamis have demonstrated their destructive power. Fortunately, today tsunamis can be detected and coastline communities can be warned. Find out what the evacuation procedures are in your area for high water levels such as flooding, hurricanes, or even tsunamis.

### For Further Reading

Ballard, R. D. "A Long Last Look at Titanic." *National Geographic* (December 1986) 170, 697. This article describes the exploration of the *Titanic*, using deep-sea submersibles such as Alvin.

Gilbreath, Alice. *The Continental Shelf: An Underwater Frontier*. Minneapolis: Dillon, 1986. This book provides an overview of the geology and ecology of the continental shelf. All the species living on the shelf are discussed.

Glaser, Michael. *The Nature of the Seashore*. Fiskdale, Mass.: Knickerbocker, 1986. The field-guide covers sand, wind, waves, and animal and plant life of the seashore.

Nelson, C. H., and K. R. Johnson. "Whales and Walruses as Tillers of the Sea Floor." *Scientific American* (February, 1987) 256:112. This article describes side-scan sonar studies of the Bering Sea that resulted in some surprising discoveries.

Sibbald, Jean H. *Homes in the Sea: From the Shore to the Deep*. Minneapolis: Dillon, 1985. This text describes the different ocean habitats and how organisms adapt to these environments.

The Oceans   **475**

**T7**

# C

**ontinual attention to the latest advances in science and technology, integrated throughout the program, helps students understand their rapidly changing world.**

## COMPUTER APPLICATION

### Element Names and Symbols Drill

**1. DESCRIPTION**

Elements are the building blocks for all objects. This program will help you remember the symbols and names of some common chemical elements.

**2. PROGRAM**

Input the following program. After it is completely input, key the computer to run the program. If the program does not run, check to make sure you have input correctly. If the program runs correctly, go on to steps 3 and 4.

**3. HELPFUL HINTS**

This program uses upper and lower case letters. Thus the symbol for Calcium is Ca and not CA. In this program the names of the elements are spelled with capital letters. Be sure there are no spaces at the end of a DATA line.

**4. GOING FURTHER**

Modify the program so that it will drill you on all the known elements.

```
10  DIM N$(41),S$(41)
12  FOR J = 1 TO 41
14  READ N$(J),S$(J)
16  NEXT J
18  PRINT  "DO YOU WANT TO TRY GIVING THE NAMES(N)"

20  INPUT "OR THE SYMBOLS(S) OF THE ELEMENTS? ";R$
22  LET RN = 40 * RND (1) + 1
24  IF R$ = "S" GOTO 28
26  IF R$ = "N" GOTO 40
28  PRINT "WHAT IS SYMBOL FOR ";N$(RN);".."

30  INPUT A$
32  IF A$ = S$(RN) THEN  PRINT "CORRECT": GOTO 22
34  IF A$ = "QUIT" THEN  END
36  IF A$ <  > S$(RN) THEN  PRINT "TRY AGAIN!"
38  GOTO 28

40  PRINT "WHAT IS NAME FOR ";S$(RN);".."
42  INPUT A$
44  IF A$ = N$(RN) THEN  PRINT "CORRECT": GOTO 22
46  IF A$ = "QUIT" THEN  END
48  IF A$ <  > N$(RN) THEN  PRINT "TRY AGAIN!"

50  GOTO 40
80  DATA ALUMINUM,Al,ANTIMONY,Sb,ARGON,Ar,BARIUM,Ba
82  DATA BERYLLIUM,Be,BISMUTH,Bi,BORON,B,BROMINE,Br
84  DATA CADMIUM,Cd,CALCIUM,Ca,CARBON,C,CHLORINE,Cl
86  DATA CHROMIUM,Cr,COBALT,Co,COPPER,Cu,FLUORINE,F

88  DATA GOLD,Au,HELIUM,He,HYDROGEN,H,MANGANESE,Mn
90  DATA KRYPTON,Kr,LEAD,Pb,LITHIUM,Li,MAGNESIUM,Mg
92  DATA IODINE,I,MERCURY,Hg,NEON,Ne,PLATINUM,Pt
94  DATA NITROGEN,N,OXYGEN,O,PHOSPHORUS,P,NICKEL,Ni
96  DATA POTASSIUM,K,RADIUM,Ra,SILICON,Si,SILVER,Ag
98  DATA SODIUM,Na,SULFUR,S,TIN,Sn,ZINC,Zn,IRON,Fe
```

Elements, Mixtures, and Compounds    **71**

Through **Computer Application,** students can enter and run computer programs related to unit topics. This unique feature includes step-by-step programming directions, as well as "Going Further," which challenges students to modify each program.

Conversion information in the *Annotated Teacher's Edition* explains how to make programs compatible with a variety of computers.

Sample pages are reduced. Actual sizes are 8" × 10".

## IS NEW YORK MOVING AWAY FROM LONDON?

Plates of the earth's crust drift slowly over the planet's surface. This movement is called *continental drift*. The movements amount to only centimeters a year. To measure this movement, scientists use lasers, satellites, and radio signals produced by stars.

### Mirrors in the Sky

A beach ball-sized satellite called Lageos (*Laser Geodynamic Satellite*) circles the earth in a high, stable orbit. Lageos is a silvery sphere covered with 426 mirrorlike devices that can reflect light beams directly back toward their sources. The satellite is part of a world-wide system used to measure the tiny changes in the positions of continents. The light Lageos is designed to reflect is laser light sent up from laser tracking stations around the world. Stations in Germany, Japan, and Australia send intense, pure pulses of laser light to Lageos. The laser pulses are transmitted all at the same time and are timed by atomic clocks. The satellite reflects them back, and the time required for a round trip is used to determine the distances between stations. The distances change over time as the sta-

tions move with the huge crustal plates on which they are located.

These measurements are more than just a subject of scientific interest. They help in the study of crustal movements that could have a serious effect on human activity. For example, although the Pa-

cific plate is sliding northwest past the North American plate at a rate of 5.6 cm each year, the San Andreas fault, which lies on the boundary between the plates, is moving only 3.5 cm per year. The difference causes rocks to bend and to break. The breaking of the rock, in turn, results in earthquakes.

Time-lapse photographs show the laser-ranging station at work.

### Signals from the Stars

Quasars are very distant stars that generate huge amounts of energy for their size. They produce radio signals. These radio signals are used in a technique known as Very *Long Baseline Interferometry*, or VLBI, to measure continental drift. Receiving stations at different locations measure the arrival times for the same signal. These data can then be used to determine the distance between stations.

### Navstar

VLBI is exact, but it also requires large, expensive, immobile radio telescopes. Earth scientists have recently started to use a new military satellite system, the Navstar GPS (*Global Positioning System*) to measure the distances between continents. Navstar

Navstar satellites (left) relay signals to radiotelescopes (right).

can take the place of a VLBI at a fraction of the cost and with far more mobility. The equipment is relatively inexpensive and extremely mobile. It can be carried in the back of a station wagon and set up virtually anywhere.

Orbiting Navstar satellites produce radio signals that serve as a navigational aid to pilots and ship captains. A satellite receiver can be used to fix latitude, longitude, and altitude within an error of 10 meters. However, earth scientists use the system by substituting the satellite signals for quasar signals. Using complicated surveying devices along with directional antennas, two temporary stations are placed at different locations. The antennas pick up the signal from one satellite and determine the distance between the sites.

Computer-generated pictures of the earth's plates show their movement.

Satellites, stars, and lasers are providing answers to questions about the earth's shifting crust. They reveal, for example, that the North American and Eurasian plates are moving apart at a rate of about 2 cm a year. Yes, New York is moving away from London.

414

Presented in a high-interest magazine format, **Science and Technology** relates new scientific discoveries and technological advances to the students' world.

Special chapters focus on the role of technology in modern medicine, the environment, the automobile industry, computers, and robotics.

# Helpful reference features facilitate learning.

Packed with helpful resources, the **Reference Section** includes information about:

- laboratory safety
- procedures for using laboratory equipment
- using mathematics in science
- metric and temperature conversions
- the five-kingdom classification of organisms

A comprehensive **Glossary** defines key terms, supplies phonetic respellings, and refers to the textbook page where each term first appears. A completely cross-referenced **Index** provides easy access to topics, skills, illustrations, tables, and special features.

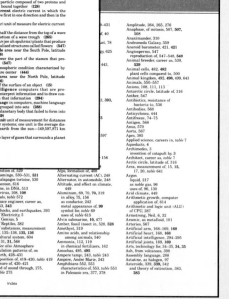

## Using Mathematics in Science

### Scientific Notation

Scientists must often work with very small or very large measurements. Scientists use a decimal system called **scientific notation** to work with these numbers. In scientific notation, all numbers are written with just one nonzero numeral before, or to the left of, the decimal point. The magnitude of numbers is indicated by a power of ten.

For example, the number 123.4 in scientific notation would be written $1.234 \times 10^2$. The first part of the number (1.234) is never smaller than 1.0 and never as large as 10.0. The number of digits indicates the number of significant figures that were recorded when the measurement was made. The second part of the number ($10^2$) is a power of ten. The ten never changes, and the small numeral written above and to the right of the 10 tells you how many spaces to the right or left you should move

the decimal point. This small numeral is called the *superscript*, or the *exponent*.

**Example:** Write the number six hundred forty-five and two-tenths in scientific notation.

**Solution:** · *Write* the number in decimal form.
645.2
· *Write* the decimal number so that there is only one nonzero digit to the left of the decimal point.
$645.2 \rightarrow 6.452$
· *Multiply* this number by the factor of ten needed to restore the decimal to the original number.
$6.452 \times 100 = 645.2$
· *Express* the factor of ten as a power of ten.
$6.452 \times 100 = 6.452 \times 10^2$

### SI Unit Prefixes

| Multiplication Factor | Prefix | Symbol | Pronunciation | Term |
|---|---|---|---|---|
| 1 000 000 000 000 000 000 = $10^{18}$ | exa | E | x uh | one quintillion |
| 1 000 000 000 000 000 = $10^{15}$ | peta | P | PENT uh | one quadrillion |
| 1 000 000 000 000 = $10^{12}$ | tera | T | TAIR uh | one trillion |
| 1 000 000 000 = $10^{9}$ | giga | G | JIHG uh | one billion |
| 1 000 000 = $10^{6}$ | mega | M | MEGH uh | one million |
| 1 000 = $10^{3}$ | kilo | k | KIHL uh | one thousand |
| 100 = $10^{2}$ | hecto | h | HEHK toh | one hundred |
| 10 = $10$ | deka | da | DEHK uh | ten |
| 0.1 = $10^{-1}$ | deci | d | DEHS uh | one tenth |
| 0.01 = $10^{-2}$ | centi | c | SEHN tuh | one hundredth |
| 0.001 = $10^{-3}$ | milli | m | MIHL uh | one thousandth |
| 0.000 001 = $10^{-6}$ | micro | u | MY kruh | one millionth |
| 0.000 000 001 = $10^{-9}$ | nano | n | NAN oh | one billionth |
| 0.000 000 000 001 = $10^{-12}$ | pico | p | PEEK oh | one trillionth |
| 0.000 000 000 000 001 = $10^{-15}$ | femto | f | FEHM toh | one quadrillionth |
| 0.000 000 000 000 000 001 = $10^{-18}$ | atto | a | AT oh | one quintillionth |

Using Mathematics in Science **639**

(phonetic respelling pronunciation key)

| | | |
|---|---|---|
| ski | ee (dee) | u pgle oo (myool) |
| ten | ee (skee) | zh treasure zh (trew uh) |
| ripe | ur (fum) | a medal uh (mehd uhl) |
| ... | ... | ... |

## A

**abiotic** those components of an ecosystem that are nonliving **(587)**

**absorption** movement of nutrient molecules through a membrane **(489)**

**acceleration** rate at which the velocity of an object changes **(175)**

**acceleration due to gravity** rate at which the velocity of an object changes due to the pull of gravity; on Earth $9.8 \text{ m/s}^2$ **(181)**

**acid** any electrolyte that releases hydrogen ions ($H^+$) in solution **(112)**

**active continental margin** shoreline located along a boundary where two plates of the earth collide, characterized by high cliffs dropping to small beaches **(457)**

**activity** measurement of the rate of nuclear disintegration, made by monitoring of the amount of radiation released **(133)**

**adaptations** changes in body parts or in behavior that better enable an organism to survive in its environment **(529)**

**air mass** large body of air with uniform temperature and humidity **(442)**

**algae** protists that contain chlorophyll and are therefore able to make their own food **(406)**

**alkali** (AL kuh ly) **metals** five elements having only one valence electron: lithium, sodium, potassium, rubidium, and cesium; categorized as Family 1 on the periodic table **(96)**

**alloy** mixture of two or more metals, or of a metal and a nonmetal **(155)**

**alpha particle** particle composed of two protons and two neutrons bound together **(128)**

**alternating current** electric current in which the electrons move first in one direction and then in the other **(248)**

**ampere** (AM pihr) unit of measure for electric current **(243)**

**amplitude** one half the distance from the top of a wave crest to the bottom of a wave trough **(265)**

**angiosperms** (AN jee oh spuhrmz) plants that produce seeds in specialized structures called flowers **(547)**

**Antarctic Circle** area near the South Pole, latitude $66°32'$ S **(316)**

**anther** on a flower the part of the stamen that produces pollen **(547)**

**anticyclone** atmospheric condition characterized by a high-pressure center **(444)**

**Arctic Circle** area near the North Pole, latitude $66°32'$ N **(316)**

**area** measure of the surface of an object **(15)**

**artificial intelligence** computers that are programmed to interpret information and to draw conclusions from that information **(294)**

**assembly language** computers, machine language instructions grouped into sets **(288)**

**asteroid** small planetary body that failed to form into a planet **(339)**

**astronomical unit** unit of measurement for distances between solar systems; one unit is the average distance of the earth from the sun—149,597,871 km **(335)**

**atmosphere** the layer of gases that surrounds a planet **(419)**

**644** Glossary

definition of, 529
of flamingo, 530–531, **531**
of Galapagos tortoise, 530
of raccoon, 616
Adenine, in DNA, 513
Adenovirus, 108, **108**
Adrenals, table 572
Aerospace engineer, career as, 343, **343**
Aftershocks, and earthquakes, 393
Age of Electricity, 5
Age of Genius, 5
Age of Reptiles, 382
Age of substances, measurement of, 135–136, **135**, **136**
Agricultural system, 604
AIDS, 31, **31**, 568
Air. *See also* Atmosphere
circulation patterns of, on earth, 428–431
composition of, 419–420, table 419
pressure of, 420–421
speed of sound through, 275, table 275

Alps, formation of, 408
Alternating current (AC), 248
Alternator, in automobile, 248
Altitude, and effect on climate, 449
Aluminum, 69, 70, 319
in alloy, 75, 156
as conductor, 242
metal appearance of, **99**
symbol for, table 69
uses of, table 615
Alvin submarine, **10**, 477
Amber, fossil insect in, 528, **528**
Amethyst, 319
Amino acids, and relationship among animals, 540
Ammonia, 112, 119
in chemical fertilizers, 162
Amoebas, 495, **495**
Ampere (amp), 243, table 243
Ampère, André Marie, 243
Amphibians 552, 553
characteristics of, 553, table 553
in Paleozoic era, 377, 378

Amplitude, 264, 265, 276
Anaphase, of mitosis, 507, **507**, 508
Anaximander, 310
Andromeda Galaxy, 359
Aneroid barometer, 421, **421**
Angiosperms, 547
reproduction of, 547–548, **548**
Animal breeder, career as, 539, **539**
Animal cells, 482, **482**
plant cells compared to, 500
Animal kingdom, 492, **498**, 499, 643
Anions, 108, 111, 113
Antarctic circle, latitude of, 316
Anther, 547
Antibiotics, resistance of bacteria to, 536
Antibodies, 568
Anticyclones, 444
Antifreeze, 74–75
Antigen, 568
Anus, 570
Aorta, 567
Apes, 385
Applied science, careers in, table 7
Aqueducts, 4
Archimedes, 3
invention of catapult by, 3
Architect, career as, table 7
Arctic circle, latitude of, 316
Area, measurement of, 15, **15**, 17, 20, table 641
Argon
liquid, 217
as noble gas, 96
uses of, 96, 130
Arid climate, 449
Arithmetic growth, computer application of, 614
Arithmetic and logic unit (ALU) of CPU, 287
Armstrong, Neil, 6, 32
Arsenic, as metalloid, 101
Arteries, 567
Artificial arm, 168–169, **168**
Artificial heart, 168, **168**
Artificial intelligence, 294–295
Artificial joints, 169, **169**
Arts, technology for, 34–35, **34**, **35**
Asbestos, as halogen, 97
Ash, from volcanoes, 398
Assembly language, 398
Astatine, as halogen, 97
Asteroids, 339, **339**, 342
and theory of extinction, 383, **383**

**656** Index

T10

Sample pages are reduced.
Actual sizes are 8" × 10".

# **M**ore than 650 photographs, illustrations, tables, and graphs promote comprehension and enhance science instruction.

Brilliant full-color **photography** sparks interest and helps students relate scientific concepts to real life.

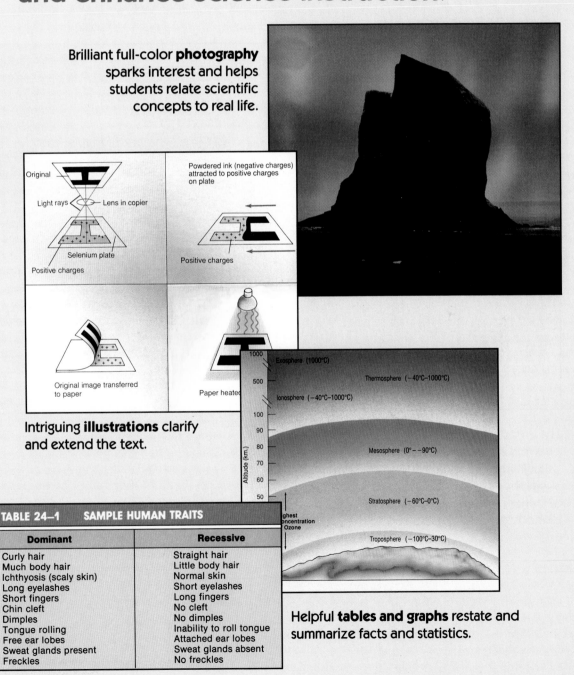

Intriguing **illustrations** clarify and extend the text.

Original

Light rays — Lens in copier

Selenium plate

Positive charges

Powdered ink (negative charges) attracted to positive charges on plate

Positive charges

Original image transferred to paper

Paper heated

Exosphere (1000°C)

Thermosphere (−40°C–1000°C)

Ionosphere (−40°C–1000°C)

Mesosphere (0°– −90°C)

Altitude (km.)

Stratosphere (−60°C–0°C)

Highest concentration Ozone

Troposphere (−100°C–30°C)

| TABLE 24–1 | SAMPLE HUMAN TRAITS |
|---|---|
| **Dominant** | **Recessive** |
| Curly hair | Straight hair |
| Much body hair | Little body hair |
| Ichthyosis (scaly skin) | Normal skin |
| Long eyelashes | Short eyelashes |
| Short fingers | Long fingers |
| Chin cleft | No cleft |
| Dimples | No dimples |
| Tongue rolling | Inability to roll tongue |
| Free ear lobes | Attached ear lobes |
| Sweat glands present | Sweat glands absent |
| Freckles | No freckles |

Helpful **tables and graphs** restate and summarize facts and statistics.

# GENERAL SCIENCE provides all the resources teachers want for successful instruction.

Deaths plus emigration is greater than births plus immigration.

**Figure 28-6.** The snake in these photographs is a limiting factor on the bird population.

Call your city or county government and get population figures for your area for the last two decades. Using the figures, construct a graph on population changes in your area. How can you determine how much change is from immigration or from emigration? Challenge students to find out. (The number of births and deaths each year are recorded in city and county records.)

**Figure 28-7.** Limiting factors vary from population to population. However, the environmental resistance is fairly constant from population to population.

Add some liquid plant food to a 1-L glass jar. Set up another jar as a control. Add 750 mL of tap water and 100 mL of pond or puddle water to each jar. Have students make daily observations of the changes in each jar.

**592**  Chapter 28

The largest population that an ecosystem can support is called its *carrying capacity.*

immigration are larger than deaths plus emigration, population size increases. What relationship among these factors would cause population size to decrease?

All organisms have the potential to produce offspring. A population's **biotic potential** is its ability to grow in an environment and to reproduce itself without any limits. For example, if bacteria were allowed to reproduce to their full biotic potential, they would cover the earth in a few weeks. A single pair of houseflies could produce almost 30 million offspring in just two months. A single pair of elephants would have over 19 million descendants after 750 years.

Fortunately, the earth is not covered with bacteria, houseflies, or elephants. Certain factors limit the biotic potential of organisms. Common **limiting factors** are space, weather, food, predation, and disease. For populations that live in water, the water temperature and the amount of dissolved oxygen are also important limiting factors.

In most cases, more than one limiting factor keeps a population from growing too large. The sum of all the limiting factors is the **environmental resistance.** Figure 28-7 shows the relationship between biotic potential and environmental resistance. The illustration shows the population growing slowly but then starting to increase very rapidly. When the population reaches a certain level, environmental resistance begins to prevent the population from increasing any more.

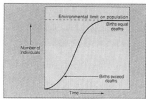

**Changes in Communities**

As populations grow and change, so do the communities of which they are a part. The change in ecological communities over time is called **succession.** There are two kinds of succession, primary and secondary.

In *primary succession,* communities are established on newly formed areas of the earth. These new areas include recent lava flows, rocky outcrops on mountains, and areas such as sand dunes where wind or water has recently deposited sand or clay. *Secondary succession* takes place on land that once supported a community that was later disturbed or destroyed. Vacant lots, roadsides, and old farmland are examples of places where secondary succession occurs.

**Figure 28-8.** The barn and trees shown on the left are an example of secondary succession. The clear lake above is an example of primary succession.

A stable community that is no longer undergoing succession is called a **climax community.** Climax communities cycle the energy and nutrients in a particular environment. Once established, climax communities may not change for hundreds of years. However, natural disasters such as wildfires or hurricanes may disturb the community. Over long periods of time, the climax community will be restored.

**Section Review**

1. List three abiotic components of ecosystems.
2. Give an example of a biotic component and an abiotic component interacting with each other in an ecosystem.
3. Define the terms ecosystem, population, and community. Explain how each is organized.
4. Define and give an example of primary succession.
5. THINKING CRITICALLY Describe how primary succession can eventually result in a climax community.

1. moisture, sunlight, and soil
2. Answers will vary. One example would be plants decaying and thereby fertilizing the soil, and the soil providing plants nutrients for growth.
3. ecosystem: a group of living and nonliving things interacting over time; population: group of organisms of a single species living in a certain area; community: all living organisms in an ecosystem
4. Primary succession is communities becoming established on a new area of the earth. Answers will vary but one example is plants beginning to grow on a recent lava flow.
5. Over time the primary growth may be supplanted by a secondary growth until no new changes take place.

Ecology  **593**

The *Annotated Teacher's Edition* includes answers at point of use, as well as background information and teaching suggestions. It also provides motivating activities, additional background, and demonstrations for each section.

The valuable *Teacher's ResourceBank*™ contains the *Teacher's Resource Book*, conveniently organized in a three-ring binder with divider tabs. The *Teacher's Resource Book* includes a wide variety of copying masters with answer keys:

- Investigations and Alternate Investigations

- Worksheets for Skill Activities, Critical Thinking, and Cross-Discipline Activities

- Student Record Sheets for textbook Investigations and Skill Activities

- Science Project Sheets

- Tests, including a Midterm Examination and a Final Examination

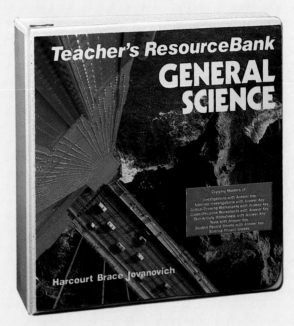

In addition, helpful ancillaries include:

- *Laboratory Manual/Workbook*

- *Annotated Teacher's Edition, Laboratory Manual/Workbook*

- *Overhead Transparencies* with accompanying copying masters

- *General Science Test Bank* (for Apple® IIe or IIc microcomputers)

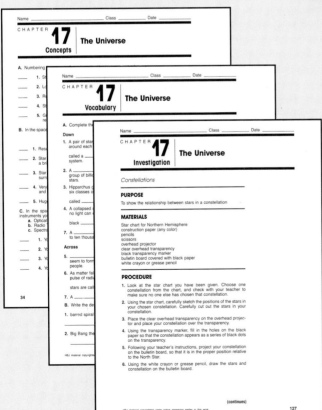

Apple® is the registered trademark of Apple Computer, Inc.

# GENERAL SCIENCE

**Patricia A. Watkins**
Science Curriculum Specialist
  and former Science Teacher
Northside Independent School District
Instructor, Department of Education
Trinity University
San Antonio, Texas

**Cesare Emiliani**
Chairperson, Department of Geology
Professor of Geological Sciences
University of Miami
Coral Gables, Florida

**Christopher J. Chiaverina**
Physics Teacher
Barrington High School
Barrington, Illinois

**Christopher T. Harper**
Instructor in Science
Phillips Exeter Academy
Exeter, New Hampshire

**David E. LaHart**
Senior Instructor
Florida Solar Energy Center
Cape Canaveral, Florida

**HBJ**

**Harcourt Brace Jovanovich, Publishers**
Orlando   San Diego   Chicago   Dallas

## AUTHORS

### Patricia A. Watkins
Ms. Watkins is an Instructor in the Department of Education at Trinity University in San Antonio, Texas, and is completing her dissertation for an Ed.D. in Instructional Management from Texas A & M University. Ms. Watkins has served as an Associate Principal of the Health Careers High School in San Antonio and as Special Education Coordinator for the Northside Independent School District, also in San Antonio. She has authored a biology textbook, has written other life science materials, and has taught general science, biology, physical science, and special education for over 20 years.

### Cesare Emiliani
Dr. Emiliani earned a D.Sc. in Geology from the University of Bologna and a Ph.D. in Geology from the University of Chicago. Since 1968, he has been Chairperson of Geological Sciences at the University of Miami. In addition, he has been Director of the Marine Science/Marine Affairs Program at the University of Miami since 1978. Dr. Emiliani is the editor of a Wiley-Interscience book on Marine Geology, has been a contributor to the *McGraw-Hill Encyclopedia of Science and Technology,* and is the author of more than 100 technical papers in the geological sciences. Dr. Emiliani is a Fellow of the American Geophysical Union and a Fellow of the American Association for the Advancement of Science, and has received the Swedish Gold Vega Medal for achievement in Geophysical Sciences.

### Christopher J. Chiaverina
Mr. Chiaverina holds an M.S. Ed. in physics from Northern Illinois University and has taught physics on the secondary level for over nineteen years. He is cofounder of The Science Place, a science museum at Barrington High School in Illinois. As an adjunct faculty member of the National College of Education, he conducts science workshops for teachers. In addition, Mr. Chiaverina has served on the editorial board of *The Physics Teacher.*

### Christopher T. Harper
Dr. Harper earned a Ph.D. in geochemistry from Oxford University. He is presently an Instructor of Science at Phillips Exeter Academy in New Hampshire. He has taught general science, earth science, physics, and chemistry on the secondary level in the United States. Dr. Harper also taught secondary science in New Zealand for eight years. Prior to his teaching in New Zealand, Dr. Harper was an associate professor of geochemistry at Florida State University.

### David E. LaHart
Dr. LaHart earned a Ph.D. in Science and Human Affairs from Florida State University. He is currently Senior Instructor at the Florida Solar Energy Center, Cape Canaveral, where he conducts teacher-training. Previously, Dr. LaHart was a consultant with the Florida Department of Education, Office of Environmental Education. Dr. LaHart earned a Bachelor's degree from Cornell University and a Master's degree in Wildlife Ecology from the University of Florida.

# Acknowledgments

## SENIOR EDITORIAL ADVISORS

**Lowell J. Bethel, Ed.D.**
Associate Professor of Science Education
Science Education Center
University of Texas at Austin
Austin, Texas

**Charles N. Kish**
General Science Teacher
Saratoga Springs
    Junior High School
Saratoga Springs, New York

## CONTENT SPECIALISTS

**Myrdene Anderson, Ph.D.**
Associate Professor,
    Department of Sociology
    and Anthropology
Purdue University
West Lafayette, Indiana

**Lorella M. Jones, Ph.D.**
Professor, Department of Physics
University of Illinois
    at Urbana-Champaign
Urbana, Illinois

**Willis J. Morrissey**
Vice President and Technical
    Director
Rio Grande Robotics
Las Cruces, New Mexico

**Lt. Colonel James Stith, D.Ed.**
Associate Professor of Physics
United States Military Academy
West Point, New York

**Joan Selverstone
    Valentine, Ph.D.**
Professor, Department of
    Chemistry and Biochemistry
University of California,
    Los Angeles
Los Angeles, California

**Tommy Elmer Wynn, Ph.D.**
Associate Professor,
    Department of Botany
North Carolina State University
Raleigh, North Carolina

## CURRICULUM SPECIALISTS

**Mildred B. Blow**
General Science Teacher
Southwest High School
St. Louis Public Schools
St. Louis, Missouri

**James J. Dolak**
Science Curriculum Subject
    Specialist
Youngstown Public Schools
Youngstown, Ohio

**Carl C. Duzen**
Physics Teacher and
    Computer Science
    Specialist
Lower Merion High School
Ardmore, Pennsylvania

**Dianne I. Hillman**
Earth Science Teacher
Cherokee High School
Lenape Regional High School
    District
Marlton, New Jersey

**Jim Nelson**
Presidential Award for
    Excellence in Science Teaching
Chemistry, Computer Science,
    and Physics Teacher
Harriton High School
Rosemont, Pennsylvania

**Joyce Pinkston**
Science Curriculum Coordinator
Memphis City Schools
Memphis, Tennessee

**Richard Russo**
Science Coordinator
Montvale School System
Montvale, New Jersey

**Ethel L. Schultz**
Program Administrator
    for K-12 Science
Marblehead Public Schools
Marblehead, Massachusetts

**Stanley Shimer, Ed.D.**
Science Educator
Science Consulting and
    Supervisor Inservice Training
Science Teaching Center
Indiana State University
Terre Haute, Indiana

**Rajee Thyagarajan**
Physics Teacher
Health Careers High School
San Antonio, Texas

## READING SPECIALIST

**Irene M. Reiter, Ph.D.**
English Department Head
Northeast High School
Philadelphia, Pennsylvania

# Contents

## Using Ancillary Materials

A complete program of supplementary materials accompanies **GENERAL SCIENCE.** The consumable **Laboratory Manual/Workbook** includes one *Investigation* keyed to each chapter of the textbook. The *Investigations* are designed to help students apply textbook concepts to everyday experiences. The **Laboratory Manual/Workbook** also includes two worksheets per chapter —one designed to review vocabulary and one designed to review concepts. The **Annotated Teacher's Edition** for the **Laboratory Manual/Workbook** contains overprinted answers to all questions, directions for preparing materials, and a complete materials list.

The **Teacher's Resource Book** is a three-hole-punched and perforated book containing over 500 blackline copying masters. This resource contains the 29 *Investigations* included in the **Laboratory Manual/Workbook** plus an additional 29 *Alternate Investigations.* The *Alternate Investigations* provide additional opportunities for laboratory experience. Also included in the **Teacher's Resource Book** are 29 *Critical-Thinking Worksheets,* 29 *Cross-Discipline Worksheets,* and 29 *Skill-Activity Worksheets.* The **Teacher's Resource Book** also contains a complete testing program consisting of chapter *Tests,* a *Midterm Examination,* and a *Final Examination.* The *Science Project Sheets* contained in the **Teacher's Resource Book** describe how to do a science project in a step-by-step manner, from formulating an idea to constructing the final display. Finally, the **Teacher's Resource Book** also contains 58 *Student Record Sheets* that parallel textbook *Skill Activities* and *Investigations.* These sheets provide students with a standardized format on which to write their responses to questions found in the *Skill Activities* and *Investigations.*

The **Teacher's ResourceBank**™ is a convenient three-ring, tabbed binder that is designed to hold and organize the entire contents of the **Teacher's Resource Book.**

Also available is **Overhead Transparencies,** a separately boxed set of 28 four-color *Overhead Transparencies* and 28 black-line *Overhead Transparency Illustrations.* The *Overhead Transparency Illustrations* are in a copying-master format and are designed for use as instructional or evaluative tools. As such, the labels found on the four-color *Transparencies* have been replaced with numbers on the illustrations.

A separate **Computer Test Bank** provides a complete testing program compatible with the Apple IIe® and IIc®. This test bank will enable teachers to test precisely the content they want by choosing questions from a comprehensive bank of test items or by adding their own questions.

## Scheduling

Each teaching situation is unique. Therefore, each individual teacher is the most appropriate person to determine the best schedule for his or her general science course. In addition, local, county, and state requirements vary. Often, predetermined curricula dictate the selection and the sequence of topics. The teacher can arrive at an appropriate course schedule by determining the ability level of the students, their previous science experience, teacher interests, teaching style, local science-related resources, and institutional requirements. The length of the class sessions and the length of the school year must also be considered.

Establishing a schedule for the school year can be an important aid in making arrangements for audiovisual aids and for guest speakers. Planning a yearly schedule will also help maintain the pace that you feel is appropriate to your class.

While **GENERAL SCIENCE** is designed with the intention that all the main topics be covered during the typical one-year general science course, the individual teacher can adapt the way in which he or she uses the textbook to the needs of the local teaching situation. No teacher should feel compelled to teach every chapter or to give equal emphasis to all chapters of the textbook. The teacher and the school system should dictate what constitutes appropriate course content.

The chart beginning on **T24** is designed to assist teachers in making decisions regarding scheduling, course content, and emphasis. The schedule is divided into several forms. One form provides for a two-semester comprehensive course. The other forms provide for a one-semester course with either a physical-science, an earth-science, or a life-science emphasis.

The sections of each chapter have been identified according to whether they are to be taught for the one-year course or for the half-year courses. Those sections to be taught for the type of course chosen are indicated with a ●. The number of recommended class sessions to be devoted to each chapter is also indicated. The teacher is cautioned to use these recommendations merely as a starting point from which to build an individual planning guide that meets his or her needs.

# Pacing Chart

| Unit | Chapter | Section Title | Comprehensive 1 Year General Science Course | days | ½ Year Physical-Science Emphasis | days | ½ Year Earth-Science Emphasis | days | ½ Year Life-Science Emphasis | days |
|------|---------|---------------|:---:|:---:|:---:|:---:|:---:|:---:|:---:|:---:|
| **1 Introduction to Science** | | | | | | | | | | |
| | **1 Science and Discovery** | | | | | | | | | |
| | | Science Throughout History | • | | • | | • | | • | |
| | | The Nature of Science | • | 5 | • | 2 | • | 5 | • | 2 |
| | | Measurement | • | | • | | • | | • | |
| | **2 Science and Modern Technology** | | | | | | | | | |
| | | The Scientific and Technological Revolution | • | | | | | | • | |
| | | The Impact of Science and Technology on Society | • | 5 | • | 2 | • | 2 | • | 5 |
| | **3 Matter, Energy, Space, and Time** | | | | | | | | | |
| | | Matter and Energy | • | 5 | • | 5 | | | • | 2 |
| | | Space and Time | • | | • | | | | | |
| **2 Matter and Change** | | | | | | | | | | |
| | **4 Elements, Mixtures, and Compounds** | | | | | | | | | |
| | | Elements | • | | • | | • | | • | |
| | | Mixtures | • | 6 | • | 6 | • | 6 | • | 6 |
| | | Compounds | • | | • | | • | | • | |

• indicates a section is to be taught

| Unit | Chapter | Section Title | Comprehensive 1 Year General Science Course | days | ½ Year Physical-Science Emphasis | days | ½ Year Earth-Science Emphasis | days | ½ Year Life-Science Emphasis | days |
|---|---|---|---|---|---|---|---|---|---|---|
| | **5 Atoms and the Periodic Table** | | | | | | | | | |
| | | Atomic Structure | ● | 7 | ● | 7 | | 1 | | 1 |
| | | The Periodic Table | ● | | ● | | ● | | ● | |
| | **6 Chemical Reactions** | | | | | | | | | |
| | | Molecules and Ions | ● | 8 | ● | 8 | ● | 1 | ● | 1 |
| | | Chemical Equations | ● | | ● | | | | ● | |
| | | Types of Reactions | ● | | ● | | | | | |
| | **7 Nuclear Reactions** | | | | | | | | | |
| | | Radioactivity | ● | 7 | ● | 7 | ● | 1 | ● | 1 |
| | | Nuclear Transformations | ● | | ● | | ● | | ● | |
| | | Fission and Fusion | ● | | ● | | | | | |
| | **8 Chemical Technology** | | | | | | | | | |
| | | Industrial Chemistry | ● | 6 | ● | 6 | | | | 2 |
| | | Metals and Alloys | ● | | ● | | | | | |
| | | Chemical Applications | ● | | ● | | | | ● | |

## 3 How Things Work

### 9 Motion

| Unit | Chapter | Section Title | Comprehensive 1 Year General Science Course | days | ½ Year Physical-Science Emphasis | days | ½ Year Earth-Science Emphasis | days | ½ Year Life-Science Emphasis | days |
|---|---|---|---|---|---|---|---|---|---|---|
| | | Motion in a Straight Line | ● | 8 | ● | 8 | | | | |
| | | The Laws of Motion | ● | | ● | | | | | |
| | | Motion Along a Curved Path | ● | | ● | | | | | |

| Unit | Chapter | Section Title | Comprehensive 1 Year General Science Course | days | ½ Year Physical-Science Emphasis | days | ½ Year Earth-Science Emphasis | days | ½ Year Life-Science Emphasis | days |
|---|---|---|---|---|---|---|---|---|---|---|
| | **10** | **Work, Energy, and Machines** | | | | | | | | |
| | | Work and Energy | • | | • | | | | | |
| | | Machines | • | 6 | • | 6 | | | | |
| | **11** | **Temperature and Heat** | | | | | | | | |
| | | Temperature | • | | • | | • | | • | |
| | | Heat | • | 6 | • | 6 | • | 3 | • | 3 |
| | | Thermodynamics | • | | • | | | | | |
| | **12** | **Electricity and Magnetism** | | | | | | | | |
| | | Static Electricity | • | | • | | | | | |
| | | Electric Current | • | 6 | • | 6 | | | • | 1 |
| | | Magnetism | • | | • | | | | | |
| | **13** | **Light and Sound** | | | | | | | | |
| | | Waves | • | | • | | • | | • | |
| | | Light | • | 6 | • | 6 | • | 6 | | 1 |
| | | Sound | • | | • | | • | | | |
| | **14** | **Computer Technology and Robotics** | | | | | | | | |
| | | What Is a Computer? | • | | • | | • | | • | |
| | | Computer Technology | • | 7 | • | 7 | | 1 | | 4 |
| | | Robotics | • | | • | | | | • | |

| Unit | Chapter | Section Title | Comprehensive 1 Year General Science Course | days | ½ Year Physical-Science Emphasis | days | ½ Year Earth-Science Emphasis | days | ½ Year Life-Science Emphasis | days |
|---|---|---|---|---|---|---|---|---|---|---|
| **4 Exploring the Universe** | | | | | | | | | | |
| | **15 Planet Earth** | | | | | | | | | |
| | | Locating Places on Earth | • | | • | | • | | • | |
| | | Earth in Space | • | 7 | • | 3 | • | 7 | | 2 |
| | | Solid Earth | • | | | | • | | | |
| | **16 The Solar System** | | | | | | | | | |
| | | The Sun | • | | | | • | | • | |
| | | The Planetary System | • | 6 | | | • | 6 | • | 6 |
| | **17 The Universe** | | | | | | | | | |
| | | Stars | • | | | | • | | | |
| | | Galaxies | • | 6 | | | • | 6 | | |
| | | The Changing Universe | • | | | | • | | | |
| | **18 Earth's History** | | | | | | | | | |
| | | The Earth's Past | • | | | | • | | • | |
| | | The Precambrian and Paleozoic Eras | • | 6 | | | • | 6 | • | 6 |
| | | The Mesozoic and Cenozoic Eras | • | | | | • | | • | |
| | **19 The Changing Earth** | | | | | | | | | |
| | | Earthquakes and Volcanoes | • | | | | • | | • | |
| | | Moving Continents | • | 7 | | | • | 7 | | 2 |
| | | Plate Tectonics | • | | | | • | | | |

| Unit | Chapter | Section Title | Comprehensive 1 Year General Science Course | days | ½ Year Physical-Science Emphasis | days | ½ Year Earth-Science Emphasis | days | ½ Year Life-Science Emphasis | days |
|---|---|---|---|---|---|---|---|---|---|---|

## 5 Weather and the Oceans

### 20 The Atmosphere

| Section Title | General | days | Physical | days | Earth | days | Life | days |
|---|---|---|---|---|---|---|---|---|
| The Composition and Structure of the Atmosphere | • | 6 | | | • | 6 | • | 2 |
| Movement of the Atmosphere | • | | | | • | | | |

### 21 Weather and Climate

| Section Title | General | days | Physical | days | Earth | days | Life | days |
|---|---|---|---|---|---|---|---|---|
| Water Vapor in the Air | • | 7 | | | • | 7 | • | 2 |
| Weather | • | | | | • | | | |
| Climate | • | | | | • | | • | |

### 22 The Oceans

| Section Title | General | days | Physical | days | Earth | days | Life | days |
|---|---|---|---|---|---|---|---|---|
| The Structure and Composition of the Oceans | • | 8 | • | 3 | • | 8 | • | 3 |
| Movement of Ocean Water | • | | | | • | | | |

## 6 The Living World

### 23 Living Things

| Section Title | General | days | Physical | days | Earth | days | Life | days |
|---|---|---|---|---|---|---|---|---|
| The Building Blocks of Life | • | 6 | | | • | 3 | • | 6 |
| The Nature of Life | • | | | | | | • | |
| The Diversity of Living Things | • | | | | • | | • | |

### 24 Continuity of Life

| Section Title | General | days | Physical | days | Earth | days | Life | days |
|---|---|---|---|---|---|---|---|---|
| Cell Reproduction | • | | | | | | • | |

| Unit | Chapter | Section Title | Comprehensive 1 Year General Science Course | | ½ Year Physical-Science Emphasis | | ½ Year Earth-Science Emphasis | | ½ Year Life-Science Emphasis | |
|---|---|---|---|---|---|---|---|---|---|---|
| | | | | days | | days | | days | | days |
| | | Genetics | ● | 7 | | | | | ● | 7 |
| | | Patterns of Heredity | ● | | | | | | ● | |
| | **25 Evolution and Natural Selection** | | | | | | | | | |
| | | Changes Over Time | ● | | | | ● | | ● | |
| | | Planned and Unplanned Changes | ● | 5 | | | | 3 | ● | 5 |
| | | A Human Time Line | ● | | | | ● | | ● | |
| | **26 Plants and Animals** | | | | | | | | | |
| | | Plants | ● | 6 | | | | | ● | 6 |
| | | Animals | ● | | | | | | ● | |
| | **27 Human Biology** | | | | | | | | | |
| | | Systems of the Body | ● | 5 | | 2 | | 2 | ● | 5 |
| | | Maintaining Wellness | ● | | ● | | ● | | ● | |
| **7 Science and Society** | | | | | | | | | | |
| | **28 Ecology** | | | | | | | | | |
| | | Organization of Ecosystems | ● | | | | ● | | ● | |
| | | Functions of Ecosystems | ● | 5 | | | | 2 | ● | 5 |
| | | Types of Ecosystems | ● | | | | ● | | ● | |
| | **29 Managing Natural Resources** | | | | | | | | | |
| | | Abiotic Resources | ● | | | | ● | | ● | |
| | | Biotic Resources | ● | 5 | | | | 3 | ● | 5 |
| | | Energy Resources | ● | | | | ● | | ● | |

# Science, Technology, and Society

For students, the present and the future loom larger and are more important than the past. Students approach the future with a sense of awe and, in many cases, anxiety as they question what their lives will be like in the years to come.

The problems of dwindling energy resources and the search for alternate energy supplies are addressed almost daily in newspapers and on television. The impact of computers and related technology on our daily lives has been significant. Social and ethical issues are constantly raised as technology progresses at a rapid pace in the fields of medicine, nuclear power, and genetic engineering.

In order to reduce anxiety about the future, to understand the role of technology, and to make informed decisions about the social implications of new scientific technologies, students first need a strong foundation in the principles and processes of science. The more a student knows about the inner workings of a computer, the more likely he or she may be to incorporate computers into daily routines. Students must do more than merely gain scientific knowledge, however. They must also develop an accurate image of the nature of science and the usefulness of science in solving problems. Finally, it is also important for students to gain confidence in their ability to identify science-related social issues and to use their own scientific knowledge to resolve these problems.

Teachers can play a vital role in helping students gain the knowledge and the skills necessary to make responsible decisions about social issues related to science and technology. The sections that follow provide suggestions to aid teachers in this role, using features from **GENERAL SCIENCE** in conjunction with a variety of classroom strategies and outside resources.

## Strategies Using
## *GENERAL SCIENCE*

**GENERAL SCIENCE** contains a wealth of information and features that can be invaluable in teaching students about the relationship of science and technology to society.

Chapter 1 provides a basis for the understanding of the history of science, the scientific method, and the metric system. This chapter is crucial for developing an understanding of what science is and how it is used to solve problems.

Chapter 2 provides an overview of how science and new technology impact our daily lives at home, at work, in medicine, in space, and in the arts. This chapter also raises questions concerning the role of technology in the future.

Other chapters in the book address the role of technology in almost all aspects of the students' lives. Chapter 7 provides an overview of atomic energy, fission reactions, nuclear reactors, and fusion reactions. A comparison is made between the relative benefits and the potential hazards of fission and fusion as possible sources of energy.

Chapter 8, *Chemical Technology,* is devoted entirely to answering one question: "What would life be like without modern chemical technology?" The chapter discusses fossil fuels, petrochemicals, polymers, metals, glass, ceramics, fiberglass, optic fibers, biological glass, and chemical fertilizers.

A discussion of simple and complex machines and how they have simplified routine tasks and improved the quality of human life is discussed in Chapter 10.

Chapter 12 presents basic information about electrical power and the technology associated with it. The full impact of how dramatically the use of electricity has affected our lives can be demonstrated by asking the students how their lives would be different without electricity.

"What is a computer?" and "How does it work?" are two questions often asked by students. Both of these questions are answered in Chapter 14. The chapter discusses various types of computer hardware and software, the different types of computers (mainframe, minis, and micros), and the use of computer technology in business, design, and manufacturing. The use of robots is also described in a way that brings the future into the present. Chapter 17 explains how computers are being combined with other technologies for the exploration and study of the universe.

Chapters 24 and 27 address how technology applies to biological knowledge in the areas of human genetics and the fight against disease.

The use of technology in the management and control of our natural resources, both renewable and nonrenewable, is discussed in Chapter 29.

## Other Classroom Strategies

One popular way to introduce social issues into the general-science classroom is to have students bring in articles on science and technology from newspapers and magazines. Class time should be set aside on a regular basis to discuss the articles and the students' views. The teacher's role is vital in these discussions. However, the teacher must remember not to make judgments or to reject or praise student responses, but rather to accept all possible answers, ideas, and positions.

Debates are another natural way of approaching the issues of science, technology, and society. For this strategy to be useful, however, students must do more than repeat the opinions of others. They must be given adequate time and direction to research the issues, collect data, formulate their own opinions, and support their position.

Students might develop a questionnaire to gather information from their peers, interested adults, the scientific community, or other groups. Students can analyze items to be included in the questionnaire, predict possible responses, and then determine the best way to administer the questionnaire. The data collected may represent a type of observation unfamiliar to many students. However, using and trying to make sense of such observations exemplifies the process of science.

The study of **GENERAL SCIENCE** may introduce students to such topics as the use of nuclear energy and the disposal of toxic wastes, about which there may be several points of view. A discussion of these topics can provide excellent learning opportunities, especially for the development of higher-level thinking skills. When such topics are encountered in the classroom, several strategies are possible. Students may need to be guided to recognize that more than one viewpoint exists. Students may also be encouraged to gather information from references. Once information has been gathered, a positive learning environment can be created if students are taught to respect the right of others to express their views.

# Computers in the General-Science Classroom

Microcomputers are powerful teaching tools. They can store, manipulate, and interpret large quantities of information. They can produce graphics, charts, and other visual materials to help the students comprehend important concepts. Computers are being used in the general-science classroom to enhance instruction, organize and manipulate data, help students prepare papers, and assist teachers with classroom preparation and organization. If you have access to only one computer, you can attach it to a large screen monitor or a 24" television set, and your class can work through computer programs. Interested students also can work independently at the computer.

## Type of Computer Programs

There are many types of computer programs that can be used in the general science classroom. Computer simulations are designed to give the students the opportunity to experience a computer version of some real event or situation. This can give the students a chance to learn about some aspect of the world in which they would normally not have experience. The students can change some of the variables in a simulation to see how these changes affect the program.

Interactive tutorials, a second type of software, help the students by providing appropriate question-and-answer techniques. The more effective tutorials provide help to the students (as necessary), assess the student's understanding of the material before permitting the student to proceed, and generally allow the student to learn material at his or her own pace.

A third type of software is drill and practice software. Effective drill and practice software can help the students review difficult concepts. It can give the students an opportunity to learn terminology, classifications, and computation and problem-solving skills.

Some types of software also can be used effectively in helping the students collect laboratory data during class experiments or while working on individual research projects. Some software also can help the students record and analyze data collected in laboratory investigations. This is an excellent use of the computer because it shows the students how to use the computer as a tool.

The microcomputer can perform time-consuming but necessary calculations quickly. Using specific programs, the computer can do tasks which otherwise would be tedious, time consuming, and perhaps frustrating to the students.

Students can also use the computer as a tool in preparing and presenting laboratory reports and term papers. Those who have access to word processing software, either at home or at school, will have an opportunity to edit their work more efficiently and to gain some computer-literacy skills.

Microcomputers can be a valuable aid in developing lessons and in classroom administration. They can also be used in many aspects of classroom management such as maintaining an inventory of science equipment and supplies. You can use some types of software to write lessons or to customize tests to suit your needs. The *General Science Test Bank,* available for Apple® computers, is a software package you can use to create your own tests.

With minor modifications, some word processing programs can be used to keep track of grades and attendance and to calculate a student's total points and final grade. While it does take some investment of time to become proficient in using word processing software, word processing will eventually save you many hours of work and enable you to produce better materials at the same time.

As software and hardware continue to improve, the computer will play an increasingly important role in the classroom.

## IBM® PC and IBM®-Compatibles Version of COMPUTER APPLICATION

In the student textbook, the Apple® version for each COMPUTER APPLICATION is provided. On the pages that follow are the same programs modified for use with an IBM® PC, Tandy® 1000, or any microcomputer that uses MS-DOS BASIC.

## Unit 1

```
100 LET E$=" = "
110 PRINT
120 PRINT"ENTER YOUR NUMBER AND PRESS RETURN"
130 INPUT A,M$
140 IF M$="KM" THEN 210
150 IF M$="M" THEN 230
160 IF M$="CM" THEN 190
170 PRINT"ERROR: UNITS NOT RECOGNIZED"
180 GOTO 240
190 PRINT A;M$;E$;A/100;"M = ";A/100000!;"KM"
200 GOTO 240
210 PRINT A;M$;E$;A*100000!;"CM = ";A*1000;"M"
220 GOTO 240
230 PRINT A;M$;E$;A*100;"CM = ";A/1000;"KM"
240 PRINT:PRINT"DO YOU WISH TO CONTINUE? TYPE (Y OR N)";
250 INPUT A$
260 IF A$="Y" THEN 110
270 END
```

## Unit 2

```
10 DIM N$(41),S$(41)
12 FOR J = 1 TO 41
14 READ N$(J),S$(J)
16 NEXT J
18 PRINT"DO YOU WANT TO TRY GIVING THE NAMES(N)"
20 INPUT"OR THE SYMBOLS(S) OF THE ELEMENTS? ";R$
22 RANDOMIZE TIMER:LET RN= 40*RND(1)+1
24 IF R$="S" GOTO 28
26 IF R$="N" GOTO 40
28 PRINT"WHAT IS THE SYMBOL FOR ";N$(RN);"..";
30 INPUT A$
32 IF A$=S$(RN) THEN PRINT"CORRECT":GOTO 22
34 IF A$="QUIT" THEN END
36 IF A$<>S$(RN) THEN PRINT"TRY AGAIN!"
38 GOTO 28
40 PRINT"WHAT IS THE NAME FOR "; S$(RN);"..";
42 INPUT A$
44 IF A$=N$(RN) THEN PRINT"CORRECT":GOTO 22
46 IF A$="QUIT"THEN END
48 IF A$<>N$(RN)THEN PRINT"TRY AGAIN!"
50 GOTO 40
80 DATA ALUMINUM,Al,ANTIMONY,Sb,ARGON,Ar,BARIUM,Ba
82 DATA BERYLLIUM,Be,BISMUTH,Bi,BORON,B,BROMINE,Br
84 DATA CADMIUM,Cd,CALCIUM,Ca,CARBON,C,CHLORINE,Cl
86 DATA CHROMIUM,Cr,COBALT,Co,COPPER,Cu,FLUORINE,F
88 DATA GOLD,Au,HELIUM,He,HYDROGEN,H,MANGANESE,Mn
90 DATA KRYPTON,Kr,LEAD,Pb,LITHIUM,Li,MAGNESIUM,Mg
92 DATA IODINE,I,MERCURY,Hg,NEON,Ne,PLATINUM,Pt
94 DATA NITROGEN,N,OXYGEN,O,PHOSPHORUS,P,NICKEL,Ni
96 DATA POTASSIUM,K,RADIUM,Ra,SILICON,Si,SILVER,Ag
98 DATA SODIUM,Na,SULFUR,S,TIN,Sn,ZINC,Zn,IRON,Fe
```

## Unit 3

```
90 LOCATE,,0:WIDTH 40
100 CLS:PRINT"WATCH THE STAR ACCELERATE."
110 LET V=5
120 PRINT:LET A=10
130 FOR T=1 TO 20
140 LET S=.5*A*T*T/10
145 IF S>39 THEN 180
150 IF S<1 THEN S=1
160 LOCATE V,S:PRINT"*";
170 FOR D=1 TO 300:NEXT D
180 NEXT T
190 PRINT:LET V=V+1:IF V=13 THEN LET V=5
200 LOCATE 15:PRINT"CHANGE THE MASS? (TYPE Y OR N)"
210 INPUT M$
220 IF M$="N" THEN 270
230 PRINT"+ FOR MORE, - FOR LESS"
240 INPUT C$
250 IF C$="+" THEN LET A = A-1
260 IF C$="-" THEN LET A = A+1
270 PRINT"CHANGE THE FORCE? (TYPE Y OR N)"
280 INPUT F$
290 IF F$="Y" THEN 320
300 IF F$="N" AND M$="N" THEN WIDTH 80:END
310 GOTO 360
320 PRINT"+ FOR MORE, - FOR LESS"
330 INPUT C$
340 IF C$ = "+" THEN LET A = A+1
350 IF C$ = "-" THEN LET A = A-1
360 GOTO 130
```

## Unit 4

```
90 WIDTH 40
100 CLS:PRINT"RICHTER EARTHQUAKE SCALE MAGNITUDES"
110 FOR K=1 TO 12:PRINT"=^=";:NEXT
120 PRINT:INPUT"ENTER MAGNITUDE LESS THAN 10: ";M
130 IF M>=10 THEN RUN
140 PRINT:PRINT:PRINT
150 PRINT:PRINT"THE INTENSITY OF THIS QUAKE IS "
155 IF M>8 THEN M=10^(M-1):N$=STR$(M):PRINT:GOTO 210
160 PRINT:M = 10^(M-1)
170 IF M < 10 THEN M = INT(10*(M+.05))/10:GOTO 190
180 M = INT(M+.5)
190 M$=STR$(M):L=LEN(M$)-1:N$=M$
200 IF L>6 THEN 270
205 IF L>3 THEN 290
210 LOCATE ,20-LEN(N$):COLOR 0,7
220 PRINT N$:COLOR 7,0:PRINT
230 PRINT"TIMES THAT OF A MAGNITUDE 1.0 QUAKE."
240 LOCATE 18:INPUT"RUN AGAIN? (Y/N) ";R$
250 IF R$="Y" THEN RUN
260 WIDTH 80:END
270 N$=LEFT$(M$,L-5)+","+MID$(M$,L-4,3)
280 N$=N$+","+RIGHT$(M$,3):GOTO 210
290 N$=LEFT$(M$,L-2)+","+RIGHT$(M$,3):GOTO 210
```

## Unit 5

```
90 WIDTH 40
100 CLS:PRINT"R E L A T I V E   O C E A N   S I Z E S"
110 LET U$="M SQ KM"
120 FOR K= 1 TO 4:READ N$(K),S$(K),RM(K),LM(K):NEXT
130 DATA "PACIFIC","166.2",38,22,"ATLANTIC","86.6",27,16
140 DATA "INDIAN","73.4",20,12,"ARCTIC","12.2",10,6
150 LOCATE 2,4
160 INPUT"ENTER: 1-4=OCEAN, 5=RERUN, 6=END ";N
170 IF N = 5 THEN RUN
180 IF N = 6 THEN LOCATE 20:WIDTH 80:END
190 LOCATE 3,1:FOR W=1 TO RM(N):PRINT"*";:NEXT
200 FOR V=3 TO LM(N):LOCATE,1:PRINT"*";
210 LOCATE,RM(N):PRINT"*":NEXT V
220 FOR W = 1 TO RM(N):PRINT"*";:NEXT W
230 LOCATE LM(N)-2,2:PRINT N$(N)
240 LOCATE LM(N)-1,3:PRINT S$(N)
250 LOCATE LM(N),2:PRINT U$
260 GOTO 150
```

## Unit 6

```
100 WIDTH 40:CLS
110 LOCATE 23,,0
120 INPUT"PRESS ENTER TO SEE DNA MOLECULE ";K9$
130 CLS
140 FOR C= 65 TO 85
150 PRINT TAB(20);CHR$(C);CHR$(C)
160 NEXT
170 LOCATE 23
180 INPUT "ENTER TO SEE MOLECULE DIVIDE ";K9$
190 LOCATE 1
200 FOR C = 65 TO 85
210 PRINT TAB(17);CHR$(C);".     .";CHR$(C)
220 FOR P=1 TO 100
230 NEXT P
240 NEXT C
250 LOCATE 23
260 INPUT"ENTER TO SEE MOLECULE REPLICATE ";K9$
270 LOCATE 1
280 FOR C= 65 TO 85
290 LOCATE,18
300 PRINT TAB(18);CHR$(C);"     ";CHR$(C)
310 FOR P=1 TO 100
320 NEXT P
330 NEXT C
340 LOCATE 23
350 PRINT"            <<< THE END >>>        "
360 FOR P=1 TO 2000:NEXT
999 WIDTH 80:END
```

## Unit 7

```
100 PRINT"PROGRAM DEMONSTRATES GROWTH OF SYSTEM:"
110 PRINT"SELECT ARITHMETIC GROWTH(A)"
120 INPUT"OR GEOMETRIC GROWTH (G) ";A$
130 IF A$="A" GOTO 500
200 PRINT TAB(12);"GEOMETRIC GROWTH"
210 LET N = 1
220 FOR J = 1 TO 11
230 FOR Z = 1 TO N
240 PRINT"G";
250 NEXT Z
260 LET N = N*2
270 INPUT K9$
280 NEXT J
290 PRINT"GEOMETRIC GROWTH!!"
300 GOTO 999
500 PRINT TAB(12);"ADDITIVE GROWTH"
510 FOR J = 1 TO 39
520 FOR Z = 1 TO J
530 PRINT"A";
540 NEXT Z
550 INPUT K9$
560 NEXT J
570 PRINT"ARITMETIC GROWTH."
999 END
```

# Language Skills and Science

The textbook is the students' primary source of information. By utilizing pre-reading strategies and guiding students in their reading assignments, teachers can significantly aid comprehension and make the task of reading the textbook easier for students. Writing assignments also develop language skills and reinforce or integrate students' learning.

## Developing Pre-Reading Strategies

Several research studies have shown that the amount of prior knowledge that students have about a topic directly influences their comprehension when reading about that topic. For example, the more students know about electricity—including concepts, vocabulary terms, functions, relationships, and dangers—the easier it is for students to understand what they are reading about electricity. Conversely, when students know very little about electricity, they find it much more difficult to read and comprehend textbook information about electricity. Because some of the information presented in the textbook is unfamiliar, students have no prior knowledge structures to link with the new information.

Other related research concerns the misconceptions students may have about a topic. This research shows that students tend to maintain their misconceptions about a topic when reading textbook information that deals with those misconceptions. In other words, students have difficulty grasping textbook information that conflicts with the ideas they already have about a topic, such as electricity. They may ignore the textbook because the new information does not fit with their existing information, or prior knowledge, about electricity. Students are able to discard or modify their misconceptions, however, when the teacher provides direct instruction that corrects the misinformation.

Helping students identify the information they already know about a topic prior to reading about that topic aids the students in at least three ways.

1. Students are able to build a framework of concepts related to the topic. As a result, students can relate the new information from the textbook to existing knowledge structures.

2. Teachers are able to identify the general awareness level of the class about a particular topic. The teacher can then plan instructional time accordingly.
3. The teacher has the opportunity to identify any misconceptions students may have about the topic. Then teachers can plan discussions, demonstrations, or other experiences to help students confront and correct their misconceptions prior to reading the information in the textbook.

## Accessing Prior Knowledge

One effective strategy for accessing prior knowledge is to brainstorm with the class as a whole to determine what the group already knows about a topic. Write student responses on the chalkboard or on an overhead-projector transparency. Ask key questions to probe relationships among the concepts the students have identified. Ask how related terms are alike and how they are different. Answer your own questions if no one knows the answers, and correct any misinformation that turns up. Using the ideas from the brainstorming, make a diagram or outline that shows visually how the terms and concepts of the chapter are related.

Use class discussions to build a common vocabulary. Many terms used in science have multiple scientific and nonscientific meanings. Providing a context for terms such as *revolution* and *fault* will help the students arrive at accurate definitions of science terms.

The Unit and Chapter Guides includes many other specific ideas for establishing students' prior knowledge about a topic. Motivating activities, demonstrations, and Teaching Suggestions not only stimulate interest and curiosity but also prepare students to understand what they are to read. You may wish to vary the methods that are used from chapter to chapter.

## Establishing a Purpose for Reading

Research on reading shows that students comprehend better when they have a purpose for reading. Making a study guide of questions that students can answer as they read is one way of establishing a purpose. You can make questions out of the *Section Objectives* at the beginning of each section or use the *Section Review* questions as a prereading guide. You can also make questions out of chapter headings, captions, and *Science Terms.* Once you have provided students with a model, they can be directed to make their own study guides for subsequent chapters.

## Providing Effective Reading Strategies

Many students have no real strategies for reading textbook materials other than simply rereading difficult sections of a chapter. Students do not generally realize that they can do things to enhance their comprehension and learning from a textbook. Students often have little awareness of higher-level cognitive strategies such as organizing, reflecting upon, or evaluating what they read. Even good readers are not much different from poor readers in the type of strategies they use, although they do differ in the number of strategies employed.

Science teachers can use three major steps to help students learn and practice effective reading strategies.

1. Help students understand how science books organize information in general. Usually, each section of a chapter contains one main idea, stated first or last. Supporting details follow or precede the main idea in a recognizable pattern. Students should look for key phrases that mark the specific type of relationship of the information being presented. For example, the phrase "there are five traits" indicates an enumerative passage; terms such as "like" and "in contrast to" indicate comparisons and contrasts.
2. Point out the basic organizational features of this textbook. Help students understand that features such as the *Chapter Outline, Section Objectives, Reading Critically,* and *Section Review* questions, can guide their reading. Important terms are printed in boldface. Important concepts are illustrated in charts, labeled drawings, or photographs with captions. Finally, use the *Skill Activity* in Chapter 1 (page 12) as a guide for studying from **GENERAL SCIENCE.**
3. Model effective reading and study practices for students. Students should be taught to preview a chapter. Previewing involves looking at all the chapter headings, illustrative material, and boldfaced terms page-by-page prior to actually reading the text. This techique helps students to gain a "feel" for the chapter and to build a basic structure of information. Later, when they read the chapter, students can fill in the details on the basic structures they have built.

## Using the Textbook for Study

Students also should be taught how to study from the textbook. If they can pick out the important information from a textbook, they can put it on cards, make study guides, write questions, or orally rehearse what they have learned. All of these methods are more effective study strategies than simply rereading a chapter.

Suggest, for example, that students put a key concept, the five steps of a process, or a difficult vocabulary term on one side of a note card. On the other side, have them list a sentence in which the concept is used, the five steps, or the definition of the term. Encourage students to put on the cards not only the boldfaced *Science Terms* but other important and unfamiliar terms. As they study the cards, have the students keep separating the cards into piles, according to what they know and what they do not know.

## Writing a Research Report

Research shows that writing is an effective way of improving reading. As students write, they are creating a text for others to read. The more they write, the more they are able to recognize compositional devices they encounter in the textbook.

A common problem that students meet in writing a science research report is a lack of practice in locating reference and resource materials. Many students also have insufficient knowledge of what a science report should contain.

(For a discussion of writing a laboratory report, see the **Laboratory Manual/Workbook** that accompanies this textbook.)

The teacher can guide the students' writing most efficiently by using a series of checkpoints. Direct the students to follow a uniform sequence of steps, such as those given below, and to seek the teacher's approval before proceeding beyond the checkpoints marked with an asterisk.

1. Choose a broad topic area.
*2. List several specific questions about the topic.
3. Do some preliminary reading about the topic in an encyclopedia or in general reference books.
4. Take notes.
*5. Narrow the focus of your topic.
6. Gather additional information, using books, magazines, filmstrips, or vertical files.
7. Take more notes on your sources. (Some teachers require a certain number of note cards to be written, according to the length or complexity of the topic.)
*8. Make an outline for your paper:
   a. Introduction—what the topic is; what kind of information will be found in the remaining sections of the paper.
   b. Three (or more) paragraphs, each telling interesting or important things about the topic.
   c. Summary/Commentary—Why did you find this topic interesting? Why is it important? What did you learn? What questions do you still have?
*9. Write the first draft of your paper. (Commenting on the students' first draft is essential, as it gives the students the opportunity to revise their work according to specific guidelines.)
10. Revise your paper.

# Teaching Mathematics in the General Science Classroom

The study of mathematics is an integral part of the teaching and understanding of science. In much the same way that a student is required to become fluent in technical vocabulary, it is necessary for the student to understand and be able to apply basic mathematical operations to the natural phenomena that occur in science. Science and mathematics should not be taught as independent, unrelated subjects. Instead, students should be shown the fundamental relationships that exist between the world of science and the basic operations of mathematics. Only when these relationships have been established can students become comfortable with the use of mathematics in the general-science classroom.

Through the effective use of mathematics in the science classroom, the teacher can focus on the application of concepts, not merely the memorization of facts. For example, once students learn and can manipulate the mathematical formula to determine average speed,

$$\text{average speed} = \frac{\text{distance}}{\text{time}}$$

they can apply this knowledge to their daily lives. They can calculate and compare the time required to travel to and from school, to and from jobs, and for long trips taken by themselves or family members. By understanding how to calculate average speed, students can gain a comprehension of how technology has impacted their lives by greatly reducing the time required to travel long distances. An easy calculation emphasizes that travel by jet over long distances is considerably faster than travel by train, or even by propeller plane. This example can be reinforced by using the same formula to calculate the time saved by traveling by supersonic jet aircraft compared to conventional jet aircraft.

Another advantage of teaching mathematics in the general-science classroom is that the teacher can focus on the problem-solving, or inquiry, approach to teaching. This approach emphasizes integrated problem solving; it is student-centered instruction. Students are required to think and apply previously learned concepts to new situations. Once a student knows and understands the steps necessary to solve a problem—in this case the correct mathematical operation—he or she can solve the problem alone, without requiring assistance from the teacher.

## Mathematics in *GENERAL SCIENCE*

*GENERAL SCIENCE* uses the metric system throughout the textbook. The metric system is the preferred system of measurement in all fields of science. Although the metric system is not in general use in the United States, students should be taught a working knowledge of this system in a scientific context.

Students are introduced to the metric system in Chapter 1 (page 13), with a table that gives metric units of measurement for length, mass, and volume. Each type of metric measure is explained in greater detail in the following sections: 1.7 Length, 1.8 Area and Volume, 1.9 Mass, and 1.10 Time and Temperature. These sections include formulas for conversions between metric units and sample problems drawn from everyday situations. For example, calculating the number of square centimeters of carpet in a room and the volume of water in a swimming pool are used as practical applications. Additional examples of the metric system are included throughout the textbook. The metric system is summarized in a Metric Conversion Table on page 640 of the *Reference Section.*

*GENERAL SCIENCE* does not place an undue emphasis on the teaching and use of mathematics. Instead, mathematical operations are included in the textbook only where necessary to emphasize a scientific concept. The concept of motion would be very difficult to explain or comprehend without some attempt to use quantitative examples. Refer to the above example on calculating average speed.

Some chapters in *GENERAL SCIENCE,* however, contain several mathematical formulas along with examples. Chapter 9, *Motion,* contains the formulas for average speed (section 9.2, page 174), acceleration (section 9.3, page 175), net force (section 9.5, page 179), and momentum (section 9.8, page 183). Chapter 10, *Work, Energy, and Machines,* contains the formulas for work (section 10.1, page 195), gravitational potential energy (section 10.2, page 197), kinetic energy (section 10.3, page 198), power (section 10.5, page 200), mechanical advantage (section 10.7, page 206), and efficiency (section 10.8, page 207). Chapter 12, *Electricity and Magnetism,* contains the formulas for current (section 12.4, page 243), electrical power (section 12.7, page 249), and energy (section 12.7, page 249). Formulas in these and other chapters should be taught to the students in context with the rest of the chapter. Rather than memorizing the formulas, encourage students to understand the concepts behind the formulas and the application of the formulas to problem solving.

The mathematics in **GENERAL SCIENCE** involves only basic skills such as conversions, decimals, division, equations, exponents, fractions, multiplication, percent, probability, and ratio and proportion. These skills are included in the textbook where appropriate.

You may find it necessary to review these basic mathematical skills before you encounter them in the textbook. A brief review exercise, in this case, would be appropriate. The following table indicates the first example in the textbook of the mathematical skills listed above. By referring to the table, you can arrange mathematical review sessions before the necessary chapter sections in which the problems appear.

| Type of Problem | Example | First Example in Textbook |
|---|---|---|
| Conversion | 1 kilometer (km) = 1000 meters (m) | Section 1.7 (page 13) |
| Decimals | $D = \dfrac{1.9 \text{ kg}}{2500 \text{ cm}^3}$ | Section 3.2 (page 47) |
| Division | $D = \dfrac{1.9 \text{ kg}}{2500 \text{ cm}^3}$ | Section 3.2 (page 47) |
| Equations | 1 km = 1000 m | Section 1.7 (page 13) |
| Exponents | $A = 5 \text{ m}^2 = 50{,}000 \text{ cm}^2$ | Section 1.8 (page 15) |
| Fractions | $20 \text{ km} = 20 \text{ km} \times \dfrac{1000 \text{ m}}{\text{km}}$ | Section 1.7 (page 13) |
| Multiplication | $20 \text{ km} = 20 \text{ km} \times \dfrac{1000 \text{ m}}{\text{km}}$ | Section 1.7 (page 13) |
| Percent | efficiency = $\dfrac{\text{useful energy output} \times 100\%}{\text{energy input}}$ | Section 10.8 (page 207) |
| Probability | Punnett square | Section 24.5 (page 511) |
| Ratio and Proportion | Punnett square | Section 24.5 (page 511) |

# Meeting the Needs of Mainstreamed Students

The science class offers mainstreamed students important information that will help them function in an increasingly more scientific and technical society. Guidance counselors and the school nurse may be consulted to help work out the best learning environment as well as realistic goals for each student.

The following recommendations apply to specific types of special students.

## Learning Disabled

- Allow for group work during oral assignments.
- Provide for simplified rephrasing of concepts, tests, and reviews.
- Make use of oral examinations.
- Make certain that easy-to-read science reference material is available.
- Provide a daily, unvarying routine so your expectations are clear.
- Establish special teaching procedures to account for a short attention span and restlessness.
- Make certain that instructions are understood before the student starts work.
- Seat the student where classroom distractions are minimized.
- Allow students to express ideas with drawings or models if their disability permits. Dyslexic students will be able to develop drawings of their own, while dysgraphic students will be more successful at labeling figures that have been prepared for them.
- Use tape recorders where appropriate.

## Mentally Retarded

- Allow for group work during oral assignments.
- Provide for simplified rephrasing of concepts, tests, and reviews.
- Make use of oral examinations.
- Make certain that easy-to-read science reference material is available.
- Give simple, clear directions.
- Encourage repeated efforts.

## Hearing Impaired

- Arrange seating that helps the student hear best or that facilitates lip reading.
- Allow for group work during oral assignments.
- Obtain closed-captioned films for the deaf.
- Provide a classroom partner who knows signing.
- Rephrase instructions. Some sounds may be heard better than others.

## Health Impaired

- Students who have diabetes, asthma, a heart condition, or other general health impairments may vary considerably in their degree of impairment. The school nurse and special education teacher can acquaint you with each student's limits.
- Become acquainted with the various symptoms of any health emergencies that might occur in the classroom.
- Obtain training in first-aid procedures to be used in the event of a health emergency.

## Orthopedically Impaired

- Arrange for seating that is comfortable for the student.
- Provide rest breaks.
- Cover the student's desk with felt so that materials do not slip.

## Visually Impaired

- Seat the student close to the chalkboard.
- Stand facing the windows to avoid putting a demonstration into shadow.
- Encourage the handling of materials before or after a demonstration.
- Assign a student to make copies of notes.
- Use verbal cues rather than nods or facial expressions.
- Provide a sighted student guide.
- Provide high-contrast copies of worksheets or chalkboard diagrams.

# Audiovisual Materials

The following audiovisuals are available from the suppliers listed below. The indicated abbreviations are used to identify suppliers in the listings.

**A & A**
Adams & Adams Films
P.O. Box 5755
Austin, TX 78703

**AIT**
Agency for Instructional Television
Box A
Bloomington, IN 47402

**ANNEN**
The Annenberg/CPB Collection
5547 Ravenswood Avenue
Chicago, IL 60640

**ASP**
Astronomical Society of the Pacific
1290 24th Avenue
San Francisco, CA 94122

**BARR**
Barr Films
P.O. Box 5667
3490 E. Foothill Boulevard
Pasadena, CA 91107

**BEAC**
Beacon Films
1250 Washington Street
P.O. Box 575
Norwood, MA 02062

**BENCH**
Benchmark Films
145 Scarborough Road
Briarcliff Manor, NY 10510

**BFI**
Bullfrog Films, Inc.
Oley, PA 19547

**CAL**
The California Video Institute
P.O. Box 7043
Mission City Annex
San Fernando, CA 91346

**CF**
Churchill Films
662 N. Robertson Boulevard
Los Angeles, CA 90069

**COR**
Coronet Films & Video
65 E. South Water Street
Chicago, IL 60601

**CPI**
Centre Productions, Inc.
1800 30th Street
Suite 207
Boulder, CO 80301

**DC**
Direct Cinema Ltd.
P.O. Box 69589
Los Angeles, CA 90069

**EA**
Educational Activities
P.O. Box 392
Reeport, NY 11520

**EB**
Encyclopedia Britannica Educational Corp.
425 N. Michigan Avenue
Chicago, IL 60611

**ED**
Educational Dimensions Group
Box 126
Stamford, CT 06904

**EI**
Educational Images Ltd.
P.O. Box 3456
West Side Station
Elmira, NY 14905

**EPRI**
Electric Power Research Institute
3412 Hillview Avenue
Palo Alto, CA 94303

**FH**
Films for the Humanities, Inc.
Box 2053
Princeton, NJ 08540

**FI**
Films Inc.
1213 Wilmette Avenue
Wilmette, IL 60091

**FL**
Filmakers Library, Inc.
133 E. 58th Street
New York, NY 10022

**FP**
Fanlight Production
47 Halifax Street
Jamaica Plain, MA 02130

**FPT**
Focal Point
Box 207
Pomfret, CT 06258

**HAWK**
Hawkhill Associates, Inc.
125 E. Gilman Street
Madison, WI 53703

**IU**
Indiana University, Audio Visual Center
Bloomington, IN 47405

**KU**
Knowledge Unlimited
Box 52
Madison, WI 53701

**LF**
Lucerne Films, Inc.
37 Gound Pine Road
Morris Plains, NJ 07950

**MEDIA**
The Media Guild
11526 Sorento Valley Road
Suite J
San Diego, CA 92121

**MSP**
Marty Stouffer Productions Ltd.
300 S. Spring Street
Aspen, CO 81611

**MTI**
MTI Film & Video
108 Wilmot Road
Deerfield, IL 60015

**MTP**
Modern Talking Picture Service
5000 Park Street
St. Petersburg, FL 33709

**NFC**
**The New Film Co., Inc.**
7 Mystic Street
Arlington, MA 02174

**NGS**
**National Geographic Society, Educational Services**
17th & M Streets, NW
Washington, DC 20036

**OCS**
**Orange Cherry Software**
P.O. Box 390
Pound Ridge, NY 10576

**OTSI**
**Office of Telecommunications, Smithsonian Institution**
Washington, DC 20560

**S & S**
**Simon & Schuster Software**
1 Gulf & Western Plaza
New York, NY 10023

**SMI**
**Science and Mankind, Inc.**
Communications Park
Box 2000
Mt. Kisco, NY 10549

**SSR**
**Science Screen Report, Inc.**
P.O. Box 691
Cooper Station, NY 10003

**SUN**
**Sunburst Communications**
39 Washington Avenue
Rm. CG
Pleasantville, NY 10570

**SVE**
**Society for Visual Education, Inc.**
1345 Diversey Parkway
Chicago, IL 60614

**TF**
**Trailwood Films**
P.O. Box 1421
Huron, SD 57350

**T–L**
**Time–Life Video**
Time & Life Building
1271 Avenue of the Americas
New York, NY 10020

**UC**
**University of California Extension Media Center**
2176 Shattuck Avenue
Berkeley, CA 94704

**UL**
**United Learning**
6633 W. Howard Street
Niles, IL 60648

**WD**
**Walt Disney Educational Media Co.**
500 S. Buena Vista Street
Burbank, CA 91521

---

**CHAPTER 1    Science and Discovery**
*Communicating in Science* **AIT**
*Decision-Making and Science* **AIT**
*Experimenting with Science* **AIT**
*Inferring in Science* **AIT**
*Observing in Science* **AIT**
*Inventors and the American Industrial Revolution* **CF**
*Imaging a Hidden World —The Light Microscope* **COR**

**CHAPTER 2    Science and Modern Technology**
*High Technology: How It Works* **ED**
*Windows in Time: Research Today for Energy Tomorrow* **EPRI**
*The Good News From Earth* **HAWK**
*Frontiers of Technology* **NGS**

**CHAPTER 3    Matter, Energy, Space, and Time**
*Physical Science: Chemical Energy* **CF**
*Physical Science: Electrical Energy* **CF**
*Energy in Physics* **WD**

**CHAPTER 4    Elements, Mixtures, and Compounds**
*Chemistry: Solution (Ionic and Molecular)* **COR**
*Chemists at Work* **HAWK**

**CHAPTER 5    Atoms and the Periodic Table**
*The Structure of Matter: A Unit of Study* **UL**

**CHAPTER 6    Chemical Reactions**
*Chemistry: Acids, Bases and Salts* **COR**
*Chem Lab* (Software) **S & S**

**CHAPTER 7    Nuclear Reactions**
*Physical Science: Chemical Energy* **CF**
*Physical Science: Electrical Energy* **CF**

**CHAPTER 8    Chemical Technology**
*Chemistry: The Quest For Synthetic Fuels* **SSR**

**CHAPTER 9    Motion**
*Falling Bodies and Projectile Motion* **BARR**
*Physicists at Work* **HAWK**
*Fundamentals of Physical Science* (Software) **OCS**

**CHAPTER 10    Work, Energy, and Machines**
*Simple Machines Series, 2nd ed.*
*Inclined Planes; Levers; Pulleys; Wheels and Axles; Working Together* **COR**
*Energy in Physics* **WD**
*Gears: Strategies in Problem Solving* (Software) **SUN**

**CHAPTER 12    Electricity and Magnetism**
*A Portrait of Small Hydro* **BFI**
*Electrical Circuits: You Can Do It!* **EB**

Have students hold up a pencil at arm's length and at eye level. Ask the students to describe the pencil's position relative to the background while they look at the pencil with both eyes open. Then keep the pencil still and have them describe the position of the pencil with the right eye closed. Have them repeat this procedure with the left eye closed.

## Demonstration (Use with section 3.6 on page 54.)

**Materials:** prepared microscope slides of *Paramecium,* hand lens, binocular microscope, 3 light microscopes (one with an oil immersion lens), electron micrographs of *Paramecium*

Prior to class, select prepared microscope slides of organisms such as *Paramecium* on which organisms can be seen using only a hand lens. Set up the slides so students can observe them with a hand lens (magnification: 5X), a binocular microscope (magnification: approximately 25–50X), a low-power light microscope (magnification: 100X), a high-power light microscope (magnification: 400X), and a light microscope with an oil emersion lens (magnification: approximately 1000X). Display electron micrographs of the same organism for students to observe. Magnifications on the electron micrographs will be indicated and should be between 2000 and 4500X. Actual magnifications of the hand lens and all microscopes will depend on equipment used.

Discuss with students how technology has expanded our world and knowledge. Ask them what kind of new knowledge has been learned and how this knowledge is beneficial to humans.

## Skill Activity (p. 53)

### Introduction
Many students have trouble visualizing and comparing quantitative data. Show students a variety of bar graphs from different sources, such as newspapers or magazines. Point out the similarities and differences among the graphs. Without going into detail about each graph, discuss with students the type of data on each graph. Make a sample bar graph on the chalkboard. Encourage students to identify parts of the graph and to explain how data is entered on the graph.

After you have completed the discussion of bar graphs with the students, have them do the Skill Activity in this chapter.

## Investigation 3 (p. 58)

### Introduction
This Investigation would best be performed after the class has discussed mass and weight on page 47. The investigation should reinforce students' skills in using scientific equipment (beakers, graduates, balance) and refine their measurement skills further.

Prior to beginning the Investigation, set up a display of laboratory equipment on a desk in front of the class. Spend some time explaining the purpose of each piece. Make sure that you carefully explain the care and proper use of the balance and graduate. You may wish to have students refer to Safety Guidelines, beginning on page 634 of the pupil's textbook, and to Laboratory Procedures, beginning on page 636.

## Answers to Writing Critically (p. 61)

1. Gravity acts between objects that have mass, and it holds together large objects such as planets, stars, and galaxies. Electromagnetism acts between objects that have charge, and it holds together small objects such as tables, books, chairs, and people. Strong nuclear force acts between protons and neutrons inside the nucleus of every atom and holds the nucleus together. Weak nuclear force acts inside the protons and neutrons to control nuclear reactions.
2. Energy is a measure of an object's ability to cause changes. Answers to the second portion of the question will vary but should indicate an understanding of various forms of energy.
3. Answers will vary. One example is that heat is stored inside the body and released through perspiration due to physical exertion.

## Planning Unit 2

| Chapter | Pupil's Edition Pages | | | Annotated Teacher's Edition Pages | Laboratory Manual/ Workbook | | | | Teacher's Resource Book | | | | | Overhead Transparencies** |
|---|---|---|---|---|---|---|---|---|---|---|---|---|---|---|
| | Skill Activity | Investigation | Chapter Review | | Investigation | Vocabulary | Concepts | Alternate Investigation | Skill Activity | Critical Thinking | Cross Discipline | Student Record Sheets | Test* | Transparency Number |
| 4 | 78 | 82 | 83–85 | T66–T67 | 27 | 121 | 122 | 133 | 256 | 336 | 296 | 457–458 | 379 | |
| 5 | 98 | 102 | 103–105 | T68–T69 | 31 | 123 | 124 | 135 | 257 | 337 | 297 | 459–460 | 381 | 2, 3 |
| 6 | 114 | 122 | 123–125 | T70–T71 | 33 | 125 | 126 | 139 | 258 | 338 | 298 | 461–462 | 383 | |
| 7 | 132 | 142 | 143–145 | T72–T73 | 35 | 127 | 128 | 143 | 259 | 339 | 299 | 463–464 | 385 | 4 |
| 8 | 157 | 164 | 165–167 | T74–T75 | 37 | 129 | 130 | 147 | 260 | 340 | 300 | 465–466 | 387 | |

Suggestions for audiovisual materials can be found on pages T41–T43.
  \* See also *Computer Testbank* for chapter tests.
  \*\* Component also includes copying masters of the transparencies for use in instruction or evaluation.

## Introducing Unit 2 (pp. 64 and 65)

### Matter and Change

Have the students look at pages 64 and 65 in their textbook. Explain that what they are looking at is a micrograph of citric acid crystals taken under polarized light. The citric acid, or tricarboxylic acid, is obtained from the juice of citrus fruits, is recrystallized, and is photographed through a light microscope.

Point out to the students that the processes used to obtain this photograph involve changes in matter. The recrystallization of the citric acid involves a physical change in the substance. Discuss with the students and have them list examples of various physical and chemical changes that they are familiar with in their lives. They might list freezing, boiling, and evaporation of water; burning of wood or other materials; and dissolving of substances in water. Ask them to explain how these changes take place and whether they think the changes are physical or chemical in nature.

Explain that this unit discusses the ways in which matter is affected in chemical and nuclear reactions. In addition, the unit discusses the characteristics of matter that influence chemical and nuclear reactions.

## Using *Science & Technology*
**(pp. 168 and 169)**

### Bioengineered Bodies

Students are often fascinated by the prospect of replacement body parts, or prosthetic devices, and are usually eager to discuss the possibilities. Point out that replacement body parts, while reaching sophisticated levels of complexity, are not new to medicine and science.

Physicians and scientists have been working on replacement body parts for centuries. Artificial arms and legs have been found in tombs thousands of years old. False teeth carved from wood or ivory also existed hundreds of years ago.

During the twentieth century, science has made tremendous advances in the development of replacement body parts. Today, people can be provided with prosthetic limbs, joints, arteries, veins, heart valves, and even hearts.

Students may be interested to know that the artificial heart was not originally intended as a permanent replacement for a natural heart. Scientists believed that the damaged muscle of the natural heart would, like other muscles, heal if it were allowed to rest. If the natural heart healed, it could be turned back on and the artificial heart could be removed. This has not yet been attempted in a human.

Discuss with the students which parts of the body probably could not be replaced with a prosthesis. (the brain and nervous system) A replacement for a damaged spinal cord is still beyond the reach of current technology, although doctors have been able to help some paraplegics to walk again through the use of computers. In the future, however, small battery packs attached to electrodes on paralyzed arms and legs may replace the cumbersome equipment pictured on page 169.

## Bibliography

**Apfel, Necia H.** *It's All Elementary: From Atoms to the Quantum World of Quarks, Leptons, and Gluons.* New York: Lothrop, Lee & Shepard Books, 1985.

**Fermi, Laura.** *Atoms in the Family: My Life with Enrico Fermi.* Woodbury, New York: American Institute of Physics, 1987.

**Levi, Primo.** *The Periodic Table.* New York: Schocken Books, 1984.

**Mebane, Robert C. and Thomas R. Rybolt.** *Adventures with Atoms and Molecules: Chemistry Experiments for Young People.* Hillside, New Jersey: Enslow Publishers, 1985.

**Puddephatt, Richard J.** *The Periodic Table of the Elements.* New York: Oxford University Press, 1986.

For additional information, see *Planning Unit 2*, pages T64–T65.

# Elements (p. 67)

## Background
Element names often indicate important properties. For example, hydrogen means "water former." This name was chosen because water is produced when hydrogen burns. Elements may also be named because of interesting facts about the elements. Two elements first produced at the University of California at Berkeley, were named *berkelium* (element #97) and *californium* (element #98). Some elements were named after famous scientists or for the persons who discovered them—curium for Marie Curie and einsteinium for Albert Einstein.

## Motivating Activity
**Materials:** paper, scissors, safety goggles, hot pad, petri dish, matches

Fold and crumple the paper into a variety of shapes. Cut the paper into small pieces.

**CAUTION: Put on safety goggles.** Place the petri dish on a hot pad. Place a small, crumpled piece of paper in a petri dish or another glass container. Light a match and ignite the paper. Have students describe which changes were physical and which were chemical.

## Demonstration (Use with section 4.1 on page 67.)
**Materials:** samples of elements such as copper, sulfur, magnesium, and aluminum

Display samples of elements such as copper, sulfur, magnesium, and aluminum. Have students suggest ways to separate these substances. Develop the idea that elements are pure substances that cannot be separated by physical or chemical means.

# Mixtures (p. 72)

## Background
A knowledge of solubility can be useful in many ways. For example, water is insoluble in gasoline.

If water gets into an automobile's gasoline tank, it can make the car run poorly or even fail to start. When dry gas—methyl alcohol—is added to the gasoline, the water dissolves in the alcohol. The alcohol/water mixture is dissolved by the gasoline. The water is removed from the tank as the gasoline is burned in the engine.

## Motivating Activity
**Materials:** bran cereal with raisins, forceps, iron filings and sand mixture, magnet, salt and pepper mixture, sand and water mixture, filter paper, beaker

Tell students that they will be examining several different mixtures. Have students suggest ways to separate the components of each mixture. Then have students carry out their suggestions.

## Demonstration (Use with section 4.4 on page 74.)
**Materials:** safety goggles, laboratory apron, protective gloves, beaker, water, sugar, spoon, ring stand, ring, and wire gauze with fireproof center, Bunsen burner, hot pad

**CAUTION: Put on safety goggles, laboratory apron, and protective gloves.** Fill a beaker half full of room temperature tap water. Stir sugar into the water a spoonful at a time until no more sugar dissolves and sugar crystals collect at the bottom of the beaker. This is an example of a saturated solution.

Place the beaker on a ring over the flame of the Bunsen burner. Heat the water until all the sugar dissolves. Stir in three or four more spoonfuls of sugar.

Place the beaker on a hot pad and allow it to cool to room temperature. If no crystals form in the cooled liquid, the mixture is supersaturated. If crystals begin to form, the solution is an unstable saturated solution.

# Compounds (p. 79)

## Background
New compounds, such as plastic, nylon, rayon, and polyester, that are formed in the laboratory are called synthetic substances. Automobile parts, clothes, electronic equipment, and household items all contain synthetic compounds.

## Motivating Activity

**Materials:**  magnet, 7 g iron filings, 4 g sulfur, safety goggles, apron, protective gloves, Bunsen burner, large test tube, tongs, toothpick

Use the magnet to separate a mixture of iron filings and sulfur. Ask students to indicate whether the combination of iron filings and sulfur is a mixture or compound and to support their choice. (mixture—can be separated by physical means)

**CAUTION:  Wear safety goggles, apron, and protective gloves when working with the Bunsen burner. Tie back long hair and loose clothing.** Place the iron filings and sulfur in the test tube. Gently heat the test tube over the flame of the Bunsen burner. Pour contents back into the petri dish. Ask students to identify the combination as a mixture or a compound and to support their choice. (compound—no longer has physical properties of individual components)

### Demonstration (Use with section 4.8 on page 80.)

**Materials:**  2 3-cm wads of coarse steel wool, timer, 50 mL vinegar in beaker, 2 large test tubes, water, 2 rubber stoppers to fit test tubes, ruler

Soak one wad of steel wool in the vinegar for one minute. Remove the steel wool and squeeze out the excess vinegar. Push the damp steel wool into the end of one test tube and the dry steel wool into the end of the other test tube.

Hold the test tubes upright. Half-fill each tube with water. Put rubber stoppers into the end of each tube and gently shake the tubes. Observe any color changes that may occur. (The steel wool soaked in vinegar oxidizes, or turns reddish brown, because the vinegar has removed the oil that coats the metal. The other sample is still coated with oil, which repels the water.)

## Computer Application (p. 71)

The computer application for this chapter will help students understand more fully the names of the elements and their symbols. For additional information on this activity, see pages T32–T34.

## Skill Activity (p. 78)

### Introduction

You can develop student confidence in reading for comprehension in stages. Begin by reading to the class a short, well-defined paragraph from a newspaper or magazine. Ask students to identify the main idea in the paragraph. Write each suggestion on the chalkboard. Repeat this procedure, reading increasingly complex paragraphs.

After the students have completed this exercise, have them do the Skill Activity in this chapter.

## Investigation 4 (p. 82)

### Introduction

This Investigation would be best performed after the class has discussed the characteristics of solutions on page 74. This Investigation should reinforce the concept that a solution, a type of mixture, can be separated by physical means.

### Conclusions

1. Answers will vary but should be between four and five colors.
2. Substances were separated according to their solubility.
3. The ink is a mixture because it was broken down by physical means.
4. black

### Applications

1. Kerosene is absorbed up the wick and burned.
2. so they do not have time to spread and create a larger stain
3. absorbency and strength

# CHAPTER 5

# Atoms and the Periodic Table

For additional information, see *Planning Unit 2*, pages T64–T65.

---

## Atomic Structure (p. 87)

---

### Background

In about 400 B.C., the Greek philosopher Democritus suggested that all matter on Earth was made of two components: empty space and tiny particles he called "atoms." (The word *atom* comes from the Greek word *atomos*, which means "that which cannot be cut or divided.")

At the same time, other Greeks, including the famous philosopher Aristotle, did not believe in atoms because they would not accept the concept of totally empty space. Instead, these Greeks believed that all matter was composed of four elements: earth, water, air, and fire. Because Aristotle and his views were so widely and highly respected, the concept of atoms was rejected. The belief that all matter was composed of the four elements was accepted and believed for almost 2000 years.

In the mid-1600s, Robert Boyle published articles on his belief in the existence of atoms. Almost 100 years later, Daniel Bernoulli made the first analytical application of the atomic theory in his study of gases. In the early 1800s, John Dalton proposed that chemical reactions involved the interaction of atoms. Dalton's work eventually led to the modern atomic theory used today.

### Motivating Activity

**Materials:** nut and bolt sets of the same size, balance

Nuts and bolts provide a good analogy for Dalton's atomic theory. They cannot be created, divided, or destroyed (at least by the students). All the bolts are of approximately identical size and mass; the same is true of the nuts. The mass of a bolt is greater than the mass of a nut. "Compounds" can be made by threading nuts on bolts. One nut represents one atom of element N. One bolt represents one atom of element B.

Have students determine the average mass of an individual nut and bolt by finding the mass of all the nuts and all the bolts. To find the average mass of one nut, divide the total mass by the number of nuts. Repeat to find the average mass of one bolt.

Thread one nut (N) on each bolt (B) to make the compound BN. Predict and then determine the mass of BN. Show how this model explains the law of constant composition.

Make a variety of compounds such as $BN_2$, $BN_3$, and $BN_4$. Compounds such as $B_2N$ and $B_3N$ cannot be made. Analyze and predict the mass of each compound. Use the balance to measure the mass of each compound. Show that the results are in accordance with the law of multiple proportions, as Dalton predicted.

### Demonstration (Use with section 5.4 on page 91.)

**Materials:** compass; ruler; 3 80-cm x 80-cm sheets of paper; marking pen; sheets of red, blue, and yellow paper; scissors

Using a compass, draw a circle with a radius of 6 cm in the center of each sheet of paper. Then, using the same center point, draw another circle with a radius of 24 cm. The small circle represents the nucleus and the large circle represents the area where the electron is found. Label the sheets of paper as follows: "hydrogen-1" (protium), "hydrogen-2" (deuterium), and "hydrogen-3" (tritium).

From the sheets of colored paper, cut circles to represent protons, neutrons, and electrons. On each paper, paste the correct number of protons, neutrons, and electrons for each isotope: hydrogen-1 = 1 proton, 0 neutron, 1 electron; hydrogen-2 = 1 proton, 1 neutron, 1 electron; and hydrogen-3 = 1 proton, 2 neutrons, 1 electron.

Add circles of colored paper to represent the two isotopes of carbon: carbon-12 (6 protons, 6 neutrons, 6 electrons) and carbon-14 (6 protons, 8 neutrons, 6 electrons).

---

## The Periodic Table (p. 93)

---

### Background

Elements were first classified early in the nineteenth century. In 1817, a German chemist, Johann Dobereiner, noted that the metals calcium, barium, and strontium had similar properties and that the atomic mass of strontium was midway between calcium and barium. These three elements formed a triad.

In 1863, John Newlands, an English chemist, arranged the elements in order of increasing atomic mass. He observed a repetition of like properties after every eighth element. From this observation, Newlands proposed the law of octaves and divided the elements known at that time into groups of eight.

Six years later, in 1869, Dimitri Mendeleev, a Russian chemist, noticed that the properties of elements are functions of atomic masses and that properties are not confined to groups of eight. Mendeleev divided the known elements into groups arranged in horizontal rows of varying length.

## Motivating Activity

**Materials:** list of first 20 elements with atomic masses

Arrange the elements in order of increasing atomic mass. Point out the repeating similarities in the properties of the elements when they are arranged according to mass.

## Demonstration (Use with section 5.6 on page 93.)

**Materials:** laboratory hood, safety goggles, apron, gloves, 2 1000-mL beakers, water, phenolphthalein, overhead projector, forceps, sodium (Na) metal (pea-sized), wire screen, potassium (K) metal (pea-sized)

**CAUTION: This demonstration should be performed under a laboratory hood for safety. The sodium and potassium will react quickly and violently with the water. Wear safety goggles, apron and gloves while doing this demonstration. Handle all metals in this demonstration with forceps only. Cover the beakers with the wire screen immediately after the metal is dropped into the water.**

Quarter-fill each beaker with water. Add 1 drop of phenolphthalein to each beaker. Place the beakers on an overhead projector. The ensuing results can best be seen in a darkened room.

With forceps, drop a very tiny piece of sodium metal into the first beaker. Immediately cover the beaker with the wire screen. Observe the reaction. Repeat, dropping a very tiny piece of potassium metal into the second beaker. Immediately cover the beaker with the wire screen.

Point out to students that both sodium and potassium belong to the same family in the periodic table. Have students predict what would happen if the same experiment were done with the elements rubidium, cesium, and francium.

## Skill Activity (p. 98)

### Introduction

Encourage students to become familiar with all the parts of the periodic table. Point out to students the location on the periodic table of the following components: element name and symbol, electron number, and atomic mass. Also point out to students the arrangement of elements into families, or groups (vertical rows), and periods, or series (horizontal rows).

After completing this discussion, have students do the Skill Activity in this chapter.

## Investigation 5 (p. 102)

### Introduction

This Investigation would be best performed after the class has discussed the structure of atoms on page 88. This Investigation should reinforce the concept and understanding of how the scientific method works in solving problems.

A shoe box with the cover taped on or a coffee can with an opaque lid will work well for a sealed container. Unknown objects may include objects of various sizes, shapes, and densities such as a piece of chalk, a lead sinker, a washer, a small glass or plastic bead, a rubber eraser, some coins, and a cork.

## Answers to Writing Critically (p. 105)

1. Answers will vary but should include a discussion of protons, neutrons, and electrons.
2. From the atomic number of the unknown element, the number of electrons in the valence shell can be determined. This will give some information about the element's ability to react chemically and whether it is a metal or nonmetal.
3. Because copper is missing electrons in its valence shell, it combines easily with other atoms—which is a feature of conductivity. Examples may include copper pots and wiring.
4. Answers will vary.
5. Answers will vary but may include changing chemical structures.

For additional information, see *Planning Unit 2*, pages T64–T65.

## Molecules and Ions (p. 107)

### Background
Acids release hydrogen ions in solution. The concentration of hydrogen ions in a solution is measured on the pH scale. Pure water has a pH of 7; it is neutral. A solution with a pH greater than 7 is basic. A solution with a pH less than 7 is acidic.

### Motivating Activity
**Materials:** litmus paper, forceps, pH color chart, milk, lemon juice, red vinegar, distilled water, white vinegar, soap solution, raw egg white, baking soda dissolved in water

On a sheet of paper, list the solutions to be tested. Use litmus paper to test the pH of the different solutions. Hold one end of the litmus paper with forceps. Dip the other end into the solution to be tested. Remove the paper and compare the color of the paper to the color chart. Record your results on the paper, next to each solution listed. (results: milk—acid; lemon juice—acid; red vinegar—acid; distilled water—neutral; white vinegar—acid; soap solution—varies but should be basic; raw egg white—basic; baking soda/water—basic)

### Demonstration (Use with section 6.5 on page 111.)
**Materials:** 3 test tubes, distilled water, test-tube rack, dropper, dilute hydrochloric acid, ammonia solution, Bromthymol blue, 250-mL beaker, antacid tablet or liquid, glass stirring rod

Half-fill two test tubes with distilled water and place them in the test tube rack. To one test tube, add 10 drops of dilute hydrochloric acid. To the other test tube, add 10 drops of ammonia solution. Add 5 drops of Bromthymol blue to each test tube. Observe the color change in each tube. (yellow in acid, blue in base)

Half-fill the third test tube with distilled water and add 10 drops of hydrochloric acid and 5 drops of Bromthymol blue. Note the color. Then add 16 drops of ammonia solution, 2 drops at a time. Note the color change as the ammonia is added. (The color will change from yellow to blue. A green color may appear as the solution changes from an acid to a base.)

Half-fill a beaker with dilute hydrochloric acid. Add 5 drops of Bromthymol blue. Stir in a crushed antacid tablet or antacid liquid. Observe the color change. (The color will change from yellow to green as the acid is neutralized. The color may change to blue if too much antacid has been added.)

## Chemical Equations (p. 115)

### Background
A chemical equation describes a chemical reaction. A chemical equation shows the relative number of atoms and molecules of the reactants and products in a chemical reaction. For example, the chemical equation for the reaction of carbon with oxygen gas to produce carbon dioxide is as follows:

$$C + O_2 \rightarrow CO_2$$

The equation says that one atom of carbon reacts with one molecule of oxygen to produce one molecule of carbon dioxide.

### Motivating Activity
**Materials:** large cards with symbols to represent atoms

Have students hold cards that represent atoms to demonstrate the following balanced equations. The arrangement of the cards is not important, but the same number of cards of each type must appear on both sides of the equation.

$$C + O_2 \rightarrow CO_2$$
$$2H_2 + O_2 \rightarrow 2H_2O$$
$$2K + Cl_2 \rightarrow 2\,KCl$$
$$N_2 + 3H_2 \rightarrow 2\,NH_3$$
$$4Al + 3O_2 \rightarrow 2Al_2O_3$$

### Demonstration (Use with section 6.7 on page 116.)
**Materials:** safety goggles, laboratory apron, fire extinguisher, graduate, beaker, 25 mL glycerine, 25 mL liquid dishwashing detergent, tape, candle, meter stick, rubber tubing, natural gas outlet, funnel, matches

**CAUTION: Put on safety goggles and a laboratory apron. Do not do this demonstration around any flammable objects. As when working with any open flame, have a fire extinguisher nearby.** Before doing the demonstration, mix equal parts of glycerine and liquid dish detergent in the beaker. You may want to add a few drops of water to dilute the glycerine and soap mixture slightly. Tape a candle to one end of a meter stick.

Connect the rubber tubing to a natural gas outlet. Connect the other end of the tubing to a small funnel. Invert the funnel in the glycerine/soap mixture. Remove the funnel from the mixture and check to make sure a thin film of the glycerine/soap mixture is stretched across the mouth of the funnel. Make a bubble of the soap mixture by opening the gas outlet carefully. Allow just enough gas to escape to create the bubble. Gently shake the bubble up and down to dislodge it from the funnel. Light the candle and pop the bubble with the flame. The following chemical reaction takes place:

$$CH_4 + O_2 \rightarrow CO_2 + 2\ H_2O$$

# Types of Reactions   (p. 119)

## Background
Substitution reactions occur when one substance is substituted for, or replaced by, another substance. This type of reaction is also called a single replacement reaction.

Exchange reactions occur when two substances replace each other in two compounds. For this reason, these reactions are often called double replacement reactions.

## Motivating Activity
**Materials:** bar of hand soap, 3 250-mL beakers, distilled water, liquid dishwashing detergent, 1 teaspoon Epsom salts, glass stirring rod

Swirl the bar of hand soap in a beaker of distilled water until the water becomes slightly cloudy. Add three or four drops of liquid dishwashing detergent to the other beaker and stir. Add the Epsom salts to the third beaker and stir. (The water and Epsom salts represent hard water.) Pour half of the Epsom salts water into each beaker and stir. Observe a precipitate form in the beaker with hand soap. The precipitation indicates that a chemical reaction took place.

## Demonstration   (Use with section 6.8 on page 119.)
**Materials:** black paper, tape, 3 test tubes, hydrogen peroxide, 3 balloons, test-tube rack, test-tube holder, $MnO_2$ as a catalyst, scoop

Wrap one test tube with black paper and tape the paper in place. Fill each test tube about half full of hydrogen peroxide. Place a balloon over the top of the test tube that has been covered with paper and over one other test tube. Place the tubes in a test-tube rack. Hold the third test tube with a test-tube holder. Use the scoop to place a few grains of $MnO_2$ into the third test tube. Gently swirl the tube and then cover the opening quickly with the balloon. Put the tube in the test-tube rack and place the rack in front of a bright light. As hydrogen peroxide breaks down into water and oxygen, the balloons will inflate. Observe the test tubes for the decomposition reaction.

# Skill Activity   (p. 114)

## Introduction
Review with students what they learned from the Chapter 2 Skill Activity: Making Tables (p. 36). After the students have completed their review, have them do the Skill Activity in this chapter.

# Investigation 6   (p. 122)

## Introduction
This Investigation would be best performed after the class has discussed chemical reactions on page 119.

Solutions of specific concentrations of NaOH and HCl can be purchased from a scientific supply company. A 0.1 M solution of both should work well. Vinegar may be substituted for acetic acid. Ethyl alcohol could be used as is from a purchased stock solution.

In procedure 2, NaOH and HCl will react to form salt (NaCl) and water. Since salt is soluable in water, it may not be visible. However, you can instruct the students to feel the test tube since heat should be generated. Magnesium will react with HCl to form $MgCl_2$ (a salt) and hydrogen gas. The bubbles will be evident immediately. A white powder should form on the magnesium ribbon. In procedure step 3, ethyl acetate, which has a characteristic odor, will form.

For additional information, see *Planning Unit 2,* pages T64–T65.

# Radioactivity  (p. 127)

## Background
In the early years of research into radioactivity, very few precautions were taken to minimize exposure to radiation. One experiment, called *Tickling the Dragon's Tail,* involved using two masses of fissionable material—each equal to one-half the amount needed to create a fission reaction. Scientists would tap the two masses closer and closer together using anything they happened to have on hand—screwdrivers, for example. When Geiger counters in the laboratory would begin to register high levels of radiation, the masses would be pushed apart—but not before everyone in the room was exposed to extremely high levels of radiation.

## Motivating Activity
**Materials:**  tapioca, salt, sieve, bright light

Mix the tapioca and salt. In this activity, tapioca represents alpha particles and salt represents beta particles. Pour the mixture through a sieve. Explain how the sieve is similar to a piece of paper in stopping the passage of alpha particles.

Hold a bright light over the sieve. The beam of light shining down through the sieve simulates gamma radiation.

## Demonstration  (Use with section 7.3 on page 129.)
**Materials:**  Geiger counter, sample of uranium mineral, cardboard, aluminum foil, glass

Hold a piece of paper between the Geiger counter and the source of radiation. Repeat using cardboard, aluminum foil, glass, and other substances. Observe how these materials reduce the intensity or stop the radiation reaching the Geiger counter.

# Nuclear Transformations  (p. 133)

## Background
The accumulated decay products from the disintegration of uranium, thorium, and potassium are found in rocks and minerals all over the earth. Samples of rock from the moon and pieces of meteorites also contain the accumulated products of radioactivity. All of the evidence points to an age of 4.5 billion years for the earth and the solar system.

## Motivating Activity
**Materials:**  250 sugar cubes, waxed paper, food coloring in dropper bottle, large bowl

Arrange the sugar cubes in a single layer on the waxed paper. Place one drop of food coloring on one side of each sugar cube. Wait a few minutes for the food coloring to dry.

Put the sugar cubes into a large bowl. Gently shake the bowl and then pour the sugar cubes onto the piece of waxed paper. Count and remove all the sugar cubes with the colored side facing up. Record the results. Place the remaining cubes into the bowl. Once again, gently shake the cubes and pour them onto the waxed paper. Count and remove the sugar cubes with the colored sides facing up. Repeat this procedure a total of 10 times. Ask students how many tosses are required to remove half the sugar cubes. This number of tosses represents the half-life of a sugar cube.

## Demonstration  (Use with section 7.5 on page 133.)
**Materials:**  35-cm x 20-cm piece of stiff cardboard or plywood, 1.4–1.8 kilograms of very fine lead shot, drill, cardboard box, books, balance

Drill about 30 holes into the piece of cardboard or plywood. Drill holes large enough for the lead shot to pass through easily. Place the drilled cardboard into a shallow cardboard box. Use books to elevate one end of the cardboard to make a ramp.

Determine the mass of the total amount of lead shot. Record this number on the chalkboard. Place the lead shot behind some kind of barrier at the top of the ramp. Remove the barrier and let the shot roll down the ramp. Determine the mass of the shot that did not fall through the holes. Return the shot to the top of the ramp. Repeat the procedure five times, determining the mass of the remaining shot each time.

Plot a graph showing mass of remaining shot versus run. The first run represents t = 1. Determine the half-life of the system from the graph.

Emphasize to the students the random nature of radioactive decay. There is no way of predicting which particular piece of lead shot will fall through a hole and "decay."

# Fission and Fusion (p. 137)

## Background
In only a fraction of a second, an atomic explosion creates a powerful blast effect. As the blast wave travels from the point of the explosion, it creates high pressure in the atmosphere. This pressure is so great that it knocks down buildings.

When an atomic bomb explodes, it also produces a glowing ball of fire that may reach temperatures of millions of degrees Celsius. The radiant energy produced in the fireball travels outward from ground zero at the speed of light, burning everything in its path.

## Motivating Activity
**Materials:** ruler, 24 dominoes

Use a ruler to set up 10 dominoes on end, about 10 cm apart from each other. Knock over the first 2 dominoes and observe what happens to the others. Ask students if this is an example of a chain reaction.

Set up all the dominoes in a row about 1 cm apart from each other. Knock over the first domino and observe what happens to the others. Compare the speed of this "reaction" to that in the first setup.

## Demonstration (Use with section 7.8 on page 137.)
**Materials:** clear plastic sandwich box with lid, black paint, two sheets of blotter paper, scissors, alcohol, radioactive source such as a piece of uranium ore, dry ice, high intensity light

Paint the bottom of the box with black paint and allow it to dry. Cut the blotter paper to fit the opposite sides of the box. Soak the pieces of blotter paper with alcohol and place them at opposite sides of the box. Place a uranium sample in the center of the box and then close the box. Keep the box level and set the box on a piece of dry ice. After a few minutes, shine a high-intensity light beam into the box from one of the sides. Darken the room to observe vapor tracks.

# Skill Activity (p. 132)

## Introduction
Review with students the Chapter 4 Skill Activity: Reading for Comprehension (p. 78). Review with students what they learned in the previous exercise about reading for comprehension. Once again, read a sample paragraph and ask students to identify the main idea(s).

After the students have reviewed what they know about reading for comprehension, have them do the Skill Activity in this chapter.

# Investigation 7 (p. 142)

## Introduction
This Investigation would be best performed after the class has discussed radioactive decay (p. 133). This Investigation should reinforce the process by which the rate of radioactive decay is used to date objects. It should also reinforce the students' skill at recording data in tabular form.

# Answers to Writing Critically (p. 145)

1. Students should mention alpha and beta particles and gamma rays and should discuss Geiger counters, scintillation counters, cloud chambers, and film badges.
2. The time required for one-half the atoms of a radioactive substance to decay; scientists can determine the age of substances by the amount of radioactive atoms it contains.
3. fission—the process of splitting atoms; fusion—the process of combining atoms; one neutron hitting uranium-235 causes it to emit two or three neutrons, which in turn hit other uranium-235 atoms, and so on.

For additional information, see *Planning Unit 2*, pages T64–T65.

# Industrial Chemistry (p. 147)

## Background
Natural gas contains methane and small amounts of other gases. To separate these gases, natural gas is cooled in the refinery. As it cools, the heavier gases condense first. As each gas becomes a liquid, it can be removed from the mixture. Long pipelines buried underground are used to move refined natural gas from the refinery to cities and towns, where it is used as a fuel.

## Motivating Activity
Display a variety of commercial products including any of the following: motor oil, automotive products, detergents, soap powder, bleach, plastics, nylon, polyester fabrics, food coloring, artificial sweeteners, medicines, cosmetics, shampoos, cleaners, cleansing agents, paints, photographic products, metals and alloys of various kinds, glass, ceramics, and fertilizers. Also have students check labels in their clothing for the presence of synthetic fibers. Discuss with students how great an impact the use of synthetic products has had on daily life.

## Demonstration (Use with section 8.1 on page 147.)
**Materials:** different grades of motor oil (such as SAE 10, SAE 20, SAE 30, SAE 40, and SAE 50), 100-mL graduates, masking tape, thermometers, forceps, 12-mm-diameter plastic spheres, timer

Fill 100-mL graduates with different grades of motor oil. Make sure the level of oil in each graduate is the same. Use pieces of masking tape to label the grade of motor oil in each graduate.

Take the temperature of each sample of motor oil and record it on the chalkboard. Use tongs to hold the plastic sphere so that it just touches the surface of the oil. Release the sphere and time how long the sphere takes to reach the bottom of the cylinder. Record the results of each trial on the chalkboard. Discuss with students the concept of viscosity—the property of having resistance to flow. Ask students to

identify which oil had the greatest viscosity and which had the least viscosity.

To test how temperature affects viscosity of the heavier grades of oil (SAE 40 or 50), fill three graduates to the same level with the same grade of oil. Place one graduate in the refrigerator overnight. Leave one graduate at room temperature. Place one graduate under a bright light for two hours to heat it. Take the temperature of the oil in each graduate. Record the temperatures. Drop a plastic sphere into each graduate and record the time it takes for the sphere to drop. Ask students how temperature affects the viscosity of motor oil.

# Metals and Alloys (p. 153)

## Background
Copper and tin are melted together to make bronze. Bronze has properties that are quite different from either copper or tin. For example, bronze is much harder than either copper or tin. Another advantage of bronze is that it does not rust easily. Although it does not rust, bronze does tarnish when exposed to the weather.

## Motivating Activity
Ask the students what they think is meant when periods of time are described as the stone age, the iron age, the bronze age, or the age of steel.

Explain that until humans were able to refine ores, tools and weapons were made from stone or bone. Eventually, someone figured out how to use iron ore, and the iron age began. Later, humans discovered how to create an alloy of copper and tin, and the bronze age began. Finally, steel was refined from iron ore and the age of steel began.

## Demonstration (Use with section 8.6 on page 155.)
**Materials:** safety goggles, laboratory apron, safety gloves, tongs, fine steel wool, Bunsen burner, copper wire, water, beaker

**CAUTION: Wear safety goggles, apron, and gloves while conducting this demonstration.** To show the formation of iron oxide, use tongs to hold a piece of fine steel wool in the flame of the Bunsen burner. Observe what happens to the steel wool. Continue heating the steel wool in the flame until there is no further change. Cool the steel wool and then feel it. Ask the students to compare the burned steel wool with an unburned sample. (The burned steel wool has oxidized and is extremely brittle. It will powder when it is touched.)

# Chemical Applications  (p. 158)

## Background
A telephone signal sent through a metal wire or the air must be regularly boosted, or amplified, using expensive equipment called repeaters. A laser signal traveling through a glass, or optic, fiber can go much farther without needing to be boosted. Today, satellites are used to beam information around the earth. Fiber optics will make communication cheaper and faster than it is with satellites.

## Motivating Activity
**Materials:**   shallow tray, aluminum foil, portland cement, plastic containers, water, sand, wooden stirring rods.

Line the bottom and sides of a shallow tray completely with aluminum foil. In a plastic container, mix a small amount of cement with a small amount of sand and just enough water to form a sticky mass. Pour the mass into the tray and spread it evenly with the wooden stirring rod. Allow the cement to harden. Have the students compare the properties of the wet concrete and hard concrete.

## Demonstration  (Use with section 8.7 on page 158.)
**Materials:**  safety goggles, laboratory apron, gloves, 50-cm piece of glass tubing, Bunsen burner

**CAUTION: Wear safety goggles, laboratory apron, and gloves while conducting this demonstration.** Tie back loose clothing and hair. Hold the glass tubing by both ends so that the burner flame is at the center of the tubing. As the glass heats, the flame turns yellow because of the sodium in the glass. Continue heating the glass until it softens. The soft glass can be bent or drawn into different shapes. Pull and twist the softened glass so that it separates, forming two pieces. Put one piece aside on a heatproof surface. Seal the hot end of the other piece of tubing by melting it together in the flame. While the glass is soft, blow gently down the open (cool) end of the tube. With practice, a bubble of very thin glass will form.

# Skill Activity  (p. 157)

## Introduction
Pose an everyday problem to the class and ask for volunteers to suggest ways to solve the problem. Point out to students that a step-by-step plan of action is helpful when solving a problem.

After you have completed the discussion with the students, have them do the Skill Activity in this chapter.

# Investigation 8  (p. 164)

## Introduction
This Investigation would be best performed after the class has discussed polymers (page 150). This Investigation should reinforce the concept of the wide and varied application of polymers and should give the students more practice in using observation skills.

Advance preparation of solutions may be desirable. Check the materials list on pages T45–T48 for a list of necessary chemicals.

# Answers to Writing Critically  (p. 167)

1. Crude oil is heated until it becomes a mixture of gases that can be separated by their densities.
2. In a blast furnace, the high temperatures cause the materials to undergo chemical reactions. Those reactions result in the separation of iron ore into molten iron and carbon dioxide.
3. Polymers are used to make fabrics. These fabrics have variety of uses, from clothing to artificial skin.
4. Cars made in the 1950s contained much more metal, making them very heavy. Cars made in the 1980s contain much plastic and less metal, making them much lighter.

## Planning Unit 3

| Chapter | Pupil's Edition Pages | | | Annotated Teacher's Edition Pages | Laboratory Manual/ Workbook | | | Teacher's Resource Book | | | | | | Overhead Transparencies** |
|---|---|---|---|---|---|---|---|---|---|---|---|---|---|---|
| | Skill Activity | Investigation | Chapter Review | | Investigation | Vocabulary | Concepts | Alternate Investigation | Skill Activity | Critical Thinking | Cross Discipline | Student Record Sheets | Test * | Transparency Number |
| 9 | 186 | 190 | 191–193 | T78–T79 | 41 | 131 | 132 | 151 | 261 | 341 | 301 | 467–468 | 389 | |
| 10 | 202 | 210 | 211–213 | T80–T81 | 43 | 133 | 134 | 157 | 262 | 342 | 302 | 469–470 | 391 | 5 |
| 11 | 222 | 234 | 235–237 | T82–T83 | 47 | 135 | 136 | 163 | 263 | 343 | 303 | 471–472 | 393 | |
| 12 | 251 | 258 | 259–261 | T84–T85 | 51 | 137 | 138 | 167 | 264 | 344 | 304 | 473–474 | 395 | 6 |
| 13 | 274 | 280 | 281–283 | T86–T87 | 55 | 139 | 140 | 173 | 265 | 345 | 305 | 475–476 | 397 | 7 |
| 14 | 291 | 300 | 301–303 | T88–T89 | 59 | 141 | 142 | 179 | 266 | 346 | 306 | 477–478 | 399 | |

Suggestions for audiovisual materials can be found on pages T41–T43.
\* See also *Computer Testbank* for chapter tests.
\*\* Component also includes copying masters of the transparencies for use in instruction or evaluation.

## Introducing Unit 3 (pp. 170 and 171)

### How Things Work

Have the students look at pages 170 and 171. Explain that what they are looking at is a photograph of the Brooklyn Bridge, which connects the boroughs of Brooklyn and Manhattan in New York City. Through the cables the twin towers of the World Trade Center can be seen. Only one building, the Sears Tower in Chicago, Illinois, is taller than the World Trade Center.

When it was completed in 1883, the Brooklyn Bridge was the largest suspension bridge in the world. Discuss with students the types of machines that they think were used to construct a bridge such as this. Ask them how technology has had to change since 1883 in order to allow for the construction of the World Trade Center.

people must give very precise and complete directions to a computer so that it can do its job correctly.

## Demonstration (Use with section 14.4 on page 292.)

**Material:** 6 index cards, scissors, marking pen

Cut each index card in half crosswise. On one side of each card, write "off"; on the other side, write "on." Arrange the cards in three rows of four each. The cards should all have "on" facing up.

Recall that a computer stores information in a series of on and off switches. Create a code for the digits 0 through 9. Each digit is represented by four on/off notations.

0 = off off off off
1 = off off off on
2 = off off on off
3 = off off on on
4 = off on off off
5 = off on off on
6 = off on on off
7 = off on on on
8 = on off off off
9 = on off off on

Arrange the cards, according to your code, to represent the numbers 325, 746, 193, and 852.

## Robotics (p. 296)

### Background

One type of sensor used by robots detects infrared radiation. Infrared rays are sometimes called heat rays. These rays are emitted by most objects but are invisible to the human eye. The warmer the object, the greater the strength of its infrared radiation. Infrared sensors detect living organisms or fire. Using an infrared detector, a guard robot can be programmed to sound an alarm if the heat of a fire is detected. An industrial robot can be programmed to stop performing a dangerous activity if it will endanger a person. A robot can also be programmed to follow paths marked by infrared reflecting paint while moving things from one place to another.

### Motivating Activity

Have the students make a list of all the activities or jobs they know robots are already capable of doing. On a separate paper, have the students make a list of activities or jobs they think robots will probably be doing by the year 2000. Make sure they consider activities in industry, medicine, publishing, sports, and the arts. Point out that while robots will eliminate some jobs, other jobs will be created in the robotics and computer industries.

## Demonstration (Use with section 14.7 on page 296.)

**Materials:** paper, pencil

Ask a student to act as a robot waiting for instructions. Have other students write detailed, step-by-step instructions for the following series of actions: rising from a chair, walking across the room, answering the telephone, saying "hello," hanging up the phone, walking back to the chair, and sitting down. Ask the "robot" student to follow the directions exactly. Students will quickly see the problems associated with developing robots that can do human tasks. Students should also realize that computers and robots are only as smart as the people who design and make them.

## Skill Activity (p. 291)

### Introduction

Have students write step-by-step directions for making a bowl of cereal with milk and a sliced banana for breakfast. Convert the written directions into the form of a flowchart. Point out to students how the flowchart saves many words and avoids confusion about sequencing of events.

After students have completed this exercise, have them do the Skill Activity in this chapter.

## Investigation 14 (p. 300)

### Introduction

This Investigation would be best performed after the class has discussed how a computer operates (page 285). This Investigation should demonstrate the amount of detailed information and directions required to make a computer work properly. This Investigation should also point out the positive impact computers have had on our society.

## Planning Unit 4

| Chapter | Pupil's Edition Pages | | | Annotated Teacher's Edition Pages | Laboratory Manual/Workbook | | | Teacher's Resource Book | | | | | | Overhead Transparencies ** |
|---|---|---|---|---|---|---|---|---|---|---|---|---|---|---|
| | Skill Activity | Investigation | Chapter Review | | Investigation | Vocabulary | Concepts | Alternate Investigation | Skill Activity | Critical Thinking | Cross Discipline | Student Record Sheets | Test* | Transparency Number |
| 15 | 317 | 324 | 325–327 | T92–T93 | 61 | 143 | 144 | 183 | 267 | 347 | 307 | 479–480 | 401 | 8, 9 |
| 16 | 333 | 344 | 345–347 | T94–T95 | 65 | 145 | 146 | 187 | 268 | 348 | 308 | 481–482 | 403 | 10 |
| 17 | 356 | 366 | 367–369 | T96–T97 | 67 | 147 | 148 | 191 | 269 | 349 | 309 | 483–484 | 405 | 11 |
| 18 | 380 | 388 | 389–391 | T98–T99 | 71 | 149 | 150 | 195 | 270 | 350 | 310 | 485–486 | 407 | 12 |
| 19 | 400 | 410 | 411–413 | T100–T101 | 73 | 151 | 152 | 199 | 271 | 351 | 311 | 487–488 | 409 | 13, 14 |

Suggestions for audiovisual materials can be found on pages T41–T43.

\* See also *Computer Testbank* for chapter tests.

\** Component also includes copying masters of the transparencies for use in instruction or evaluation.

## Introducing Unit 4 (pp. 306 and 307)

### Exploring the Universe

Have the students look at pages 306 and 307. Explain that what they are looking at is a photograph of the Blue Mesa in the Painted Desert, region of the Petrified Forest National Monument in northern Arizona.

Ask the students what they would consider to be a long time. How old is old? Point out that the rocks in this photograph tell a story that is billions of years old. The rocks and the fossils in the rocks tell the 4.5-billion-year-old story of the earth. The light from the stars in the sky tells a story that is even older—perhaps 20 billion years old.

Ask the students what object they would consider to be really big. After discussion, point out that the planet Jupiter is 11 times larger than Earth and that the size of either of these planets is small when compared with the size of a galaxy or with that of the Universe.

# Using *Science & Technology*

**(pp. 414 and 415)**

## Is New York Moving Away from London?

This concept is very difficult for many people to imagine. Whole continents are moving over the surface of the earth. Review with the students the concept of plate tectonics. Reinforce the idea that these changes are occurring very slowly. Tell the students that there is no chance that they are going to wake up one morning and find that southern California has drifted out into the Pacific Ocean.

Point out, however, that southern California is, in fact, slowly moving up the western coast of North America. About 25 million years from now, this portion of the United States will be an island off the coast of Alaska. You may wish to explain that the earthquakes that periodically occur in California are evidence of this movement.

This article describes the methods by which scientists measure the movement of the continents. Based upon the information in the article, ask the students to determine how much farther apart North America and Europe have drifted since they were born. How much farther apart have the two plates drifted since the United States Constitution was signed in 1787?

# Bibliography

**Arduini, Paolo.** *Simon & Schuster's Guide to Fossils.* New York: Simon & Schuster, 1986.

**Blong, R. J.** *Volcanic Hazards: A Sourcebook on the Effects of Eruptions.* Orlando, Florida: Academic Press, 1984.

**Chester, David K.** *Mount Etna, the Anatomy of a Volcano.* New York: Chapman and Hall, 1985.

**Colbert, Edwin Harris.** *Wandering Lands and Animals: The Story of Continental Drift and Animal Populations.* New York: Dover, 1985.

**DeCamp, L. Sprague.** *Day of the Dinosaur.* New York: Bonanza Books, 1985.

**Denison, Rodger E.** *Geology and Geochronology of Precambrian Rocks in the Central Interior Region of the United States.* Washington, D.C.: United States Government Printing Office, 1984.

**Martin, J. S. Rudwick.** *The Meaning of Fossils: Episodes in the History of Palaeontology.* Chicago: University of Chicago Press, 1985.

**Windley, B. F.** *The Evolving Continents.* New York: Wiley, 1984.

For additional information, see *Planning Unit 4,* pages T90–T91.

## Locating Places on Earth (p. 309)

### Background

In about 240 B.C., Eratosthenes, a Greek scientist, calculated the circumference of the earth. Eratosthenes based his calculations on the angles of a triangle. Eratosthenes lived in Alexandria, Egypt. He had heard that in the city of Syene, the sun was directly overhead at high noon on midsummer day (June 21) each year. He measured the angle of the sun at high noon in Alexandria and the angle of the sun at noon in Syene. He also knew that Syene was 910 km south of Alexandria. Using this information, he figured out that the circumference of the earth was 45,500 km. This number is close to the modern calculated value of 40,030 km. (Inform students that the metric system was not used in 240 B.C. These measurements are equivalent to those made by Eratosthenes.)

### Motivating Activity

**Materials:** ball, tape

With tape, mark two locations on the ball on the same side, several centimeters apart. Ask, "If this ball is our planet and we are at point A, how can we find our way to point B?" Remember that "up" is away from the surface and "down" is into the center of the ball. Right, left, and straight are relative terms that could lead anywhere on the surface of the ball. Explain that ancient people lived with this same handicap. They did not know about the compass and had no lines of latitude or longitude to use as reference.

### Demonstration (Use with section 15.2 on page 311.)
**Materials:** wall map, string, tape measure, world globe

Tell the students that two planes are flying from New York City to Cairo, Egypt. On a wall map, tack a piece of string showing a straight route from New York to Cairo. This is the route of plane A. Using a second piece of string, mark a route from New York to Cairo that forms a smooth arc passing across the border between France and Spain, the island of Sardinia in the Mediterranean, and the "toe" of Italy. This is the route of plane B. Ask students which plane is taking the shorter route. (the route taken by plane A)

Now have students look at a globe of the earth. Locate New York and Cairo on the globe. Using string, trace the two routes on the globe. Ask the students to measure the two routes. Which is shorter? (The route taken by plane B is shorter.) Explain that on a sphere, the shortest distance between two points lies along a great circle. The part of the great circle between two cities is a great circle arc.

## Earth in Science (p. 313)

### Background

In 1543, the Polish astronomer Nicholas Copernicus concluded that all the planets, including the earth, revolve around the sun in circular orbits. Copernicus was proven correct in 1610 by the Italian astronomer, Galileo Galilei. Galileo had constructed a telescope in 1609, and he used it to observe the moon, the planets, and the stars. He discovered that he could see only parts of Venus at certain times, just as only parts of the moon are visible at certain times in a month. Similar observations of Mercury showed that it, too, was only partly visible at certain times. The portion of Venus, the moon, and Mercury facing away from the sun were in shadow. Galileo's observations about Venus and Mars proved that they moved around the sun.

### Motivating Activity

**Materials:** tape, paper, corrugated cardboard, 2 thumbtacks, string, pencil

Tape a large piece of paper to a large piece of corrugated cardboard. Place a thumbtack in the center of the paper. Tie the two ends of the piece of string together. Loop the string over the tack and draw a circle with a pencil using the string as a guide. Place a second tack about 5 cm from the first one. Loop the string around both tacks. Try to draw the circle again. This time, what is drawn is an ellipse. The two tacks in the center form the foci of the ellipse. Label the aphelion (the point of the ellipse farthest from the foci) and the perihelion (the point of the ellipse closest to the foci).

Explain to students that the orbits around the sun of the earth and other planets are ellipses. At aphelion, the Northern Hemisphere of earth experiences summer. At perihelion, the Northern Hemisphere experiences winter.

## Demonstration (Use with section 15.4 on page 315.)

**Materials:** tape, 2 thermometers, black construction paper, light, timer

Tape two thermometers to a piece of black construction paper. Place the thermometers under a bright light. Position the thermometers so that the first is directly under the light and the second is at an angle to the light. Turn on the light. After 15 minutes, read the temperatures on the thermometers. Which thermometer has the higher reading? Ask the students to explain why. Move the second thermometer to a greater angle away from the light. Repeat the procedure. How does the temperature compare with the first reading? Have the students explain why. (As the angle increases, the temperature decreases, because the light rays are indirect.)

## Solid Earth (p. 318)

### Background

Paleomagnetism is the study of ancient magnetic fields that are preserved in rock. When lava hardens, or iron minerals are deposited in a body of water, or iron oxide is heated, the iron minerals align themselves so the north-seeking end of the mineral is pointing northward. The orientation of these minerals does not change if the earth's poles reverse themselves or if the earth's poles wander. By using delicate instruments, scientists can tell the polarity and location of the poles during ancient times.

### Motivating Activity

**Materials:** tall, clear container; water; sediments such as sand, pebbles, silt, and clay; timer

Fill a tall, clear container about three-fourths full of water. Drop a small amount of various sediments such as sand, pebbles, silt, and clay into the water. Time how long it takes for each type of sediment to fall through the water and hit the bottom. Ask the students where the largest particles

are likely to settle in relation to the mouth of a river.

## Demonstration (Use with section 15.5 on page 318.)

**Materials:** mineral samples such as galena, hematite, quartz, talc, graphite, pyrite, halite, and hornblende; streak plate or unglazed porcelain tile; paper towels; metal pick

Have students examine and compare the characteristics of the different minerals. Make a chart on the chalkboard to record the color, streak, luster, and hardness of each mineral. First, ask students to record the color of each mineral. Then have students rub each mineral across the streak plate. Wipe the streak plate clean with paper towels between each trial. Record the results on the chalkboard. Have the students determine the luster of each mineral and then record their results. Then have students scrape each mineral with the pick to determine hardness. Record these results to finish the chart.

## Skill Activity (p. 317)

### Introduction

Discuss with students the importance of knowing how to calculate the time in different time zones. Point out to students that many businesses along the west coast of the United States must adjust their working hours to be able to conduct business with companies on the east coast. Discuss with students what problems might arise for employees on the west coast.

When you have completed the discussion, have students do the Skill Activity in this chapter.

## Investigation 15 (p. 324)

### Introduction

This Investigation would be best performed after the class has discussed the seasons (page 315). The Investigation should help students understand how the inclination of the earth's axis affects the angle of the sun's rays.

For additional information, see *Planning Unit 4*, pages T90–T91.

## The Sun (p. 329)

### Background

During the sun's 4.5 billion years of existence, about half the hydrogen originally contained in the core has been used up. Eventually, the entire amount will be exhausted. When this happens, the core of the sun will contract, the sun will become hotter, and it will increase in size, becoming a red giant star. As the sun increases in size, it will destroy first Mercury, then Venus, and eventually Earth. Scientists believe that the sun will not run out of hydrogen for about another 5 billion years. After the sun expands, it will gradually shrink in size, becoming a white dwarf star. In the end, the sun will cool off and become a cold, dark mass called a black dwarf.

### Motivating Activity

**Materials:** paper, pencil, meter stick

Make a scale model of the solar system. Use any scale you wish. Calculate the distances of all the planets from the sun before you make the actual model. The following are distances of the planets in astronomical units (A.U.) as they compare to the distance of the earth from the sun.

| | |
|---|---|
| Mercury | 0.4 A.U. |
| Venus | 0.7 A.U. |
| Earth | 1.0 A.U. |
| Mars | 1.5 A.U. |
| Jupiter | 5.2 A.U. |
| Saturn | 9.5 A.U. |
| Uranus | 19.2 A.U. |
| Neptune | 30.1 A.U. |
| Pluto | 39.5 A.U. |

Students will soon see that the earth is very close to the sun, compared with the outer planets. Have students suggest scales they might use to compare the distances of the planets. For example, if the earth is 1 cm from the sun, Pluto is 39.5 cm away from the sun. If the earth is 1 km from the sun, Pluto is 39.5 km away from the sun.

### Demonstration (Use with section 16.2 on page 331.)

**Materials:** tape, unlined paper, binoculars, masking tape, pencil

**CAUTION: Never look directly into the sun. It can permanently damage the eyes.** This demonstration must be done on a sunny day. Tape paper over both lenses on one side of a pair of binoculars. Tape an unlined piece of paper to a desk or table in front of a sunny window. With the wide end of the binoculars toward the sun, focus the image of the sun onto the sheet of paper. Hold the binoculars 20–30 cm away from the paper. Trial and error will result in the sharpest focus of the sun's image. The image should be at least 3 cm in diameter. Sun spots appear in the sun's image as dark spots. With a pencil, draw around the sun spots. Repeat the procedure in two or three days. Once again, circle the position of the sun spots. Have the sun spots changed position?

## Planetary System (p. 334)

### Background

Asteroids revolve around the sun in elliptical orbits, frequently colliding with each other. These collisions cause the asteroids to fragment and to change orbit. As a result, over 700 asteroids have orbits that cross Earth's orbit.

Just as other planets and moons have been struck by asteroids, Earth must have had a similar past. Wind, rain, and other erosional processes on Earth, however, have erased most traces of the impact craters. However, some impact craters, caused by asteroids, are still visible on the surface of the earth. Barringer Meteor Crater in Winslow, Arizona, is more than a kilometer across and 180 m deep. Barringer Crater was formed 50,000 years ago when an asteroid weighing 484,000,000 kg struck the earth. This asteroid had the mass of a medium-sized office building.

Asteroids range in size from less than one km in diameter to almost 1000 km. The largest recorded asteroid, Ceres, is 974 km in diameter, or about the size of Texas. Most asteroids have diameters of around 10 km. The asteroids consist of iron-magnesium silicates and iron-nickel metal.

Fragments of asteroids that fall to Earth are called meteorites. Meteorites may also be fragments of comets. Over 3000 meteorites have been collected. However, only 1000 of these were actually seen falling. Over 90 percent of meteorites consist of rock that is similar in composition to earth's mantle. These meteorites are called stony meteorites. The other 10 percent of meteorites are mainly iron meteorites, consisting of iron with small amounts of nickel.

## Motivating Activity
**Materials:**  bright light, ball

To show the phases of the moon, have the students sit in the middle of the room with a large light bulb glowing in the front of the room. The bright bulb represents the sun. Hold a ball—representing the moon—and walk around the class. As you do so, ask what portion of the ball is lit, what side is lit, and what shape the lit portion has. Relate students' answers to the phases of the moon.

## Demonstration  (Use with section 16.3 on page 334.)
**Materials:**  flour, water, flat pan, flour sifter

Make lumps of flour by adding droplets of water to the flour and rolling it in the palm of your hand. Let the lumps dry for a day or two. Add about 2 cm of water to a flat pan. With a flour sifter, sift a layer of flour about 1 cm thick over the surface of the water. Drop the lumps from various heights and different angles. Describe the craters you see. Some flour balls may break through the surface, and the water may come through. If so, compare the water to lava that might flow because a meteorite broke through a thin-crusted planet or moon.

# Skill Activity  (p. 333)

## Introduction
Throughout their school years, most students have seen diagrams of the solar system and the planets. Unfortunately, these diagrams are rarely drawn to scale because of space limitations. By using this Skill Activity, the students will first learn how to determine scale on a graph. They will also develop an understanding of the planets in comparison with one another.

# Investigation 16  (p. 344)

## Introduction
This Investigation would be best performed after the class has discussed the composition and structure of the sun (page 329). The Investigation should reinforce student's measurement skills and refine their ability to follow directions.

## Conclusions
1. Answers will vary but should approximate the focal length of the lens used.
2. Answers will vary.
3. Answers will vary but should be approximately 1,380,000 km.

## Application
Students should explain that they would be able to use the ratio provided in the investigation. Since the actual diameter is known, they would simply repeat the Investigation to determine the average diameter and the average distance.

# CHAPTER 17 The Universe

For additional information, see *Planning Unit 4*, pages T90–T91.

## Stars (p. 349)

### Background

Early Greek astronomers tried to measure the distance to the stars but failed. In about 1600, the German astronomer Johann Kepler estimated that the closest stars are at least 6300 times farther away from Earth than the sun is. Isaac Newton increased this value to 125,000 times farther away, equivalent to about 2 light years.

Measuring such great distances was a difficult task. In 1838, the German astronomer Friedrich Bessel was successful in determining that a star known as 61 Cygni was 11 light years away from Earth. He chose 61 Cygni because it seemed to move very fast with respect to nearby stars. The speed of 61 Cygni suggested that it might be close to Earth. However, there are stars even closer to Earth than 61 Cygni. Other than the sun, the closest is Proxima Centauri, which is 4.26 light years away.

### Motivating Activity

**Materials:** binoculars or telescope, constellation map

On a clear, starry night, look at the stars in the sky through binoculars or a telescope. Refer to a constellation map. Locate as many constellations as possible using the unaided eye. Make observations at different times of night. How do the constellations move? (Earth's rotation causes the apparent movement.)

### Demonstration (Use with section 17.2 on page 351.)

**Materials:** safety goggles, safety gloves, laboratory apron, Bunsen burner, insulated tongs, metal strip

**CAUTION: Put on safety goggles, laboratory apron, and safety gloves. Tie back loose clothing and hair while doing this demonstration.** Light a Bunsen burner and adjust the flame so that it is as hot as possible. Using insulated tongs, hold a strip of metal in the flame. Have students describe what they see. The metal should start to glow from the red end of the spectrum and move up to the blue end. If a spectroscope is available, have the students observe the flame through the scope. Have them describe what they see.

## Galaxies (p. 357)

### Background

The German philosopher Immanuel Kant (1724–1804) believed that nebulae lay within the region of the fixed stars. He thought that nebulae were "island universes" outside the galaxy. Kant believed that each nebula was a vast system of stars just like a galaxy.

One nebula, M31, which is easily visible with the naked eye, lies in the Andromeda constellation. On December 30, 1924, a young American astronomer, Edwin Hubble, announced that he had calculated the distance to M31. He had determined that M31 definitely lies outside our galaxy, just as Kant had predicted.

Edwin Hubble applied his findings to many other disk-shaped nebulae and showed that they all lie outside our galaxy. With these observations, the size of the known universe was expanded enormously. Today, astronomers have shown that the radius of the universe is at least 16.5 billion light years and that it contains about 100 billion known galaxies. On the average, a galaxy contains 100 billion stars. The total number of stars in the universe is about one sextillion ($10^{22}$).

### Motivating Activity

**Materials:** chalk, black construction paper

Have each student select one of the galaxies that is pictured in the text and draw an accurate picture of it on the black paper. Have the students exchange diagrams with a classmate. Ask the students to identify the galaxies they now have. Explain to students that before the camera was used in astronomy, scientists depended upon their artistic abilities to record information. Ask the students if they can imagine finding one star, based on someone's drawing, from the night sky.

### Demonstration (Use with section 17.4 on page 359.)

**Materials:** 1 self-adhesive dot, plastic flying disk, marking pen

Attach a self-adhesive dot to a plastic flying disk. Draw arrows on the surface of the disk going out in all directions from the dot. The dot represents Earth, and the arrows represent the direction away from Earth's surface where the Milky Way can be seen. The disk represents the Milky Way. If you look up from the dot, you would see the few stars above Earth in the flattest part of the Milky Way. If you were to look toward the center of the disk, many more stars would be visible. Have students compare this model of Earth in the Milky Way to the observations of early astronomers.

# The Changing Universe (p. 361)

## Background

Time measured from the beginning of the universe is called *cosmologic time*. According to the Big Bang theory, within the first millionth of a second, the universe began expanding. At the high temperatures of the early universe, matter was not stable. Energy changed into elementary particles with electric charges—particles such as protons and electrons. However, these elementary particles immediately combined and changed back to energy.

Within the first ten seconds after the universe began expanding, however, the temperature decreased. At this lower temperature, protons, neutrons, and electrons could form. Within four minutes, the universe had cooled enough to allow protons and neutrons to form the nuclei of hydrogen and helium.

By the time the universe was 700,000 years old, the temperature in the expanding universe had dropped below 3000°C. At this lower temperature, neutral atoms of hydrogen and helium could form. The universe then was simply a rapidly expanding gas cloud consisting of 74 percent hydrogen and 26 percent helium.

## Motivating Activity
**Materials:** television

Explain to students that the explosion that formed the universe produced large amounts of radiation. Some of this radiation, called *microwave background radiation,* still exists. Turn on a television set to an unused channel. Turn down the brightness until the screen is almost black. One in a hundred of the little flashes seen on the screen is caused by microwave background radiation left over from the Big Bang. The other 99 percent of the radiation is from electronic communication equipment.

## Demonstration (Use with section 17.6 on page 362.)
**Materials:** water-base marker, balloon

Using the marker, place three dots on the top, bottom, and side of a balloon to represent galaxies. Blow up the balloon. What happens to the distance between the dots? (It increases.) If this balloon represents the universe as it expands, what is left in the center? (empty space) How does the size of the dots change as the balloon is blown up? (The size increases, just as galaxies spread out and become diffuse as they age.)

# Skill Activity (p. 356)

## Introduction

Explain to students that ancient travelers and navigators did not have accurate maps of the land and oceans. They did, however, have fairly accurate maps of the stars and constellations. Ancient navigators found their way by referring to their position in relation to the stars. Discuss with students the obvious drawbacks of this type of navigation. Ask students how these ancient people would navigate on cloudy nights. (They would not. They would anchor and wait for the clouds to pass.)

After completing the discussion, have students do the Skill Activity in this chapter.

# Investigation 17 (p. 366)

## Introduction

This Investigation would be best performed after the class has discussed stars and constellations (page 350). The Investigation should reinforce the concept that accurate study and measurement of stars is complicated by their great distance from Earth. The Investigation should also reinforce students' skills in measurement and recording data in a table.

For additional information, see *Planning Unit 4,* pages T90–T91.

# The Earth's Past (p. 371)

## Background

Many scientists think the moon was formed in the same way as the earth. However, others believe that the moon was formed when an asteroid collided with the earth.

If an asteroid had struck the earth, the impact would have thrown a great deal of crustal material into orbit. Eventually, these materials could have condensed to form the moon. When Apollo astronauts brought back moon rocks, scientists discovered that moon rocks were, in fact, very similar to crustal rocks on Earth.

Still other scientists hypothesize that the moon was formed in another part of the solar system and later was captured by Earth's gravity. Since the likelihood of the earth's capturing the moon is small, this theory is less likely to be correct.

## Motivating Activity

**Materials:** 6.5-m piece of adding machine tape, meter stick, colored pens or pencils

Make a time scale of the dominant species and events that have shaped the spectrum of life. At one end of the adding machine tape, mark 650 million years ago (m.y.a.) to represent the beginning of the time scale. At the other end, mark 0 to represent the present. Use the meter stick to mark dates on the tape. Each centimeter represents 1 million years. Plot the following organisms and events on the scale.

| Millions of Years Ago | Animals/Events |
|---|---|
| 620 | Blue-green bacteria |
| 600 | Worms, jellyfish, bivalves, ammonites |
| 500 | Trilobites |
| 424 | Fishes with bony plates |
| 400 | Amphibians appeared |
| 350 | Forests became swampland |
| 340 | First reptiles appeared |
| 248 | Pangaea broke up |
| 230 | Birds, dinosaurs, mammals first appeared |
| 172 | North Atlantic Ocean formed |
| 156 | South America and Africa broke away from Antarctica |
| 70 | Emperor-Hawaiian Chain started to form |
| 3 | North and South America became connected |

Discuss with students the changes that have taken place. For example, point out that while simple plants and animals still exist, more complex plants and animals have also evolved. Discuss as well the changes resulting from the breakup of Pangaea. Mention the variations in plant and animal species that occurred as a result of their isolation on separate continents.

## Demonstration (Use with section 18.3 on page 373.)

**Materials:** examples of fossils

Display as many types of fossils as available. Fossils should include casts, molds, organisms preserved in amber, and pieces of petrified wood. Discuss with students how the fossils were formed. Also discuss some of the characteristics and habitats of the organisms preserved in the fossils.

# The Precambrian and Paleozoic Eras (p. 375)

## Background

Most rocks from the Precambrian Era contain few, if any, fossils. Two factors account for this. First, most rocks that formed during this time were metamorphic or igneous. Living tissues trapped in these kinds of rock were destroyed, not preserved. Second, most Precambrian organisms had soft bodies. These organisms were not preserved as fossils. However, some fossils do exist from this time. One example is a stromatolite—a structure composed of fine layers of calcium carbonates and silt deposited by algae or bacteria.

## Motivating Activity

**Materials:** water, freezer, pieces of fruit, 2 plastic containers with lids

clothing and hair while doing this demonstration. Remove the top of the shoe box and lay the box on its side. In what is now the top of the box, and about 5 cm from either end, cut circles large enough to fit the cardboard tubing. Push the tubing into the holes so that it just extends into the box. Tape the tubes in place. Light the candle and place it in the box below the left tube. Be very careful not to ignite the cardboard. Coat one end of the piece of stiff fabric with petroleum jelly. Light that end of the fabric and wait until smoke is produced. Hold the smoking cloth midway between the two cardboard tubes. Observe the motion of the smoke. (The smoke will move up the left tube.) Ask students why the smoke went up this tube and not the right tube. (The air heated by the candle was rising up the left tube. Cooler air was flowing down the right tube.)

# Climate (p. 449)

## Background

In addition to chemical weathering, thermal weathering also takes place. Thermal weathering results from the fact that darker minerals, when exposed to sunlight, heat up more than lighter minerals do. The darker minerals expand and contract more in a given temperature range than the lighter ones do. In time, this process breaks down the rocks into individual grains.

## Motivating Activity

**Materials:** string, scissors, small weight, protractor, tape, plastic drinking straw

Cut a piece of string about as long as the protractor is wide. Tie the weight to one end of the string. Tape the other end of the string to the center of the protractor. When the protractor is turned upside down, the string should hang at the 90° mark. Tape the drinking straw to the straight edge of the protractor.

On a clear night, locate Polaris, the North Star. Look at Polaris through the straw. Have a partner record the angle where the string crosses the protractor. To determine the latitude, subtract the number from 90°. This number represents the degrees above the horizon at which Polaris is located. This number is the same as the latitude where you took the reading. Relate your latitude to the climate in your area. (If the degree of latitude were between 0° and 30°, the climate would

be tropical; if the degree of latitude were between 30° and 60°, the climate would be temperate; above 60° the climate would be polar.)

## Demonstration (Use with section 21.8 on page 450.)

**Materials:** crushed samples of limestone, sandstone, feldspar, and classroom chalk, 4 large test tubes with stoppers, test tube rack, dilute hydrochloric acid, dropper, fine strainer, 4 petri dishes, paper towels

Place a crushed sample in each of the test tubes. Note: Retain enough of each sample for comparison at the end of the demonstration. Add just enough dilute hydrochloric acid to cover each sample. Let the test tubes stand for a few minutes. Observe the reaction in each tube. Stopper the test tubes and shake each for 5 minutes. Pour each sample through a fine strainer and rinse thoroughly with water. Line each petri dish with a paper towel. Pour each sample into a petri dish and allow the sample to dry. Pass the dishes around for students to observe. Compare the weathered samples with the unweathered specimens.

# Skill Activity (p. 448)

## Introduction

Encourage students to explain why it is important for them to know what the weather will be like in the future. Show students weather maps taken from the newspaper. Point out the main features of each map. Ask students to compare the information on the map with the actual weather that day. Were the weather maps accurate?

After the discussion, have students do the Skill Activity in this chapter.

# Investigation 21 (p. 452)

## Introduction

This Investigation would be best performed after the class has discussed humidity (page 437). The Investigation should reinforce the concept that relative humidity is just one of several factors that determine weather.

# CHAPTER 22 The Oceans

For additional information, see *Planning Unit 5*, pages T102–T103.

## The Structure and Composition of the Oceans (p. 457)

### Background

Sea water is a complex solution with positive and negative ions. Chemical bonds are formed between these ions and water molecules. These bonds interfere with the bonding of water molecules to one another. As a result, sea water freezes at -1.872°C instead of 0°C, the freezing point of pure water. Brines, which are salt solutions even saltier than sea water, freeze at even lower temperatures.

If sea water freezes slowly, the ions are left out. In fact, water can be purified by freezing. As water freezes, materials dissolved in the water are frozen out of the ice. Ice formed on the ocean surface has the same composition as fresh water. The water immediately below the ice is very cold and is rich in sea salts. The low temperature and extra salt make this water unusually dense. As a result, this water sinks to the bottom of the ocean and is responsible for the top-to-bottom circulation of the ocean. This type of circulation causes the deep water of the ocean to be as cold as the coldest surface water.

### Motivating Activity

**Materials:** petri dish, sea water (or table salt, Epsom salts, and borax), distilled water, heat lamp, hand lens

Before students do this activity, collect actual sea water or make sea water by adding 1.2 g table salt, 1.2 g Epsom salts, and 1.2 g borax to one liter of water.

Half-fill the top of the petri dish with sea water. Half-fill the bottom with distilled water. Place the two dishes under a heat lamp. Allow the water to evaporate completely from each dish. Use a hand lens to examine the sediments that remain in each dish after the water has evaporated. When the sea water has evaporated, several kinds of crystals should remain. Table salt forms

cubic crystals. Epsom salts form long, needle-like crystals. Borax forms a powdery substance.

Discuss with students how this procss could be used commercially to obtain salt. Mention that the great salt flats that surround Great Salt Lake in Utah were once the bottom of an inland sea. As the water evaporated, the salt was left behind.

The class might also be interested in discussing how evaporation might be used to purify water. (Evaporation as part of a distillation process separates salt from water; the pure water can then be used for drinking or cooking.)

### Demonstration (Use with section 22.1 on page 457.)

**Materials:** stream table, sand, water, rubber tubing, toy boat with moving propeller

Set up the stream table so it and the sand slope gently down hill. Slowly pour water through rubber tubing over the land. Notice that sand is deposited at the edge of the land. As the water level in the stream table builds up, a delta will form where the stream meets the ocean. Hold a toy boat with a moving propeller near the mouth of the stream. The current caused by the moving propeller should be enough to prevent the sand from being deposited at the mouth of the stream.

## Movement of Ocean Water (p. 465)

### Background

A cubic meter of water, which is about the size of a classroom desk, has about the same mass as an elephant. Therefore, a tsunami, which consists of thousands of square meters of water moving at speeds approaching 800 km per hour, hits with a tremendous force. No manufactured structure can survive such pounding. When a tsunami struck Alaska after the earthquake in 1964, the waterfronts of all coastal towns and villages in the area of the tsunami were destroyed. The Alaskan pipeline terminal at Valdez caught fire and exploded.

In 1896 more than 100,000 homes were smashed and 26,000 people killed when 35-m-may have spilled. This bag represents a cell. Fill a beaker half full of tap water. Add about 20 drops of iodine to the water in the beaker. Float the plastic bag in the beaker of water. The next day, observe any color change that takes place in the water in the beaker. Note: Iodine reacts with starch to produce a blue-black color.

The next day, observe any color change that takes place in the beaker or in the plastic bag. Point out to students that starch cannot move across a cell membrane.

# The Diversity of Living Things (p. 492)

## Background
One of the earliest systems of classification was proposed by the Greek philosopher Aristotle in about 350 B.C. Aristotle divided all living things into two groups, or kingdoms: plants and animals. Animals were further divided into three groups based on their habitats: those that lived on land, those that lived in water, and those that lived in the air. Theophrastus, a student of Aristotle, divided the plants into three groups based on their growth habits: herbs—those with no woody stems; shrubs—those with many woody stems; and trees—those with one main wood stem. This system of classification proposed by Aristotle and Theophrastus was used for more than 2000 years.

## Motivating Activity
**Materials:** microscope, oil immersion lens, prepared slides of cocci, bacilli, and spirilla bacteria, paper, pencil

Observe the prepared slides of the different types of bacteria under the oil immersion lens of the microscope. Draw the different shapes of the bacteria that you can recognize. Look at different prepared slides of bacteria. How can bacteria be classified into groups?

## Demonstration (Use with section 23.7 on page 492.)
**Materials:** variety of classroom and laboratory materials—tables, chairs, desks, pencils, pens, beakers, flasks, graduates, thermometers

Have the students develop a system of classification for all the material. They can use any categories they wish. For example, they might group the materials by size, shape, and color; by whether they are glass, wood, or plastic; or by whether the materials are organic or inorganic. Have the students describe and defend their classification system.

## Demonstration (Use with section 23.8 on page 494.)
**Materials:** organisms from each of the five kingdoms

Display live or preserved organisms from each of the five kingdoms for students to observe. Encourage students to notice the similar characteristics of organisms in the same kingdom. Also encourage students to notice the differences within each kingdom. Have students list the major characteristics of each kingdom.

# Skill Activity (p. 491)

## Introduction
The branched, or dichotomous, key is a simple two-choice method of identifying or classifying an organism. At each step of the key, the organism is compared to two different characteristics. As a choice is made at each step of the key, the organism is eventually classified. Show students a sample branched key. Work through the key with them.

When students have completed this exercise, have them do the Skill Activity in this chapter.

# Investigation 23 (p. 500)

## Introduction
This Investigation would be best performed after the class has discussed the structure of cells and the similarities and differences of plant and animal cells (page 482). The Investigation should acquaint students with the use of the compound microscope and refine their observation skills. If the students are not familiar with the microscope, refer them to Using a Compound Light Microscope on page 636 in the Reference Section.

Prior to the class doing the Investigation, you will need to obtain two plant cell slides and two animal cell slides. One plant cell slide and one animal cell slide should be marked as such. The other two slides should be unknowns. See the list of laboratory suppliers on page T49 for sources of these slides.

For additional information, see *Planning Unit 6*, pages T110–T111

# Cell Reproduction (p. 505)

## Background
When a cell is not dividing, or undergoing mitosis, it is said to be in interphase. Interphase can be divided into three distinct phases. Immediately following division, the cell enters into the $G_1$, or first-growth, phase. During this phase, the cell undergoes rapid growth. The cell generally doubles in size. Organelles such as the ribosomes and the mitochondria increase in number. The stage following the $G_1$ phase is the S, or synthesis, phase. The chromosomes within the cell replicate during this phase. The final stage of the cell cycle that occurs before mitosis begins is the second-growth, or $G_2$, phase. During this phase, the cellular structures involved in mitosis are produced.

## Motivating Activity
**Materials:** paper, pencil, calculator

Have students compute how much money they would have at the end of 30 days if they were given a penny a day, doubled every day. ($5,368,709.12 in 30 days.) Relate this number to how many bacteria there would be in 12 hours if you started with one bacterium and reproduction occurred every 20 minutes. (68,719,000,000 bacteria.)

## Demonstration (Use with section 24.2 on page 507.)
**Materials:** prepared slides of dividing onion root tip or whitefish (showing stages of mitosis), slide projector or compound microscope

Show students prepared slides of the stages of mitosis for an onion root tip or a whitefish. Point out the various structures in each cell involved with mitosis. Discuss with students the movement and arrangement of the chromosomes in each stage.

# Genetics (p. 510)

## Background
In 1865, Gregor Mendel presented his findings to a meeting of prestigious scientists of his time. Mendel's findings were not accepted by the biological community at that time for two main reasons. First, Mendel kept very accurate mathematical records of his findings. Many biologists at the time believed that biological processes were too complex to be explained mathematically. Second, scientists had not yet discovered chromosomes within cells. Biologists had a hard time accepting and understanding a process for which there existed no physical means of confirmation.

It was not until 1900 that Mendel's work was independently rediscovered by three botanists: Hugo DeVries, Carl Correns, and Erich Tschermak. These three botanists can be credited with the support and attention Mendel's work finally achieved—and deserved.

## Motivating Activity
**Materials:** 2 pennies, pencil, paper

Toss the two pennies and let them land on the desk. Record whether the pennies are heads/heads, heads/tails, or tails/tails. Toss the pennies 10 times. Record the results of each toss in a table. Toss the pennies 50 times. Record the results each time in the table. Toss the pennies 100 times. Again, record the results of each toss in the table. Calculate the ratio of heads to heads, heads to tails, and tails to tails in each group of tosses. Relate your findings to Mendel's Law of Independent Assortment.

## Demonstration (Use with section 24.5 on page 511.)
**Materials:** chalkboard

Draw a Punnett square on the board for the cross GGSS (green, short) x ggss (striped, long). The gametes for this cross are as follows: GS and gs. All the offspring of this cross have the genotype GgSs and the phenotype green/short.

Draw a second Punnett square on the board for the cross GgSs x GgSs. The gametes for this cross are as follows: GS, Gs, gS, and gs. The genotypes of the offspring are as follows: 1 GGSS, 2 GGSs, 1 GGss, 2 GgSS, 4 GgSs, 2 Ggss, 1 ggSS, 2 ggSs, and 1 ggss. The ratio of the phenotypes of the offspring is 9 green/short: 3 green/long: 3 striped/short: 1 striped/long.

# Patterns of Heredity (p. 517)

## Background
Twin brothers both named Jim were brought up in two completely different environments. After 39 years they were reunited. When they met for the first time, they both wore short-sleeved blue shirts. They discovered that they both had sons named James, enjoyed woodworking, disliked baseball, and even drove the same kind of car.

Scientists are still trying to discover the strong behavioral similarities between twins. Many believe the similarities are a result of the genetic code received by each twin. Others believe that the behavioral traits are determined by the environment.

## Motivating Activity
**Materials:** human karyotype, scissors, tape, paper

Carefully and closely study the karyotype of human chromosomes. Count the pairs of chromosomes. How many pairs are there? (23) Carefully cut out the pairs of chromosomes and tape them together on a piece of paper. You may want to arrange the chromosomes from smallest to largest. After you have cut out and taped all of the chromosome pairs, number them in sequence. Explain how a geneticist studying human chromosomes could use a karyotype to discover genetic abnormalities.

## Demonstration (Use with section 24.8 on page 518.)
Take a class survey of common dominant and recessive traits found in humans. Record the results on the chalkboard. The following table shows the dominant and recessive expressions of some easily determined human traits.

| Dominant | Recessive |
| --- | --- |
| finger hair | no finger hair |
| can roll tongue | cannot roll tongue |
| free earlobes | attached earlobes |
| dimples | no dimples |
| cleft chin | no cleft chin |
| freckles | no freckles |

Discuss with students the results of the survey. Ask students why a dominant trait, such as cleft chin or dimples, may not show up in the majority of students. (If very few people carry the trait—low incidence—there is little chance that an offspring will have the trait.)

# Computer Application (p. 515)

The Computer Application for this chapter will help students visualize the replication of the DNA molecule. For additional information, see pages T32–T34.

# Skill Activity (p. 516)

## Introduction
Explain to students that notetaking is a skill that is not only important in school but also in daily life. Discuss with students the types of information that should be recorded while taking notes. Refer students back to the Skill Activities on reading for comprehension—finding the main idea and supporting facts. Explain to students that notes can be taken in many ways—in outline form, in longhand, and in a variety of different types of shorthand.

After students have completed this exercise, have them do the Skill Activity in this chapter.

# Investigation 24 (p. 522)

## Introduction
This Investigation would be best performed after the class has discussed genetic principles (page 510). Students learn from the Investigation that even though chance is involved in genetic traits, if the genotypes of the parents are known, the genotypes of the offspring can be predicted with some accuracy.

For additional information, see *Planning Unit 6,* pages T110–T111.

## Changes Over Time (p. 527)

### Background
Some biologists have suggested that new species evolve fairly quickly on the fringes of an existing species' territory. The new species may evolve quickly enough to replace the existing organisms. Other biologists believe that all species evolve through the process of natural selection. Among these two groups of biologists, almost all agree that the rate of evolution of an organism depends on the organism itself and the environment in which it lives.

### Motivating Activity
**Materials:** 1 sheet of black construction paper, 1 sheet of white paper, 2 sheets of red construction paper, scissors, blindfold

To demonstrate natural selection at work, cut each sheet of construction paper into 64 equal-size rectangles. Scatter the rectangles onto the sheet of newspaper. The rectangles represent organisms and the newspaper represents the environment in which they live. Blindfold one student at a time. Have the blindfolded student pick five organisms from the environment. Repeat for four or five students. Record how many of each type of organism (black, white, or red) the students selected. Count how many of each type of organism remain in the environment. Did any one type of organism survive in greater numbers than the others? Ask students to explain how this might have happened. (Answers will vary, but predation is often random and involves whatever food source is available.)

### Demonstration (Use with section 25.2 on page 529.)
**Materials:** models or drawings of homologous structures, such as the flipper of a whale, the leg of a dog, and the arm of a human, and analogous structures, such as the wing of a bird and the wing of an insect

Explain to students that an additional type of evidence for evolution is the study of homologous and analogous structures in animals. Homol-ogous structures are similar body parts with the same basic structure. Point out the similarities in structure and function of the flipper, leg, and arm. Analagous structures, on the other hand, are structures that have similar functions but different structures. Point out the similarity in function but difference in structure of the wing of the bird and insect. Homologous structures indicate common ancestry of the organisms in which they are found. Analogous structures do not indicate common ancestry.

## Planned and Unplanned Changes (p. 533)

### Background
Organisms can be improved by changing the quantity of DNA in their cells. In a process called polyploidy, an organism has more than two complete sets of chromosomes in its cells. Diploid organisms normally have two sets of chromosomes in their cells. Polyploid organisms may have as many as four complete sets of chromosomes.

Polyploidy is not possible in animals. Even a slight variation in the number of chromosomes in an animal cell often produces fatal results.

### Motivating Activity
**Materials:** dog magazines, scissors, tape or glue, paper

Students should list the desirable characteristics of various dog breeds with which they are familiar. Possible characteristics might include size, length or thickness of hair (consider local climate), temperament, food and shelter requirements, hair color, and eye color. Genetic concepts such as dominant and recessive genes should be discussed.

### Demonstration (Use with section 25.4 on page 535.)
**Materials:** samples of fruits and vegetables produced by genetic engineering

Bring to class examples or pictures of fruits and vegetables that have been improved by breeders. Note: Seed catalogs are good sources for pictures of these organisms. These catalogs also describe the trait for which the plant was developed. Discuss with students the traits for which each fruit or vegetable was selected. Ask students to suggest possible traits for which fruits and/or vegetables might be bred.

# Human Time Line (p. 537)

## Background
One of the most important events that took place in the evolution of humans was the development of agriculture.

No one is quite sure what caused the development of agriculture. One factor that may have contributed to this development was a change in the climate. As the great glaciers began retreating about 18,000 years ago, the grasslands that once dominated the landscape were replaced with dense forests. Many animals that roamed the grasslands were hunted by early humans for food. These animals moved to new habitats or became extinct due to lack of food. Humans were forced to find new sources of food. Because they were no longer following large herds of animals across the grasslands, these early humans gradually became less nomadic. The development of agriculture was a logical adaptation that allowed early humans to survive.

## Motivating Activity
**Materials:** adding machine tape, colored pens or pencils, meter stick, magazine, scissors, tape or glue

Make a time line of human evolution. Include the following organisms on the time line: *Ramapithecus* (17 to 8 million years ago), *Australopithecus afarensis* (3.6 million years ago), *Australopithecus africanus* (2.5 million years ago), *Australopithecus robustus* (2.2 to 1.4 million years ago), *Homo erectus* (1.6 million years ago), *Homo sapiens* (400,000 to 200,000 years ago), Neanderthals (130,000 to 35,000 years ago), and Cro-Magnons (35,000 years ago). Use the meter stick to mark a time scale on the adding machine tape. For example, 1 cm = 500 years. If possible, cut out pictures of human ancestors and tape them to the time line.

## Demonstration (Use with section 25.6 on page 538.)
**Materials:** 2-m long piece of butcher paper, meter stick, color pencils or pens

Tell students that a fossil was discovered in the Great Rift Valley in Africa in 1977 that is believed to be the oldest known hominid. The skeleton, which was 3.6 million years old, was of a female who was about 1 meter tall and weighed about 22.5 kg. This skeleton has been named Lucy.

Tape the butcher paper on the wall. Demonstrate Lucy's size by drawing a line on the paper about 1 meter from the bottom. Compare Lucy's size to the size of students in your class by having volunteers come forward and be measured. Mark the heights of the volunteers on the paper. Tell students that scientists believe that Lucy was an adult—about 22 years old—when she died.

# Skill Activity (p. 532)

## Introduction
Tell students that illustrations often summarize or expand upon information presented in the text. Show students a variety of illustrations from different textbooks. Ask students to describe the information presented in each illustration. Explain to students that illustrations are useful for explaining procedures that require several different steps or stages.

After you have completed the discussion, have students do the Skill Activity in this chapter.

# Investigation 25 (p. 540)

## Introduction
This Investigation would be best performed after the class has discussed the theories of evolution (page 529). The Investigation should reinforce the concept that the study of amino acids in different organisms is one of the types of evidence used to support the theory of evolution.

# CHAPTER 26

**Plants and Animals**

For additional information, see *Planning Unit 6*, pages T110–T111.

# Plants (p. 545)

## Background
The flowers of flowering plants come in a tremendous variety of shapes, sizes, colors, and odors. This variety is the result of adaptations of the flowers to encourage pollination by birds and insects. Some flowers are long and cup-shaped; they hold nectar at their base. These flowers are pollinated by butterflies and hummingbirds whose long tongues can reach the nectar at the base of the flower.

Red, yellow, or purple flowers attract bees and other insects from great distances. Once a bee is near the flower, the flower's scent attracts the bee directly to it. Some plants, such as pansies and violets, even provide "landing pads" for the bees to rest on while they are drinking the nectar.

One flower exhibits a very unique adaptation to ensure pollination. The flower, an orchid, looks almost exactly like the female of a certain species of wasp. Male wasps attempt to mate with the female "wasp," pollinating the flower in the process.

## Motivating Activity
**Materials:**  complete flower, scissors, hand lens

Dissect a flower to identify its essential (reproductive) and nonessential (nonreproductive) parts. Observe and count the petals on the flower. Locate the receptacle and the sepals on the flower. The petals, receptacle, and sepals are nonessential flower parts. Carefully pull off the petals and set them aside.

Locate the stamens—the male reproductive parts of the flower. On each stamen, locate the stemlike filament and the oblong structure called the anther. Touch your finger to the anther. The yellow powder that comes off on your finger is pollen.

Locate the pistil—the female reproductive part of the flower. The ovary is located at the base of the pistil. The style is the slender central part of the pistil. The stigma is located at the tip of the style.

With scissors, carefully cut out the pistil at the base of the flower. Then cut the pistil in half lengthwise. Use a hand lens to observe the ovules within the ovary.

Note: You can often obtain complete flowers, such as tulips and lilies, for this activity from local florists free of charge.

## Demonstration (Use with section 26.3 on page 547.)
**Materials:**  live samples or models of monocotyledons and dicotyledons

Explain to students that the angiosperms can be divided into two groups based on the number of cotyledons in their seeds. The first group of plants are the monocotyledons, or monocots, that have one cotyledon, or seed leaf. The second group is the dicotyledons, or dicots, that have two cotyledons. In addition to being recognizable by their seeds, monocots and dicots can be identified by other characteristics. These characteristics are listed in the following table.

| Monocots | Dicots |
|---|---|
| one cotyledon | two cotyledons |
| flower parts in 3s | flower parts in 4s or 5s |
| parallel veins in leaves | net veins in leaves |
| diffuse roots | taproots |
| stem bundles scattered | stem bundles in circle |

Show students a variety of plants. Have them identify each plant as a monocot or a dicot. Have students give reasons to support their choices.

# Animals (p. 550)

## Background
When zoologists study animals, they observe the symmetry of the animal's body. Symmetry is the arrangement of body parts around a central point. Very few animals are asymmetrical. Sponges are an example of asymmetrical animals. Their bodies are not arranged around a central point. The symmetry of an animal's body often provides clues to the animal's way of life.

A round organism with no distinct front or back, or right or left side, exhibits spherical symmetry. Such animals face all directions at once. Animals that have spherical symmetry include protozoans that roll and float in water.

Animals that have body parts arranged like spokes around a wheel exhibit radial symmetry. Jellyfish and starfish have radial symmetry. These animals usually move very little, if at all, or they float in the water.

Most animals exhibit bilateral symmetry. One half of the body is an almost exact mirror image of the other half. Most animals that are bilaterally symmetrical also have an upper, or dorsal, side and a lower, or ventral, side. The front end of an animal with bilateral symmetry is called anterior; the opposite end is called posterior.

Vertebrates can be divided into two groups based on the internal temperatures of their bodies. Animals that maintain a constant internal body temperature are warm blooded, or endothermic. Warm-blooded animals include birds and mammals. Animals that cannot maintain a constant internal body temperature are cold blooded, or ectothermic. Cold-blooded animals have a body temperature that is within a few degrees of the temperature of their surroundings. Cold-blooded animals include all fish, reptiles, and amphibians.

## Motivating Activity
**Materials:** culture dish, culture of brown or green hydra, dropper, brine shrimp, hand lens or binocular microscope

Observe the movement and behavior of a hydra, a common invertebrate. Place a small amount of the hydra culture in a culture dish. Observe the hydra with a hand lens or binocular microscope. Notice the animal's body and tentacles, or arms. Observe how the animal moves through the water. Add a few drops of brine shrimp to the culture dish. Observe how the hydra reacts.

## Demonstration (Use with section 26.5 on page 552.)
**Materials:** 5–10 gallon aquarium, tadpoles, dry fish food

Before acquiring the tadpoles, set up a freshwater aquarium. Fill the aquarium with pond water or tap water that has been allowed to stand for at least 24 hours. Place some plants and rocks in the aquarium. Add about 10 tadpoles at an early stage of development to the aquarium. Maintain the aquarium at room temperature. Feed the tadpoles a small amount of dry fish food twice a day. Observe the development of the tadpoles over the next several days. Discuss with students the changes that take place.

## Skill Activity (p. 549)

### Introduction
Show students a completed outline. Point out the various levels of headings in the outline. Read a paragraph or two from the textbook. Outline the paragraphs, with student help, on the chalkboard.

After students have completed this exercise, have them do the Skill Activity in this chapter.

## Investigation 26 (p. 558)

### Introduction
This Investigation would be best performed after the class has discussed the differences between vascular and nonvascular plants (page 545). The Investigation should reinforce the concept of fluid movement through vascular plants.

Prior to the class doing the Investigation, obtain several stalks of fresh celery. Do not cut the celery until just before the Investigation is performed.

For additional information, see *Planning Unit 6*, pages T110–T111.

# Systems of the Body (p. 563)

## Background

The human body is often compared to a sophisticated, complex machine. Like a machine, the body functions properly only when all of its parts are well and are working properly. When a machine breaks down, it can be shut off and the damaged parts repaired or replaced. When a part of the human body misfunctions, the body cannot be shut down. However, with increased knowledge and advanced technology, the damaged part can often be replaced with a healthy, functioning part from another human. This procedure is called an organ transplant. The part also can be replaced with an artificial part called a *prosthesis*. Biomedical engineering is the field of medicine that designs and develops artificial body parts.

The first organ transplant in a human took place in 1954. The organ transplanted was a kidney. Since that time, kidney transplants have become almost commonplace, with over 70,000 patients successfully receiving transplants. Today, other organs, including the heart, lungs, liver, skin, and bone, can be transplanted successfully.

Artificial body parts have been used for centuries. But it has only been since the early 1970s that the number of artificial body parts has increased dramatically. Today, biomedical engineers can provide artificial replacements for bone, skin, joints, limbs, teeth, blood, and the heart.

The artificial parts used today are marvels of modern technology. They often contain new synthetic materials and electronic equipment. One sophisticated example of an electronic prosthesis is the Utah Arm. This arm is used to replace missing limbs. It is equipped with microprocessors that pick up nerve impulses from muscles. These microprocessors then interpret the impulses as movements that closely resemble those of a natural arm.

## Motivating Activity

**Materials:** paper clip, blindfold, metric ruler

Unfold a paper clip into a U shape with the two arms even. The two ends should be about 2 mm apart. Blindfold a student. Test the sensitivity of the student's skin by gently pressing with the two ends of the paper clip. Press at the following locations: palm of hand, back of hand, tip of finger, inside elbow, outside elbow, cheek, forehead, chin, and back of neck. Ask the student to describe how many points of the paper clip he or she felt. Separate the ends by another 2 mm and repeat the procedure at each location. Continue separating the points an additional 2 mm until he or she can feel two points. Explain that while the nervous system is very sensitive, if stimuli are too close together, the system cannot distinguish between them.

## Demonstration (Use with section 27.5 on page 569.)

**Materials:** beef heart, red and blue yarn, large needle

Obtain a beef heart from a butcher. Ask the butcher to leave as many arteries and veins in place on the heart as possible. Also ask the butcher to cut the heart in half lengthwise.

Show the beef heart to the class. Point out as many of the following structures as possible: aorta, inferior vena cava, pulmonary artery, superior vena cava, right and left atria, right and left ventricles, tricuspid valve, semilunar valves, mitral valve. Use red yarn to represent oxygenated blood and blue to represent deoxygenated blood. Use a needle to thread the yarn through the heart as it would normally flow. Discuss with students each structure of the heart the blood flows through. Point out the different locations of oxygenated and deoxygenated blood.

# Maintaining Wellness (p. 574)

## Background

The indirect spread of a disease between organisms involves living or nonliving intermediate agents. For example, a person can get tetanus by stepping on a nail. Water infected with certain bacteria causes typhoid fever. Animals such as fleas, ticks, flies, and mosquitoes often carry pathogens. Bites from these organisms can write the name and a drawing of each organism on a card. Two samples of food webs follow:

Food Web #1
    plankton ← blue whale
    plankton ← jellyfish ← eel ← puffin
    plankton ← herring ← gull
    herring ← tuna
    herring ← sperm whale

Food Web #2
    grass ← bird ← snake ← hawk
    grass ← rabbit ← hawk
    grass ← grasshopper ← lizard ← snake
    grass ← mouse ← hawk
    mouse ← snake
    bird ← hawk

Discuss with students the primary and secondary consumers in each of these food webs.

# Types of Ecosystems (p. 600)

## Background
As the latitude changes both north and south of the equator, the biomes also change. As one moves away from the equator (either north or south), the biomes change from rain forest to deciduous forest to coniferous forest to tundra. One reason for the change in biomes is the change in temperature.

Temperature also decreases as altitude increases. As a result, a mountain at the equator would have rain forest at the bottom and tundra on the top. In between would be deciduous and coniferous forests.

## Motivating Activity
**Materials:** biome map of the United States

Locate your home state on the biome map. In what biome do you live? Locate the home states of friends and relatives around the country. In which biomes do your friends and relatives live? Compare the kinds of plants and animals that live near you with those that live near your friends and relatives. How does the climate near you compare with that near your friends or relatives?

# Demonstration (Use with section 28.6 on page 600.)
**Materials:** planting trays (2), sand, soil, cactus (2), grass seed

Demonstrate the dependence of organisms on the conditions in their particular biome. Fill one planting tray with sand and the other with soil. Plant a cactus in each tray. Spread grass seed on the sand and on the soil. Provide each tray with an equal amount of water when the planting is completed. On each subsequent day, provide the same amount of water to the soil tray. Do not water the sand tray. At the end of one week, have the students record their observations. (In the soil, the grass should have started to sprout and the cactus to rot. In the sand, the grass should not have sprouted and cactus should be very healthy.)

# Skill Activity (p. 594)

## Introduction
Explain to students that being able to calculate percentages is an important mathematical tool. Percentages are used both in science and in our daily lives. Give students step-by-step directions on how to calculate percentages. Work several problems on the chalkboard with the class.

After students have completed this exercise, have them do the Skill Activity in this chapter.

# Investigation 28 (p. 606)

## Introduction
This Investigation would be best performed after the class has discussed the water cycle (page 595). The Investigation should reinforce the importance of water and oxygen to living things.

Prior to this lab, obtain water samples from the tap, from a lake, from a stream, and from a pond. Mark each sample clearly.

For additional information, see *Planning Unit 7*, pages T122–T123.

# Abiotic Resources (p. 611)

## Background

Natural resources are any form of matter or energy obtained from the environment. Most natural resources are used to meet human needs of one kind or another. Technology depends on resources, and the availability of resources often depends on technology. For example, at one time, oil was just a strange liquid that people avoided. When people learned to burn oil, it became a resource. As oil becomes more difficult to find, newer and better technologies are being developed to locate, pump, transport, and use it.

## Motivating Activity

Write the words *Natural Resources* on the chalkboard. Ask the students to name the natural resources they have used today. List the resources that students name until a dozen or so are on the board. Start another column headed *Alternatives*. Ask students to name some things they could use instead of the resources they identified earlier. Most alternatives require the use of other resources. Add these resources to the bottom of the *Natural Resources* column. Discuss with students the alternatives to the alternatives.

Point out that North America uses 25 times more natural resources than a typical third-world country. After discussing how our modern lifestyle is supported by using large amounts of dwindling natural resources, have each student write a letter to a student in a third-world country justifying his or her life style and the use of natural resources.

## Demonstration (Use with section 29.2 on page 611.)
**Materials:** 3 soil samples from different areas, 3 beakers, balance, oven

Collect soil samples from three different areas in the community. Areas to collect soil samples might include the school grounds, a vegetable or flower garden, a lawn, or an open field. Determine and record the mass of each of the soil samples. Place each soil sample in a labeled beaker. Place the labeled beakers of soil in a 300° oven for about 2 hours. Remove the beakers and allow them to cool. Again, determine the mass of each soil sample. Compare the difference in mass before and after each soil sample was heated. Discuss with students the possible explanations for the differences. (Organic material was chemically changed by the heating.) Which soil sample contained the most organic matter and living organisms?

# Biotic Resources (p. 616)

## Background

One example of human intervention causing the extinction of an animal species is that of the dusky seaside sparrow. At one time, more than 6000 of these birds lived in the grassy flats along the St. Johns River and on Merritt Island in central Florida. The sparrows' natural habitat and food source were destroyed by fires, the flooding of marshes, and the spraying of insecticides to control mosquitoes. These events all took place because humans chose to live or work in these areas. The last dusky seaside sparrow died in August 1987. It had been kept in a selective breeding area in southern Florida. Prior to its death, it had been cross-bred with similar sparrows. As a result, some of the characteristics of the dusky seaside sparrow may survive.

## Motivating Activity

**Materials:** 250-mL beaker, isopropyl alcohol, funnel, 10 cm x 10 cm piece of cheesecloth, ring stand, 2 clamps, light source with 25-watt bulb, soil sample, paper towel, hand lens, forceps

Pour about 5 cm of isopropyl alcohol into the beaker. Line the funnel with the cheesecloth. Set up the apparatus as follows. Place the beaker of alcohol on the base of the ring stand. With a clamp, position the funnel so that its base is about halfway into the beaker. With the second clamp, position the light source about 5 cm above the top of the funnel.

Pour the soil sample onto the paper towel. With the hand lens, carefully examine the soil sample for any living organisms. With forceps, remove the organisms, such as worms, sow bugs, and so on, from the soil. Break up any large clumps in the soil.

Put the soil in the cheesecloth-lined funnel. Turn on the light. Leave the light on for at least 24 hours. After that amount of time, observe the organisms in the collecting beaker of alcohol. What caused the organisms to fall into the beaker? Identify as many of the organisms as possible.

## Demonstration
**Materials:** aquarium with hood, small potted plant, wood splints, matches

Place a small potted plant in an aquarium. Provide the plant with sufficient amounts of water over a one-week period. Several times each day, place four or five lit wooden splints in the aquarium and place the hood on the aquarium. Allow the aquarium to fill with smoke. At the end of a week, have the students observe the effects of the smoke on the plant. Discuss with students how forest fires affect the woodland resources.

# Energy Resources (p. 621)

## Background
In 1985, about 9 percent of the total amount of the world's electricity was being provided by more than 300 nuclear power plants located in 25 countries. This production of electricity amounts to less than 3 percent of the world's primary energy. Countries such as France, where energy resources are low, rely heavily on power from nuclear reactors. Many countries are realizing that the amount of energy produced by a nuclear power plant is not enough to offset the high cost of its construction.

## Motivating Activity
Write the words *Energy Resources* on the chalkboard. Ask students to name the kinds of energy they use in their homes and school. Then ask students to identify the resource responsible for each source of energy and whether that resource is renewable or nonrenewable. Ask students if they know of any use of solar, geothermal, or wind energy in their community. Ask students to investigate the primary energy resource used in energy production for their community.

## Demonstration (Use with section 29.10 on page 623.)

**Materials:** 5 250-ml beakers, 5 thermometers, light-colored sand, dark-colored soil, water, shredded newspaper

Fill one beaker almost full with light-colored sand. Fill three more beakers using dark-colored soil, water, and shredded newspaper. Leave the fifth beaker empty. Place a thermometer in each beaker so that it touches the bottom. Place the five beakers in front of a sunny window. Record the temperature on each thermometer as soon as you place the beakers in front of the window. Record the temperatures again after 30 minutes. Move the beakers out of the sun. Record the temperature in each beaker after 5 minutes. Repeat after 10 minutes, after 15 minutes, and after 30 minutes. Discuss how these observations can be applied to the use of solar energy.

# Computer Application (p. 614)

The Computer Application for this chapter will help students more fully understand the concepts of geometric and arithmetic growth. For additional information, see pages T32–T34.

# Skill Activity (p. 620)

## Introduction
Bar graphs are often used to provide information visually. The bars provide easy comparison among the quantities being graphed. Have the students bring examples of bar graphs into class. Discuss what information is being presented in the graphs and how the graphs make that information easy to understand.

After completing the discussion, have the students do the Skill Activity.

# Investigation 29 (p. 626)

## Introduction
This Investigation would be best performed after the class has discussed natural resources (page 611) and water (page 613). The Investigation should reinforce the concept that some resources, including water, are renewable when used with proper care.

# GENERAL SCIENCE

# GENERAL SCIENCE

**Patricia A. Watkins**
Science Curriculum Specialist
   and former Science Teacher
Northside Independent School District
Instructor, Department of Education
Trinity University
San Antonio, Texas

**Cesare Emiliani**
Chairperson, Department of Geology
Professor of Geological Sciences
University of Miami
Coral Gables, Florida

**Christopher J. Chiaverina**
Physics Teacher
Barrington High School
Barrington, Illinois

**Christopher T. Harper**
Instructor in Science
Phillips Exeter Academy
Exeter, New Hampshire

**David E. LaHart**
Senior Instructor
Florida Solar Energy Center
Cape Canaveral, Florida

**Harcourt Brace Jovanovich, Publishers**
Orlando   San Diego   Chicago   Dallas

Requests for permission to make copies of any part of the work should
be mailed to: Permissions, Harcourt Brace Jovanovich, Publishers,
Orlando, Florida 32887

Printed in the United States of America
ISBN 0-15-364305-6

# Acknowledgments

## SENIOR EDITORIAL ADVISORS

**Lowell J. Bethel, Ed.D.**
Associate Professor of Science Education
Science Education Center
University of Texas at Austin
Austin, Texas

**Charles N. Kish**
General Science Teacher
Saratoga Springs
Junior High School
Saratoga Springs, New York

## CONTENT SPECIALISTS

**Myrdene Anderson, Ph.D.**
Associate Professor,
Department of Sociology
and Anthropology
Purdue University
West Lafayette, Indiana

**Lorella M. Jones, Ph.D.**
Professor, Department of Physics
University of Illinois
at Urbana-Champaign
Urbana, Illinois

**Willis J. Morrissey**
Vice President and Technical
Director
Rio Grande Robotics
Las Cruces, New Mexico

**Lt. Colonel James Stith, D.Ed.**
Associate Professor of Physics
United States Military Academy
West Point, New York

**Joan Selverstone
Valentine, Ph.D.**
Professor, Department of
Chemistry and Biochemistry
University of California,
Los Angeles
Los Angeles, California

**Tommy Elmer Wynn, Ph.D.**
Associate Professor,
Department of Botany
North Carolina State University
Raleigh, North Carolina

## CURRICULUM SPECIALISTS

**Mildred B. Blow**
General Science Teacher
Southwest High School
St. Louis Public Schools
St. Louis, Missouri

**James J. Dolak**
Science Curriculum Subject
Specialist
Youngstown Public Schools
Youngstown, Ohio

**Carl C. Duzen**
Physics Teacher and
Computer Science
Specialist
Lower Merion High School
Ardmore, Pennsylvania

**Dianne I. Hillman**
Earth Science Teacher
Cherokee High School
Lenape Regional High School
District
Marlton, New Jersey

**Jim Nelson**
Presidential Award for
Excellence in Science Teaching
Chemistry, Computer Science,
and Physics Teacher
Harriton High School
Rosemont, Pennsylvania

**Joyce Pinkston**
Science Curriculum Coordinator
Memphis City Schools
Memphis, Tennessee

**Richard Russo**
Science Coordinator
Montvale School System
Montvale, New Jersey

**Ethel L. Schultz**
Program Administrator
for K-12 Science
Marblehead Public Schools
Marblehead, Massachusetts

**Stanley Shimer, Ed.D.**
Science Educator
Science Consulting and
Supervisor Inservice Training
Science Teaching Center
Indiana State University
Terre Haute, Indiana

**Rajee Thyagarajan**
Physics Teacher
Health Careers High School
San Antonio, Texas

## READING SPECIALIST

**Irene M. Reiter, Ph.D.**
English Department Head
Northeast High School
Philadelphia, Pennsylvania

# Contents

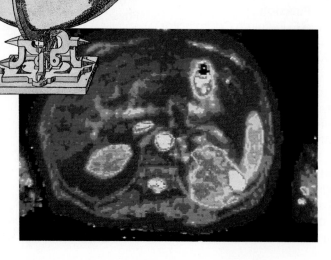

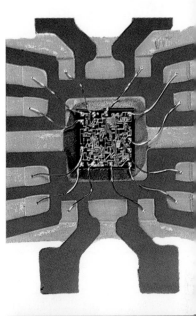
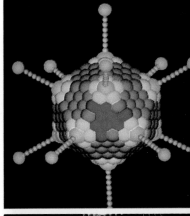
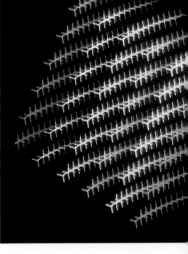

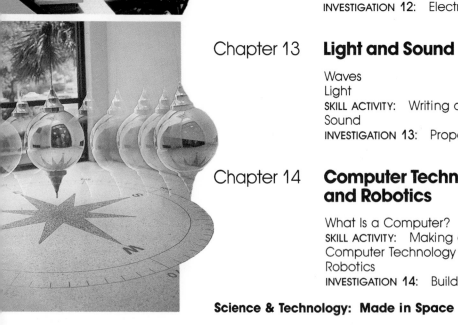

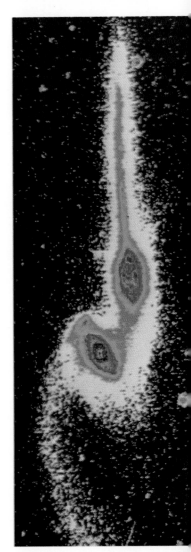

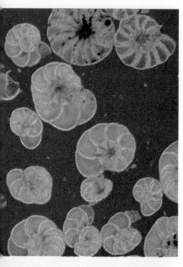

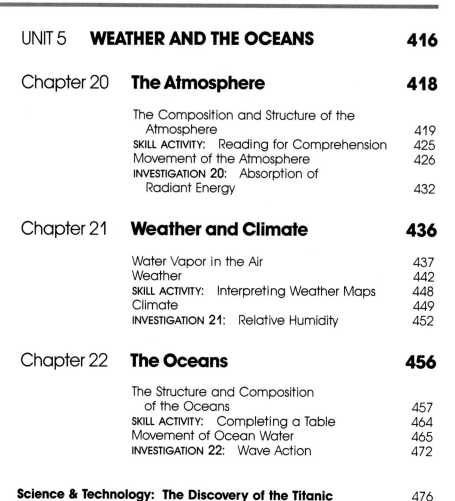

# Activities

These Activities provide opportunities for developing multiple process skills. For example, in Calculating Density (Chapter 3) students use not only problem-solving skills but also predicting and inferring skills. For more information about skills development, see page T21 and the lists of Investigations and Skill Activities in this Table of Contents.

# Science in Your Life

Do you use science every day of your life? At first you might answer "No." If you really thought about it, however, you might admit that there are many things you do and many items you use every day that are closely related to science.

Most modern conveniences were developed through technology, the application of science. The appliances that you use to cook food, wash clothes, and heat homes, for example, could have been developed only after an understanding of the basic principles of science.

The mechanical or electrical devices that you use are obvious applications of science. However, science affects other aspects of your life as well. Knowledge of science helps you understand not only how a vehicle such as a car or a bicycle works but also how to keep that vehicle in good working order.

Science also is useful in sports and recreation. A knowledge of the physics of motion can help you become a better diver, skater, or skier. The use and understanding of science can be applied as you enjoy your favorite movie on your VCR or listen to your favorite group on the latest CD.

A knowledge of science can even help you learn more about science and the other subjects you study in school. The use of personal computers is increasing steadily. Such computers can help you study, review material for tests, increase your understanding of certain concepts, and write reports.

A knowledge of human biology can help you maintain the health of your body. Such knowledge can help you choose healthful foods and realize why the use of alcohol, tobacco, and other drugs can be harmful.

# You and GENERAL SCIENCE

You may be taking this course because you are interested in science. You may be taking the course because it is required by your school. Whatever the reason, you will find that you will learn many things that you can apply to your life every day. You may even develop interest in a science-related career.

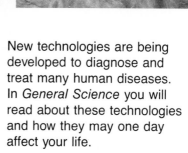

In *General Science* you will find some topics with which you are already familiar. For example, you probably know about insulation; in *General Science* you will find how the use of insulation in homes is related to energy transfer. You will acquire knowledge of electrical circuits to help you realize the energy capacity of your home.

New technologies are being developed to diagnose and treat many human diseases. In *General Science* you will read about these technologies and how they may one day affect your life.

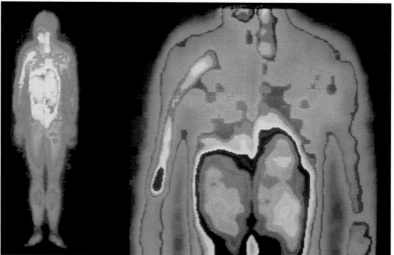

As the population of the world continues to increase, the need for food and energy supplies will also increase. *General Science* presents concepts that will be vital to decisions about the sources and uses of these supplies.

In *General Science* you will also develop many lifelong skills that you can use now and in the future. For example, you will learn skills such as reading for comprehension, making and reading tables and graphs, and understanding photographs and diagrams. In addition, *General Science* will give you many opportunities to use thinking skills such as comparing and contrasting, interpreting data, evaluating information, and determining cause and effect.

The authors of *General Science* wrote this book with you in mind. They hope you enjoy reading it and that you learn concepts you can use today and in the future. They also hope you will begin to understand that almost every aspect of your life is related to a knowledge and an application of science.

# UNIT 1

# Introduction to Science

What is science? *Science* is a method of obtaining knowledge—knowledge of what things are made of and of how things work. With this knowledge, people have developed technologies to take them to the moon and to take their machines even further. This unit discusses how people can use scientific knowledge to make informed decisions on how technology affects their lives.

1

# Science and Discovery

Humans have explored the greatest ocean depths and have walked on the moon. Studying the other planets of our solar system is another step in this quest to discover and explore. This photograph of the planet Uranus was sent by the *Voyager 2* space probe. After visiting the planet Neptune in 1990, this tiny spacecraft will begin a 350,000-year journey to a distant star.

For additional information, see pages T58–T59.

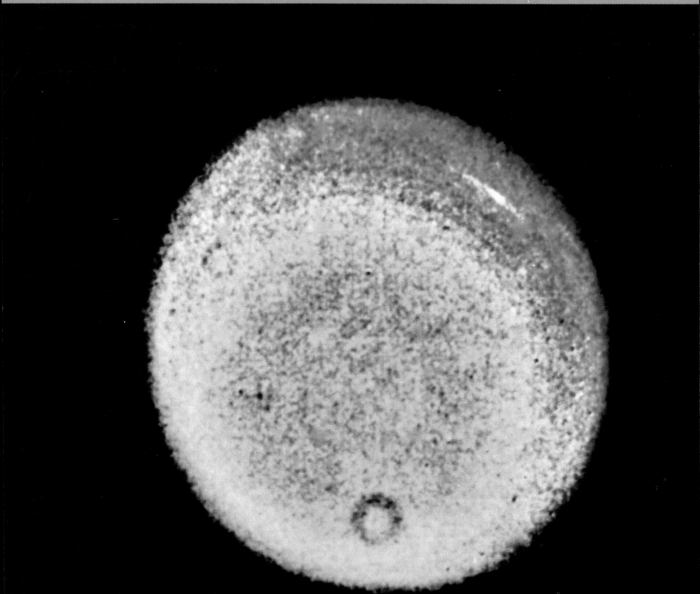

To be useful, a scientific theory must be able to explain known events and to predict new events. Scientists can test a theory by comparing a theory's prediction with observation. For example, the British astronomer Edmund Halley (HAL ee) calculated the orbit of a comet that he observed in 1682. Based upon his findings, he predicted that the comet would return every 76 years. If the comet did not return when predicted, the theory would have to be changed. Although Halley did not live long enough to witness the comet's return in 1758, Halley's comet is named after him.

It is important to remember that a scientific theory is not an opinion, or an untested guess. It is based on the results of many experiments by different scientists throughout the world. A scientific theory is the best scientific explanation presently available to explain some natural event.

Ask the students what usually happens when an object is dropped. (it falls) Next, drop a helium-filled balloon. Ask the students to modify their theory and to use their findings to predict what should happen when an air-filled balloon is dropped. (Objects lighter than air float, objects heavier than air fall. An air-filled balloon is slightly heavier than air and should therefore fall.)

## READING CRITICALLY

Halley's comet most recently was seen from Earth in 1986. When will it be visible again?

2062

**Figure 1–9.** This photograph of Halley's comet was taken in Bishop, California on January 8, 1986.

## Section Review

1. Briefly describe the steps of a scientific method.
2. Why did the scientists in the Clark's nutcrackers experiment move only half of the rocks?
3. What is the difference between an opinion and a scientific theory?
4. THINKING CRITICALLY List at least three variables that might explain why people in rural areas tend to live longer than people in cities.

1. identify a problem, gather data, form a hypothesis, perform experiments, form a conclusion
2. If the scientists had moved all the rocks, they would not have shown that the birds could find the seeds when the rocks were not moved.
3. An opinion is an untested guess; a scientific theory is based on the results of many experiments.
4. Answers will vary but may include pollution, food, type of work performed.

Science and Discovery **11**

# SKILL *ACTIVITY*  Studying from Your Textbook

**INTRODUCTION**

Using good study skills can make learning about science and technology, or any subject, easier. This textbook has a number of features that can help you to study more effectively.

**PROCEDURE**

1. Spend some time becoming familiar with your textbook and how each chapter is organized.

2. Each chapter begins with a *Chapter Outline* such as that found on page 3. Review the outline. This will help you to determine the major ideas covered within the chapter.

3. Next, turn to the *Summary* in the *Chapter Review* on page 21. Read through the *Summary* to preview what you will be learning in the chapter.

4. Now turn back to the *Section Objectives* on pages 3, 8, and 13. Section Objectives describe the important concepts that you should understand in each section.

5. Turn to page 3. *Science Terms* are in **boldface** type throughout the chapter. They call your attention to the important terms related to each concept. Each *Science Term* is defined in the sentence in which it is boldfaced. The *Science Terms* and their page references are included in the *Chapter Review* on page 21.

6. Each section includes at least one *Reading Critically* question. Reading Critically questions are located in the margin (see page 6) and are designed so that the answer must be inferred from what you have just read.

7. At the end of each section are *Section Review* questions that test your understanding of the material in each section. The questions range from simple recall to *Thinking Critically.* Thinking Critically questions challenge you to apply the information in the section. If you have trouble answering a question, reread the section.

8. When you are studying for a test, start by rereading the *Chapter Outline, Section Objectives, Summary,* and *Science Terms.* If you are unsure of any concept or term, reread the appropriate section. Another good way to study from this textbook is to expand the *Chapter Outline* by listing the major ideas contained in each section. Then check your understanding by completing the *Chapter Review.*

**APPLICATIONS**

2. Reading and rereading does not organize the material. Reading the material does not mean you have learned the concepts; without using the features, you have no way of knowing if you understand the material.

1. Outline Sections 1.1, 1.2, and 1.3 according to your teacher's directions.

2. Why is using the method described above more effective than just reading and rereading the chapter until you think that you understand the material?

**12**  Chapter 1

# Measurement

## SECTION OBJECTIVES

- **Explain** some advantages of using the metric system of measurement.
- **List** the basic metric units for length, mass, time, temperature, and volume.
- **Demonstrate** an ability to convert from one metric unit to another.

## 1.6 The Metric System

The **metric system** of measurement originated in France in 1791. In 1960, the metric system was standardized by international agreement. This standardized system is called *SI* from the French name, *Le Système Internationale d'Unités*.

Today, nearly all scientists and most countries use the metric system. One reason why so many countries have switched to the metric system is that it is easy to use. Because metric units use decimals, converting from one metric unit to another is simple.

Many businesses in the United States have already changed to the metric system. The next time you go to a grocery store, see how many products show their metric weights or volumes. When businesses use the same measurement system, their products can usually be bought and sold more easily. Businesses that use metric standards to make products are better able to sell these products in different countries. For example, most United States automobile manufacturers now use metric standards in building automobiles. Even the United States government has begun the switch to the metric system.

**Figure 1-10.** This expensive sports car was built to metric specifications.

The United States has adopted the metric system as the official system. However, it has not been officially implemented. Ask the students to discuss why they agree or disagree that the United States should "go metric."

## 1.7 Length

The **meter** (m) is the standard unit of length in the metric system. Originally, a meter was defined as one ten-millionth of the distance between the equator and the North Pole. Later, a meter was redefined as the distance between two lines marked on a platinum bar stored in Paris. This bar was used as the standard of length. In 1960 the meter was redefined in terms of the wavelength of orange light emitted by a certain krypton atom. In 1986 the meter was again redefined. As in the past,

## SCIENCE FACT

The star PKS 3000-330 is about 100 sextillion km from Earth. The light from this star takes 12 billion years to reach Earth.

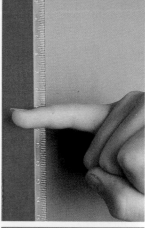

**Figure 1–11.** The Sears Tower in Chicago is slightly less than 0.5 km high. The height of most doorknobs is about 1 m above the floor. The width of your smallest finger is about 1 cm. The thickness of a dime is about 1 mm.

There are seven fundamental quantities in the metric system. They are mass, length, time, temperature, electrical current, light intensity, and number of particles (moles). All other quantities are derived from these seven.

scientists were looking for the most accurate method of determining length. This time the meter was defined in terms of the speed of light. Specifically, the meter was defined as being the distance light travels through space in 1/299,792,458th of a second. If, in the future, the speed of light can be measured with greater accuracy, then the length of the meter will change.

Other units of length in the metric system include the kilometer (KIHL uh meet uhr), the centimeter (SEHNT uh meet uhr), and the millimeter (MIHL uh meet uhr). To develop a feeling for the size of these units, see Figure 1–11. Table 1–3 lists conversions and some other metric units of length. Using a metric ruler, measure the height of several students.

## *READING CRITICALLY*

What are some common units of length in the metric system?

meter, kilometer, centimeter, millimeter

| TABLE 1–3 | SOME METRIC UNITS |
|---|---|
| **Length** | |
| 1 kilometer (km) = 1000 meters (m) | |
| 1 meter (m) = 100 centimeters (cm) | |
| 1 centimeter (cm) = 10 millimeters (mm) | |
| **Mass** | |
| 1 kilogram (kg) = 1000 grams (g) | |
| 1 gram (g) = 1000 milligrams (mg) | |
| 1 milligram (mg) = 1/1000 gram (g) | |
| 1 microgram (μg) = 1/1,000,000 gram (g) | |
| **Volume** | |
| 1 liter (L) = 1000 milliliters (mL) | |
| 1 cubic centimeter ($cm^3$) = 1 milliliter (mL) | |

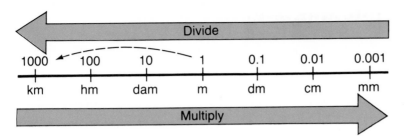

Display a set of metric wrenches and a set of customary (English) wrenches. Ask the students to order each set according to size. Explain that metric tools are calibrated in whole numbers rather than in fractions, which makes selecting the correct size easier.

In the metric system, measurements can be converted easily from larger to smaller units or from smaller to larger units. To convert from a larger unit to a smaller unit, multiply. To convert from a smaller unit to a larger unit, divide. This method for converting between metric units is shown in Figure 1–12.

**Example:** Convert 20 km to meters.

**Solution:** • *Write* the equation that relates kilometers and meters.

1 km = 1000 m

• *Solve* by multiplying. [Reason: The change is to a smaller unit (km to m).]

$$20 \text{ km} = 20 \text{ km} \times \frac{1000 \text{ m}}{\text{km}}$$

20 km = 20,000 m

**Example:** Convert 400 mm to centimeters.

**Solution:** • *Write* the equation that relates millimeters and centimeters.

10 mm = 1 cm

• *Solve* by dividing. [Reason: The change is to a larger unit (mm to cm).]

$$400 \text{ mm} = 400 \text{ mm} \times \frac{1 \text{ cm}}{10 \text{ mm}}$$

400 mm = 40 cm

## 1.8 Area and Volume

Suppose you owned a rug-cleaning shop. How would you set a price for cleaning rugs? You might charge by the length of a rug. However, not all rugs are the same width.

When you clean a rug, you are cleaning an area. **Area** is a measure of the surface of an object. Area, which is related to length, is expressed in square units, such as cm² and m². Figure 1–13 illustrates the idea of area.

To calculate area, all measurements must be in the same unit. If not, convert the measurements to the same unit. Then calculate the area. Formulas for area and volume are given on page 641 in the Reference Section.

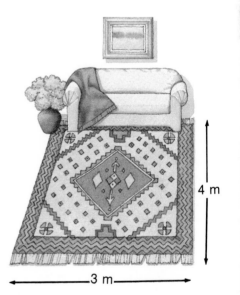

4 m

3 m

**Figure 1–13.** Area is the measure of a surface. The area of a rectangular object is calculated by multiplying its length by its width.

 **APPLICATION**

# Metric Conversion

## 1. DESCRIPTION

This program calculates length in centimeters (cm), meters (m), and kilometers (km). You can enter a length in centimeters, meters, or kilometers. The program will then calculate this length in each unit.

To use this program, enter a number followed by a comma and the unit symbol. For example, enter *5,cm* or *5,m* or *5,km*.

## 2. PROGRAM

Input the following program. After it is completely input, key the computer to run the program. If the program does not run, check to make sure you have input correctly. If the program runs correctly, go on to steps 3 and 4.

## 3. HELPFUL HINTS

You must be sure to place a comma between the number and the unit. The program will not work correctly without the comma. Remember, to enter 5 m, you must type *5,m.* Then press the return key. If you have entered the program correctly, then the computer will print *5 m = .005 km = 500 cm.*

## 4. GOING FURTHER

Change the program so that it can also convert millimeters to the other units.

Hints: In order to make this change, you will need to change *Dim (2)* to *Dim (3)*. You will also need to insert the following step *LET M$(3) = "MM"* after step 120. Also, it might be helpful to remember that a mm = 0.1 cm = 0.001 m = 0.000001 km.

```
100   DIM M$(2)
110   LET M$(1) = "KM"
120   LET M$(2) = "M"

130   PRINT
140   PRINT "ENTER YOUR NUMBER AND PRESS RETURN"
150   INPUT A,M$
160   IF M$="KM" THEN 200

170   IF M$="M" THEN 220
180   PRINT A;"CM = ";A/100;"M = ";A/100000;"KM"
190   GO TO 230
200   PRINT A;M$(1);" = ";A*1000;"M = ";A*100000;"CM"

210   GO TO 230
220   PRINT A;M$(2);" = ";A/1000;"KM = ";A*100;"CM"
230   PRINT "DO YOU WISH TO CONTINUE? TYPE (Y OR N)";
240   INPUT A$

250   IF A$="Y" THEN 130
260   END
```

**Example:** Calculate the area (*A*) of a rectangular carpet that is 2.5 m long (*l*) and 200 cm wide (*w*). Remember, the length and the width must be in the same units.

**Solution:**
- *Write* the equation for the area of a rectangle.
  - Area = length x width
  - $A = l \times w$
- *Substitute* the values for *l* and *w* in the equation.
  - $A = 2.5$ m x 2 m *or*
  - $A = 250$ cm x 200 cm
- *Solve* by multiplying.
  - $A = 5$ m$^2$ = 50,000 cm$^2$

**Volume** is another quantity related to length. Volume is the amount of space that an object takes up. The idea of volume is shown in Figure 1–14. The volume of solids is measured in cubic units, such as cubic meters (m$^3$). The volume of liquids is measured in **liters** (LEET uhrz). Many liquids are sold in one-liter and two-liter bottles. See Table 1–3 for conversions and other units of volume.

An understanding of volume is often important. For example, suppose you are planning to build a swimming pool. If you decide to double the length, width, and depth of your pool, how much more water will you need to use? The answer is not twice as much, as you might have thought. For the correct answer, see the example that follows.

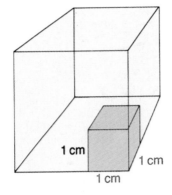

**Figure 1–14.** Volume is the amount of space an object takes up.

**Example:** Using the illustration in the margin, calculate the volume of a rectangular swimming pool that is 10 m long, 5 m wide, and 2 m deep. Next, calculate the volume of a pool that is 20 m long, 10 m wide, and 4 m deep.

**Solution:**
- *Write* the equation for the volume of a rectangular solid.
  - Volume = length x width x height
  - $V = l \times w \times h$
- *Substitute* the values for *l*, *w*, and *h* in the equation.
  - *V* (pool one) = 10 m x 5 m x 2 m
  - *V* (pool two) = 20 m x 10 m x 4 m
- *Solve* by multiplying.
  - *V* (pool one) = 100 m$^3$
  - *V* (pool two) = 800 m$^3$

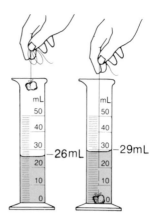

**Figure 1–15.** The volume of an irregular solid is the difference between the volume of the liquid alone and the volume of the liquid plus the solid.

**Figure 1–16.** The mass of one raisin is approximately 0.5 g. The mass of this container is approximately 1 kg.

By how much does the volume of water increase when the measurements of the pool are doubled? by eight times

The volume of a liquid is often measured using a **graduate**, or graduated cylinder. Figure 1–15 shows that the surface of the liquid curves up the side of the graduate. This curved liquid surface is called the **meniscus** (muh NIHS kuhs). The volume of most liquids is read at the lowest level of the meniscus. Liquid mercury is, however, an exception. The mercury meniscus curves up in the middle and down at the sides.

The volume of a regularly shaped object can be calculated from measurements of the object. However, how would you measure the volume of an irregularly shaped object, such as a person?

A method to determine the volume of some irregularly shaped solids is shown in Figure 1–15. This method is called the **displacement method**. When a solid is placed into a liquid, the solid displaces, or takes the place of, some of the liquid. The difference between the volume of the liquid alone and the volume of the liquid and the solid together is equal to the volume of the solid.

## 1.9 Mass

In the metric system, the **kilogram** (KIHL uh gram) is the standard unit of mass. The symbol for kilogram is kg. The kilogram was once defined as the mass of a liter of water. It is now defined as the mass of a small cylinder of platinum-iridium kept in France. **Mass** is the amount of matter that an object contains. Other metric units of mass are the gram (g) and the milligram (mg).

The mass of an average high-school female is about 50 kg and the mass of an average high-school male is about 60 kg. Mass, which is measured on an instrument called a **balance**, will be discussed more fully in Chapter 3. Based on Figure 1–16, approximately how many raisins are contained in 1 kg of raisins? 2,000 raisins

## 1.10 Time and Temperature

The **second** is the standard unit of time in the metric system. Originally, the second was defined in terms of the length of a year. However, the length of a year varies slightly. Therefore, the second was redefined in 1969. The second is now based on the time it takes a certain atom to move in a particular way.

**Temperature**, or the hotness or coldness of an object, is measured with a thermometer. Most scientists measure temperature in **Celsius** (SEHL see uhs) **degrees**.

There are 100 Celsius degrees between the freezing point and the boiling point of water. On the Celsius temperature scale, water freezes at 0°C and boils at 100°C. Other temperatures are shown in Figure 1–17.

The Kelvin scale is another metric temperature scale. On the Kelvin scale, water freezes at 273 K and boils at 373 K. To convert a temperature given in Celsius to Kelvin, add 273 to the Celsius temperature.

## Section Review

1. List the following units in order from smallest to largest: cm, km, m, mm.
2. Name three units of mass in the metric system.
3. How many Celsius degrees are there between the freezing and boiling points of water?
4. A room is 7.2 m long, 5.0 m wide, and 2.5 m high. Calculate the area of the floor and the volume of the room. Be sure to include the proper units for area and volume.
5. THINKING CRITICALLY  How many inches are there in a foot? feet in a yard? yards in a mile? Use these results to explain an advantage of using the metric system.

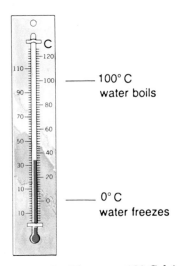

**Figure 1–17.** There are 100 Celsius degrees between the freezing point and the boiling point of water.

1. mm, cm, m, km
2. Answers will vary but may include kilogram (kg), gram (g), milligram (mg).
3. 100
4. $A = 36\ m^2$; $V = 90\ m^3$
5. 12 in/foot, 3 ft/yd, 1760 yds/mile. The use of decimals makes converting from one metric unit to another simple.

# CAREER

## Medical Laboratory Technician

**DESCRIPTION**  A medical laboratory technician performs medical tests. Medical laboratory technicians work in hospitals, as well as in industrial and in governmental laboratories. Such technicians analyze body fluids and tissue samples. These tests assist physicians in diagnosing certain health problems.

**REQUIREMENTS**  To prepare to be a medical laboratory technician, a high-school student should take courses in science, such as biology and chemistry, as well as courses in mathematics. Upon graduation the student enrolls in a one- or two-year training course in a college or technical school.

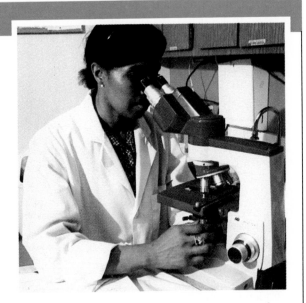

**INFORMATION**  National Association of Trades and Technical Schools, 2021 I Street, N.W., Washington, DC 20036.

# INVESTIGATION 1: Finding Area and Volume

*How would you find the area and volume of variously shaped objects?*

## PURPOSE

To determine the area and volume of regularly and irregularly shaped objects

## MATERIALS

metric ruler
card (7 cm x 12 cm)
wooden block
metal cube
   (1cm x 1cm x 1cm)

sponge
   (2 cm x 2 cm x 2 cm)
50-mL graduate
pebble
string (30 cm)
water

## PROCEDURE

1. Copy Table 1 onto a sheet of paper. Enter all data from this investigation onto your table.

2. Using a metric ruler, measure in millimeters and centimeters the length, width, and height of the card, wooden block, metal cube, and sponge.

3. Determine the volume of the metal cube, sponge, and pebble by displacement, as shown in Figure 1–15 on page 18. Use a string to gently lower the pebble into the graduate. **Do not drop the pebble into the graduate.** Dropping the pebble may break the graduate. Record your data in cubic centimeters (1 mL = 1 cm$^3$).

## RESULTS

1. Place your completed Table 1 in the results section of your laboratory report.

2. Calculate the area of the largest flat surface of the card, wooden block, metal cube, and sponge in square centimeters.

3. Calculate the volume of the card, wooden block, metal cube, and sponge in cubic centimeters.

## CONCLUSIONS

1. What is an effective way to determine the volume of a regularly shaped object, such as a cube? Defend your method. Measure the sides and use these measurements to calculate the volume.

2. What is the best way to determine the volume of an irregularly shaped object, such as a class ring? Explain. the displacement method, because it is accurate when you cannot measure the sides of an object

3. For what types of materials might the displacement method give incorrect results? Why? for materials that absorb water; the materials absorb water and make it appear that more water has been displaced than actually was

## APPLICATIONS

1. State one reason why breakfast cereal is sold by mass rather than by volume. Cereals usually settle during shipping, causing volume to change.

2. Suppose a certain paint sells for $7.00 per can. Two coats of this paint are needed to cover a certain wall. A second paint sells for $12.50 per can, but only one coat of this paint is needed to cover the same wall. Discuss two advantages of using the more expensive paint. one can less expensive to use than two cans of other paint; less time to paint

| TABLE 1 | CALCULATIONS OF AREA AND VOLUME | | | | |
|---|---|---|---|---|---|
| Item | Width (mm) (cm) | Length (mm) (cm) | Height (cm) | Area of Largest Flat Surface (cm²) | Volume (cm³) |
| Card | | | | | |
| Wooden Block | | | | | |
| Metal Cube | | | | | |
| Sponge | | | | | |
| Pebble | | | | | |

## Summary

1. The study of science first became widespread in ancient Greece. **(1.1)**
2. Since 1900, scientific knowledge and discoveries have increased rapidly. **(1.2)**
3. Many career opportunities exist in the fields of science and engineering. **(1.3)**
4. Scientists follow a series of steps called a scientific method to study problems. **(1.4)**
5. Scientific theories must be modified or rejected if data do not support them. **(1.5)**
6. The metric system is a measuring system based on decimals. **(1.6)**
7. In the metric system, the unit of length is the meter, the unit of mass is the gram, the unit of time is the second, and the units of volume are the cubic meter and the liter. **(1.7–1.10)**
8. Area is a measure of an object's surface, while volume is a measure of the amount of space that an object takes up. **(1.8)**
9. Most scientists measure temperature in Celsius degrees. **(1.10)**

## Science Terms

On a separate sheet of paper, define each term in a sentence.

area **(15)**
balance **(18)**
basic research **(6)**
Celsius degree **(18)**
conclusion **(10)**
control **(9)**
data **(8)**
displacement method **(18)**
engineer **(6)**

experiment **(9)**
graduate **(18)**
hypothesis **(8)**
kilogram (kg) **(18)**
liter (L) **(17)**
mass **(18)**
meniscus **(18)**
meter (m) **(13)**
metric system **(13)**

science **(3)**
scientific method **(8)**
second **(18)**
technology **(6)**
temperature **(18)**
theory **(10)**
variable **(9)**
volume **(17)**

## Modified True-False

On a separate sheet of paper, mark each true statement *TRUE* and each false statement *FALSE*. If false, change the underlined term to make the statement true.

1. The <u>Greeks</u> used scientific discoveries to build improved buildings and roads. F, Romans
2. The use of <u>computers</u> has become important in business and industry. T
3. Using new materials to build a better building is an example of <u>technology</u>. T
4. The conditions in an experiment or test that are changed are called <u>data</u>. F, variables
5. In the experiment with Clark's nutcrackers, moving the rocks was one part of the <u>conclusion</u>. F, variables
6. <u>Scientific theories</u> that have been verified by many experiments are usually accepted by most scientists. T
7. The metric system is used by a <u>few</u> countries throughout the world. F, most
8. A millimeter is <u>one-tenth</u> of a centimeter. T
9. The kilogram is the basic unit of <u>length</u> in the metric system. F, mass
10. Water freezes at <u>32°C</u>. F, 0°

*(continues)*

# CHAPTER REVIEW

## Multiple Choice

On a separate sheet of paper, write the letter of the term that best answers the question or completes the statement.

1. The time between the invention of the automobile and the first space flight was about _____ years.
   a. 5
   b. 50
   c. 500
   d. 5000

2. Basic research is most likely to be done by
   a. engineers.
   b. teachers.
   c. technicians.
   d. scientists.

3. After gathering data, a scientist forms a _____ that can be tested.
   a. conclusion
   b. result
   c. hypothesis
   d. problem

4. A scientist uses the results of an experiment to form
   a. a hypothesis.
   b. results.
   c. data.
   d. conclusions.

5. If an athlete runs 20 kilometers per day, how many meters will the athlete run in 3 days?
   a. 6
   b. 6000
   c. 60
   d. 60,000

6. The amount of matter that is contained within an object is its
   a. volume.
   b. mass.
   c. area.
   d. temperature.

7. Which one of the following would be used to find the number of seconds in a week?
   a. 60 x 7
   b. 60 x 60 x 24
   c. 60 x 60 x 7
   d. 60 x 60 x 24 x 7

8. Which one of the following relationships does not fit with the others?
   a. kg—balance
   b. mL—graduate
   c. °C—temperature
   d. mm—metric ruler

9. The amount of time required to paint a wall depends mostly upon the _____ of the wall.
   a. area
   b. volume
   c. mass
   d. temperature

10. The area of the surface of a baseball could be which of the following?
    a. 150 cm$^2$
    b. 150 mL
    c. 150 m
    d. 150 m$^3$

## Completion

On a separate sheet of paper, complete each statement by supplying the correct term.

1. The theory that the earth revolves around the sun was proposed by Copernicus.

2. The *Space Age* began in the middle of the twentieth century when *Sputnik* was placed into orbit.

3. Discovering scientific principles is part of basic research.

4. If you record student attendance to see if a pattern exists, then the information you have gathered is called data.

5. In an experiment that studies the relationship between acne and diet, the variable is diet.

6. An opinion is different from a theory because theories are based on the results of many experiments.

7. A scientific question can never be answered without data.

8. Businesses that make products to metric standards are better able to sell these products in other countries.

9. If one nail weighs 5 g, 200 nails would be contained in a 1-kg box of nails.

10. A kilogram is equal to 1,000,000 milligrams.

# Writing Critically

1. Summarize the history of scientific discoveries over the last three thousand years. Include within your discussion periods of time during which the rate of scientific discoveries increased or decreased. Suggest some possible reasons for these increases or decreases.

2. Describe some advantages and disadvantages of the United States' changing to the metric system of measurement.

3. CHALLENGE A newly discovered substance is reported to reduce tooth decay. Using a scientific method, describe an experiment that could test this hypothesis.

4. CHALLENGE Write an essay about how technology has improved the way in which you live, as well as some ways in which technology has caused pollution problems.

## Skill Reinforcement

The Skill Activity on page 12 describes how to improve your study skills by getting to know your textbook. Use the steps in that activity to become familiar with the books you use in other classes. Become familiar with their features so you can improve your study skills in those subjects, as well.

## Research Ideas

1. Investigate some contributions of Chinese or Arabian scientists prior to the 1500s.

2. Find the origin of the following units of measurement: angstrom, bushel, carat, dram, fathom, furlong, light year, millennium, ounce, yard.

3. CHALLENGE Nicolaus Copernicus and Galileo Galilei each proposed that the sun was the center of the universe. Investigate why this idea was not accepted by most people of their times. Find out what trouble Galileo's idea caused for him.

## For Further Reading

Asimov, Isaac. *Change! Seventy-one Glimpses of the Future.* Boston: Houghton Mifflin, 1981. In a collection of essays, Isaac Asimov considers problems and opportunities that people may face in the future. Asimov discusses such topics as natural resources, environmental issues, health, space, energy, and time.

Blohm, Hans and others. *Pebbles to Computers: the Thread.* New York: Oxford, 1987. This book discusses the connections between early machines and high-technology computers.

Papacosta, Pangratios. *The Splendid Voyage: an Introduction to New Sciences and New Technologies.* Englewood Cliffs, New Jersey: Prentice Hall Press, 1987. This book discusses science and technology topics of every-day-appeal in easy-to-understand language.

# CHAPTER 2

# Science and Modern Technology

Science and technology go hand in hand. An understanding of scientific concepts is vital to the development and wise use of new technologies. Such an understanding is necessary to make informed decisions on topics ranging from nuclear power to mass transportation.

# The Scientific and Technological Revolution

| NEW TERMS IN | transistor | integrated circuit | computer | CAT scanner |
| THIS SECTION | electronic devices | chip | computer network | NMR |

## SECTION OBJECTIVES

- **List** examples of modern technology in the home.
- **Explain** how modern technology is used in industry and transportation.
- **Describe** how developments in medical technology have improved health care.
- **Summarize** the ways in which space technology is used on Earth.
- **Identify** ways in which computer technology is used in the arts.

Photograph left: Metro, Washington, D.C.

**Figure 2–1.** Advances in technology have meant great improvements in home appliances. Washing clothes is no longer the chore it was when only manual machines were available.

## 2.1 Technology for the Home

The relationship between science and technology is a continuous cycle of discovery and development. Advances in science and technology have made everyday life much easier than it was in the past. For example, many of the appliances we take for granted are the result of new technologies made possible by scientific discoveries. Consider, for example, the washing machine. In your great-great-grandparents' day, doing laundry was a very time-consuming chore. It would take all day to wash clothes. Wood had to be gathered, a fire had to be built to heat the water, and the clothes had to be stirred and scrubbed in a tub. Today, your family simply places clothes in a machine and, with the turn of a dial or push of a button, the clothes are washed in a matter of minutes.

Lead a discussion of the changes in cooking appliances, from the old wood- or coal-burning stove to electric or microwave appliances.

## Surveying Home Technology

Survey your home and make a list of items that have transistors or integrated circuits. Create a master list from the findings of the class.

## Electronic Technology

Today's washing machines and many other time-saving and labor-saving devices are the result of scientific developments in the use of electricity. A major improvement in these machines was the invention of the transistor. A **transistor** is a tiny device used to control electric current. Transistors are used to control the speed of many appliances, such as kitchen mixers, vacuum cleaners, and electric drills. In washing machines, clothes dryers, electric stoves, and refrigerators, transistors are also used to control temperature. Machines that use transistors are called **electronic devices.**

Electronic devices have been improved even further by the development of the integrated circuit. An **integrated circuit**, or **chip**, is an electrical unit that contains many transistors. Figure 2–2 shows a single chip, which is often no larger than a fingernail. Transistors, integrated circuits, and other electronic components used in developing today's technology are discussed in greater detail in Chapter 12.

**Figure 2–2.** Integrated circuits began as bulky hardware (left). Today, technology has reduced the size of circuits (right).

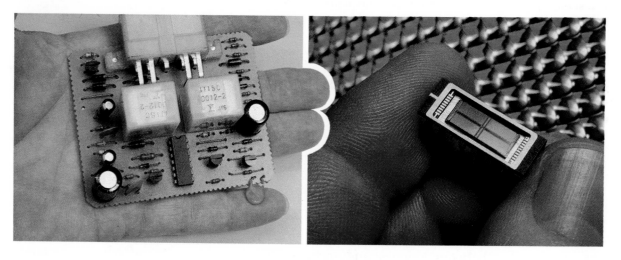

## Personal Computers

With the development of the integrated circuit, it became possible to make electronic parts smaller and more powerful. One of the most important applications of integrated circuits was their use in the personal computer. **Computers** are electronic devices that can store and use information. In homes, computers can be used to program appliances such as ovens, alarm clocks, and videotape recorders. In addition, personal computers can be used to calculate the household budget and income tax. Students may use information from a computer's memory bank to do homework.

Students can use computers to keep records and accounts, use for homework and as a tutor, learn about computer programs.

## READING CRITICALLY

How can a student make good use of a computer?

Figure 2–3. Personal computers are used in a wide variety of situations for many activities.

Personal computers can be linked through telephone wires with other computers to form **computer networks.** Through a computer network, students may "attend" classes using their home computers. People may also work from their homes, using personal computers to connect them with their business office. Computer networks can also bring news and information into the home. For example, users of electronic newspaper and magazine services can view selected news stories and other features on home-computer screens. Television lines may connect home computers with computers at banks or stores. Through such systems, it is possible to bank and shop from your home. What are some ways in which these uses of computers might change small family-owned businesses? fewer employees needed, more work can be done at home

### Home Entertainment

Improvements in electronics technology have also had a great impact on home entertainment equipment. Only since the 1950s have television sets become common in most homes. While early television screens measured only 18 cm or 25 cm, their electronic parts took up so much room that sets were much larger than today's televisions with similar screen sizes. Programs could be broadcast only in black and white. Scientific discoveries based on the properties of light made color television

Lead a discussion describing technological changes that have affected the students' lives in the last five years. For example, discuss how videocassette recorders have changed their movie habits. Do they see more movies now? Do they go to a movie theater less often?

**Figure 2–4.** Televisions have both increased and decreased in picture size since they were first introduced (top left).

possible. Transistor technology has made television sets smaller, more reliable, and less expensive. Recent developments in television technology have resulted in *high-definition television* (HDTV). High-definition television produces pictures that are much sharper and clearer than those produced by regular picture tubes.

Other types of home entertainment equipment have been developed by using scientific knowledge of sound-waves. Stereo systems use the latest in electronic technology to reproduce high-quality sound. Stereo speakers are now commonly found in television sets. Sound and light are combined in *laser disc* technology. Compact disc (CD) players use a laser beam instead of a record needle to reproduce sound. CDs last longer than records due to this technology. Video games, videotape recorders, and portable video cameras are also part of the modern home entertainment system. These devices combine the latest in electronic and computer technology.

**Figure 2–5.** CDs such as these are "read" by lasers. The sound quality of a CD is much better than that of a record or tape because the laser precisely reads the information on the disc. Unlike a phonograph needle, the laser beam will not wear out or cause scratches on a CD.

## 2.2 Technology for Industry and Transportation

Developments in science and technology have changed the way many products are produced and transported. Computer technology has had perhaps the greatest impact on industry and transportation.

An application of computers in industry that affects everyone is the use of computerized cash registers. Information about each product is contained in the *bar code* on each item. An electronic scanner built into the checkout stand reads this information and sends it to the computer. Some registers even "talk," calling out the name and price of each item as the clerk passes it over the scanner. Your receipt not only tells you how much you spent, but it also tells you what day and time you bought your groceries. In addition, the receipt tells you what each item was, whether the item was taxable, how much money you gave the clerk, and your change.

The design, fuel efficiency, and construction of automobiles and aircraft also have been improved through the use of a technology called *CAD/CAM* (*Computer-Aided Design/Computer-Aided Manufacturing*). CAD/CAM helps engineers produce drawings and designs quickly. With CAD/CAM, designers do not have to go "back to the drawing board" each time a change must be made. Because the computer stores the original drawing in its memory, changes can be made easily. Many other technologies, such as the use of lasers, are also used in designing cars and other products. Chapter 14 explains CAD/CAM in greater detail.

**Figure 2–6.** CAD/CAMs (top), bar-code readers (left), and lasers (bottom) are all examples of technology currently used in industry.

Lead a discussion comparing the bar-code system with manual price entry. (faster service, fewer cashier errors)

Lead a discussion with students on the positive and negative effects of computers in transportation. For example, computer-controlled radar allows more planes to fly at once, but the increase of flights causes delays and near misses.

Computers help keep things moving in the field of transportation. Air-traffic controllers use sophisticated computer-controlled radar devices to keep track of incoming and outgoing planes. Automobile traffic may also be controlled by computer. Many traffic lights are programmed by computer to operate based on the local speed limit. This type of programming keeps the traffic flowing smoothly. Automatic switching controls in railroad systems are run by computers to help keep trains on the right track.

## 2.3 Technology for Medicine

Some of the most important applications of science to technology are in the field of health care. For example, physicians may now use computers to help them decide, or diagnose, the cause of an illness by comparing a patient's symptoms with computer data on all known diseases. Such technology has made the diagnosis of disease faster and more accurate. The computer can also provide the physician with information about treatment once a disease has been diagnosed. What might be some benefits and some limitations of computer diagnoses?

The benefits of computer diagnoses include accurate, fast results. The limitations include the fact that the computer can base diagnosis only on information it has received. It cannot guess and it could misdiagnose.

## SCIENCE FACT

The CAT scanner was invented by Allan H. Cormack in 1973. Cormack received the 1979 Nobel Prize for Physiology and Medicine for his contributions to the CAT scanner.

You may have heard of a CAT scanner being used in a hospital. CAT stands for the **computerized axial tomography (CAT) scanner,** a diagnostic tool that uses both computer and X-ray technology. CAT scanners can "map" the structure of internal organs in a matter of minutes. They can show where small tumors and other diseased tissue may exist. Figure 2–7 shows the CAT-scan image of a brain.

Before CAT scanners exploratory surgery was often necessary to diagnose illnesses.

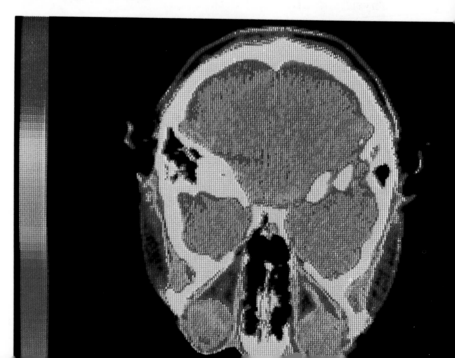

**Figure 2–7.** In this CAT-scan image of the human brain, a computer processes a series of X rays to build one composite X ray of the brain.

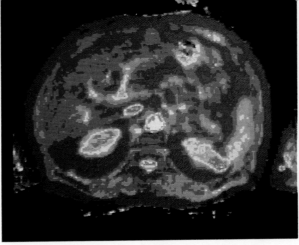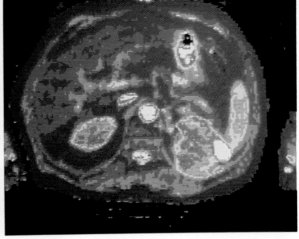

Scientists have discovered that certain substances in the body can be identified by the way they vibrate. These vibrations are recorded by **nuclear magnetic resonance imaging,** or **NMR.** Through the use of NMR imaging, doctors can get cross-sectional pictures that show differences among tissues on a chemical level. From these pictures, medical researchers can tell the difference between healthy and diseased tissue. NMR is also useful in determining how well medicines work. Figure 2–8 shows an NMR image of a liver that has been treated with a medicine, and one that has not.

Scientific discoveries in biology and chemistry have helped doctors to develop drugs to treat, cure, and prevent many diseases. Diseases such as polio, tetanus, smallpox, and diphtheria are now almost nonexistent in the United States due to the development of special *vaccines.* Research is now going on to discover a treatment and cure for one of the world's most serious health threats, *AIDS* (*A*cquired *I*mmune *D*eficiency *S*yndrome). Physicians are hopeful that with continuing research and today's technology, a cure will be found in the near future.

**Figure 2–8.** The NMR image on the left shows a normal human liver. The image on the right shows a liver with tumors. The tumors are the yellow spots on the image.

AIDS is caused by a virus that destroys the body's natural immune system. Patients with AIDS contract diseases that the body would normally fight off.

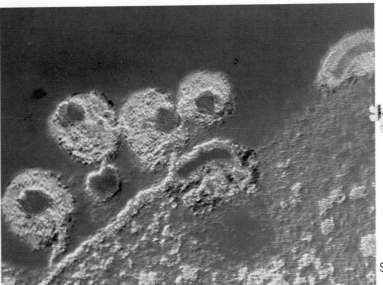

**Figure 2–9.** On the left is a computer-enhanced photograph of the AIDS virus. The medicines being developed to treat AIDS include the drug zidovudine, which is shown here.

Developments in technology have improved other branches of medicine as well. Surgeons use *optical-fiber* devices, such as the one shown in Figure 2–10, to "see" into the body without having to cut through the skin. When it is necessary to operate, this same instrument is used to guide the surgeon to the area needing treatment.

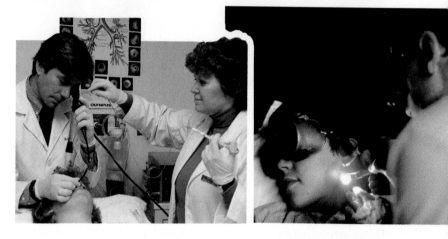

**Figure 2–10.** These physicians are using optical fibers to see inside the nose and ear of the patients.

Using lasers in surgery causes less blood loss that can translate to less recovery time in the hospital.

## *READING CRITICALLY*
How can lasers help decrease the cost of health care?

Laser technology is also used in surgery. Instead of scalpels, lasers are often used to cut through tissue. As the laser cuts through the skin, the heat from the laser also seals broken blood vessels, which keeps bleeding to a minimum. Lasers are now used in many types of surgery, including eye surgery and the removal of kidney stones. Lasers are explained more fully in Chapter 13.

## 2.4 Technology for Space

In 1969, Neil Armstrong became the first man to walk on the moon. In the 1980s, space-shuttle flights became a common event. But it was not so long ago that such things were the material of science fiction. The United

**Figure 2–11.** Space technology has come a long way from the space ship writer Jules Verne pictured in 1865.

States space program is probably the best example of how science and technology work together. For instance, scientific discoveries have allowed engineers to design and build the spacecraft that have taken astronauts to the moon and back. A knowledge of physics and chemistry made it possible to produce the high-energy fuels needed to power the engines that carry rockets into space.

Computers are an important part of the space program. The calculations needed to place objects in their proper orbits must be made quickly and accurately. Only computers have the necessary speed and accuracy to do this. Computers control almost every part of space flight, from launch to landing. Astronauts use computers to navigate their spacecraft and to perform many experiments in space. Many spacecraft are sent into orbit without crews and are controlled completely by computer. Engineers on Earth follow the flight of all spacecraft with the use of computerized tracking stations. Tracking stations are placed in different spots around the world so spacecraft can be monitored continuously. Why must tracking stations be placed around the world in order to continuously monitor spacecraft?

Much of the technology developed for space has been put to use in everyday applications here on Earth. For example, satellite technology has had a great impact on our lives. Satellites are used in communications to relay, or send, radio, television, and telephone signals around the world. One satellite can do the work of hundreds of relay stations on Earth.

Technology designed to monitor the vital signs of astronauts in space is now used in hospitals. Ask students what other ways hospitals might use computers. (record keeping, billing, in surgery)

Explain the efficiency of a satellite over a ground-base relay station by explaining how intervening hills and mountains can block off line-of-sight transmissions, while a satellite can "look over" such obstructions.

One tracking station cannot monitor spacecraft around the earth. Instead the tracking of a spacecraft is passed from one station to the next.

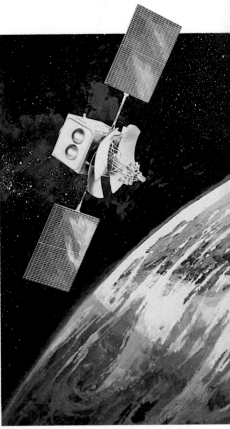

**Figure 2–12.** Satellites in space transmit electrical impulses to satellite dishes on the earth. Satellites enable people to watch television programs from all over the world.

Satellites may also be equipped with cameras. Photographs of weather patterns across entire continents help forecasters predict the weather. Satellite photographs of distant planets have provided scientists with important information. Photographs such as the one in Figure 2–13 are sometimes the only means of learning more about the solar system.

Satellite photographs are also used to make maps and to study the earth's land and sea resources. For example, from satellite photographs, scientists discovered a new fishing ground near the Philippines. This area now provides thousands of tons of seafood for the people of Southeast Asia.

Other space program spinoffs include solar-energy devices, better insulating materials for buildings, and freeze-dried foods. Scientists believe that further space exploration will open the door to many more discoveries and technologies for use on Earth. Space exploration and space technology are discussed further in Chapters 16 and 17.

**Figure 2–13.** This photograph of Jupiter was taken by a camera aboard a satellite.

## 2.5 Technology for the Arts

From musicians to film directors, artists of all types use modern technology to produce their art. A good example of art and technology is the scientific research on sound that led to the development of the music *synthesizer* (SIHN thuh sy zuhr). This electronic device can produce sounds that closely match the sounds of musical instruments.

**Figure 2–14.** Dancers may use computers to plan the step in a dance or to show correct position in dance, as this dancer is demonstrating.

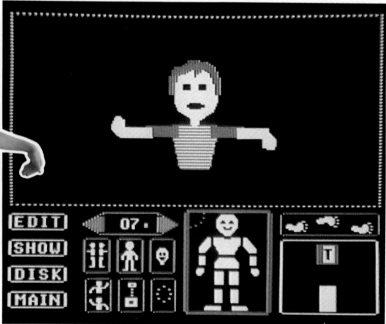

Synthesizers can also produce tones that ordinary musical instruments cannot. Because they are so versatile, synthesizers are used in the production of all types of music, from classical to rock.

**Figure 2–15.** Herbie Hancock uses a variety of synthesizers to create his unique music.

There are many uses for computer technology in the arts. Computers are used by musicians to help them compose music. In recording studios, computers control complex recording equipment. Writers use computers to revise and edit their stories. For example, this textbook was written, edited, and typeset on a computer. Movie directors use computers to edit film. Computers have been used with laser technology to produce laser light shows.

Cartoonists and animators use computer graphics to develop high-quality pictures. Computers are also used for special effects in television and movies. Have the students name programs and movies they have used or seen that use computer graphics.

As this section has shown, science and technology affect every part of your life. The continuing study of science will lead to new technologies that will have a strong impact on your future.

## Section Review

1. List some ways that modern technology has influenced everyday life.
2. Explain the benefits of computers in industry and transportation.
3. Name two devices that enable physicians to "see" inside the body without X rays.
4. List three applications of satellite technology.
5. THINKING CRITICALLY Scientific discoveries often lead to the development of new technology. Give some examples of new technology that could lead to new scientific discoveries.

1. Answers will vary, but may include VCRs, microwaves, food packaging and preserving, and surgery and medicine.
2. Computers take efficient inventory, perform boring tasks, regulate traffic, and aid engineers in car and aircraft designs.
3. CAT scans and NMR
4. satellite photography, satellite communication relays, satellite weather maps
5. CAT scans and NMR help us learn more about the human body, while satellites give more information about outer space.

# SKILL *ACTIVITY*   Making Tables

**INTRODUCTION**

Tables are used to organize information. The use of tables often makes data easier to understand. Table 1 is an example of how a table should be set up.

| TABLE 1 | ENERGY RATINGS OF SOME ACTIVITIES |
|---|---|
| **Activity** | **Energy Used (Calories per hour)** |
| Swimming | 750 |
| Basketball | 700 |
| Jogging | 600 |
| Bicycling | 400 |
| Walking (briskly) | 360 |
| Bowling | 240 |

**PROCEDURE**

1. To make a table, decide on a title for the table. Each table should be numbered in order.
2. Next, decide how many columns the table should have. Each column should have a heading.
3. List the material to be presented under the proper heading. When your table includes measurements, be sure to include the correct units.

**APPLICATION**

Organize the information in the following letter into a table. Then answer the questions below.

Dear Subscriber:

On our cable service, television network WCBS is on channel 6, television network WNBC is on channel 2, television network WABC is on channel 5, television network WPBS is on channel 3, television network WTBS is on channel 7, and television network WNEW is on channel 4.

1. television call letters and their corresponding channel numbers
2. Answers will vary.

1. What two types of information does your table contain?
2. In Table 1 above, the information could have been arranged alphabetically. Instead, it was arranged by the amount of energy used. Explain how you arranged the television information in your table.

# The Impact of Science and Technology on Society

## SECTION OBJECTIVES

- **Debate** some social questions raised by developments in science and technology.
- **Discuss** environmental problems caused by advances in technology.
- **Evaluate** the impact of science and technology on society.

## 2.6 Social and Environmental Questions

Science and technology have had a strong influence on the development of modern society. Most scientific and technological developments have led to an improved quality of life for almost all people. However, some technological changes also raise serious questions for society.

As shown in Figure 2–16, nuclear energy is a striking example of the positive and negative applications of technology. Nuclear power plants were developed as an additional means of providing electrical power. Nuclear power plants can generate more electricity than other types of power plants.

Technology has also used the scientific knowledge of nuclear energy in the development of nuclear weapons that have tremendous destructive power. Some scientists think that a worldwide nuclear war would change the earth's climate and destroy all life on Earth. Other people believe that nuclear weapons are needed to prevent one country from attacking another. People who support

### SCIENCE FACT

About 345 nuclear power plants operate in 22 countries. The United States has about 85 nuclear power plants, which generate about 13 percent of the country's electricity.

**Figure 2–16.** Nuclear power plants and nuclear explosions are both expressions of nuclear technology.

**Figure 2–17.** Every citizen has the right to examine his or her computer credit records. This right allows everyone to ensure that the records are accurate.

Erroneous information about a person may cause him or her credit problems and legal difficulties.

**ACTIVITY**

**Predicting Future Technology**

Make some predictions of new technology and discoveries that you think will take place over the next few years. You may wish to write down your predictions and put them in an envelope to be opened on your thirtieth birthday. Give some reasons for your predictions.

the development of nuclear arms believe that these weapons are so terrible that no country will ever actually use them. People who oppose nuclear arms reason that if the weapons are available, they may eventually be used. The nuclear weapons issue raises many questions for which there are no easy answers. Chapter 7 explains how nuclear energy is used and describes the effects of its power.

The computer has played a large part in the development of many different technologies. However, the availability of information put into computer banks has raised many questions. A person's school record, driving history, credit-card purchases, and financial status are recorded by computers. This and other information is readily available to credit companies, retailers, and law enforcement agencies, among others. Most people are not even aware of the information computer banks may contain about them. How might having all this information in a computer affect a person's privacy?

To get into most computer files, a person must know a certain code. Anyone with the correct code can look at and change your personal records. Many people believe that it is an invasion of privacy to have such information recorded in computer files. In this case, technology has raced ahead of the society that created it. Laws are now being proposed that would limit the availability of computer files already in use and control the amount of information put into new files.

## 2.7 Future Technology

Technological advances in the future will be based on increased demand for the products and services created by today's technology. These advances will also be based on some of the problems today's technology has created. For example, scientists in all fields will be working on safer ways in which to work with nuclear energy and to deal with the harmful effects of a nuclear accident.

Scientists are already working on alternative materials to use in place of natural resources. For example, some plant products may be used to replace fossil fuels, such as petroleum. Petroleum is made of large carbon molecules, which can be changed into many different chemicals. Very similar carbon molecules are found in many living plants. In the future, machines may use oil removed from peanuts or other plants rather than the petroleum products used today. The development and use of new synthetic materials will also increase as natural resources decrease. The management of natural resources is discussed more fully in Chapter 29.

New areas of scientific research will open up as technology takes us from the vastness of outer space to the depths of the world's oceans. How will continued uses of and improvements in computers aid scientists in exploring new discoveries?

These examples have given you a brief look at what the future may hold. How society manages the development of technology is critical. Each person should be aware of how technology affects everyday life so that informed decisions can be made.

## Section Review

1. Describe an example of technology that could have both positive and negative applications.
2. Explain how the widespread use of computers could invade a person's privacy.
3. THINKING CRITICALLY How would an understanding of scientific principles help you analyze the effects of new technologies?
4. THINKING CRITICALLY Describe how you think advances in technology will change your life in the next 20 years.

1. nuclear energy—cheap energy, nuclear accidents
2. Unauthorized people can access personal information about an individual.
3. If you understand the principles, you can make an informed decision and determine the advantages and disadvantages.
4. Answers will vary.

# CAREER

## Word-Processing Operator

**DESCRIPTION** A word-processing operator uses a computer to write, edit, and store different types of documents. Word-processing equipment consists of a keyboard, a computer, a video display screen, a storage system, and a printer. Word-processing operators can find jobs in business, government, and education.

**REQUIREMENTS** If you plan on a career as a word-processing operator, you should take typing courses to become a good typist. You should also learn how to operate word-processing equipment. Many business schools and community colleges offer courses after high-school graduation.

**INFORMATION** Information Management and Processing Association, P.O. Box 16267, Lansing, MI 48901

# INVESTIGATION 2: Designing Paper Airplanes

*What kind of plane will fly further, a paper plane or a tissue-paper plane?*

## PURPOSE

To design two paper airplanes and to determine which of the two will fly the farthest

## MATERIALS

| | |
|---|---|
| typing paper | transparent tape |
| waxed paper | aluminum foil |
| tissue paper | plastic wrap |
| construction paper | scissors |
| glue | meter stick |
| toothpicks | |

## PROCEDURE

1. Copy Table 1 onto a sheet of paper. Enter all data from this investigation on your table.

2. Using any of the materials listed above, design and construct two different airplanes.

3. Number your completed airplanes 1 and 2.

4. Test airplane 1 by standing at a given point. Throw the airplane as far as you can. Measure the distance the plane flew with a meter stick. Record the distance on Table 1.

5. Repeat step 4 using airplane 2.

6. Fly each airplane three times. Record the distance for each flight in Table 1.

7. After you have recorded three trial flights for each airplane, average the distances and record the average in the space provided on Table 1.

## RESULTS

1. Using the scientific method, outline the steps taken in designing, building, and testing your airplanes.

2. From the average distance each plane flew, determine which airplane flew the farthest.

3. Did the results of your trial flights support your prediction at the beginning of the investigation?

## CONCLUSIONS

1. What features did your winning airplane have that the other plane did not have?

2. Using the same materials, how would you redesign the other plane so that it goes further?

   1. Answers will vary but may include the plane's light weight and streamlined design.
   2. Answers will vary.

## APPLICATIONS

1. Test your winning airplane against your classmates' airplanes to determine a class winner.   1. Answers will vary.

2. Discuss how professional engineers would go about designing a real airplane.

   2. Some possible answers might be that they would use computers to produce graphics to help design an airplane.

| TABLE 1 | FLIGHT TRIALS | | |
|---|---|---|---|
| | **Plane 1** | **Plane 2** | **Distance (cm)** |
| Trial 1 | | | |
| Trial 2 | | | |
| Trial 3 | | | |
| Total | | | |
| Average | | | |

## Writing Critically

1. Computer records about a person are available from many data banks. Explain why computer records can pose a threat to individual privacy that did not exist when only written records were available.

2. Describe some ways in which nuclear energy can affect your life. Discuss arguments for and against using this technology.

3. **CHALLENGE** Write a story about what life might be like twenty years from now. Describe what technological advances would have been made and how these advances would change your life style.

1. Anybody can get access to files, and can tamper with them without the individual's knowledge.
2. Answers will vary but should discuss benefits of nuclear power plants as well as potential for accidents. Destructive effects of nuclear war should also be discussed, as well as deterent value of nuclear arms.
3. Answers will vary.

## Skill Reinforcement

The Skill Activity on page 36 describes how to make a table. Using the information in this chapter, make a table showing the different areas in which computer technology is used. Also list the applications of computers in each area. (Note: There may be more than one application for each area.) Be sure you follow the steps outlined in the Skill Activity when setting up your table. Compare your table with those of your classmates. Describe some other ways in which this information could be presented.

## Research Ideas

1. Talk with your parents, grandparents, or other adults to find out what technological advances have taken place in their lifetime. Compare some of the devices that resulted from these technologies to the same or similar devices used today.

2. Find out how modern technology is being used in some local businesses and industries in your area. Report on how similar technologies are used in different environments.

3. **CHALLENGE** Research the problem of world energy supplies and propose ways in which different technologies might be improved to help provide a solution.

## For Further Reading

Bailey, David, and Laura Castoro. *Careers in Computers*. New York: Julian Messner, 1985. If you are interested in a career working with computers, this book is a good guide to the various opportunities available in the field. It describes types of computer-related jobs in industry, business, government, education, and research.

Hayden, Richard, and Thierry Despont. *Restoring the Statue of Liberty: Sculpture, Structure, and Symbol*. New York: McGraw-Hill, 1986. This fascinating book is the story of the step-by-step restoration of the Statue of Liberty. A team of architects, engineers, metallurgists, chemists, and artisans used traditional craftsmanship and new technologies to restore the statue from top to bottom.

# CHAPTER 3

# Matter, Energy, Space, and Time

Matter, energy, space, and time affect everyone's life. The universe is made of matter and energy and is located in space and time. With the aid of modern technology, scientists are learning more about how matter and energy act together and how the universe operates within space and time.

For additional information, see pages T62–T63.

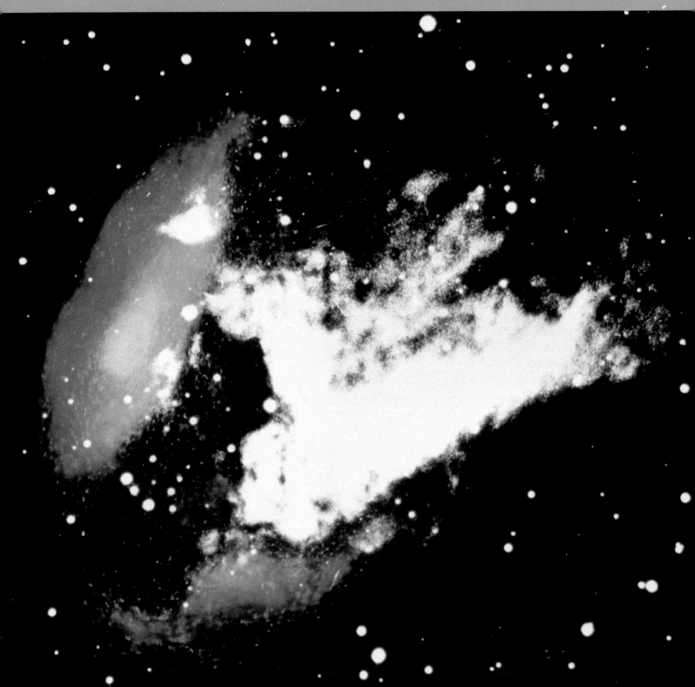

# Matter and Energy

## SECTION OBJECTIVES

- **Identify** the three states of matter.
- **Define** and **calculate** *density*.
- **Define** the terms *mass* and *energy*.
- **Name** the four forces of nature.
- **Describe** the relationship between energy and mass.

Photograph left: an irregular galaxy

NEW TERMS IN THIS SECTION

| | |
|---|---|
| matter | gravity |
| law of conservation of mass | electromagnetism |
| solid | strong nuclear force |
| liquid | weak nuclear force |
| gas | kinetic energy |
| phase change | potential energy |
| balance | heat |
| density | law of conservation of |
| weight | energy |

## 3.1 Three States of Matter

Anything that takes up space and has mass is called **matter**. There are three basic states of matter on Earth—solids, liquids, and gases. There is a fourth state of matter with which you are probably less familiar. It is called *plasma*. Plasma occurs only under special circumstances, such as in a flame, in fluorescent lights, or on the sun.

Matter can be changed from one form to another, but it cannot be created or destroyed. This is called the **law of conservation of mass**.

### Solids, Liquids, and Gases

A **solid** has a definite shape and volume and is therefore incompressible (ihn kuhm PREHS uh buhl). Matter that is incompressible cannot be squeezed into a smaller volume. Like a solid, a **liquid** has a definite volume and is also incompressible. However, liquids do not have a definite shape. The shape of a liquid is determined by the shape of its container.

A **gas** has neither a definite shape nor a definite volume. A gas always expands to fill its container. Unlike

**Figure 3–1.** The ancient Greeks and Romans made use of the incompressible nature of solids. They recognized the possibilities of stone as a means of supporting very large structures.

Liquids and gases are classed together as *fluids*. A fluid is any substance that flows.

a solid or a liquid, a gas is compressible. This property of gases makes them useful in shock absorbers and air-brake systems for cars and trucks.

## Phase Changes

Any substance may exist as a solid, a liquid, or a gas. Water is found in nature in all three states. The state of matter of any substance is determined by temperature and pressure. Most substances are solids or liquids at room temperature. When these substances become hot enough, they change into gases. The change from one state of matter to another is known as a **phase change**. A phase change occurs at a definite temperature for each substance at a given pressure. For example, at sea level, water changes from a solid to a liquid at 0°C and from a liquid to a gas at 100°C. However, the temperature at which a liquid boils or freezes will change as the pressure increases or decreases.

When any substance that is normally a solid or a liquid changes into a gas, the gas is called a *vapor*. For example, water in the gaseous state is called *water vapor*. A few solids (e.g., iodine, dry ice) will change directly into a gas at normal pressure, without becoming a liquid. This process is called *sublimation*.

**Figure 3–2.** At pressures greater than atmospheric pressure, water can remain liquid at temperatures greater than 100°C. If your car radiator has overheated, never remove the cap while the radiator is still hot. Removing the cap reduces the pressure inside the radiator, causing the water to boil immediately.

How are temperature and pressure related in causing changes in phase? At high elevations, atmospheric pressure is lower than at sea level. As a result, water at high elevations will boil at temperatures lower than 100°C. For this reason, mountain climbers often cannot cook eggs by boiling them. The temperature of boiling water on a mountaintop may be too low to cook eggs or other food. By comparison, food cooks faster at higher pressures than the pressure at sea level. Pressure cookers work on this principle.

Modern technology has made it possible to produce intermediate states of matter. Liquid crystals, used in digital watches, are liquids that behave like solids in many ways.

At very high pressures, water melts below 0°C, its normal freezing point. Ice skaters make use of this fact. The blade of an ice skate exerts a very high pressure on the surface of ice. This high pressure causes the ice to melt. As a result, an ice skater actually glides on a thin film of water. The water refreezes as soon as the pressure from the skate blade is removed.

# 3.2 Mass, Density, and Weight

There are other properties of matter that are important to your understanding of how nature works. Properties that can be observed without changing the material in any way are called *physical properties*. Color, size, and melting point are all physical properties. Some physical properties can be changed. For instance, suppose you have brown hair and you dye it red. You still have hair, you have just changed its color.

Some physical properties cannot be changed. Unchanging physical properties that help you to identify a particular object or material are called characteristic properties. For instance, your fingerprints are characteristic of you. People can identify you just by examining your fingerprints. Your fingerprints are a characteristic property. Similarly, matter has characteristic properties that can be used to identify different materials regardless of size, shape, or color.

## Mass and Density

You may recall from Chapter 1 that mass is a measure of the amount of matter an object contains. Mass is a physical property and can be measured in kilograms (kg). A **balance** is an instrument used to measure mass.

*READING CRITICALLY*
If you lived in a bubble of air under the ocean, what problems might you have when cooking?

Food would cook very quickly due to the high pressures found below the sea.

Ask the students to form small groups. Each group should then create a list of physical properties that are characteristic properties, and give examples of each. When all groups have completed their lists, make a composite list.

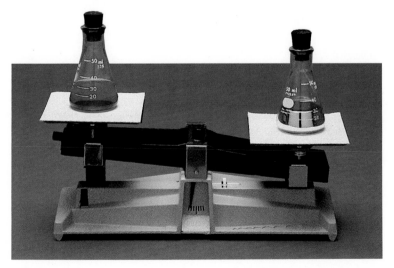

**Figure 3–3.** Although these two flasks contain the same volume of liquid, their densities are very different. The flask on the left contains colored water while the flask on the right contains mercury.

**Calculating Density**

Using a balance, determine the mass of three unknown rectangular solids that your teacher will give you. Calculate the density of each solid.

The density of the sun (100 g/cm³) is much greater than the density of the earth (5.52 g/cm³).

Another physical characteristic of matter is density. **Density** is a measure of the amount of matter in a given volume of a substance. As stated in Chapter 1, volume is the amount of space matter occupies. If you divide the mass of an object by its volume, you get the density of the object. In other words, density is mass per unit volume. Density is a characteristic property of matter. All samples of the same material, whatever their size and shape, have the same density. If the mass increases, the volume also increases and vice versa, so the ratio of mass to volume remains the same.

Suppose you wanted to find the density of water. First you must know the mass and the volume. One cubic meter (1 m³) of fresh water has a mass of 1000 kg. Therefore, the density of water must be 1000 kg/m³. However, because the cubic meter is such a large unit of volume, densities are usually given in grams divided by cubic centimeters (g/cm³). In these units, the density of water is 1 g/cm³.

**Example:** Calculate the density of a block of wood. The volume of the block is 2500 cm³. The mass of the block is 1.9 kg.

**Solution:**
- *Write* the equation for density.

$$\text{Density} = \frac{\text{mass}}{\text{volume}}$$

$$D = \frac{m}{V}$$

- *Substitute* the values for $m$ and $V$ in the equation.

$$D = \frac{1.9 \text{ kg}}{2500 \text{ cm}^3}$$

$$D = \frac{1900 \text{ g}}{2500 \text{ cm}^3}$$

- *Solve* by dividing.

$$D = 0.76 \text{ g/cm}^3$$

**Figure 3–4.** If astronauts lost strength and mass in space, as well as weight, they would never be able to perform tasks such as the one shown here. Astronauts report that such tasks require all their strength despite the reduced weight of the objects they are maneuvering.

**Weight**

Many people confuse mass and weight. You now know that mass is the amount of matter an object contains. The **weight** of an object is a measure of the force it exerts on anything that supports it. Weight is caused by the force of gravity acting on the mass of an object. Unlike density, weight is not a characteristic property of matter. You can lose weight simply by going to the moon. The force due to the moon's gravity is much less than the force due to the earth's gravity. Astronauts standing on the moon's surface weigh only one-sixth their weight on Earth. However, their mass and their strength remain the same as on Earth. How is an astronaut's density affected by going to the moon? The astronaut's density does not change.

**READING CRITICALLY**
How much would an 82-kg astronaut weigh on the moon?

13.7 kg

## 3.3 Four Fundamental Forces

The universe is controlled by forces. The word *force* often means "push" or "pull." However, scientists use the word *force* to describe how objects affect, or interact with, one another. There are many different kinds of forces. For example, substances that return to their original shape after being distorted are experiencing *elastic* force.

**Figure 3–5.** Due to elastic force, this fishing rod will return to its original shape when the fish gets away.

To measure the strength of an elastic force, hang known weights on a large elastic band. Measure the extension. Elastic energy is stored in the stretched rubber band.

*Friction* is another kind of force. It exists wherever two substances come in contact. It enables you to walk, run, and jump. Friction also slows down fast-moving objects. For instance, space-shuttle pilots use air friction to slow their craft before landing. Friction can also produce large amounts of heat. You can prove this yourself by rubbing your hands together quickly for a few seconds. What are some other ways that friction produces heat?

Elastic force, friction, and all other forces are the result of one or another of four fundamental forces. The four fundamental forces are gravity, electromagnetism, strong nuclear force, and weak nuclear force.

Answers will vary but may include dragging an object along the ground and the reentry of the space shuttle into the atmosphere.

**Figure 3–6.** Friction between the surface of the long-jump runway and this athlete's feet enables her to gain speed as she runs toward the pit.

## Gravity and Electromagnetism

A force that acts on objects with mass is called **gravity.** The sun, moon, planets, stars, and galaxies are all held together by, and move under, the control of gravity. When you drop something, it falls because the gravity of the earth pulls it down. The earth's gravity also keeps you and everything else on the planet from floating off into space.

A force acting on electrically charged particles of matter is **electromagnetism** (ih lehk troh MAG nuh tihz uhm). Both electromagnetism and gravity can act on an object that has both an electric charge and mass.

## Nuclear Forces

Two other fundamental forces, the strong nuclear force and the weak nuclear force, were not discovered until the twentieth century. The discovery of these forces did not occur until developments in modern technology made investigation of atomic structure possible. Nuclear forces act only over very short distances. In fact, the nuclear forces do not act beyond the atom.

The **strong nuclear force** binds the protons and the neutrons in the nucleus (NOO klee uhs) of the atom together. The **weak nuclear force** is found within the particles of the nucleus and is involved in the breaking apart of some nuclei. As a result, this force is responsible for the control of radioactivity and of the nuclear reactions that fuel the sun and all the stars.

In comparison to other forces, gravity is a relatively weak force. It takes a large amount of mass to produce a strong gravitational force. This explains why gravity has a greater effect on objects with very large mass, like planets and stars.

Ask the students to prove the statement "Matter itself would not exist without force." Their answers should relate to the fact that force binds everything together. There would be no stars, planets, or living things without forces to bind everything together.

**Figure 3–7.** The weak nuclear force is responsible for the nuclear reactions taking place in this power plant. These reactions produce heat that can be converted into electricity.

nate to locate the object. For example, suppose you are trying to find a location on a certain street. You need to know only the number of the address. You could find a house on Beacon Street, as long as you knew the number of the house.

To locate a place on a surface, you need two coordinates. Places are located on the surface of the earth using two coordinates, latitude and longitude. Latitude and longitude are discussed more fully in Chapter 15. In cities and towns, streets and avenues are often used to locate places. For example, the New York Public Library is located at the intersection of Forty-second Street and Fifth Avenue.

To locate an object in space, you need three coordinates. For instance, to locate a submarine, you must know its latitude, longitude, and depth.

Measurements of position and time are always made from a starting point. For instance, both height and depth are measured starting from sea level. Latitude starts from the equator. Any set of points, lines, or planes from which coordinates can be measured is called a **frame of reference.** For example, when you point to something, you become a frame of reference. Your body is a reference point, and your pointing finger is a reference line.

Three coordinates are needed to locate an object in three-dimensional space. However, there is a fourth dimension. That fourth dimension is time. As a simple example of this idea, think of the submarine mentioned earlier. If you were to look at the correct longitude, latitude, and depth, you might expect to find the submarine if it were not moving. If the submarine is moving, you will not find it at that location if you were a minute or two early or late. Time becomes a very important coordinate for moving objects.

### ACTIVITY

**Using Coordinates**

Draw a map of your school on graph paper. Give the coordinates for locating the library and the cafeteria on your map.

---

Discuss with the students how many coordinates they would need to locate a moving heliocopter. (4)

Discuss with the students how we determine that the earth moves. The perception of the earth's movement depends on the frame of reference used to define the earth's position. The earth does not move beneath our feet. Relative to any frame of reference attached to the earth, such as a person or a classroom, the earth is stationary. Relative to a frame of reference attached to the sun, the earth does move. It all depends on your point of view.

## 3.7 Einstein's Theory of Relativity

Albert Einstein showed that the dimensions of space and time are related. According to Einstein's **theory of relativity,** space and time both change for objects traveling at very high speeds. Time is measured by a clock, and space is measured by meter sticks. At very high speeds, clocks slow down and meter sticks get shorter. Measurement of length and time depends on the speed of the object being measured relative to the speed of the observer. This is why Einstein's theory is called the *theory of relativity.*

Einstein developed two theories of relativity. The special theory deals with how objects and events appear when viewed from different frames of reference that are moving with constant speed relative to one another. The general theory deals with accelerated frames of reference and gravity.

**Figure 3–11.** If you were traveling at the speed of light, everything around you would appear as in the photograph on the left. Anyone viewing you moving at that speed would see you as in the photograph on the right.

Help the students understand the theory of relativity with the following example. Imagine looking at a large stopwatch. If we moved at the speed of light away from the stopwatch, the hands would appear to stand still. The stopwatch would appear to be frozen in time. From the moving observer's point of view, time would have stopped.

## *READING CRITICALLY*

Who would age faster—a twin taking a trip at the speed of light or a twin staying behind?

the twin staying home

## SCIENCE FACT

During the 1980s, our model of the solar system changed dramatically. *Voyager 1* and *2* space probes discovered many new moons around Jupiter, Saturn, and Uranus. The space probes also discovered rings around Jupiter.

The theory of relativity is very confusing for many people. In our common experience, length and time do not appear to change with speed. A racing car moving past us at high speed does not appear to be shorter than a car that is standing still. The watch on the driver's wrist keeps exactly the same time as our own. Yet it has been shown that length and time do change for objects moving at speeds approaching the speed of light.

## 3.8 Scientific Models

Artists and architects use models to help them see, or visualize, people and buildings. Scientists use models to visualize the objects they study. A **scientific model** is a mental picture or physical representation of an object or a set of objects.

Scientists often use physical models to help them visualize things they cannot see. In addition, some scientific models are described in mathematical language.

The structure of the atom, the interior of the sun, and the interior of the earth are all examples of things that scientists cannot see directly. Scientists have collected as much indirect evidence as they could about these things. Using this information, scientists can then hypothesize models of what they think these things look like. As they receive more or different information, their models may change.

Most of these models can never be tested directly. The scientists can only determine if the model satisfactorily explains the evidence and information about the object, and if the model can make predictions that can be tested.

Scientific models can be changed as more information becomes available. Figure 3–12 shows an early scientific model of the solar system. This model is now out of date. It was used by early astronomers to help them visualize all the facts then known about the planets and the stars. What evidence can you think of to prove that the model in Figure 3–12 is incorrect? the movements of the planets relative to the earth and sun

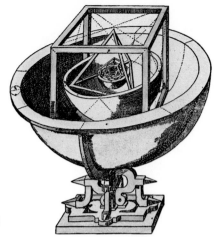

**Figure 3–12.** Although we now know that Kepler's model of the solar system was inaccurate, it was a model that represented the known facts of that time. As more information was obtained, the model was changed.

## Section Review

1. How many coordinates must be specified in order to locate a point in space?
2. Describe what is meant by frame of reference.
3. How does a scientific model differ from an artist's model?
4. THINKING CRITICALLY Why is distance distorted at the speed of light?

1. three
2. A frame of reference is a set of points, lines, or planes from which coordinates can be measured.
3. Artists' models are always physical representations of visible objects. Scientific models can be a mental or mathematical description of something that cannot be seen.
4. Speed causes objects to appear smaller than they are, thus distorting them.

## CAREER

# Physicist

**DESCRIPTION** A physicist uses mathematical terms to describe the structure and behavior of the universe, as well as the interaction of matter and energy. Physicists develop theories that describe the forces of nature, such as gravity and electromagnetism. Physicists work for educational institutions, government, and industry. Their work has led to discoveries that have advanced electronics, communications, aerospace technology, and medicine.

**REQUIREMENTS** A student planning a career as a physicist should take chemistry, physics, and mathematics courses in high school. Completion of college work leading to a master of science degree in physics is essential. Many physicists have doctoral degrees.

**INFORMATION** American Physics Society, 335 East 45th Street, New York, NY 10017

# INVESTIGATION 3: Weighing Different Water Volumes

## How are the mass and volume of a substance related?

### PURPOSE
To discover how to predict the mass of different volumes of water

### MATERIALS
100-mL graduate
250-mL beaker
equal arm balance, with weights if necessary
water

### PROCEDURE
1. Copy Table 1 onto a sheet of paper. Enter all data from this investigation on your table.
2. Measure the mass of the empty graduate and record the value in your data table.
3. Pour about 200 mL of water in a beaker. This beaker of water will be your source of water for the investigation.
4. As shown in the data table, pour various amounts of water from your beaker into the graduate and then use the balance to find the mass of the graduate with the water. Record each value in your data table.
5. Plot a graph of the mass of the graduate and water versus the volume of the water. If you need help plotting the graph, ask your teacher.
6. Using the same graph, plot a graph of the mass of the water only versus the volume of the water.

### RESULTS
1. How are the two graphs similar? How are they different?
2. Use your graph to predict the mass of 100 mL of water.
3. Use your graph to predict the mass of 55 mL of water.
4. Use your graph to predict the volume of 100 g of water.
5. Use your graph to predict the volume of 55 g of water. Answers to numbers 1 through 5 will vary.

### CONCLUSIONS
1. What generalization can be stated as a result of doing this investigation?
2. How could you use your graphs to find the density of water? 1. Mass increases with volume.
   2. Use volume and mass to find density.

### APPLICATION
1. This investigation could be done with other liquids (e.g., alcohol, glycerine) in order to find their density. Density is one of the characteristic properties of a substance that is used to distinguish it from other substances. What are other properties that are used to distinguish one substance from another? Mass and volume.
2. In this chapter you learned that matter exists in three basic states. This investigation shows how to determine the density of a liquid. How could the densities of gases and solids be determined? With your teacher's approval, you could perform investigations to find the density of other substances.

| Volume of Water (mL) | Mass of Water and Graduate (g) | Mass of Water Only (g) |
|---|---|---|
| 0 | | |
| 10 | | |
| 20 | | |
| 30 | | |
| 40 | | |
| 50 | | |
| 60 | | |
| 70 | | |
| 80 | | |
| 90 | | |

TABLE 1    DETERMINATION OF THE MASS OF WATER

# CHAPTER **3** REVIEW

## Summary

1. Matter exists in three different states: solid, liquid, and gas. Matter cannot be created or destroyed. **(3.1)**

2. States of matter are determined by pressure and temperature. **(3.1)**

3. Mass is the amount of matter in an object. **(3.2)**

4. Density is the mass of an object divided by its volume. All samples of the same substance have the same density. **(3.2)**

5. The weight of an object is a measure of the force it exerts on anything that supports it. **(3.2)**

6. The four fundamental forces of nature are gravity, electromagnetism, strong nuclear force, and weak nuclear force. **(3.3)**

7. All changes involve energy. Energy is a measure of an object's ability to cause changes. **(3.4)**

8. Energy can be changed from kinetic to potential and back again. Energy can also be transferred from one place to another. However, energy cannot be created or destroyed. **(3.4)**

9. Mass and energy are different forms of the same thing. **(3.5)**

10. The location of any object is described by coordinates measured from a frame of reference. **(3.6)**

11. According to Einstein's theory of relativity, measurements of length and time depend on the speed of the object being measured relative to the speed of the observer. **(3.7)**

12. Scientific models are used to help scientists visualize an object or a set of objects. **(3.8)**

## Science Terms

On a separate sheet of paper, define each term in a sentence.

balance **(47)**
coordinates **(54)**
density **(48)**
electromagnetism **(50)**
frame of reference **(55)**
gas **(45)**
gravity **(50)**

heat **(51)**
kinetic energy **(51)**
law of conservation of energy **(52)**
law of conservation of mass **(45)**
liquid **(45)**
matter **(45)**
phase change **(46)**

potential energy **(51)**
scientific model **(56)**
solid **(45)**
strong nuclear force **(50)**
theory of relativity **(55)**
weak nuclear force **(50)**
weight **(48)**

## Modified True-False

On a separate sheet of paper, mark each true statement *TRUE* and each false statement *FALSE*. If false, change the underlined term to make the statement true.

1. A <u>liquid</u> will always expand to fill its container.   F, gas

2. The temperature at which a liquid boils <u>increases</u> as atmospheric pressure decreases.   F, decreases

3. Density is mass per unit <u>volume</u>.   T

4. <u>Strong</u> nuclear force binds the nucleus of an atom together.   T

5. A <u>moving</u> object has kinetic energy.   T
*(continues)*

6. Energy can be <u>transformed</u> but not destroyed.   T

7. When particles of matter are brought to very high speeds, <u>both</u> their mass and their energy increase.   T

8. <u>Two</u> coordinates are required to locate an object in space.   F, Three

9. The <u>weight</u> of an object is a measure of the force it exerts on anything that supports it.   T

10. Length and time <u>change</u> for objects moving at speeds approaching the speed of light.   T

## Multiple Choice

On a separate sheet of paper, write the letter of the term that best answers the question or completes the statement.

1. Anything that takes up space and has mass is the definition of
   a. solid.
   b. liquid.
   (c.) matter.
   d. gas.

2. The law of conservation of energy states that
   a. energy can be transformed from kinetic energy to potential energy.
   b. energy can be transferred between two objects at different temperatures.
   (c.) energy cannot be created or destroyed.
   d. mass and energy are the same thing.

3. Which of the following is not a physical characteristic?
   a. color
   b. size
   c. shape
   (d.) energy

4. The fourth dimension is
   a. space.
   (b.) time.
   c. length.
   d. height.

5. The state of matter that occurs on the sun is
   a. gas.
   b. solid.
   (c.) plasma.
   d. liquid.

6. At speeds approaching the speed of light,
   (a.) time slows down and mass increases.
   b. time speeds up and mass decreases.
   c. time slows down and mass decreases.
   d. time speeds up and mass increases.

7. A cube of metal 2 cm on a side has a mass of 64 g. The density of the metal is
   a. $2 \text{ g/cm}^3$.
   (b.) $8 \text{ g/cm}^3$.
   c. $32 \text{ g/cm}^3$.
   d. $64 \text{ g/cm}^3$.

8. Which of the following is *not* a fundamental force?
   a. gravity
   (b.) friction
   c. electromagnetism
   d. weak nuclear force

9. A car moves at 50 km/h up a hill. The car's _____ increases.
   (a.) potential energy
   b. weight
   c. density
   d. kinetic energy

10. Which of the following is *not* a model?
    a. a world globe
    b. a world map
    c. a toy doll
    (d.) a chair

## Completion

On a separate sheet of paper, complete each statement by supplying the correct term.

1. Because solids and liquids have a definite volume, they are <u>incompressible</u>.

2. Liquids have a definite <u>volume</u> but no definite shape.

3. A change from one state of matter to another is known as a <u>phase</u> change.

4. The state of any substance is determined by <u>temperature</u> and pressure.

5. The quantity of matter in any object determines its  mass  .

6. A measure of the force an object exerts on anything supporting it, is that object's  weight  .

7. When objects move at speeds approaching the speed of light, clocks  slow down  .

8. A force that acts on electrically charged particles of matter is  electromagnetism

9. Time has been recognized as the  fourth  dimension.

10. Water at elevations higher than sea level will boil at temperatures lower than  100°C.

## Writing Critically   Answers: page T63.

1. Describe the four fundamental forces found in the universe and how they affect the existence of the universe.

2. What is energy? Describe some of the energy changes that you see taking place in the classroom.

3. **CHALLENGE** Describe ways in which heat is stored and released.

## Skill Reinforcement

The Skill Activity on page 53 describes how to make a bar graph. Using the information in that activity, make another bar graph, but graph the information in a different way.

## Research Ideas

1. Find out more about plasma and its role as a state of matter.

2. Discover what coordinates are used in airplane radar.

3. **CHALLENGE** How was Einstein's theory of relativity tested? How does this theory link space, time, matter, and energy?

## For Further Reading

Asimov, Isaac. *The Measure of the Universe.* New York: Harper and Row, 1983. This book includes a full discussion of mass, length, time, area, volume, and density. It covers the vast scale of the physical universe from the micro to the cosmic domain.

Bishop, Owen. *Yardsticks of the Universe.* New York: Peter Bedrick, 1984. This book shows how the ability to measure has been an essential element in the discovery of scientific knowledge. It includes five do-it-yourself projects.

Gribbin, John. *In Search of the Double Helix: Quantum Physics and Life.* New York: Mc-Graw-Hill, 1985. This book is an account of the major scientific discoveries of the twentieth century. The work of Einstein, Pauling, Crick, and Watson is included.

Kahan, Gerald. *E = mc²: Picture Book of Relativity.* Blue Ridge Summit, PA: Tab, 1983. This text is an excellent introduction to relativity. It shows what happens to mass, length, and time as objects are accelerated to speeds near the speed of light.

# MOVING THE FAIRMOUNT HOTEL

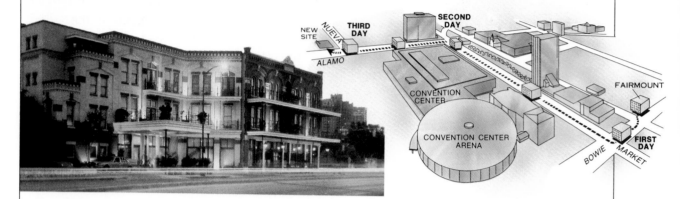

March 30, 1985: The three-story Fairmount Hotel began
a trip through the streets of San Antonio, Texas. Heavy-duty
technology, an understanding of engineering, and efficient use
of energy was required for its record-setting move to a site five blocks away.

## Preparation

The historic Fairmount Hotel, built in 1906, was in the way. Developers were ready to build a shopping mall on its site. Could it be moved? The job seemed nearly impossible: the hotel weighed more than 1.4 million kg. A company specializing in moving heavy buildings was brought in and agreed to attempt the relocation.

The old brick structure was reinforced inside and out. It was wrapped in a steel cage made of 15-cm thick beams and adjustable steel cables. The hotel's doors and windows were braced in place by wood beams. Hydraulic, or fluid-filled, jacks on railroad ties raised the building at 34 places around its foundation and set it on a network of steel beams. In all, the hotel was hoisted 2.6 meters above its previous level. The steel beams added 280 metric tons to the weight to be moved.

## Ready to Roll

Thirty-six dollies were used to accomplish the actual move.

Each dolly, designed to support 70 metric tons, had eight wheels. The wheels would distribute the load evenly over the roadbed to be traveled. As a result, the weight of the hotel would apply no more pressure to the street surfaces than would an 18-wheel tractor-trailer.

The dollies are placed in position.

Each dolly had a hydraulic jack that could be used in lifting. The dollies were slipped one by one under the beams supporting the hotel.

The dollies had hydraulic suspension systems that would absorb the shock of movement. In addition, the dollies were designed to keep the hotel stable at a constant 2.6 m above ground level. Most important, the hydraulic systems were linked together. If one dolly failed, hydraulic fluid would flow from other nearby dollies to balance the load.

Bracing the windows helps keep the structure rigid.

## Moving Day

The actual move required a large crane and seven dump trucks connected to the hotel through a system of pulleys and cables. The hotel was hauled at a leisurely 6.4 kilometers per hour toward its destination five blocks away.

Since the hotel was more than 3 m wider than the roadbed, it hung over the sidewalk on both sides as it moved along. The dollies, each with the capability of being raised, lowered, or turned independently, were carefully controlled as they moved down this narrow pathway and around two corners.

## Making Way

To clear the way for the hotel, light poles, traffic lights, and parking meters were removed. A weak point in the hotel's path was the Market Street Bridge over the San Antonio River. The problem was solved by paving the bridge's surface with steel plates that directed the hotel's load to concrete beams supporting the bridge. These beams were themselves reinforced for the move.

## Heaviest Move on Wheels

Three days after the hotel began to roll, it reached its destination. Workers began setting it into place on its new foundation. The move set a record for the heaviest building ever moved on pneumatic tires over city streets. The move also preserved one of San Antonio's historic buildings. The Fairmount was refurbished and reopened as a luxury hotel in the fall of 1986.

The hotel approaches its final destination.

# UNIT 2

# Matter and Change

Photograph right: polarized light micrograph of citric acid crystals

What causes substances to react with one another? *Chemistry* is the science that deals with the structures of different substances and with how these substances react. Chemical reactions take place everywhere— inside stars, inside a car's engine, even inside your body. This unit explains the effects of some of these reactions and the new technologies that have resulted from them.

# CHAPTER 4

# Elements, Mixtures, and Compounds

Gold was the first known element. For thousands of years, people have been attracted by the shiny yellow color and soft glow of this metal. Gold is valuable because it is scarce and does not tarnish easily. The gold shown below is worth over a billion dollars.

For additional information, see pages T66–T67.

# Elements

## SECTION OBJECTIVES

- **Define** the term *element*.
- **Compare** and **contrast** physical properties and chemical properties.
- **Recognize** the names of some common elements and their chemical symbols.
- **Identify** three main elements found in the human body.

NEW TERMS IN THIS SECTION
element
physical properties
chemical properties
homogeneous
pure substance
chemical symbol

Photograph left: gold at Fort Knox

## 4.1 Identifying Elements

Early Greeks believed that all matter was made of a few simple substances, which they called *elements*. Any substance that cannot be broken down by chemical means into a simpler substance is an **element**. Modern science has identified more than 108 elements. However, only 90 elements occur naturally on Earth. The remaining elements have been made in laboratories by scientists experimenting with nuclear reactions. Nuclear reactions are discussed more fully in Chapter 7.

Each element has characteristics that are special to that particular element. These characteristics can be classified into two groups—physical properties and chemical properties.

### Physical Properties

As was discussed in the previous chapter, **physical properties** are those characteristics that can be observed or measured without changing the composition of a substance. Physical properties include such things as color, hardness, luster, density, and freezing, melting, or

### *ACTIVITY*

**Identifying Elements**

Using Table 4–1 on page 69, select three elements that are unfamiliar to you. Find out where they were first discovered and how they may be used.

Elements 93-108 are synthetic. Elements 43 (technetium), 61 (promethium), and 85 (astatine) are unstable and are not found naturally on Earth.

Pure gold is so soft it can be molded in one's hands. Because of its softness, a variable proportion of copper or another metal is mixed with gold to give it added strength. The proportion of gold in a sample is measured in units called karats. Pure gold is 24-karat; 14-karat gold contains 14/24 or 58.3% gold.

Have different groups of students write descriptions of objects, such as a piece of chalk, a lake, or a fingernail using the objects' physical characteristics. Ask the class to identify the objects from the descriptions.

boiling points. These properties are used to identify elements and to determine their purity. Gold, for example, is yellow, soft, and shiny. The purity of gold can be determined by melting a sample of it. The melting point of gold is 1064.43°C. If the sample melts at a temperature other than 1064.43°C, the gold is not pure. Even a small impurity will change both the melting point and the boiling point of gold. The differences in temperature may be used to identify other substances in the gold.

Elements and other substances can be changed physically. A *physical change* is any change that does not produce a new kind of substance. For example, when gold is melted to make jewelry, the liquid gold is still gold. As Figure 4–1 shows, other substances, like water, can also be changed physically.

**Figure 4–1.** Water can be found naturally on Earth in all three states: liquid, solid, and gas. The physical properties of water—a low boiling point and high freezing point—make all three states possible.

READING CRITICALLY

Explain why boiling water is not a chemical change.

Boiling water is not a chemical change because it does not produce a new substance. Liquid water and water vapor are both water.

## Chemical Properties

An element can be identified by its chemical properties. **Chemical properties** are those characteristics that are observed or measured when a substance changes its composition. Such changes are called *chemical changes*. Chemical changes produce new kinds of substances. For example, when charcoal is burned in air, the charcoal is changed into carbon dioxide, water vapor, and ashes. These substances have physical and chemical properties different fron one another and from the original charcoal. Rusting iron, digesting food, and burning wood all undergo chemical changes.

Elements are **homogeneous** (hoh muh JEE nee uhs), which means that they have the same, or uniform, properties throughout. In addition, an element is made up of one particular kind of matter. A **pure substance** is any

**Figure 4–2.** Cutting wood (left) involves a physical change. Burning wood (right) involves a chemical change.

substance that is made of either a single element or one particular kind of matter. All samples of a pure substance have the same chemical properties. Gold, copper, water, and sugar are examples of pure substances.

Another property of a pure substance is that it cannot be broken down into different substances by normal physical changes. Water, for example, cannot be changed into hydrogen and oxygen by freezing, boiling, filtering, or any other physical method.

### Names and Symbols of Elements

Each element has a chemical symbol. A **chemical symbol** is a shorthand way to represent an element. Chemical symbols consist of one or two letters. The first letter is always written as a capital letter. The second letter, if there is one, is always written as a lower-case letter.

## 4.2 Distribution of Elements

The elements are not distributed evenly throughout the universe. Ninety-eight percent of the earth's surface is made from only eight elements. Of these eight elements, silicon and oxygen make up about 75 percent of the earth's surface. Aluminum, iron, calcium, sodium, potassium, and magnesium make up about 23 percent of the materials in the earth's surface. These eight elements are found in many rocks and minerals.

Some elements, such as gold, are often found in their pure state. However, most elements found in nature are mixed with other elements in the form of rocklike substances called *ores*. Ores are formed at the surface of the earth or inside the earth. Pure elements can be obtained

To avoid international disputes, all elements beyond element 103 are named by their atomic number. For example, element 104 is called *unnilquadium*, which is Latin for 104.

| TABLE 4–1 | SYMBOLS FOR SOME ELEMENTS |
|---|---|
| **Element** | **Symbol** |
| Aluminum | Al |
| Barium | Ba |
| Boron | B |
| Bromine | Br |
| Calcium | Ca |
| Carbon | C |
| Chlorine | Cl |
| Copper | Cu |
| Fluorine | F |
| Helium | He |
| Hydrogen | H |
| Iodine | I |
| Iron | Fe |
| Lithium | Li |
| Mercury | Hg |
| Nickel | Ni |
| Nitrogen | N |
| Oxygen | O |
| Phosphorus | P |
| Platinum | Pt |
| Radium | Ra |
| Silicon | Si |
| Sodium | Na |
| Sulfur | S |
| Uranium | U |
| Zinc | Zn |

The two lightest elements, hydrogen and helium, make up 99 percent of the mass of our solar system.

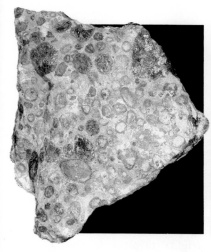

**Figure 4–3.** These photographs show the progression of a pure substance in its natural state to a finished product. Aluminum begins as bauxite ore (left), is then refined to aluminum (middle), and ultimately becomes aluminum sheets (right) that have a variety of uses.

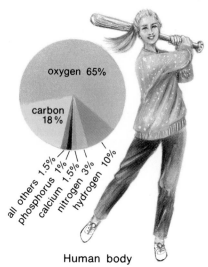

oxygen 65%

carbon 18%

all others 1.5%
phosphorus 1%
calcium 1.5%
nitrogen 3%
hydrogen 10%

Human body

**Figure 4–4.** Because oxygen, carbon, and hydrogen make up 90 percent of the human body, the total worth of all elements in the body is about fifty dollars.

1. An element is a substance that cannot be broken down by chemical means into simpler stustances.
2. A chemical property describes how a substance changes its composition; a physical property can be observed or measured without changing the composition of a substance.
3. mercury, bromine, sulfur, sodium, platinum
4. carbon, oxygen, and hydrogen
5. chemical changes: burning; physical changes: freezing, melting, boiling

from ores after the ores have been refined. For example, aluminum is obtained from an ore called *bauxite*. Which element is obtained from iron ore? iron

Elements also make up the human body. You breathe oxygen to live. Your bones and teeth are made of calcium and phosphorus. Your blood has iron in it. As Figure 4–4 shows, your body is made mostly of the elements carbon, oxygen, and hydrogen. These three elements make up more than 90 percent of your body. Other elements needed for a healthy body include nitrogen, phosphorus, calcium, potassium, sodium, sulfur, and chlorine. A total of ten elements account for more than 99 percent of all the matter in living things.

Elements that are essential for life, but only in very small amounts, are called *trace elements*. Trace elements essential to the human body are iron, magnesium, cobalt, copper, zinc, and molybdenum. Trace elements are necessary to carry out special functions in the body. For example, iron is needed for healthy red blood cells. Magnesium is needed for healthy bones and teeth. Your body needs zinc to regulate nerve and muscle function.

## Section Review

1. What is an element?
2. What is the difference between a chemical property and a physical property?
3. Give the names of the elements represented by the following symbols: Hg, Br, S, Na, and Pt.
4. What three elements make up more than 90 percent of your body?
5. THINKING CRITICALLY  Classify each of the following as a chemical or physical change—burning, freezing, melting, and boiling.

ference how a compound is made. For example, iron reacts with sulfur to produce iron sulfide. No matter how much iron and sulfur are used, the iron-sulfide compound is always 63.5 percent iron and 36.5 percent sulfur by weight.

Proust's observations have been confirmed by many experiments. His finding is now called the **law of definite proportions**. This law states that when two or more elements combine to form a compound, their relative weights are always the same.

The law of definite proportions makes it possible to predict the amounts of chemicals needed to manufacture a given amount of any compound. For example, sulfuric acid always contains 65 percent sulfur, 33 percent oxygen, and 2 percent hydrogen by weight. The law of definite proportions predicts that 0.65 kg of sulfur will be needed for each kilogram of sulfuric acid produced. Sulfuric acid is used largely in fertilizers.

## Section Review

1. Describe the two classes of compounds.
2. What are the differences and similarities between a compound, a mixture, and an element?
3. THINKING CRITICALLY Table salt (NaCl) can be produced from salt mines or evaporated from sea water. Compare the composition of table salt produced in each of these methods. Explain the reason for your answer.

### ACTIVITY

**Determining Chemical Composition**

Research the composition of the following acids: acetic acid, ethanoic acid, and hydrochloric acid.

1. Organic compounds contain carbon combined with hydrogen; inorganic compounds do not contain carbon.
2. Differences: elements cannot be broken down by chemical means, while compounds and mixtures can be broken down into elements by chemical means. Only mixtures can be broken down by physical means. There are millions of compounds, but only about 108 elements. Similarity: all are composed of elements; compounds and elements are pure substances.
3. By the law of definite proportion, the proportion of the table salt is always the same regardless of how it is produced.

## CAREER

### Exterminator

**DESCRIPTION** An exterminator uses chemicals or traps to rid homes and other buildings of rodents, insects, and other pests. Exterminators must know how to use these chemicals safely. Most exterminators work for firms specializing in pest control.

**REQUIREMENTS** A special training course or on-the-job training is required to become an exterminator. Many pest-control firms require their exterminators to have a high-school diploma. Some states require exterminators to be licensed and to pass an examination on the use and handling of toxic substances.

**INFORMATION** National Pest Control Association, Inc., 8150 Leesburg Pike, Suite 1100, Vienna, VA 22184

# INVESTIGATION 4: Paper Chromatography

*Is an unknown liquid a compound or a mixture?*

## PURPOSE

To separate the substances in an unknown liquid by the method of paper chromatography

## MATERIALS

filter paper
black India ink
water
beaker (500 mL)
wooden splint or thin wire
aluminum foil

## PROCEDURE

1. Cut a strip of filter paper 1 cm wide and 20 cm long. Taper the paper at one end as shown in the figure. Draw a line with a pencil (not a pen) across the paper about 2 cm above the tip of the paper.

2. Squeeze a drop of ink along this line. Allow it to dry. Repeat the procedure until a dark line is obtained across the paper.

3. Place 5 mL of water in a beaker.

4. Hang the filter paper over a wooden splint placed across the top of the beaker, as shown in the figure. The tip of the paper should be in the water. Make sure the paper strip hangs in the middle of the beaker and does not touch the walls of the beaker.

5. Cover the beaker with aluminum foil to prevent evaporation of the water.

6. Let the solution stand until the color has risen almost to the top of the paper.

7. Remove the paper, and hang it in a safe place to dry.

## RESULTS

Carefully inspect the filter paper. List the colors in order from the top of the paper down.
Answers will vary but may include blue, red, yellow, green, and orange.

## CONCLUSIONS    Answers: see page T67.

1. How many different-colored substances were you able to separate?

2. Explain why this procedure could be used to separate the different colors.

3. Does your experiment lead you to conclude that ink is a compound or a mixture? Explain.

4. What color do you think you would get if you combined the colors you have separated? (To test your hypothesis, you could put the used filter strip in a test tube. Then add 1 mL of water and shake the mixture.)

## APPLICATIONS    Answers: see page T67.

1. Describe how a kerosene lamp works.

2. Explain why ink or other chemicals spilled on clothes should be wiped up immediately rather than waiting until the chemical dries.

3. What are two qualities to look for in paper towels?

## Summary

1. An element is a substance that cannot be broken down into simpler substances by ordinary chemical means. **(4.1)**

2. An element can be described by its physical and chemical properties. **(4.1)**

3. Each element has a name and a chemical symbol. **(4.1)**

4. Ten elements make up 99 percent of all living things; three elements make up more than 90 percent of your body. **(4.2)**

5. The components of a mixture can be separated by physical means. **(4.3)**

6. Methods for separating the components of a mixture include filtration and distillation. **(4.3)**

7. Homogeneous mixtures are called solutions. **(4.4)**

8. A suspension is a heterogeneous mixture. **(4.5)**

9. Elements can chemically combine to form compounds. Both elements and compounds are pure substances. **(4.6)**

10. The names of compounds containing only two elements end in *-ide*. Compounds containing three different elements usually have names ending in *-ate*. **(4.7)**

11. The law of definite proportions describes how elements combine to form compounds. **(4.8)**

## Science Terms

On a separate sheet of paper, define each term in a sentence.

chemical properties **(68)**
chemical symbol **(69)**
colloid **(76)**
compound **(79)**
distillation **(73)**
element **(67)**
evaporation **(74)**

filtration **(73)**
heterogeneous **(73)**
homogeneous **(68)**
insoluble **(75)**
law of definite proportions **(81)**
mixture **(72)**
physical properties **(67)**

pure substance **(68)**
solubility **(75)**
soluble **(75)**
solute **(74)**
solution **(74)**
solvent **(74)**
suspension **(76)**

## Modified True-False

On a separate sheet of paper, mark each true statement *TRUE* and each false statement *FALSE*. If false, change the underlined term to make the statement true.

1. <u>Ninety</u> elements occur naturally on Earth. T

2. When elements combine chemically, <u>suspensions</u> are formed. F, compounds

3. Wood is <u>homogeneous</u>. F, heterogeneous

4. According to the the law of definite proportion, the composition of a <u>colloid</u> is always the same, no matter how it is formed. F, compound

5. The components of a mixture of pure substances can usually be separated by <u>physical</u> means. T

6. Pure substances may be either <u>solutions</u> or compounds. F, elements

7. Some mixtures can be separated by <u>filtration</u>. T

8. A colloid is a special type of <u>solution</u>. F, suspension

9. A <u>chemical</u> change is one in which a substance changes its composition. T

10. A <u>chemical symbol</u> is a shorthand way to represent an element. T

*(continues)*

## Multiple Choice

On a separate sheet of paper, write the letter of the term that best answers the question or completes the statement.

1. Evaporation is an example of a
   a. physical change.
   b. chemical change.
   c. heterogeneous mixing.
   d. formation of a gel.

2. Which of the following compounds is an organic compound?
   a. $H_2O$
   b. NaCl
   c. $H_2O_2$
   d. $CH_3$

3. Which of the following shows evidence that water is not an element?
   a. Water reacts with many metals.
   b. Water is formed when hydrogen and oxygen combine.
   c. Water dissolves many other substances.
   d. Water does not burn.

4. Which of the following is a compound?
   a. sodium
   b. chlorine
   c. iodine
   d. copper sulfide

5. Which of the following is a mixture?
   a. air
   b. salt
   c. water
   d. sulfur

6. The rust on an iron nail is made from iron and oxygen. Rust is a
   a. compound.
   b. mixture.
   c. pure substance.
   d. crystal.

7. Which of the following compounds does not contain oxygen?
   a. lithium nitrate
   b. potassium fluoride
   c. water
   d. carbon dioxide

8. Compounds with names ending in -ate contain
   a. two elements.
   b. three elements.
   c. oxygen.
   d. carbon.

9. A mixture whose properties are not the same throughout is called
   a. homogeneous.
   b. heterogeneous.
   c. soluble.
   d. insoluble.

10. The technique of separating mixtures by changing a liquid to a gas is called
    a. filtration.
    b. distillation.
    c. evaporation.
    d. panning.

## Completion

On a separate sheet of paper, complete each statement by supplying the correct term.

1. Carbon, oxygen, and _hydrogen_ make up more than 90 percent of all living matter.

2. In a compound, the elements always combine in the _same_ proportions.

3. The law of definite proportions applies to elements and _compounds_.

4. The element _carbon_ is the basis of all life on Earth.

5. A cloudy liquid is a _suspension_.

6. A technique that separates a liquid mixture by boiling the liquid and condensing it back is called _distillation_.

7. Elements that are essential for life, but only in small amounts, are called _trace elements_.

8. A mixture whose properties are not the same throughout is a _heterogeneous_ mixture.

9. The symbols for carbon, oxygen, nitrogen, and hydrogen are _C, O, N, H_.

10. When water is used to dissolve another substance, the water acts as a _solvent_.

## Writing Critically

1. Compare and contrast an element, a compound, and a mixture. Use examples that are familiar to you to demonstrate the similarities and differences.

2. Describe what information can be obtained from the chemical name of a compound.

1. Students should describe the basic characteristics of each. Examples of each may include: elements: gold, lead, aluminum; compounds: water, aluminum foil; mixtures: salad dressing, air, kitty litter

3. **CHALLENGE** Compare the methods of separating mixtures. Describe some mixtures that are best suited to each process.

2. what elements make up that compound, the number of different elements that compound contains, and the proportion each of those elements within the compound

3. Distillation: making alcohol; evaporation: obtaining salt from salt water; filtration: purifying water or separating coffee grinds from coffee

## Skill Reinforcement

The Skill Activity on page 78 describes how to find the main idea in a paragraph. It also describes how to draw conclusions from what you have read. Find the main idea of the first paragraph on page 67. What conclusion can you draw from the statement that only 90 elements occur naturally on Earth, but that there are 108 elements? that 18 elements are made artificially

## Research Ideas

1. Do a survey on the use of chemicals in your own home. You might organize your survey on a room-to-room basis. List which chemicals are elements, which are mixtures, and which are compounds. How can you determine the category of each chemical? What safety precautions should be taken with these chemicals?

2. An element is sometimes named for a property of the element. An element may be named for an interesting fact about the element or for the person who first discovered the element. Research the origin of the name of each of the following elements: cobalt, copper, curium, einsteinium, francium, germanium, hydrogen, polonium, and strontium.

3. **CHALLENGE** Evaluate the nutritional information given on various brands of a certain kind of food or beverage. Distinguish between elements, minerals, nutrients, vitamins, preservatives, and artificial flavoring and coloring. Develop a system to rank the various brands by their nutritional value.

4. **CHALLENGE** Earth's atmosphere is very different in chemical composition from the atmosphere of other planets. Find out what is known about the atmospheres of other planets. Suggest reasons that might account for the observed differences.

## For Further Reading

Bodanis, David. *The Secret House*: New York, Simon and Schuster, 1986. The author describes amazing physical, chemical, and biological events that go on around you all the time in your home.

Cobb, Vicki. *Chemically Active! Experiments You Can Do at Home*. New York: Lippincott, 1985. This book provides a series of experiments that can be done using materials readily available at home.

Cotterill, Rodney. *The Cambridge Guide to the Material World*. New York: Cambridge University Press, 1985. The book is well illustrated, and topics include crystals, minerals, metals, ceramics, and glass.

CHAPTER **5**

# Atoms and the Periodic Table

Do atoms exist? Until recently no one had ever seen an atom because an atom is too small to be seen using an ordinary light microscope. The picture on this page is a computer-generated image of an atom that was first seen using an electron microscope.

For additional information, see pages T68–T69.

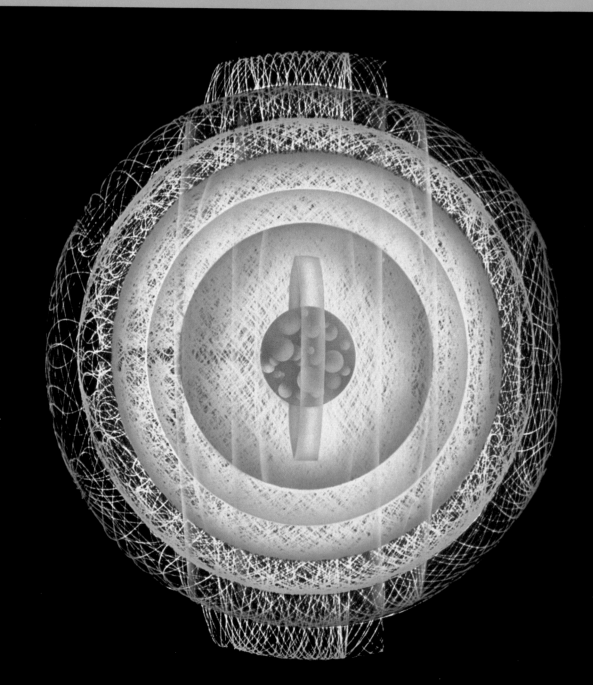

## Halogens

Group 17 is often called the **halogens**. The elements fluorine, chlorine, bromine, iodine, and astatine are all halogens. All the halogens have seven valence electrons in their outer electron shell. These valence electrons give the halogens their similar chemical and physical properties. Although the halogens have many characteristics in common, they are found in different forms in nature. Fluorine and chlorine are both gases. Bromine is a liquid that eats away, or corrodes, many substances. Iodine and astatine are solids.

All halogens dissolve in either water or alcohol. A solution of iodine and alcohol, called *tincture* (TIHNK chuhr) *of iodine*, is used as an antiseptic, or bacteria killer. Bromine is an important part of such various compounds as sleeping pills and shoe polish. Some chlorine compounds are widely used to purify drinking water and to keep swimming-pool water clean. Fluorine compounds are added to drinking water and toothpaste to prevent tooth decay. Both chlorine and fluorine have important uses in the manufacture of plastics. For example, the chemical polyvinyl chloride (PVC) is made with chlorine. PVC pipes are often used to replace metal pipes because PVC pipes are easier to install and resist corrosion. Astatine is so rare that not much is known about this element. What property do all halogens have in common?

**Figure 5–9.** When an electric current is passed through neon, the gas glows red. The addition of other noble gases produces different colors.

all dissolve in water or alcohol

**Figure 5–10.** PVC pipes are being used in the construction of most new buildings. PVC pipe is also used in the manufacture of outdoor furniture because PVC does not rust or stain.

# SKILL ACTIVITY   Interpreting the Periodic Table

**INTRODUCTION**
It is often easier to see relationships within data when the information is presented in the form of a table. The periodic table is one such example. Knowing how to read the periodic table will enable you to quickly obtain important information about the elements.

**PROCEDURE**
The periodic table classifies elements according to their properties. In the periodic table on pages 94–95, the number above the symbol of the element stands for the atomic mass of the element. The number below the element is the atomic number of the element. Remember that the total number of electrons is equal to the atomic number. The number above the element represents the group.

**APPLICATION**
Copy Table 1 onto a separate sheet of paper and fill in the missing information. Then answer the questions that follow.

| TABLE 1 | ELEMENTS | | | | |
|---|---|---|---|---|---|
| Element | Symbol | Atomic Number | Mass Number | Total Number of Electrons | Valence Electrons |
| Lithium | Li | 3 | 6.94 | 3 | 1 |
| Silicon | Si | 14 | 28.09 | 14 | 4 |
| Chlorine | Cl | 17 | 35.45 | 17 | 7 |
| Calcium | Ca | 20 | 40.08 | 20 | 2 |
| Krypton | Kr | 36 | 83.80 | 36 | 8 |

**1.** What is the name of the group that contains the element with 36 electrons? Group 18, or noble gases

**2.** Explain whether it is easier for silicon or chlorine to get a completed outer shell. chlorine, because it needs only one electron to fill its valence shell

# 5.7 Metals and Nonmetals

More than three-quarters of all the known chemical elements are metals. Most of the rest of the elements are classified as nonmetals. The most important difference between metals and nonmetals is the ability to conduct heat and electricity. Metals are good conductors. Nonmetals are poor conductors.

In addition to their conductivity, metals have two other important characteristics. First, metals are *malleable* (MAL ee uh buhl), which means they can be bent or flattened into sheets. Second, metals are *ductile* (DUHK tuhl), which means they can be drawn into thin wires.

Why are metals good conductors of heat and electricity? Why are they malleable and ductile? Atomic structure explains the difference between metals and nonmetals. All the metallic elements have atoms that contain only a few valence electrons in the outer electron shell. In metals, these electrons are not firmly bound to the nucleus and can jump from one atom to another. This movement of electrons through a solid is what causes metals to conduct heat and electricity. It also explains why metals are malleable and ductile.

Metallic character varies across the periodic table. Across any period, metallic character decreases from left to right as the number of valence electrons increases. The metallic character decreases because the valence electrons become more firmly bound to the nucleus as the number of protons in the nucleus increases.

Down any group, metallic character increases from top to bottom. It increases because the force that binds the electrons to the nucleus becomes weaker as the distance from the nucleus increases. Since the electrons in the outer shells are farther from the nucleus, these electrons can escape from the atom more easily.

Ask the students to explain why copper is widely used in cookware and electrical wiring. (Copper is a good conductor of heat and electricity.)

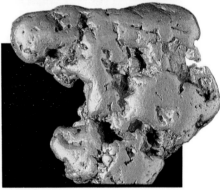

**Figure 5–11.** Elements can be divided into metals and nonmetals. One way to distinguish metals from nonmetals is by their appearance. Metals such as copper (top), silver (middle), and gold (bottom) have a shiny look. Nonmetals such as sulfur (left) and carbon (right) have a dull appearance.

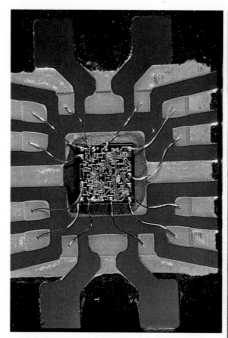

**Figure 5–12.** Gold is a valuable metal that is both malleable and ductile. It can be hammered into very thin sheets called gold leaf. Gold leaf is used to gild such items as books, furniture, and buildings (right). Gold can also be drawn into fine wires such as those used in computer chips (top).

Not all nonmetals are equally nonmetallic. The extent to which an element displays the properties of a nonmetal depends on its distance from fluorine on the periodic table. Have the students classify the following elements as metals or nonmetals: Mg (metal), S (nonmetal), Ne (nonmetal), Cs (metal), C (nonmetal), P (nonmetal), I (nonmetal).

ability to jump electron shells and bond with other atoms

## *READING CRITICALLY*

What is the most important difference between a metallic element and a nonmetallic element?

Atoms of the nonmetallic elements have four or more valence electrons. All the electrons in a nonmetallic atom are firmly bound to the nucleus. Such electrons cannot easily jump from atom to atom. Table 5–1 summarizes some of the properties that make metals different from nonmetals.

| TABLE 5–1 | A COMPARISON OF METALS AND NONMETALS | |
|---|---|---|
| **Metals** | **Nonmetals** | |
| Solids at room temperature (except mercury) | Gases, liquids, or solids at room temperature | |
| Good conductors of heat and electricity | Poor conductors of heat and electricity | |
| Malleable and ductile in the solid state | Brittle and nonductile in the solid state | |
| Opaque | Can be transparent or translucent | |
| Shiny appearance, with a metallic luster | Dull in appearance, no metallic luster | |

Some elements have the properties of both metals and nonmetals. These elements are classified as metalloids (MEHT uhl oyds). Examples are silicon, germanium, boron, and arsenic. The electrical conductivity of metalloids is lower than that of metals but higher than that of nonmetals. Metalloids play a vital role in the electronics industry. For example, silicon chips are vital components of computers. They are also used in the electric eyes that open doors at stores.

## Section Review

1. How does atomic structure explain similarities in the properties of a group of elements?
2. What electron arrangements make the alkali metals different from the halogens?
3. Why do the noble gases not combine readily with other elements?
4. Describe the main difference between a metal and a nonmetal in terms of atomic structure.
5. THINKING CRITICALLY  Why are all the nonmetals found in the upper right-hand corner of the periodic table?

SCIENCE FACT

The existence of germanium was predicted by Mendeleev when he developed the periodic table. However, germanium was not discovered until 1886 by Clemens Winkler, who named the element germanium after his native country, Germany.

1. Elements in the same chemical family all have atoms with the same number of electrons in the valence shell.
2. Alkali metals have only one valence electron; halogens have seven valence electrons.
3. Noble gases have eight valence electrons, the maximum in the outer shell of any atom. This makes for a stable atom, and interactions with other atoms are unlikely.
4. Electrons of metals are free to move through the solid, jumping from atom to atom. Electrons of nonmetals are more firmly bound to the nucleus.
5. Nonmetals occur when valence electrons are firmly bound to the nucleus. Valence electrons become more firmly attached when the number of protons in the nucleus increases and when the electrons are closer to the nucleus.

# CAREER

## Chemistry Teacher

**DESCRIPTION**  A chemistry teacher uses many kinds of equipment and techniques in teaching chemistry to students. Chemistry teachers carry out classroom demonstrations, plan and supervise student laboratory work, and develop lesson plans.

**REQUIREMENTS**  A student planning to become a chemistry teacher should take science and mathematics courses in high school. After graduation, the student completes a four-year college course. All 50 states require chemistry teachers to be certified. Some states require education courses, student teaching, and a certain number of college credits in chemistry. Other states require entrants to have a college degree with a major in chemistry.

**INFORMATION**  National Science Teachers Association, 1742 Connecticut Avenue, N.W., Washington, DC 20009

# INVESTIGATION 5: Indirect Evidence

*How can you learn about things you cannot see?*

## PURPOSE

To identify an item in a closed container. Because atoms and molecules are too small to be seen, they must be studied indirectly that is, by how they behave, not by how they are seen. In this experiment you will have to use indirect methods to learn about an unseen item in a closed container.

## MATERIALS

sealed container
unknown object or objects

## PROCEDURE

1. Copy Table 1 onto a sheet of paper. Enter all observations from this investigation on your table.

2. Your teacher will give you a sealed container that has one or more objects inside. Since you cannot open the container, you can only learn about what is inside the container indirectly.

| TABLE 1 | INVESTIGATION OF AN UNKNOWN OBJECT(S) | |
|---|---|
| **Description of Test** | **Conclusion** |
| | |
| | |
| | |
| | |
| | |
| | |

3. You may do anything with the container as long as you do not open or damage it. If you need any additional materials or equipment, ask your teacher. Record each test you make in Table 1. In addition to describing your test, record what you were able to conclude about the object(s). Do not overlook negative results. For example, if you turn the container slightly and the contents do not move, this may indicate that the contents are not round but flat.

## RESULTS   Answers will vary.

1. Your description of your tests should allow anyone else to repeat your test. Give your descriptions of your tests to another student. By reading your description, can the other student do the tests as you did? Does the other student arrive at the same conclusion that you did?

2. Based on all your tests and observations, write a description of the unknown object(s) in your container. You may name the object(s), but you must also give a complete description.

## CONCLUSIONS

1. Your teacher will identify the unknown object(s). How complete and correct was your description of the object(s) based on indirect evidence?

2. List some objects that scientists study indirectly. Answers will vary but may include atoms, space, and viruses.

## APPLICATION

You may have noticed that learning by indirect evidence is rather like a detective story. In fact, searching for clues to solve mysteries is what makes science so exciting to many people. Using a detective story from a book or television show, describe the indirect evidence that was used to solve the crime.

## Summary

1. All matter is composed of tiny, invisible particles called atoms. **(5.1)**
2. Dalton's atomic theory explains the chemical behavior of matter. **(5.1)**
3. Atoms are made of smaller, subatomic particles called protons, neutrons, and electrons. Protons and neutrons are packed together in the nucleus; while electrons orbit around the nucleus. **(5.2)**
4. Rutherford's model pictured the atom as a tiny planetary system with electrons orbiting a central nucleus. **(5.2)**
5. All atoms of the same element have the same number of protons, or atomic number. Atoms of an element that differ in the number of neutrons are called isotopes. Their atomic numbers are the same, but isotopes of the same element have different atomic masses. **(5.3)**
6. A scale of relative mass units (amu), based on the carbon-12 atom, is used to express the mass of atoms and subatomic particles. **(5.3)**
7. The Bohr model explains that electrons move around the nucleus in fixed paths called orbitals. **(5.4)**
8. Electrons are located in shells around the nucleus of the atom. **(5.5)**
9. The periodic table is an arrangement of elements by groups according to the atomic numbers of the elements. **(5.6)**
10. In the periodic table, metallic character decreases across the rows and increases down the columns of elements. **(5.7)**

## Science Terms

On a separate sheet of paper, define each term in a sentence.

alkali metals **(96)**
atom **(87)**
atomic mass **(90)**
atomic mass unit **(90)**
atomic number **(89)**
electron **(88)**
electron cloud **(92)**
family **(93)**
group **(93)**
halogen **(97)**
isotope **(90)**
mass number **(89)**
neutron **(89)**
noble gases **(96)**
nucleus **(88)**
octet **(92)**
period **(93)**
proton **(88)**
series **(93)**
subatomic particle **(88)**
valence electrons **(92)**

## Modified True-False

On a separate sheet of paper, mark each true statement *TRUE* and each false statement *FALSE*. If false, change the underlined term to make the statement true.

1. An atom is the smallest piece of matter that has the chemical properties of an element. T
2. According to Dalton's theory, all atoms of a given element are identical in size and mass. T
3. Dalton's atomic theory gave no explanation of the chemical properties of matter. F, electrical
4. Electrons are positively charged particles. F, negatively
5. The nucleus of an atom contains electrons and protons. F, neutrons
6. The number of protons in the nucleus is called the atomic number. T
7. All atoms of the same element contain the same number of neutrons. F, protons
8. The relative mass of an element, based on the atomic scale, is called its atomic number. F, mass
9. The total number of electrons and neutrons inside the nucleus of an atom equals the mass number. F, protons
10. On the periodic table, periods are columns of elements. F, families or groups

*(continues)*

## Multiple Choice

On a separate sheet of paper, write the letter of the term that best answers the question or completes the statement.

1. The mass number of an atom is equal to the number of
   a. protons.
   b. neutrons.
   c. protons and neutrons.
   d. protons and electrons.

2. All atoms of the same element have the same number of
   a. protons, neutrons, and electrons.
   b. neutrons.
   c. protons.
   d. neutrons and protons.

3. An atom with an atomic number of 8 and a mass number of 17 has _____ neutrons in the nucleus.
   a. 8      b. 9      c. 17      d. 25

4. Which of the following of Dalton's statements about the atom was proven wrong by the discovery of the electron?
   a. Atoms cannot be created, divided, or destroyed.
   b. All the atoms of an element have the same size and mass.
   c. The atoms of different elements have different size and mass.
   d. When a chemical reaction occurs, atoms are not destroyed.

5. The number of electrons is equal to the number of _____ in an atom.
   a. neutrons      c. shells
   b. protons       d. orbits

6. When an electron jumps from a higher energy level to a lower energy level,
   a. it gives off heat.
   b. it gives off light.
   c. it explodes.
   d. nothing happens.

7. Sodium (atomic number 11) has _____ electrons located in the outer shell.
   a. 1      b. 2      c. 7      d. 8

8. The carbon-12 isotope has an atomic mass of exactly _____ amu.
   a. 1      b. 10      c. 12      d. 100

9. Which of the following statements about the periodic table is true?
   a. Elements are arranged by mass number.
   b. Metallic elements are placed on the right-hand side.
   c. Elements in the same group have the same number of valence electrons.
   d. All the gases are in the same group.

10. Most of the known elements are
    a. nonmetals.       c. metals.
    b. gases.           d. halogens.

## Completion

On a separate sheet of paper, complete each statement by supplying the correct term.

1. An _atom_ is the smallest particle of an element that has the chemical properties of that element.

2. Some elements have the properties of both metals and nonmetals and are therefore classified as _metalloids_.

3. The nucleus contains _neutrons_ and protons.

4. A valence shell with eight electrons is called an _octet_.

5. Positively charged particles found in the _nucleus_ of an atom are called protons.

6. Atoms of the same element that differ in mass are called _isotopes_.

7. An atom is in the _ground_ state when all its electrons are in their lowest possible orbits.

8. The maximum number of _valence_ electrons is eight.

9. All noble gases have eight valence electrons except for the element _helium_.

10. The _noble gas_ group of elements do not readily combine with other elements.

## Writing Critically Answers: see page T69.

1. Write a newspaper article describing a model of the atom. Illustrate your article.

2. Explain how the periodic table can be used to predict the properties of an unknown element.

3. Copper is one of the best conductors of both heat and electricity. Describe the characteristics of the copper atom that give the element these conductive properties. List items made from copper that make use of the element's conductive properties.

4. CHALLENGE Write a letter to convince a doubtful friend that atoms really exist.

5. CHALLENGE What effects might the discovery of the actual structure of the atom have on science?

## Skill Reinforcement

The Skill Activity on page 98 describes how to locate information in the periodic table. Make a table listing the following elements: hydrogen, lithium, sodium, helium, neon, and argon. Include in your table the symbol, atomic number, atomic weight, total number of electrons, and valence electrons for each element.

Hydrogen H 1 1.01 1 1; Lithium Li 3 6.94 3 1
Sodium Na 11 22.99 1 1; Helium He 2 4.00 2 2
Neon Ne 10 20.18 10 8; Argon Ar 18 39.95 18 8

## Research Ideas

1. Find out how Rutherford discovered that the mass of an atom is concentrated in the nucleus.

2. Choose a group of related elements and find out how each element was discovered and named. What properties are shared by all members of the group? How are these properties related to the atomic structure of the elements?

3. Investigate the history and early uses of copper, silver, and gold. Report on additional modern uses of these valuable metals.

4. CHALLENGE Look up a copy of Mendeleev's original periodic table. Compare this original with the modern version given in this textbook. List and explain all the differences you can find.

5. CHALLENGE A spectrum, such as a rainbow, is produced when white light is separated into its component colors. Find out what an atomic spectrum is and how atomic spectra can be used to identify elements.

## For Further Reading

Asimov, Isaac. *The Search for the Elements.* NY: Basic Books, 1962. A classic in its field. Dr. Asimov tells the story of the 2,000-year-long quest to identify the basic ingredients out of which the universe is made.

Berger, Melvin. *Atoms, Molecules, and Quarks.* NY: Putnam, 1986. Writing in an interesting manner, the author explains the composition of natural materials. The book is well illustrated and includes a few experiments that can be performed at home.

Gannes, Stuart. "People at the Frontiers of Science." *Fortune* Magazine, Oct. 13, 1986, pp. 47–57. Ten scientists are profiled in this special report on the high-tech race between the U.S. and other nations. Included is a story on Gerd Binnig, the physicist who invented the scanning tunneling microscope that can create three-dimensional images of atoms.

# CHAPTER 6

# Chemical Reactions

Chemical reactions take place in the home, in industrial plants, and in all living things. In this series of pictures, construction workers use a chemical reaction to destroy an old building. The dynamite explosion causes the building to collapse in seconds.

For additional information, see pages T70–T71.

# Molecules and Ions

NEW TERMS IN THIS SECTION

| | | | |
|---|---|---|---|
| molecule | chemical bonds | molecular formula | base |
| macromolecules | covalent bonds | empirical formula | pH |
| ion | ionic bonds | electrolyte | neutralization |
| ionization | chemical formula | acid | salt |

## SECTION OBJECTIVES

- **Describe** the difference between a molecule and an ion.
- **Identify** molecules by their molecular formula.
- **Distinguish** between covalent and ionic bonds.
- **Define** *acid*, *base*, and *salt*.

Photograph left: planned destruction of a building using explosives

## 6.1 Atoms in Combination

With the exception of the noble gases, which exist as single atoms, atoms rarely exist alone. Atoms usually combine to form molecules. A **molecule** (MAHL ih kyool) is a group of atoms that act as a unit. A molecule is the smallest unit of an element or a compound that has the characteristics of the element or compound. A molecule of water, for example, has the same characteristics as all other water molecules.

Like atoms, molecules are very small. A typical raindrop may contain 300 million trillion molecules of water. This number is so large that, if you were able to line up this many raindrops end to end, they would reach to the stars.

The simplest molecules are made up of only two atoms. These atoms may be of the same element or of different elements. For example, a molecule of oxygen is made up of two atoms of oxygen. A molecule of carbon monoxide is made up of one atom of carbon and one atom of oxygen.

More complex molecules are made up of three or more atoms. A water molecule is made up of two atoms of hydrogen and one of oxygen. A molecule of carbon

Emphasize that models and diagrams of molecules and ions are only representations. Individual molecules and ions are smaller than the wave length of light.

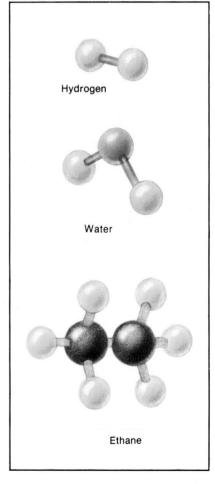

Hydrogen

Water

Ethane

**Figure 6–1.** Shown here from top to bottom are models of hydrogen ($H_2$), water ($H_2O$), and ethane ($C_2H_6$) molecules.

dioxide has one atom of carbon and two atoms of oxygen. A molecule of glucose, a simple sugar, contains six atoms of carbon, twelve atoms of hydrogen, and six atoms of oxygen—a total of 24 atoms. A molecule of sucrose, or table sugar, contains 45 atoms—12 atoms of carbon, 22 atoms of hydrogen, and 11 atoms of oxygen.

In the largest molecules, many hundreds of thousands of atoms are joined. Such molecules are called **macromolecules** (MAK roh MAHL ih kyools). Figure 6–2 shows the structure of an adenovirus. This macromolecule is responsible for the common cold. Other giant molecules include plastics and certain crystals. Some plastic molecules contain more than 100,000 atoms joined together like a string of pearls. The structure of plastics is also discussed in Chapter 8. Some giant molecules contain billions and billions of atoms. Since macromolecules are made of many smaller units, they are also called polymers. Polymers are also discussed in Chapter 8.

**Figure 6–2.** The molecular structure of a single adenovirus is shown in the computer graphic on the left. Adenoviruses cause sore throats and other cold symptoms. On the right is a densely packed group of adenoviruses magnified 7,300 times.

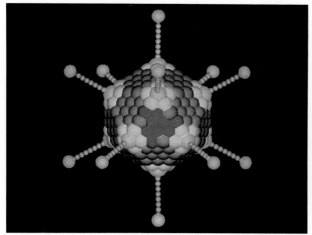
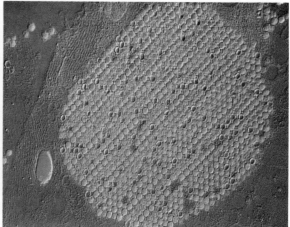

## 6.2 Ions

Positively charged ions are called *cations* because they are attracted toward negatively charged electrodes called *cathodes*. Anions are attracted toward positively charged electrodes called *anodes*.

As you read in Chapter 5, an atom is electrically neutral because it has equal numbers of electrons and protons. However, atoms can gain or lose their outermost, or valence, electrons. When an atom gains or loses valence electrons, it becomes an electrically charged particle called an **ion** (EYE uhn). For example, a sodium atom can lose one electron to become a positively charged sodium ion. Positively charged ions are called *cations* (KAT eye uhns). A chlorine atom can gain one electron to become a negatively charged chloride ion. Negatively charged ions are called *anions* (AN eye uhns). The process of gaining or losing an electron is called **ionization** (eye uhn ih ZAY shuhn).

# 6.3 Chemical Bonds

Only valence electrons are involved when atoms form molecules or ions. The outer shell of an atom is complete when it has eight electrons. Atoms that do not have eight electrons in their outer shell will transfer or share electrons with another atom. This transferring and sharing of valence electrons produces **chemical bonds** between atoms.

Atoms gain, lose, or share electrons until they have a complete valence shell of eight electrons. Atoms with five or more valence electrons usually gain electrons to complete their outer shells. These atoms form stable anions. Atoms with four valence electrons usually share electrons with other atoms. Atoms with three or fewer valence electrons usually lose them to leave behind a complete shell. These atoms then become stable cations.

## Covalent Bonds

Chemical bonds formed when atoms share valence electrons are called **covalent** (koh VAY luhnt) **bonds**. Compounds in which two or more different atoms are joined by covalent bonds are called *covalent compounds*. Covalent bonds can also form between atoms of the same kind. In a hydrogen molecule, for example, two hydrogen atoms share their valence electrons with one another. A diagram of the structure of a hydrogen molecule is shown in Figure 6–3. The covalent bond holds the two hydrogen atoms together in a hydrogen molecule.

In an oxygen molecule, not just one, but two pairs of electrons are shared between the oxygen atoms. The result is a double covalent bond. In Figure 6–3, how does the double bond give each oxygen atom eight electrons?

## ACTIVITY

**Making Models of Molecules**

Using toothpicks and plastic-foam spheres, construct a model each of hydrogen, oxygen, and nitrogen molecules.

As discussed in Chapter 5, a shell of eight valence electrons is called an *octet*. Atoms with an octet tend to be very stable. An exception is helium, which has a complete valence shell of only two electrons.

## READING CRITICALLY

In a nitrogen molecule, two atoms of nitrogen share three pairs of electrons. What kind of bond would this be?

a triple covalent bond

Covalent bonding occurs when the valence shells of two atoms overlap and two nuclei share the same pair of valence electrons.

Each bond represents the sharing of an electron. Therefore, each atom shares two electrons, giving both atoms a total of eight electrons.

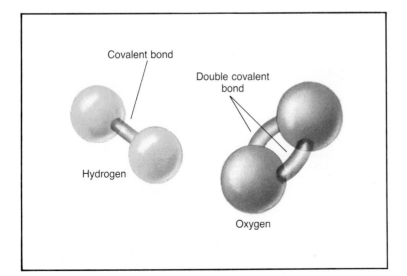

Covalent bond

Double covalent bond

Hydrogen

Oxygen

**Figure 6–3.** A hydrogen molecule ($H_2$) consists of two hydrogen atoms joined by a covalent bond. An oxygen molecule ($O_2$) consists of two oxygen atoms joined by a double covalent bond.

**Figure 6–4.** A sodium chloride crystal consists of an array of sodium ions (smaller, blue spheres) and chlorine ions (larger, green spheres). This arrangement is called a *crystal lattice*.

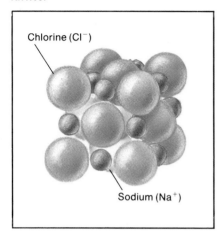

Chlorine (Cl⁻)

Sodium (Na⁺)

The intermolecular forces between covalently bonded molecules are not very strong. As a result, covalent substances are generally gases or liquids at room temperature, while ionic compounds are generally solid.

Review the law of definite proportions from Chapter 4.

Have students memorize the formulas for some of the common molecules such as $O_2$, $N_2$, $H_2O$, etc. This information will be helpful later in the chapter to write equations.

## Ionic Bonds

A different type of chemical bond occurs when atoms lose or gain electrons to form ions. A chemical bond between ions is called an **ionic bond**. Compounds formed in this way are called *ionic compounds*.

Ionic compounds do not form molecules. Instead, billions of ions combine to form crystals, which are discussed more fully in Chapter 15. The size and shape of a crystal depend upon the number and arrangement of ions in the crystal. For example, sodium chloride, which is shown in Figure 6–4, is a cube-shaped crystal.

# 6.4 Chemical Formulas

A **chemical formula** is a short way of showing the number and kinds of atoms in a substance. Formulas are also used to represent individual molecules and ions. A chemical formula contains a great deal of information about the makeup of a substance. Chemical formulas are used to represent chemical compounds because of the law of definite proportions. Different samples of a pure substance always have identical combinations of atoms. Therefore, all samples of a pure substance have the same chemical formula.

## Molecular Formulas

Just as chemical symbols are used to represent individual atoms, chemical formulas are used to show combinations of atoms. For example, the symbol H represents one atom of hydrogen. The formula $H_2$ represents one molecule of hydrogen. This formula shows that a molecule of hydrogen is made up of two atoms of hydrogen joined by a chemical bond.

A **molecular formula** indicates the number and kinds of atoms present in one molecule of a substance. The formula $H_2$ is an example of a molecular formula.

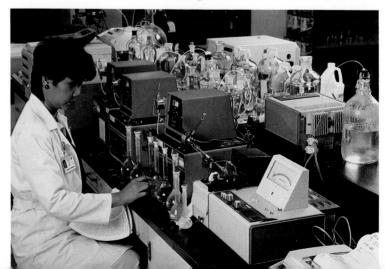

**Figure 6–5.** Pharmacists use chemical formulas when preparing medicines. Industrial chemists use chemical formulas in manufacturing soaps, cosmetics, paints, and many other products.

**Figure 6–6.** The *Hindenberg,* an early airship that was filled with hydrogen ($H_2$), exploded over Lakehurst, New Jersey on May 6, 1937. Modern airships, or blimps, are filled with helium (He) gas, which does not explode.

The number 2 in this formula is called a *subscript*. Subscripts are written below and to the right of a symbol. In a formula, subscripts show the number of atoms that are combined in a molecule. For example, the formula for water is $H_2O$. This formula is read as "h two oh." The formula shows that a water molecule is made of two hydrogen atoms and one oxygen atom. What is the molecular formula for sucrose, which is described in Section 6.1 on page 108? The molecular formula is $C_{12}H_{22}O_{11}$.

### Empirical Formulas

Since ionic compounds do not form molecules, a chemical formula for an ionic compound shows the relative proportions of ions in the compound. A chemical formula for an ionic compound is called an **empirical** (ehm PIHR ihk uhl) **formula**. For example, there are no molecules of sodium chloride. A grain of salt contains billions of sodium and chloride ions in equal numbers. The empirical formula for sodium chloride is NaCl. The empirical formula for magnesium chloride is $MgCl_2$. What is the relative number of chloride ions compared to magnesium ions in this compound? 2:1

*Superscripts*, or numbers written above and to the right of ions, show the charge on an ion. The sign of the number tells if the ion is positively charged ($+$) or negatively charged ($-$). For example, a hydrogen ion, $H^+$, has a single positive charge. A nitrate ion, $NO_3{}^{2-}$, has two negative charges. Nitrates are used in fertilizers.

## 6.5 Acids, Bases, and Salts

Many compounds are soluble in water. When an ionic compound dissolves in water, the ionic bonds that hold the ions together are broken. As a result, the cations and anions separate from one another and are free to move.

**Figure 6–7.** The effects of acid rain can be devastating to plants, animals, and buildings. The trees in this forest have been damaged by acid rain.

Acids are essential to health. HCl in the stomach aids in the digestion of proteins. Ascorbic acid (vitamin C) serves as a coenzyme in many reactions. Acids have a sour taste. Excess acid in the stomach is the cause of acid indigestion.

Bases have a bitter taste. Examples of bases are caffeine, nicotine, and quinine.

Therefore, the solution can conduct electricity. Any substance that releases ions when it dissolves is called an **electrolyte.**

Body fluids, such as blood and perspiration, contain electrolytes. Electrolytes are necessary for certain reactions to occur in the body. Since electrolytes can be lost by sweating, they need to be replaced after strenuous exercise. Sea water is also an electrolyte.

### Acids and Bases

An **acid** is an electrolyte that releases hydrogen ions ($H^+$) in solution. You have probably heard of many types of acids. Hydrochloric acid is found in your stomach and aids in the digestion of foods. Vinegar, tomato juice, and citrus juices are also acids. Carbonic acid is found in soft drinks. Carbon dioxide reacts with water to form carbonic acid, which gives soft drinks their "fizz."

Some acids are harmful and can cause severe burns. Acids that react with metal are used in many industries. Hydrochloric acid is used to etch metals, such as brass. Hydrofluoric acid is used to etch glass. Acids may also affect the environment. *Acid rain* is formed when oxides of sulfur and nitrogen react with water in the air to form acids. These acids fall to the earth with rainwater.

A **base** is an electrolyte that releases hydroxide ions ($OH^-$) in solution. Soaps, detergents, and other cleaning products contain bases. Sodium hydroxide and ammonia are examples of bases. Like acids, bases may be very harmful and can cause severe burns and corrosion.

Acids and bases may be useful, but they may also be harmful. *Never try to identify an acid or a base by tasting or touching it.*

### pH

When an acid dissolves in water, it releases hydrogen ions. When a base dissolves in water, it takes up hydrogen ions. The concentration, or amount, of hydrogen ions in a solution is called the **pH** of the solution. pH can be measured on a scale called the pH scale. On this scale, pH of 7 is considered neutral. Pure water has a pH of 7. A solution with a pH greater than 7 is a base. A solution with a pH less than 7 is an acid.

pH can also be measured by using a special instrument called a pH meter or by using an indicator. An indicator is a chemical that determines the presence of a certain substance in a solution. One indicator of the pH of a solution is litmus. Litmus paper will turn red in the presence of an acid and blue in the presence of a base.

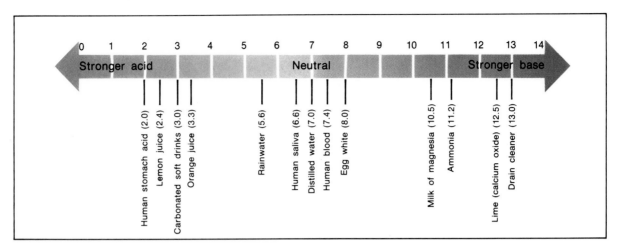

## Salts

In a chemical change called **neutralization**, the properties of the acids and bases are destroyed. When an acid and a base react, salt and water are formed. A **salt** is an ionic compound containing a cation and an anion. Sodium chloride, or table salt, is an example of a typical salt. A list of some common acids, bases, and salts is given in Table 6–1. What patterns can you discover in this table? All acids contain hydrogen, all bases contain hydroxide, all salts are mixes of bases and salts.

In recent years, sodium in food has been linked with high blood pressure. For this reason, many people have reduced the amount of sodium in their diets. Salt substitutes contain potassium chloride, which can be substituted for table salt.

| TABLE 6–1 | | ACIDS, BASES, AND SALTS | | | |
|---|---|---|---|---|---|
| **Acids** | | **Bases** | | **Salts** | |
| **Name** | **Formula** | **Name** | **Formula** | **Name** | **Formula** |
| Hydrochloric | HCl | Sodium hydroxide | NaOH | Sodium chloride | NaCl |
| Hydrofluoric | HF | Calcium hydroxide | $Ca(OH)_2$ | Calcium chloride | $CaCl_2$ |
| Boric | $H_3BO_3$ | Aluminum hydroxide | $Al(OH)_3$ | Copper sulfate | $CuSO_4$ |
| Acetic | $CH_3COOH$ | Potassium hydroxide | KOH | Potassium acetate | $CH_3COOK$ |
| Nitric | $HNO_3$ | Ammonium hydroxide | $NH_4OH$ | Ammonium nitrate | $NH_4NO_3$ |
| Phosphoric | $H_3PO_4$ | Magnesium hydroxide | $Mg(OH)_2$ | Magnesium phosphate | $Mg_3(PO_4)_2$ |
| Sulfuric | $H_2SO_4$ | Zinc hydroxide | $Zn(OH)_2$ | Zinc sulfate | $ZnSO_4$ |

## Section Review

1. What is the main difference between a molecule and an ion? How are they alike?

2. How does a covalent bond differ from an ionic bond?

3. What is the difference between an empirical formula and a molecular formula?

4. Describe what happens when an ionic substance dissolves in water.

5. THINKING CRITICALLY Using nitrogen as an example, show how chemical symbols and formulas are used to distinguish between atoms, molecules, and ions.

1. A molecule is electrically neutral, while an ion has an electrical charge. Both are made of atoms.

2. In a covalent bond, atoms share valence electrons; in an ionic bond, valence electrons are transferred from one atom to another; the resulting ions are attracted to one another.

3. A molecular formula gives the exact number of atoms in a molecule, while an empirical formula shows the relative number of ions in a compound.

4. The bonds are broken, which allows the ions to move. The solution can therefore conduct electricity.

5. N stands for a nitrogen atom, $N_2$ for a nitrogen molecule, and $NO_3^-$ for a nitrate ion.

# SKILL ACTIVITY   Understanding Tables

**INTRODUCTION**

When reading a table, the table title and the headings of the columns tell you what the table is about. If you take the time to understand this information, it will help you to follow the table.

**PROCEDURE**

1. When studying a table, first look at the title. The title will tell you what the information is about.

2. The title of a table should be brief, but still completely summarize what the table is about.

3. Next study the column headings. The headings will tell you the specific information that the table contains.

**APPLICATION**

Copy the table below onto a sheet of paper. Decide on a title that best describes the information presented, and add your title to the table. The title should be accurate but brief. In the third column to the right of each mineral, name a metal found in the mineral. For example, for bauxite, you should list *aluminum*. Decide on a heading for the third column and include this heading in your table. Then answer the questions that follow.

**TABLE 1**

| Mineral | Chemical Formula | Metal in the Mineral |
|---------|------------------|----------------------|
| Bauxite | $Al(OH)_3$ | Aluminum |
| Chalcocite | $Cu_2S$ | Copper |
| Hematite | $Fe_2O_3$ | Iron |
| Galena | $PbS$ | Lead |
| Pyrolusite | $MnO_2$ | Manganese |
| Cinnabar | $HgS$ | Mercury |
| Argentite | $Ag_2S$ | Silver |
| Cassiterite | $SnO_2$ | Tin |
| Pitchblende | $UO_2$ | Uranium |
| Sphalerite | $ZnS$ | Zinc |

1. column 2
2. oxygen, hydrogen, and sulfur
3. This title does not tell the reader what the table is about, namely common minerals.

1. Which column in the table helped you to decide which metal is in each ore?

2. What other elements, besides metals, are found in the minerals in the table?

3. Analyze whether "Some Common Metals" is a good title for your table.

# Chemical Equations

NEW TERMS IN THIS SECTION
reactants
products
law of conservation of mass
chemical equation
coefficients

## SECTION OBJECTIVES

● **State** the law of conservation of mass.

● **Write** balanced chemical equations, using chemical formulas.

## 6.6 The Law of Conservation of Mass

In the 1700s, French chemist Antoine Lavoisier (an TWAHN lah vawh ZYAY) studied chemical reactions. Lavoisier kept careful records of the masses of all the materials involved in chemical reactions. The original substances that react together in a chemical reaction are called the **reactants**. The substances produced by a chemical reaction are called the **products**.

Lavoisier found that when he compared the mass of the products with the mass of the reactants, the masses were the same. Repeated experiments have demonstrated that atoms are not destroyed in a chemical reaction. This discovery is known as the **law of conservation of mass**.

Tell students that because atoms are not destroyed in chemical reactions, atoms are very old. The atoms in their bodies are older than the earth itself.

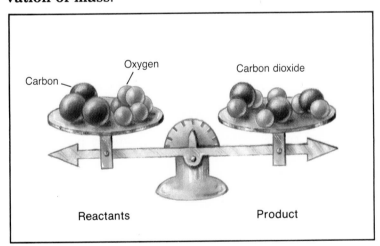

**Figure 6–9.** In all chemical reactions, the mass of the products equals the mass of the reactants. Atoms are simply rearranged, not destroyed, in chemical reactions.

According to the law of conservation of mass, you can never get rid of anything. Chemicals dumped into rivers end up in the ocean. Gases from smokestacks and chimneys go into the air. Today, no place on Earth is free from the danger of harmful chemicals. In the Antarctic, for example, the bodies of penguins have been found to contain harmful chemicals. These chemicals were carried thousands of kilometers from other places in the world to Antarctica. How do you think these chemicals got to Antarctica? from pollutants carried by way of air and water currents

## ACTIVITY

**Conserving Mass**

**CAUTION: Put on safety goggles and leave them on throughout this activity. This activity should be done in a well-ventilated area or under a lab hood.**

Place 4 mL of lead nitrate and 4 mL of potassium iodide in separate 10 mL graduates. Use a balance to determine the mass of the graduates. Mix the chemicals into one graduate. Determine the masses again. How do the masses compare?

They should be equal.

**Figure 6–10.** The problem of toxic waste disposal is posing an increasing threat to the environment.

The disposal of chemicals is a serious problem. In order to prevent harmful chemicals from getting into the air and water, these substances must either be stored or changed into harmless products. Some cities have special chemical disposal centers where used engine oil and other household chemicals may be recycled or changed into other products. Disposing of poisonous, or *toxic*, waste chemicals is more difficult. Toxic wastes are often stored in containers and placed in open ponds or buried under ground. Over time, the chemicals may leak out and contaminate the water, soil, and air. Such leakage can damage the environment and cause serious health problems in humans. Scientists and society must work together to solve the problem of toxic-waste disposal.

*READING CRITICALLY*
Why are toxic chemical pesticides such as DDT and chlordane carefully controlled and even banned in some parts of the world?

Because they take a long time to break down and therefore remain in the environment for long periods of time. The presence of these toxic substances can contaminate the water, soil, and air and in some cases may be carcinogenic to humans and animals.

An equation is not truly an equation unless it is balanced.

## 6.7 Balancing Chemical Equations

The law of conservation of mass makes it possible to write chemical equations for chemical reactions. A **chemical equation** describes a chemical reaction. When an equation has equal numbers of atoms on each side, the equation is balanced. An equation must be balanced in order to show the correct proportion of reactants and products.

For example, the chemical equation for the reaction of carbon with oxygen gas to produce carbon dioxide is

$$C + O_2 \rightarrow CO_2$$

The equation says that one atom of carbon reacts with one molecule of oxygen to yield one molecule of carbon dioxide. In this equation, the plus sign means "reacts with" and the arrow means "to produce," or "to yield." The chemical formula $O_2$ is used for oxygen because oxygen exists as oxygen molecules.

Chemical equations are balanced by changing the amount, not the composition, of the substances. In order to show the amount of a substance in a chemical equation, numbers called **coefficients** (koh uh FIHSH uhnts) are placed in front of the formulas. The number 1 is never used as a coefficient. When no number appears before a formula, it means that the coefficient is 1. When the coefficients are correct, the total number of atoms of each element is the same on both sides of the equation.

The coefficients in a chemical equation indicate the proportions of reactants and products.

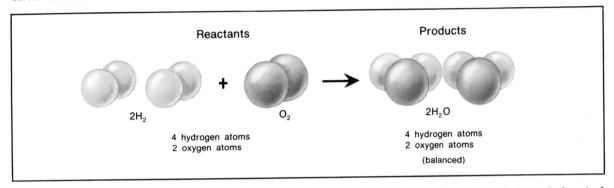

The following steps show how to balance an equation. In these steps, the reaction between aluminum and oxygen to produce aluminum oxide ($Al_2O_3$) is used as an example.

**Figure 6–11.** A balanced chemical equation obeys the law of conservation of mass. The same number of hydrogen and oxygen atoms is on each side of the equation.

1. Write the formulas of all reactants on the left side of the equation and connect them with a plus sign. Write the formulas of all the products on the right side of the equation. Connect the products with plus signs, if necessary. In this example, only one product is formed, so a plus sign will not be necessary. Draw an arrow pointing from the reactants to the products. The arrow shows the direction of the reaction.

$$Al + O_2 \rightarrow Al_2O_3$$

This equation is read "aluminum plus oxygen yields aluminum oxide."

2. Balance the equation. Remember that there must be an equal number of atoms for each element on both sides of the equation. To balance an equation, only the coefficients can be changed. *Never change the subscripts.* Changing the subscripts would change the composition of the substance. In this example, there are two aluminum atoms on the right side of the equation, but only one aluminum atom on the left side. Remember that since no number appears before the aluminum on the left, its coefficient is 1. Change the coefficient so the aluminum atoms on both sides are equal.

To balance a complicated equation, balance all elements, except hydrogen and oxygen. Then balance hydrogen and finally oxygen.

To do this, you must determine the number by which you would multiply the aluminum on the left to equal the number of atoms on the right. Since there are two atoms on the right, multiplying by 2 will give you an equal number of aluminum atoms on the right ($2 \times 1Al = 2Al$).

$$2Al + O_2 \rightarrow Al_2O_3$$

Now the oxygen atoms must be balanced. There are three oxygen atoms on the right side and two on the left side of the equation. Multiplying the two oxygen atoms on the left by 1.5 will give you three oxygen atoms. Therefore, place a 1.5 in front of the oxygen formula on the left. Now there are three oxygen atoms on both sides.

$$2Al + 1.5O_2 \rightarrow Al_2O_3$$

3. Every coefficient in the equation must be a whole number. Since 1.5 is not a whole number, you must multiply the entire equation by a number that will give you the closest whole number. In this case, multiplying 1.5 by 2 will result in three which is the closest whole number.

$$(2)2Al + (2)1.5O_2 \rightarrow (2)Al_2O_3$$

equals

$$4Al + 3O_2 \rightarrow 2Al_2O_3$$

The equation is now balanced. Each side of the equation now contains four aluminum atoms and six oxygen atoms.

4. To check the equation, multiply the coefficients by the subscripts for each element to see if there is an equal number of atoms on each side of the equation.

## Section Review

1. Using the law of conservation of mass, explain why it is possible to write a balanced chemical equation.

2. Why is it incorrect to change the subscripts in a chemical formula to balance an equation?

3. THINKING CRITICALLY Write a balanced equation for the reaction in which carbon reacts with oxygen to produce carbon monoxide (CO).

4. THINKING CRITICALLY If a chemical equation shows more oxygen atoms on the right side of the equation than on the left, what does the equation imply?

## Summary

1. Atoms join together to form molecules. **(6.1)**
2. Atoms gain or lose valence electrons to form ions. **(6.2)**
3. Chemical bonds are formed when valence electrons are transferred or shared between atoms; covalent bonds hold atoms together; ionic bonds join ions. **(6.3)**
4. Chemical formulas are used to represent compounds. Molecular formulas are used to represent molecules. Empirical formulas are used to represent ionic compounds. **(6.4)**
5. Compounds that release ions in water are called electrolytes. Acids, bases, and salts are electrolytes. **(6.5)**
6. The law of conservation of mass states that atoms are not created or destroyed in a chemical reaction. The mass of the products always equals the mass of the reactants. **(6.6)**
7. A balanced chemical equation is used to represent a chemical reaction. **(6.7)**
8. There are four types of chemical reactions: synthesis, decomposition, substitution, and exchange. **(6.8, 6.9)**
9. Many reactions take place in a series of steps that may involve more than one type of reaction. **(6.9)**

## Science Terms

On a separate sheet of paper, define each term in a sentence.

acid **(112)**
base **(112)**
chemical bond **(109)**
chemical equation **(116)**
chemical formula **(110)**
coefficient **(117)**
covalent bond **(109)**
decomposition reaction **(120)**
electrolyte **(112)**

empirical formula **(111)**
exchange reaction **(120)**
ion **(108)**
ionic bond **(110)**
ionization **(108)**
law of conservation of mass **(115)**
macromolecule **(108)**
molecular formula **(110)**
molecule **(107)**

neutralization **(113)**
pH **(112)**
precipitate **(120)**
product **(115)**
reactant **(115)**
salt **(113)**
substitution reaction **(120)**
synthesis reaction **(119)**

## Modified True-False

On a separate sheet of paper, mark each true statement *TRUE* and each false statement *FALSE*. If false, change the underlined term to make the statement true.

1. A <u>molecule</u> is the smallest piece of an element or compound that can exist by itself. T
2. Negatively charged ions are called <u>cations</u>. F, anions
3. Covalent bonds can occur between <u>ions</u> of the same type. F, atoms
4. Substances that have <u>ionic</u> bonds do not form molecules. T
5. The formula $H_2O$ represents an <u>atom</u> of water. F, molecule
6. Electrolytes are compounds that dissolve in water to form solutions that conduct <u>electricity</u>. T
7. An acid is an electrolyte that releases <u>hydrogen</u> ions in solution. T
8. In a chemical reaction, <u>molecules</u> cannot be broken down. F, atoms
9. A chemical equation cannot be balanced by changing chemical <u>formulas</u>. T
10. When two or more substances combine, a <u>decomposition</u> reaction takes place. F, synthesis

*(continues)*

## Multiple Choice

On a separate sheet of paper, write the letter of the term that best answers the question or completes the statement.

1. Magnesium is weighed and then heated strongly and weighed again. A gain in mass occurs because the magnesium
   a. is replaced by a heavier substance.
   b. melts and forms a solid lump.
   c. expands due to heat.
   d. combines with oxygen.

2. Which of the following properties is *not* typical of an acid?
   a. corrosive
   b. turns litmus blue
   c. releases hydrogen ions in water
   d. with bases, forms salt and water

3. Anions are _____ .
   a. positively charged ions.
   b. negatively charged ions.
   c. acids.
   d. bases.

4. Many hundreds of atoms joined together are called
   a. ionic compounds.
   b. macromolecules.
   c. covalent compounds.
   d. electrolytes.

5. Hydrogen peroxide ($H_2O_2$) decomposes to produce water ($H_2O$) and oxygen ($O_2$). The balanced equation for this reaction is
   a. $H_2O_2 \rightarrow H_2O + O_2$.
   b. $2H_2O_2 \rightarrow 2H_2O + O_2$.
   c. $2H_2O_2 \rightarrow H_2O + 2O_2$.
   d. $2H_2O_2 \rightarrow 2H_2O \rightarrow 2O_2$.

6. The transferring of valence electrons produces
   a. ionic bonds.          c. covalent bonds.
   b. empirical bonds.      d. valence bonds.

7. The number of atoms in a molecule of $C_6H_{12}O_6$ is _____ .
   a. 1.      b. 3.      c. 12.      d. 24

8. In a $CuSO_4$ crystal, the number of sulfate ions is _____ the number of copper ions.
   a. the same as      c. twice
   b. less than        d. four times

9. Which type of chemical change destroys the properties of acids and bases?
   a. neutralization      c. synthesis
   b. decomposition       d. substitution

10. When a chemical reaction occurs, atoms are never
    a. ionized.         c. precipitated.
    b. destroyed.       d. rearranged.

## Completion

On a separate sheet of paper, complete each statement by supplying the correct term.

1. The process of gaining or losing an electron is called _ionization_ .

2. When two atoms share the same valence electrons, a _covalent_ bond is formed.

3. The pH of an acid is always less than _7_ .

4. Sodium hydroxide is an example of a _base_ .

5. A balanced chemical equation shows equal numbers of _atoms_ on each side of the equation.

6. The reaction in which calcium carbonate ($CaCO_3$) breaks down into calcium oxide ($CaO$) and carbon dioxide ($CO_2$) is an example of a _____ reaction. _decomposition_

7. When a base reacts with an acid, the products of the reaction are salt and _water_ .

8. Water is broken down into hydrogen and _oxygen_ .

9. A balanced chemical equation for the synthesis of ammonia is $N_2 + $ _3_ $H_2 \rightarrow 2NH_3$.

10. Insoluble compounds produced in chemical reactions are called _precipitates_ .

## Writing Critically

1. Compare and contrast substances formed by the formation of covalent and ionic bonds.

2. Explain the relationship between acids, bases, and salts.

3. **CHALLENGE** Discuss some similarities and differences among the four major types of chemical reactions. Give an example of each type of reaction.

4. **CHALLENGE** Barium sulfate ($BaSO_4$) does not dissolve in water. What would happen if a solution of barium chloride ($BaCl_2$) was mixed with a solution of copper sulfate ($CuSO_4$)?

1. Covalent compounds are formed when atoms share valence electrons. In ionic compounds, the atoms do not share electrons; they either gain or lose electrons. 2. Acids and bases are both electrolytes; they release ions in solution. A salt is the result of the reaction of an acid and a base. 3. All four reactions involve the rearrangement of atoms. Answers to the second part will vary, but examples from the chapter may be used. 4. Barium sulfate would form as a precipitate in this exchange reaction.

## Skill Reinforcement

The Skill Activity on page 114 describes how to title and label a table. Take a survey of any chemicals you may have in your home. Identify the chemicals as an acid, base, or salt. Make a table showing the uses of the chemicals. Be sure to include a title and column heads. Compare your table with those of your classmates to see how they organized their tables.

## Research Ideas

1. Investigate how limestone caves are formed through the chemical action of water. How are stalactites and stalagmites formed inside the caves?

2. How did Antoine Lavoisier discover the law of mass conservation? As part of your investigation, find out what chemical reactions he observed to make this discovery.

3. **CHALLENGE** The proper chemical balance in a swimming pool is essential to keep the water clear and safe to swim in. Find out what chemicals are added to the water and why. Include some of the chemical reactions that take place when these chemicals are added.

## For Further Reading

"Checking Out Acids and Bases." *ChemMatters* (April 1983), American Chemical Society. This issue has a number of different articles about acid-base chemistry. Various articles discuss antacids, acid rain, and shampoo pH.

Corrick, James A. *Recent Revolutions in Chemistry.* NY: Watts, 1986. The science of chemistry has yielded exciting new discoveries such as silicon chips, polymers, and synthetic drugs. These and other developments are discussed in an understandable way for the nonchemist.

Sherman, A., and S.J. Sherman. *Chemistry and Our Changing World.* Englewood Cliffs, New Jersey: Prentice-Hall, 1983. The authors describe how chemistry is helping to change the way in which we live.

Tocci, Salvatore. *Chemistry Around You.* New York: Arco Publishing, 1985. The author describes different chemical reactions that take place in the home. Step-by-step instructions are given for a variety of experiments that can be done at home.

# CHAPTER 7

# Nuclear Reactions

At temperatures greater than 110 million degrees centigrade, atoms join, or fuse, together. Tremendous amounts of energy are released in this nuclear reaction. Today, fusion reactions take place only in the sun. The experimental chamber shown below uses ion beams to create these intense temperatures. Researchers are still working on ways to create and harness this energy.

For additional information, see pages T72–T73.

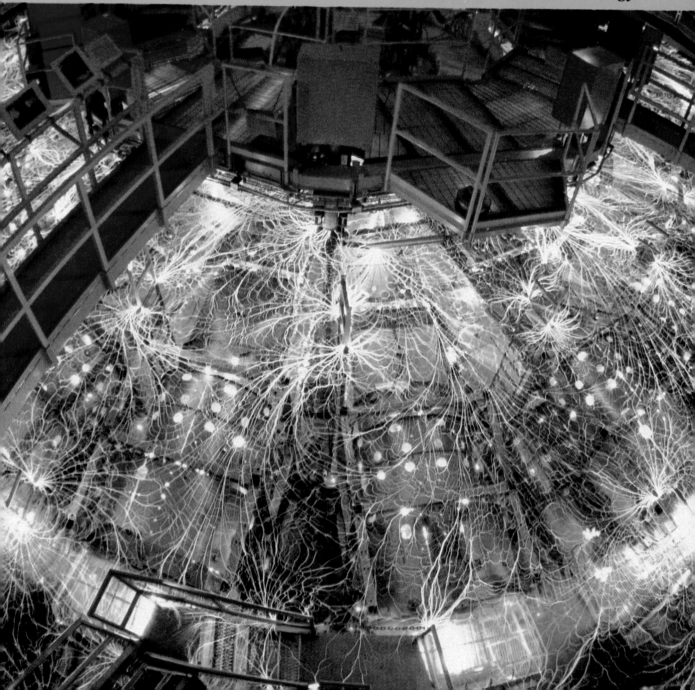

# Radioactivity

NEW TERMS IN THIS SECTION
radioactivity
radioactive decay
radioisotope
alpha particle
beta particle
gamma ray
background radiation
rems
Geiger counter
scintillation counter
cloud chamber
film badge

## SECTION OBJECTIVES

- **Describe** how radioactivity was discovered.
- **Distinguish** between alpha, beta, and gamma radiation.
- **Recognize** the dangers of exposure to radiation.
- **Name** the methods used to detect radiation.

Photograph left: ion beams creating a temperature exceeding 111,100,000°C

## 7.1 The Discovery of Radioactivity

The atomic age began in 1896 with a discovery by the French scientist Antoine Henri Becquerel (an TWAHN ahn REE beh KREHL). Becquerel placed a uranium compound on top of a photographic plate that was wrapped in black paper. When the plate was developed, it was fogged, as if the plate had been partially exposed to light. Becquerel concluded that invisible rays from the uranium had passed through the paper and had affected the photographic plate.

   The Polish chemist Marie Sklodowska Curie (skluh DAHF skuh kyu REE) gave a name to the invisible rays that Becquerel had discovered. She called the invisible rays **radioactivity**. In 1898 Curie and her husband, Pierre, a French scientist, discovered two new, highly radioactive elements. They called one of the new elements *polonium*, after Madame Curie's native country, Poland. They named the other *radium* because it was so highly radioactive. Marie Curie also discovered that the element thorium is radioactive. For their discoveries, Marie and Pierre Curie were awarded the Nobel prize. The prize was awarded in 1903 for research on radioactivity and was shared jointly with Henri Becquerel.

The discovery of radioactivity was not accidental. Becquerel was systematically and deliberately investigating uranium compounds, searching for an expected connection between phosphorescence and the emission of X rays.

**Figure 7–1.** In 1911, Marie Curie became the first person to receive two Nobel prizes when she received the prize for the discovery of polonium and radium. Pierre Curie had been killed in an accident and did not live to share the second Nobel prize.

Nuclear Reactions    **127**

# 7.2 Nuclear Radiation

The work of Becquerel and of the Curies did not explain why certain atoms are radioactive, while others are not. The answer involves the number of protons and neutrons in the nucleus of the atom. The force required to hold the nucleus together depends on two factors. Those two factors are the size of the nucleus and the number of protons compared to the number of neutrons found in the nucleus.

As discussed in Chapter 3, the strong nuclear force is involved with holding the nucleus together. The larger the nucleus, the stronger the force must be. For this reason, very large nuclei are very difficult to hold together. In fact, elements with atomic numbers higher than 82 are unstable and will lose neutrons, a process called **radioactive decay.** For example, all uranium nuclei have 92 protons. One uranium isotope has 146 neutrons. Another uranium isotope has only 143 neutrons. The strong nuclear force is not powerful enough to hold all these nuclear particles together. For this reason, the nuclei of all uranium atoms decay into lighter elements.

When unstable radioactive nuclei decay, they release high-energy radiation. Since the number of atoms in a given radioactive sample is so great, the total amount of radiation released can be very large.

Different isotopes of the same element may be radioactive, while others are not. Those isotopes that are radioactive are called **radioisotopes**. Some radioactive isotopes of the lighter elements are found in nature. Naturally occurring radioisotopes of some lighter elements include carbon-14, potassium-40, and rubidium-87. All of these isotopes are radioactive because their atoms have more neutrons than can be held by the strong nuclear force.

The nucleus of a radioactive atom emits three different types of radiation. The types of radiation are named alpha (AL fuh) particles ($\alpha$), beta (BAYT uh) particles ($\beta$), and gamma (GAM uh) rays ($\gamma$). Figure 7–2 illustrates the three types of radiation.

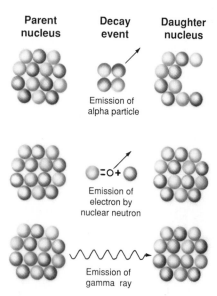

| Parent nucleus | Decay event | Daughter nucleus |

Emission of alpha particle

Emission of electron by nuclear neutron

Emission of gamma ray

**Figure 7–2.** In alpha radiation (top), two protons and two neutrons are emitted carrying a positive charge. In beta radiation (middle), a single electron is emitted with a single negative charge. Gamma radiation (bottom) occurs when pure energy is released from the nucleus.

### Alpha Particles

An **alpha particle** consists of two protons and two neutrons bound together. An alpha particle, which is identical to the stable nucleus of a helium atom, has a positive charge of 2. Alpha particles are emitted from the nucleus of a radioactive atom at very high speeds. However, they are easily stopped by a piece of paper or by a person's skin.

## Beta Particles

A **beta particle** is identical to an electron. Unlike alpha particles, beta particles have a single negative charge. A beta particle is emitted from an atom when a neutron in the nucleus changes into a proton. Beta particles can pass through paper and skin, but not through wood, heavy clothing, or a metal plate.

Emphasize to the students that the nucleus changes when radiation is emitted.

## Gamma Rays

Pure energy released from the nucleus is called **gamma rays**. Gamma rays are similar to X rays. Like X rays, gamma rays have no mass and no electric charge. However, gamma rays have much more energy than X rays. Gamma rays can pass straight through most materials. Thick lead plates and concrete walls are used to stop gamma rays.

### READING CRITICALLY

Which form of radiation poses the greatest threat to a person's health?

gamma rays, because they are able to penetrate through most materials

## 7.3 Exposure to Radiation

Small amounts of radioactive elements are found in the earth and in all living things. In addition, cosmic radiation reaches the earth from outer space. Together, these sources produce a natural level of radiation, called **background radiation**. The amount of background radiation is so slight that it presents no health risk to humans. However, exposure to increased amounts of radiation can present serious health risks.

When radiation passes through a living cell, the cell can be damaged or destroyed. If molecules that regulate growth of the cell are damaged by radiation, cancer can develop. Cancer is the abnormal and uncontrolled growth and reproduction of cells. If radiation damages the nucleus of a reproductive cell, this damage may be passed on from one generation to the next.

The amount of cellular damage caused by exposure to radiation depends upon the level of the radiation and the length of exposure to the radiation. A brief exposure to very strong radiation can cause serious injury or death. However, small doses of radiation repeated over long periods of time can be just as dangerous as large, single doses. The next time you receive an X ray, notice that the technician wears a lead apron and stands behind a shield. Why do you think this is done?

Radiation can be used to treat certain types of cancer. Sometimes it is possible to use radiation to destroy cancer cells without destroying normal cells. This type of treatment, known as *radiation therapy,* involves focusing the radiation on only the cancer cells.

to protect him or her from prolonged exposure to gamma rays

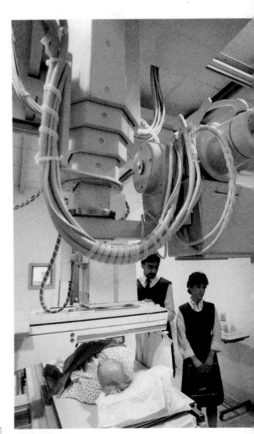

**Figure 7–3.** Although radiation is known to cause cancer, technology has devised ways to use radiation to combat cancer. This patient is undergoing radiation therapy that kills cancer cells.

A brief exposure to very strong radiation can cause serious injury or death. However, small doses repeated over long periods of time can be just as dangerous.

**Figure 7–4.** The symbol indicating a radiation hazard is universally recognized.

The biological effect of exposure to radiation is measured in units called **rems**. The rem is a measure of the amount of radiation received and the biological damage caused by the radiation.

The National Safety Council on Radiation Protection warns that no individual should be exposed to more than 500 millirems (0.5 rems) of radiation in any one year. This amount does not include natural background radiation. One dental or chest X ray would be equal to about 0.045 rems.

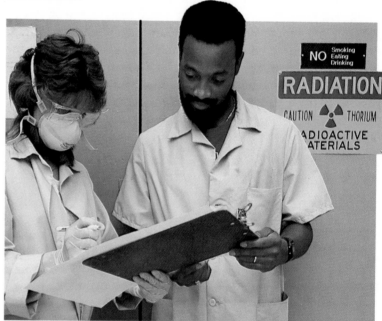

## 7.4 Detecting Radiation

Since alpha, beta, and gamma radiation are invisible, special instruments are needed to detect and measure such radiation. The **Geiger** (GY guhr) **counter** is one type of instrument that measures radiation. In a Geiger counter, radiation enters a special tube that contains argon gas. Electrons in the argon atoms absorb the radiation, causing the argon electrons to jump to higher energy levels. Some of these electrons escape from the atoms. The clicking sound that a Geiger counter makes when it is exposed to radiation is due to bursts of electric current carried by these electrons.

A scintillation (sihnt uhl AY shuhn) counter is another type of radiation-measuring instrument. A **scintillation counter** measures radiation by counting tiny flashes of light, called *scintillations*. These flashes are produced when special substances are exposed to radiation. Scintillation counters are useful because they are

smaller than Geiger counters and because they can measure low-level radiation more efficiently.

**Cloud chambers** are instruments that show the tracks left by radiation. Charged alpha and beta particles are so small that they cannot be seen. However, charged particles produce tracks when they pass through a cloud chamber.

People who work in areas exposed to radiation usually wear a **film badge** to detect radiation. The film in the badge is developed each day to show how much radiation the person has received. <u>If the film is very dark when developed, what would that tell you about the amount of radiation received?</u> that the individual wearing the badge had been exposed to a significant amount of radiation

**Figure 7–5.** These tracks left by radiation were produced in a cloud chamber, an instrument scientists use to study radiation.

Compare tracks of radiation to vapor trails made by high-flying aircraft. Even though the plane is too high to be seen, the condensed water vapor from its exhaust clearly marks its path.

## Section Review

1. What did Becquerel conclude from his discovery that uranium could fog a photographic plate?

2. List and briefly describe the three types of nuclear radiation.

3. Explain why nuclear radiation can be harmful to living things.

4. Describe two methods that are used to detect nuclear radiation.

5. THINKING CRITICALLY A large sample of radioactive carbon-14 is broken down into individual atoms. How is the radioactivity of each atom affected? Explain your answer.

1. Invisible rays from the uranium had caused the fogging.
2. alpha particles: positively charged particles ejected at high speeds from nuclei of heavy atoms; beta particles: negatively charged particles ejected when a neutron inside the nucleus changes into a proton; gamma rays: radiant energy emitted by unstable nuclei; similar to X rays
3. When radiation passes through a living cell, cell damage occurs. If the cell damage is not automatically repaired, genetic damage may be passed on when cells multiply, resulting in the development of cancer.
4. Geiger counters, scintillation counters, cloud chambers, and film badges
5. There is no change in the amount of radioactivity given off by each atom. Each atom still has too many neutrons.

# SKILL ACTIVITY   Reading for Comprehension

**INTRODUCTION**

You can better understand what you read by identifying the purpose of the writer. A writer may write to inform you, to vividly describe something, or to persuade you. The writer's purpose will determine both the content and the words used to express the ideas.

**PROCEDURE**

1. To write to inform the reader, include specific details and write in a fairly formal way. Example: Exposure to sunlight can cause sunburn, skin aging, and even cancer.

2. To write to describe something, include details that create an image for the reader. Example: The soft, white bunny twitched its moist, red nose as it sniffed the clear morning air.

3. To write to persuade, write in a concise style and express your ideas clearly. Support your opinions with reasons and evidence. Example: All Americans should vote not only because it is their right, but also because it is their duty.

**APPLICATION**

Read the article below. Then answer the questions that follow.

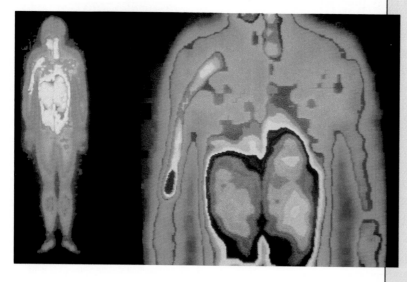

**Using Radioisotopes in Medicine**
Doctors use radioisotopes, such as thallium-201, to determine how much heart damage has occurred from a heart attack. In this procedure radioactive thallium is injected into a patient's vein. The blood then carries the radioisotope to the patient's heart. A radiation monitor is then used to determine how much radiation has been absorbed by different parts of the heart.

Healthy heart muscle readily absorbs thallium-201. Damaged parts of the heart absorb less thallium. For this reason damaged parts of the heart show up as dark spots on the radiation monitor. By studying these images, doctors learn how much heart damage has occurred.

1. how radioisotopes are used to measure heart damage
2. how thallium-20 works within the body
3. This passage is informative. Examples may include "healthy heart muscle readily absorbs thallium, radioactive thallium is injected into a patients vein"

1. What is the main idea in the first paragraph?
2. What is the main idea in the second paragraph?
3. Explain whether the article is written to inform, to describe, or to persuade. Give examples to support your reason.

# Nuclear Transformations

NEW TERMS IN THIS SECTION
activity
curies
half-life
particle accelerator
tracer
radiometric dating

## SECTION OBJECTIVES

● **State** what is meant by the terms *radiactive decay* and *half-life.*

● **Explain** the two ways in which nuclear reactions can take place.

● **Describe** some of the uses for radioisotopes.

## 7.5 Radioactive Decay

The continual loss of radioactive atoms when the nuclei decay is called radioactive decay. Although all radioactive atoms decay, those with very unstable nuclei decay faster than those with more stable nuclei. Scientists can find no way to tell which atom in a large group of radioactive atoms will decay at any given moment.

The rate of nuclear decay is measured by the amount of radiation released. This amount is called the **activity**. Activity is measured in units called **curies**. One curie is the amount of radiation released by 1 gram of pure radium in one second. A curie is equal to 37 billion nuclear disintegrations per second. A smaller unit, the microcurie, is equal to 37,000 disintegrations per second.

The activity of a radioactive substance does not remain constant. That is, the amount of radiation does not stay the same over the life of the substance. In time the activity decreases as the number of radioactive atoms remaining becomes smaller. The time required for one-half the atoms of a radioactive substance to decay is called the **half-life**. For example, the half-life of iodine-

The first three types of decay products discovered were alpha rays, beta rays, and gamma rays. Some beta rays were found to be positrons, or positive electrons. The positron is called the antiparticle of the electron. If a positron meets an electron, they are both annihilated. Both disappear and two gamma rays are created that carry off their energy, including the energy of their mass.

### ACTIVITY

**Calculating Half-Life**

On a sheet of paper draw a square that is 10 cm on a side. Assume that the square represents a radioactive element with a half-life of two years. By dividing the square in half repeatedly, find the area that represents the amount of the substance remaining after eight years.

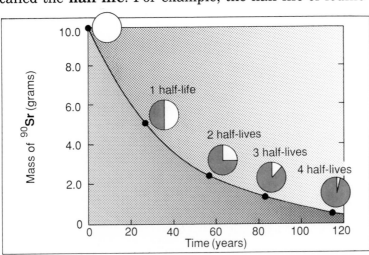

**Figure 7–6.** This graph shows the decay curve of a 10-g sample of strontium-90. The half-life of strontium-90 is 28.8 years.

As the number of neutrons increases, an isotope becomes more unstable and decays more rapidly. For example, iodine-129 has a half-life of 17 million years; iodine-131, which has two more neutrons, has a half-life of eight days; and iodine-133, which has another two neutrons, has a half-life of 21 hours.

In 1919, Ernest Rutherford observed that alpha particles traveling through nitrogen were absorbed and protons were emitted. He concluded that some of the nitrogen nuclei had been transformed into oxygen nuclei. This was the first artificial nuclear reaction ever observed in the laboratory.

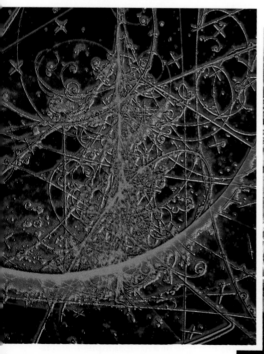

**Figure 7–7.** Particle accelerators, like the Fermi National Accelerator Laboratory near Batavia, Illinois (below right), are also called *atom smashers*. Electrically charged particles are accelerated around an underground tunnel that forms a circle 2 km in diameter. The actual tracks made by atomic particles in an accelerator are shown below.

131 is 8 days. After 8 days, the amount of radioactive iodine-131 in any sample will have decreased by 50 percent. After 16 days, only one quarter of the radioactive iodine will remain. After about 10 half-lives, the amount of radioactive material is less than one-thousandth of the original amount.

The relationship between half-life and the amount of radioactive isotope remaining in shown in Figure 7-6. Each radioisotope has its own half-life. Half-lives range from billionths of a second to billions of years. Iodine-133, for example, has a half-life of 21 hours. Iodine-129 has a half-life of 17 million years.

## 7.6 Nuclear Reactions

Nuclear reactions can take place in two ways—by spontaneous reaction and by collision. A *spontaneous reaction* is one that occurs without external causes. Radioactive decay is a spontaneous reaction. When the nucleus of a radioactive atom releases an alpha particle, it becomes a different kind of nucleus. For example, when an atom of uranium decays by emitting an alpha particle, it loses two protons and two neutrons. Its mass number is reduced by four units. The new nucleus has 90 protons instead of the 92 that uranium had. It is now an isotope of a different element, thorium.

## Summary

1. Uranium emits invisible radiation called radioactivity. **(7.1)**

2. Radioactive atoms have unstable nuclei and emit three different types of radiation: alpha particles, beta particles, and gamma rays. **(7.2)**

3. Radiation can damage or destroy cells inside the body, causing cancer and genetic damage. The biological effect of radiation is measured in units called rems. **(7.3)**

4. Radiation can be detected by Geiger counters, scintillation counters, cloud chambers, and film badges. **(7.4)**

5. The amount of radiation released by radioactive material is called the activity. The half-life is the time required for half the atoms of a radioactive substance to decay. **(7.5)**

6. Nuclear reactions take place in two ways: spontaneously in the decay of radioactive material and artificially in particle accelerators. **(7.6)**

7. Radioisotopes are used as tracers and for radiometric dating. **(7.7)**

8. Nuclear reactions release much more energy than do chemical reactions. This happens because much more mass is converted into energy in a nuclear reaction. **(7.8)**

9. Nuclear fission occurs when a heavy nucleus splits into two parts. A nuclear reactor converts the energy from nuclear fission into useful electric energy. **(7.9, 7.10)**

10. Nuclear fusion occurs when two nuclei combine. This process occurs only at very high temperatures. **(7.11)**

## Science Terms

On a separate sheet of paper, define each term in a sentence.

activity **(133)**
alpha particle **(128)**
background radiation **(129)**
beta particle **(129)**
chain reaction **(138)**
cloud chamber **(131)**
control rods **(139)**
curie **(133)**

film badge **(131)**
fission **(138)**
fusion **(140)**
gamma rays **(129)**
Geiger counter **(130)**
half-life **(133)**
particle accelerator **(135)**
radioactive decay **(128)**

radioactivity **(127)**
radioisotopes **(128)**
radiometric dating **(135)**
rems **(130)**
scintillation counter **(130)**
tracer **(135)**

## Modified True-False

On a separate sheet of paper, mark each true statement *TRUE* and each false statement *FALSE*. If false, change the underlined term to make the statement true.

1. Radioactivity is the underlined visible radiation that comes from radioactive substances. F, invisible

2. Radioactivity involves the underlined nucleus of the atom, not the orbiting electrons. T

3. Underlined Alpha particles have a negative charge and can pass through paper and skin. F, beta

4. Underlined Gamma rays are the most dangerous form of radiation. T

5. An instrument that measures radiation by counting tiny flashes of light is called a underlined Geiger counter. F, scintillation

*(continues)*

6. The time required for three-quarters of the atoms of a radioactive isotope to decay would be <u>three</u> half-lives.  T

7. The activity of a radioactive sample is a measure of the rate of disintegration. The activity always <u>decreases</u> with time.  T

8. Pure energy released from the nucleus of an atom is called <u>beta rays</u>.  F, gamma rays

9. When two atomic nuclei combine, the reaction is a <u>fission</u> reaction.  F, fusion

10. The chain reaction in a nuclear power plant is controlled by absorbing some of the <u>neutrons</u> that cause the fission reaction.  T

## Multiple Choice

On a separate sheet of paper, write the letter of the term that best completes the statement.

1. One effect of radiation on humans is
   a. weight loss.
   b. weight gain.
   (c.) cancer.
   d. growth.

2. Activity is measured in units called
   (a.) curies.
   b. rems.
   c. half-lives.
   d. tracers.

3. Nuclear radiation that can pass through paper, skin, and heavy clothing is
   a. alpha radiation.
   b. beta radiation.
   (c.) gamma radiation.
   d. X radiation.

4. As a sample of radioisotope decays, its half-life
   (a.) slowly decreases.
   b. slowly increases.
   c. remains the same.
   d. remains constant.

5. The Chernobyl incident is an example of
   (a.) meltdown.
   b. half-life.
   c. electricity.
   d. nuclear waste.

6. An example of a naturally occurring radioisotope used for radiometric dating is
   (a.) carbon-14.
   b. nitrogen-14.
   c. oxygen-16.
   d. potassium-40.

7. A partial meltdown of a reactor occurred at
   a. Salem Island.
   b. Chernobyl.
   c. Oyster Creek.
   (d.) Three Mile Island.

8. The process in which a heavy nucleus splits into two lighter nuclei is called
   (a.) fission.
   b. fusion.
   c. alpha decay.
   d. chain reaction.

9. A nuclear power station changes
   a. heat energy into nuclear energy.
   b. electrical energy into nuclear energy.
   (c.) nuclear energy into electrical energy.
   d. fission energy into fusion energy.

10. No individual should be exposed to more than _____ millirems of radiation in any one year.
   a. 50  (b.) 500  c. 5  d. 0.5

## Completion

On a separate sheet of paper, complete each statement by supplying the correct term.

1. All atoms with an atomic number greater than ___82___ are radioactive.

2. The carbon-14 isotope is radioactive because it has too many ___neutrons___ in its nucleus.

3. Gamma rays are similar to ___X rays___, but they carry much more energy.

4. The biological effect of exposure to radiation is measured in units called ___rems___.

5. An instrument used to show the tracks left by nuclear particles is called a ___cloud chamber___.

6. The rate of nuclear disintegration is measured in units called ___curies___.

7. The half-life of strontium-90 is 28.8 years. It takes __28.8__ years for the amount of Sr-90 in any sample to decrease by 50 percent.

8. All radioactive disintegrations are __spontaneous__ reactions.

9. A machine designed to study nuclear reactions by causing particles to collide at high speeds is called a __particle accelerator__.

10. When a nuclear reaction occurs, some of the nuclear mass is changed into __energy__.

## Writing Critically   Answers: page T73.

1. Differentiate the three types of nuclear radiation. Describe methods that are used to detect and measure nuclear radiation.

2. What is meant by the term half-life? Explain how radioisotopes with different half-lives are used as clocks to measure time.

3. CHALLENGE   Distinguish between nuclear fission and nuclear fusion. How is a controlled chain reaction used to produce large amounts of energy from the fission of uranium-235?

## Skill Reinforcement

The Skill Activity on page 132 describes how an article may be written to inform, to describe, or to persuade. Use the information from "Using Radioisotopes in Medicine" in the Skill Activity to write an article that describes an imaginary personal experience or that is intended to persuade the reader about a point of view.

## Research Ideas

1. Find out how particle accelerators are used to create transuranium elements. How many of these radioactive elements, which have a number greater than 92, have been made? What is the future for this field of research?

2. Find out how Marie Curie and her husband discovered radium. How was radium used in the early decades of the twentieth century?

3. Find out where the nuclear power station nearest your school is located. How many years has it been operating? What are some of the potential dangers of a nuclear reactor?

4. CHALLENGE   Find out how radiometric dating helped scientists determine the age of the Dead Sea scrolls and measure the age of the earth.

## For Further Reading

Jackson, J. D., M. Tigner, and S. Wojcicki. "The Superconducting Supercollider." *Scientific American* 254, (March 1986): 66. This article provides an account of plans to build a giant particle accelerator to explore the hidden depths of the nucleus.

Wolkomir, Richard. "Quark City." *Omni*, February 1984: 40-44, 80-83. This interesting and informative article discusses subatomic particles in an easy-to-understand manner.

"Deadly Meltdown," *Time*, May 12, 1986: 39-59. This article provides a step-by-step account of the Chernobyl disaster.

# Chemical Technology

What would your life be like without modern chemical technology? Look around your classroom or your home. Think about things you wear or use. How many items can you identify that are made only of natural materials such as wood, wool, cotton, or stone? How many are a result of chemical technology?

For additional information, see pages T74–T75.

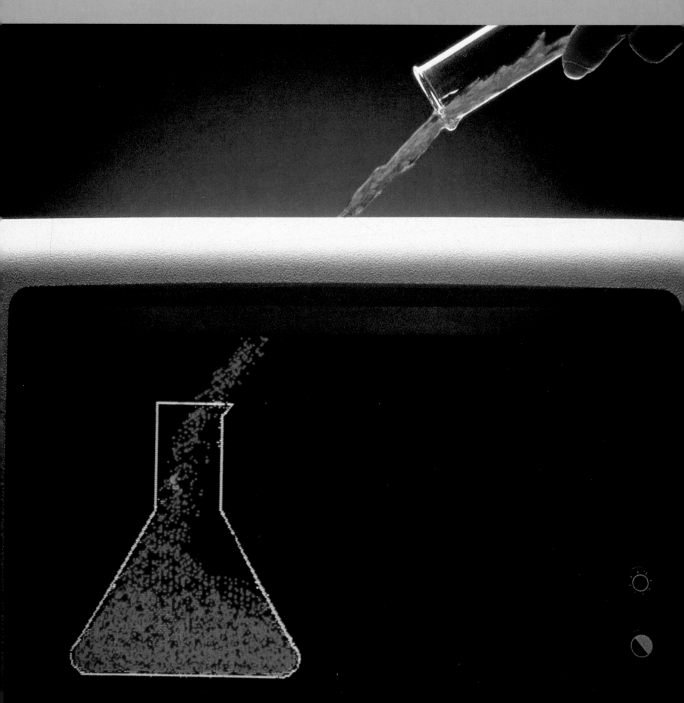

# Industrial Chemistry

**SECTION OBJECTIVES**

- **Compare** the various fossil fuels with regard to how they are formed and how they are used.
- **Distinguish** between the terms *cracking* and *polymerization*.
- **Explain** what a polymer is.
- **Identify** and give some uses of four polymers.

NEW TERMS IN THIS SECTION
fossil fuel
coal
petroleum
natural gas
polymer
plastic
synthetic fiber
rubber

Photograph left: computer-simulated laboratory procedure

## 8.1 Fossil Fuels

Coal, petroleum, and natural gas are all fossil fuels. A **fossil fuel** is an energy source that is formed from the remains of living organisms. These fuels are trapped under layers of rocks and are found by drilling or mining. Today, fossil fuels provide more than 80 percent of the world's energy needs. Fossil fuels take millions of years to form. Therefore, these fuels should be used wisely. When the current supplies of coal, petroleum, and natural gas are used up, there will be no more.

### Coal

**Coal** is a solid formed from the remains of plants. It is found underground in layers called *beds* or *seams*. Coal beds range in thickness from less than one centimeter to massive beds of more than 10 m. Scientists estimate that a layer of plants about 12 m thick is needed to make a coal bed 1 m thick. In North America and Russia, coal beds may extend over areas of 1000 km² or more. Before coal can be used, it must first be mined, or dug from the ground. Figure 8–1 shows a piece of equipment used in the mining and moving of coal.

**Figure 8–1.** Mining coal requires enormous labor as well as heavy equipment.

Coal is used as a fuel because it gives off heat when burned. Coal is also used to make other chemicals. When heated in ovens where it cannot burn, coal breaks down into three substances—coke, coal tar, and coal gas. All of these components of coal have practical uses. Coke can be used as a fuel and in the manufacture of iron and steel. Coal tar is needed to make some types of dyes, medicines, perfumes, and insecticides. Some dandruff shampoos contain coal tar. Coal gas can be burned as a fuel. Before the days of electricity, lamps that burned coal gas were used to light streets and homes.

900 kg of coal yield about 16 kg of coal tar. This material is the natural source of heavy, aromatic organic compounds such as napthalene, benzene, phenol, cresol, toluene, and xylene.

## Petroleum

Crude oil, or **petroleum**, is a dark, oily, liquid mixture of chemical substances containing carbon and hydrogen. These substances are called *hydrocarbons*. The word *petroleum* comes from two Greek words—*petra*, meaning "rock" and *oleum*, meaning "oil." Hydrocarbons can be separated into many types of fuels, such as gasoline, naphtha, and propane.

To be used as an energy source, petroleum must be removed from the ground. Petroleum is formed deep within the ground between layers of rock. It is removed from the ground by way of a well.

**Figure 8–2.** Petroleum is recovered in a way similar to the way in which underground water is obtained. If natural pressure provides most of the energy necessary to bring the petroleum to the surface, the recovery of the petroleum is called *primary recovery*. If artificial means are used, the process is known as *enhanced recovery*.

Because coal, petroleum, and natural gas are derived from the remains of living organisms, deposits of these materials are not expected to be found on other planets in the solar system.

## Natural Gas

**Natural gas** is a mixture of light hydrocarbons. Petroleum and natural gas are often found together, trapped between rock layers beneath the surface of the earth. One of the main uses of natural gas is to heat buildings. Natural gas has an advantage over coal in that it is a "clean" fuel. When natural gas burns, carbon dioxide and water are formed, but unlike petroleum, no harmful pollutants are given off.

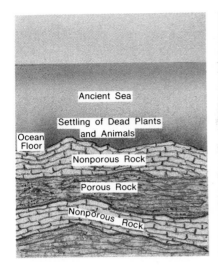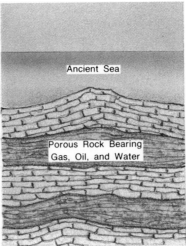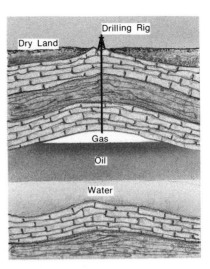

Petroleum and natural gas were probably made from tiny animals that lived millions of years ago in the sea. When these animals died, they settled to the sea floor. As time passed, their bodies were covered by deposits of sand and silt. Over millions of years, these organic remains were changed into petroleum and natural gas by pressure and temperature. Figure 8–3 shows how petroleum and natural gas are formed.

**Figure 8–3.** Because the same process that produces petroleum also produces natural gas, natural gas is often found on top of oil deposits or dissolved in them.

## 8.2 Petrochemicals

Aside from being good fuel sources, petroleum and natural gas can be separated into different useful chemicals called *petrochemicals*. Petroleum is heated until it becomes a mixture of gases. The chemicals in the gases can then be separated by their densities. The chemical products obtained from this process are made in manufacturing plants called *refineries*. Table 8–1 lists the substances obtained from petroleum.

One of the substances produced when petroleum is separated is gasoline. Gasoline is used as a fuel for automobiles, airplanes, and other machines. The amount of gasoline made from crude oil can be increased by two methods called *cracking* and *polymerization*. Cracking is a method that breaks down, or "cracks," large, heavy molecules to make smaller molecules for gasoline mixtures. Polymerization is the reverse of cracking. Polymerization makes larger molecules for gasoline mixtures by joining smaller molecules of crude oil.

Fuel oil and heating oil are also separated from petroleum. Fuel oil is burned to power machines in factories and power plants. Heating oil is used to heat homes and other buildings.

**TABLE 8–1**
**SUBSTANCES OBTAINED FROM PETROLEUM**

| Substance | Uses |
|---|---|
| Petroleum gas | Gaseous fuel |
| Gasoline | Motor fuel |
| Kerosene | Diesel fuel |
| Lubricants | Motor oil and greases |
| Paraffins | Waxes |
| Asphalt | Tar |

Natural gas contains methane and small amounts of other gases. To separate these gases, natural gas is cooled in the refinery. As it cools, the heavier gases condense first. As each gas becomes a liquid, it can be removed from the mixture. Long pipelines buried underground are used to move natural gas from the refinery to cities and towns, where it is used as a fuel.

Dietary fiber is cellulose, a natural polymer. Cellulose is found in the cell walls of fruits, vegetables, grains, and cereals.

**Figure 8–4.** As can be seen from the computer graphic representation (left), a polymer is a large, long, chainlike molecule. Plastic bags and wrapping material (right) are made by heating the plastic until it is a liquid that can be poured into molds.

# 8.3 Polymers

Some of the most useful petrochemicals are polymers. **Polymers** are giant molecules made by chemically joining many identical smaller molecules. You can think of a polymer as a chain with thousands of identical links. The polyester in a shirt is a polymer. A foam cooler is made of polymers, as is the rubber in your bicycle tires.

### Polyethylene

One widely used polymer is *polyethylene* (pahl ee EHTH uh leen). The sandwich in your lunch may be packed in a polyethylene bag. Polyethylene is made of long chains of ethylene molecules. The prefix *poly-* means "many." Although ethylene is a gas, long polyethylene molecules form a solid.

### Plastics

Many plastics are polymers. A **plastic** is a solid that can be molded when heated. Some plastics, called *thermoplastics,* can be repeatedly molded by heating and cooling. *Polystyrene* is a thermoplastic. You may drink hot chocolate from a polystyrene cup at a football game.

Other plastics, such as *polyurethane* (pahl ee YUHR uh thayn), can be molded only once. When polyurethane is heated, it becomes perfectly rigid. Would polyurethane make a good bumper for a car? Why?

No, because it is rigid and would shatter on contact.

Some plastics have properties that make them useful for special purposes. For example, in World War II airplanes, the cockpit cover was made of plastic. Sometimes during combat the cover shattered and pieces were embedded in the pilot's eyes. A British physician observed that the pilot's eyes were not damaged or infected by the plastic fragments. As a result of this observation, scientists used this plastic to make artificial lenses, including contact lenses, for people's eyes.

Sunlight can damage plastics. Ultraviolet radiation in the sunlight has sufficient energy to break the chemical bonds that join the polymer molecules together.

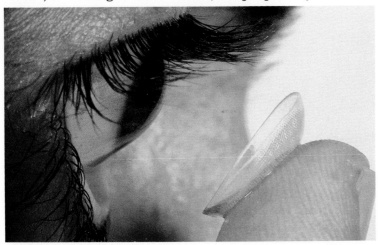

**Figure 8–5.** This person is inserting a soft contact lens, which is made from water and plastic.

## Synthetic Fibers

*Nylon* and *polyester* are polymers that can be drawn out into long threads. Nylon and polyester are synthetic fibers. **Synthetic fibers** are not made from natural plant or animal products. They are made from petroleum products or from coal. Synthetic fibers are used to manufacture fabrics. Many of your shirts, pants, or skirts contain synthetic fibers.

## Polymers in Medicine

Medical scientists are using polymers to solve many problems. For example, polymers can be used to help replace the skin on your body. Skin protects the body from infection. People with severe burns often die because they have lost this protection. Physicians can help burn victims by giving them a temporary skin made of polymers.

A covering of polymers is applied to the burned area. Underneath this temporary covering, the body creates a new layer of inner skin. Eventually the body's cells break down the polymer shield. By the time the shield is broken down, the body is ready to grow its own outer skin. Observe your skin the next time you cut or scrape it. How does your body protect the wound while it replaces the damaged skin? A scab forms over the wound. New skin forms under the scab.

**ACTIVITY**

**Locating Natural Materials**

Try to find some object or material in the classroom or in your home that has not been changed in some way by chemical technology. On what did you base your decision?

Answers will vary.

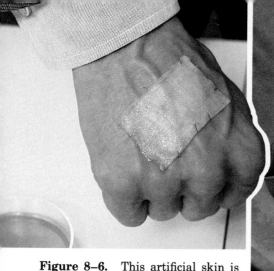

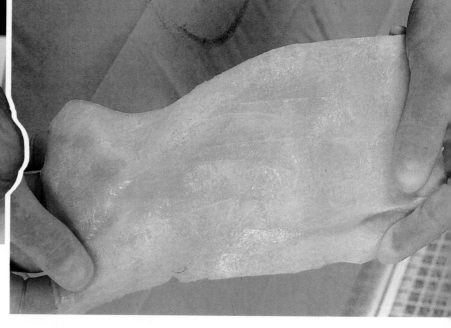

**Figure 8–6.** This artificial skin is made from a polymer of certain molecules of a cow. Using this skin helps burn victims recover by helping new skin to grow and protecting wounds from infection.

When a small cut is made in the trunk of a rubber tree, a milky liquid oozes out. This liquid, called *latex*, is a suspension of resinous rubber particles in water.

## READING CRITICALLY
Why does synthetic rubber last longer than natural rubber?

Synthetic rubber is more elastic and less sticky. It does not dissolve in the presence of other chemicals.

1. because, like all fossils, they are formed from the remains of organisms trapped underground in layers of rock
2. Polymerization and cracking. They are similar in that they both increase the amount of gasoline that can be made from crude oil. They are different in that cracking breaks down large molecules and polymerization joins molecules together.
3. A polymer is a giant molecule many thousands of atoms long. Answers to the second part will vary, but may include examples taken from the text.
4. Answers will vary, but may include a discussion of the growth in transportation due to gasoline that enabled products and ideas to be shared quickly, spurring on technology.

### Rubber

Both synthetic and natural **rubber** are polymers that are elastic. A substance that is elastic will return to its original shape after being bent, stretched, or compressed.

Natural rubber, which comes from certain tropical trees, is mixed with other materials and then heated. This process, known as *vulcanization,* makes the rubber more elastic and less sticky. Vulcanized, or synthetic, rubber is used in tires, shoes, and many other products.

Synthetic rubber has replaced natural rubber for many uses. Synthetic rubber is used for car tires because it wears longer than natural rubber. Another advantage of synthetic rubber is that, unlike natural rubber, it does not dissolve in the presence of petroleum products. *Neoprene*, a synthetic rubber, was first produced in 1931. Since oil and grease do not dissolve neoprene, it is used for gasoline hoses.

## Section Review

1. Why are petroleum, natural gas, and coal called fossil fuels?
2. List two processes that increase the amount of gasoline made from crude oil. Discuss the differences and similarities of these methods.
3. Define polymers and give some uses of them.
4. THINKING CRITICALLY The first major oil wells were drilled in the United States in 1859. How do you think the discovery of oil in the U.S. affected the life style of that time and since?

# Metals and Alloys

## SECTION OBJECTIVES

● **Define** *metallurgy.*
● **Explain** how metals are separated from ores.
● **Distinguish** between iron and steel.
● **Name** and **describe** three alloys.

NEW TERMS IN THIS SECTION
ore
metallurgy
steel
alloy

## 8.4 Separating Metals

The aluminum in a softball bat, the steel in the blades of ice skates, and the lead in your pencil are all products of chemical technology. You may recall from Chapter 4 that all metals other than gold, silver, copper, and platinum are found only in compounds. That is, most metals are combined with other metals or other elements in ores. An **ore** is any natural combination of minerals from which a metal may be separated or extracted.

Metals must be chemically separated from their ores. The science of separating a metal from its ore and preparing it for use is called **metallurgy** (MEHT uhl uhr jee). The first step in separating a metal from its ore is to remove unwanted sand and clay. Next, chemical reactions are used to separate the metal from the remaining material. The separated metal is then purified by removing any remaining trace elements. After this step the metal can be formed into bars. Figure 8–7 shows copper being prepared from its ore.

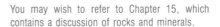

You may wish to refer to Chapter 15, which contains a discussion of rocks and minerals.

### SCIENCE FACT

Metallurgists have been able to make glass out of metal by cooling the hot metal at a rate of nearly 1,000,000°C per second. This new substance is more resistant to corrosion and is a better insulator.

**Figure 8–7.** This photograph shows the purification process of copper from copper ore. The metal is extracted from the ore through a melting process. Other metals are freed from ore by using electric current or dissolving the ore with acids.

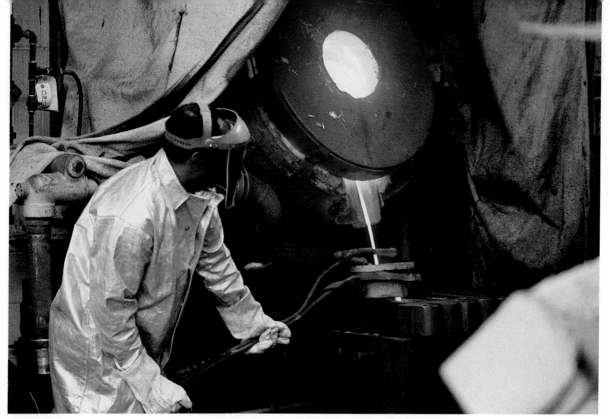

**Figure 8–8.** Hot air is added to this white-hot mixture of ore, coke, and limestone in the process of making pig iron.

In the United States, deposits of hematite are found in northern Minnesota near Lake Superior and around Birmingham, Alabama.

Limestone is added to the mixture inside the blast furnace to remove silica ($SiO_2$), one of the major impurities in ore. Limestone and silica react to produce calcium silicate which floats to the top of the molten iron. When it cools and solidifies, the calcium silicate forms slag.

## *READING CRITICALLY*
Why is coke a necessary ingredient in making pig iron?

Coke is needed to react with oxygen to make carbon monoxide. This in turn reacts with iron ore to separate the ore into iron and carbon dioxide.

## 8.5 Iron and Steel

Iron is an element that can be separated from the ore hematite (HEE muh tyt). Hematite is an oxide of iron. Iron is separated from its ore in a huge furnace called a *blast furnace*. A mixture of the ore, coke, and limestone is put into the top of the blast furnace, as shown in Figure 8–8. Hot air is forced into the furnace near the bottom. Inside the furnace the coke reacts with oxygen from the air to form carbon monoxide. The carbon monoxide reacts with the iron ore, producing iron and carbon dioxide. Since temperatures inside a blast furnace are more than 1500°C, the iron is liquid, or molten.

The molten iron runs out the bottom of the furnace into open containers. These containers are shaped like the troughs from which pigs feed. For this reason, iron from a blast furnace is called *pig iron*. Pig iron contains 3 to 4 percent carbon in addition to a number of other impurities. Because of its high carbon content, pig iron is brittle. Therefore, pig iron cannot withstand a great deal of stress or pressure.

**Steel** is purified iron with only 0.5–1.5 percent of carbon. Steel beams are used to construct large buildings and other structures. Steel is also used to make machinery, automobiles, and many other items. What things can you think of that are made of steel?

Answers will vary but may include light poles, pots, and bicycles.

Different kinds of steel can be made by varying the amounts of other chemicals mixed with the iron in the steel. For example, stainless steel is a mixture of iron with 13–27 percent chromium and 1 percent carbon. Because is it very resistant to corrosion, stainless steel is often used to make sinks, pots, pans, and surgical instruments.

## 8.6 Alloys

A mixture of two or more metals, or of a metal and a nonmetal, is called an **alloy.** Steel is an example of an alloy because it is a mixture of iron, other metals, and carbon.

Copper and tin are melted together to make another alloy called *bronze*. Bronze has properties that are quite different from either copper or tin. For example, bronze is much harder than either copper or tin. Another advantage of bronze is that it does not rust easily.

Although gold found in nature is pure, the gold jewelry that you may be wearing is not pure gold, but an alloy. Because pure gold is so soft that it can be molded in your hands, it is usually mixed with other metals, such as silver or nickel, to make it harder. Mixing gold may change its color. Yellow gold is an alloy of gold and copper. White gold is made of gold and silver.

The percent of gold in an alloy is measured in *karats*. Pure gold is 24 karat. A 14-karat gold necklace is made of 14 parts gold and 10 parts alloy. What percentage of that necklace is gold? Why would you expect to pay more for an 18-karat necklace than a 14-karat necklace?

Alloys play an important part in advanced technologies, such as jet aviation. Scientists are experimenting with alloys that perform well under the heat and strain inside a jet engine. Better alloys will result in improved jet performance and safety. because it contains a higher percentage of gold

**Figure 8–9.** This statue is made of bronze, an alloy of chiefly copper and tin. Bronze turns green due to the properties of copper. However, this film of green protects the alloy from further corrosion.

Emphasize the importance of alloys in modern technology. Metals are seldom used in the pure state.

**Figure 8–10.** This sheet of gold leaf is thin and may look very fragile; but gold is very resistant to weathering.

### Observing Metal Fatigue

Find a piece of coat hanger or other metal wire. Create "metal fatigue" in the wire by bending it several times in the same spot. What do you think happens to the molecules in the wire to make it soft?

| TABLE 8–2 | SOME COMMON ALLOYS | | |
|---|---|---|---|
| **Alloy** | **Elements** | **Composition** | **Uses** |
| Stainless steel | Iron (Fe)<br>Chromium (Cr)<br>Nickel (Ni)<br>Carbon (C) | 80.0%<br>18.0%<br>1.6%<br>0.4% | Tableware,<br>sink tops |
| Brass | Copper (Cu)<br>Zinc (Zn) | 67.0%<br>33.0% | Hardware,<br>lamps |
| Pewter | Tin (Sn)<br>Copper (Cu)<br>Bismuth (Bi)<br>Lead (Pb) | 85.0%<br>7.8%<br>6.0%<br>1.2% | Cups, mugs,<br>utensils |
| Sterling silver | Silver (Ag)<br>Copper (Cu) | 92.5%<br>7.5% | Tableware,<br>jewelry |
| Plumber's solder | Lead (Pb)<br>Tin (Sn) | 67.0%<br>33.0% | Soldering |

**Figure 8–11.** The metal in this bridge experienced extreme fatigue to the point at which the metal supports snapped and the bridge fell into the water.

1. Metallurgy is the science of separating metal from ore.
2. Iron is separated in a blast furnace that heats the ore with coke and limestone. The chemical reactions cause pure iron to separate out.
3. Carbon makes the iron hard but also very brittle.
4. Iron is an element, steel is an alloy—a mixture of iron with other metallic and non-metallic elements.
5. Bronze, steel, and gold are some examples of alloys. Their uses vary, but they are largely used in industry because of their high resistance to heat and stress.
6. Gold and silver are attractive in color; they do not corrode; they are both very malleable and ductile so they can be easily fashioned into any desired shape.

The metal fans, or turbines, inside a jet engine spin at very high speeds. The force of the spinning blades actually causes the turbine blades to stretch out of shape. Scientists have created an alloy that resists this stretching. Nickel and aluminum are melted together at high temperatures. Then the alloy is chilled so that the atoms crystallize like snowflakes. The alloy is then heated again to "age" it. The result is an alloy that actually gets stronger as it gets hotter.

Another problem in jet engines is created by *metal fatigue* (fah TEEG). Metal engine parts get "tired" because jet engines are heated and cooled rapidly each time the jet takes off and lands. Scientists have learned that alloys with special kinds of structures resist fatigue. These alloys help prevent jet engine failure due to metal fatigue. The use of advanced alloys such as these is making air travel safer.

## Section Review

1. What is metallurgy?
2. Describe how iron is separated from its ore to make pig iron.
3. Why is it important to remove carbon impurities from pig iron?
4. What is the difference between iron and steel?
5. List some common alloys and explain their uses.
6. THINKING CRITICALLY  Why are gold and silver the metals most often used for jewelry and coins?

# SKILL ACTIVITY     Solving Problems

**INTRODUCTION** _____ A neat, orderly approach to solving math problems reduces errors and makes it easier to check your work. The method described below, which is used throughout this textbook, is a good way to solve math problems.

**PROCEDURE** _____ 
1. The first step in solving a problem is to write down the information and the equation that relates the information. For example, suppose you want to find the area of a rectangular room that is 8 m long and 5 m wide. Write the equation for the area of a rectangle, $A = l \times w$, where $A$ is the perimeter, $l$ is the length, and $w$ is the width.
2. The next step in solving an equation is to fill in the numbers, keeping all units. The units are an important way of checking your problem. Fill in $l = 8$ m and $w = 5$ m, so that the equation reads $A = 8$ m $\times$ 5 m.
3. The last step in solving an equation is to complete the math. When you solve this equation, your answer should be $A = 40$ m$^2$.

**APPLICATION** _____ You own a company that puts ceramic tile down. Your company charges \$8/m$^2$ for tiling. Fill in the estimate form to arrive at the cost of tiling a floor. Follow the steps outlined in the procedure to write a correct estimate that you could give to your customer. Then answer the questions that follow.

---

### C & C CONSTRUCTION CO.
**Estimate for Floor Tiling**

Customer: Mr. Arthur Faulkner     Estimate Preparer: Liz Heeter

Address: Andy Lane     Date: June 6

Hoe Gunn, Arizona

Job Description: Floor is 12 m by 14 m.

Total area: 168 m$^2$

---

1. After you have determined the total area of the floor, calculate the cost of the job, if each m$^2$ costs \$8. \$1,344
2. What other companies can you think of that would need estimates of area in order to know what to charge the customer? carpeting, painting, wall papering, custom draperies

# Chemical Applications

## SECTION OBJECTIVES

- **Describe** the properties of glass, ceramics, and composites and **list** two uses for each.
- **Discuss** how cars of the future will be better due to advanced materials.
- **Summarize** the purpose and importance of chemical fertilizers.

## 8.7 Glass

One of the most easily recognizable sounds is that of breaking glass. Although it may be hard to realize, glass is actually one of the strongest compounds known. It is amazing that a substance as fragile as glass can withstand the heat of lasers and the pressure of the ocean's depths.

Commercial glass is made from silicon dioxide, or *silica*. Flint, opal, and quartz are all forms of silica. Quartz sand is the material most often used to make glass. When quartz sand is heated to about 1610°C, it melts to form a colorless, sticky liquid. If this liquid is cooled rapidly, the liquid solidifies to a clear, colorless glass called *quartz glass*.

Many different substances can be added to quartz to make glass with different physical properties. Window glass is a mixture of silica and oxides of sodium and calcium. Colored glass is made by mixing different metals with the silica.

The structure of solids, including all metals, is based on *crystals*. In crystals, which are discussed in Chapter 15, the atoms are arranged in a particular order. However, glass atoms do not form crystals. When glass hardens, the atoms are not in a fixed pattern.

One of the most exciting new technologies involving glass is fiber optics. Fiber optics move information such as phone calls and computer data over a light wave instead of an electric wave. **Optical fibers,** which are made of ultra-thin rods of glass, are used to move a beam of laser light. Light moves through an optical fiber much faster than electricity can move through a metal wire. A strand of hair-thin optical fiber can carry 1000 times more information than a metal wire.

Communication by glass has a number of advantages. A telephone signal sent through a metal wire or

**Figure 8–12.** Medieval artisans were masters in the use of stained glass, as illustrated in this window from the cathedral in Chartres, France.

Like any viscous fluid, sheets of glass flow slowly. This explains why glass windows in old colonial homes are thicker at the bottom than at the top.

Another important chemical used by farmers to help plants grow is *slaked lime*. Slaked lime is made from limestone—a common rock. To make slaked lime, the limestone is heated to temperatures between 1200°C and 1300°C. At these temperatures, the limestone breaks down to form calcium oxide or *quicklime*. When added to water, quicklime will form slaked lime.

## Section Review

1. What is the difference between a glass and a ceramic?
2. What advantage do glass telephone lines have over metal wire?
3. List two uses of ceramics.
4. Explain why chemical fertilizers are important to farming.
5. THINKING CRITICALLY Describe some ways in which cars in the year 2000 might be better than the cars of today.

1. Commercial glass is made from quartz (silca) sand. A ceramic is any material made from clay.
2. Light moves faster through glass than electricity does through metal. Glass fibers can carry more information than metal.
3. Answers will vary, but may include porcelain, china, reactor shields, and spark plugs.
4. Fertilizers put all the nutrients back in the soil so that it can continue to be farmed.
5. Answers will vary.

# CAREER

## Automobile Assembly-Line Worker

**DESCRIPTION** An automobile assembly-line worker carries out one step in the production of automobiles or other vehicles. Some assembly-line workers, known as *precision assemblers,* must use specifications and follow detailed instructions, often relying on their own judgment to complete a task. New manufacturing technology, including the use of chemistry, robots, and computers, is changing the way some automobile assembly-line jobs are done.

**REQUIREMENTS** Many assembly-line jobs require only on-the-job training. For precision-assembly jobs, an employer may require that an applicant have a technical-school diploma or equivalent experience received in the military.

**INFORMATION** United Auto Workers, 8000 East Jefferson, Detroit, MI 48214

# INVESTIGATION 8: Making a Blueprint

*How can you use a chemical reaction to make a blueprint?*

## PURPOSE

In this investigation you will make a blueprint. Blueprints can be used to show how a building is to be constructed. Blueprints are made by chemical reactions. This investigation shows that a chemical reaction using light can be used to record an image. Photography is another very common example of using a chemical reaction involving light to record an image.

## MATERIALS

2 beakers (100 or 250 mL)
4.0 g of potassium ferricyanide
5.0 g of iron(III) ammonium citrate
2 stirring rods
graduate (50 mL)
2 or 3 paper towels
1 piece notebook paper

## PROCEDURE

1. **CAUTION: Put on safety goggles, rubber gloves, and a laboratory apron.** Place the 4.0 g of potassium ferricyanide in a clean beaker. Add 25 mL of water. Stir gently until the potassium ferricyanide has dissolved. Set this beaker aside until step 3.

2. Place the 5.0 g of iron(III) ammonium citrate in another beaker. Add 25 mL of water. Stir gently until the iron(III) ammonium citrate has dissolved.

3. In a location away from direct lighting, such as in a closet or under a desk, add the solution made in step 2 to the solution made in step 1 above.

4. Using a paper towel, soak up some of the mixture made in step 3. Using the soaked paper towel as a brush, coat a piece of paper with the solution.

5. Place the coated piece of paper in a dark area, such as inside a desk drawer, until it is dry.

6. When the paper is dry, place the paper on a flat surface under the room lights. Place one or more objects, such as coins or paper clips, on the paper. Leave the paper with the objects exposed to the light for about 5 minutes.

7. At the end of the 5 minutes, remove the objects from the paper. Wash the exposed paper with cool water to remove any leftover chemicals.

8. Wash your hands to remove any chemicals.

9. Set the paper aside to dry.

## RESULTS AND CONCLUSIONS

1. When the paper is dry, record your observations of the images produced. Attach your paper to your laboratory report.

2. How is the image on your blueprint helpful? gives precise images of objects

3. What is not shown by the image on your blueprint? color

4. Why should you combine the two solutions in a location removed from direct light? Light would cause a chemical reaction of the solutions causing them not to expose the paper.

## APPLICATIONS

1. Why are blueprints sometimes used to show the construction plans of buildings? show measurements and correct positions

2. What other techniques use chemicals and light to produce images? photographs and films

3. Would it be possible to make an image of a glass object using the technique you just performed? No, because light would pass through the glass and expose the paper.

## Summary

1. Coal, petroleum, and natural gas are fossil fuels found in the earth. **(8.1)**

2. Refineries process crude oil and natural gas into many different useful products such as gasoline. **(8.2)**

3. Organic molecules can be joined together chemically to make giant molecules called polymers. Plastics, synthetic fibers, and rubber are all polymers. **(8.3)**

4. Metals are extracted from ores by chemical processes. The science of separating a metal from its ore and preparing it for use is called metallurgy. **(8.4)**

5. Iron is extracted from iron ore in a blast furnace. Steel is a specially prepared mixture of purified iron with other metals and nonmetals dissolved in it. **(8.5)**

6. Mixtures of two or more metals, or of metals and nonmetals, are called alloys. **(8.6)**

7. Glass is made from quartz sand. Glass has no internal crystal structure. Glass softens when heated and can be formed or blown into different shapes. **(8.7)**

8. A ceramic is any object made from clay. Ceramics are good insulators. **(8.8)**

9. A composite is a combination of two or more different materials. Scientists can combine materials to make a new material with all the advantages of the old materials. **(8.9)**

10. Chemical fertilizers such as ammonia, phosphate, potash, and lime can now be made in large quantities to help farmers grow better and larger crops. **(8.10)**

## Science Terms

On a separate sheet of paper, define each term in a sentence.

| | | | |
|---|---|---|---|
| alloy **(155)** | fertilizer **(162)** | optical fiber **(158)** | polymer **(150)** |
| ceramic **(160)** | fossil fuel **(147)** | ore **(153)** | rubber **(152)** |
| coal **(147)** | metallurgy **(153)** | petroleum **(148)** | steel **(154)** |
| composite **(161)** | natural gas **(148)** | plastic **(150)** | synthetic fiber **(151)** |

## Modified True-False

On a separate sheet of paper, mark each true statement *TRUE* and each false statement *FALSE*. If false, change the underlined term to make the statement true.

1. Fossil fuels are complex mixtures found underground. T

2. In an oil refinery, crude oil is separated into natural gas. T

3. Iron is extracted from limestone in a blast furnace. F, hematite

4. The science of separating a metal from its ore and preparing it for use is called metallurgy. T

5. Nylon and polyester are both polymers. T

6. Substances formed by dissolving one metal in another are called alloys. T

7. Pure gold is 18 karat. F, 24 karat

8. Any material made from clay is called potash. F, ceramic

9. Slaked lime is used as a food. F, fertilizer

10. Gold is mixed with copper to make white gold. F, silver

*(continues)*

# CHAPTER REVIEW

## Multiple Choice

On a separate sheet of paper, write the letter of the term that best answers the question or completes the statement.

1. Which of the following is NOT a fossil fuel?
   a. coal
   b. crude oil
   c. natural gas
   d. corn oil

2. Ultra-thin rods of glass used to move a beam of light are
   a. composites.
   b. optical fibers.
   c. polyurethane.
   d. fiberglass.

3. Which of the following is NOT a polymer?
   a. nylon
   b. polyester
   c. ethylene
   d. polyethylene

4. A naturally occurring material from which a metal can be extracted is called
   a. an alloy.
   b. an ingot.
   c. an ore.
   d. a karat.

5. Which of the following is a composite?
   a. porcelain
   b. fiberglass
   c. steel
   d. nylon

6. A process for joining a large number of organic molecules is called
   a. fertilization.
   b. fixation.
   c. polymerization.
   d. vulcanization.

7. Which of the following is an alloy?
   a. iron
   b. aluminum
   c. magnesium
   d. steel

8. Which of the following is a fertilizer?
   a. sodium chloride
   b. potassium carbonate
   c. calcium hydroxide
   d. silicon dioxide

9. Steel is an alloy of carbon and
   a. iron.
   b. tin.
   c. silver.
   d. lead.

10. When metals are rapidly heated and rapidly cooled, they may experience
    a. metal fatigue.
    b. polymerization.
    c. vulcanization.
    d. cracking.

11. A type of synthetic rubber used for gasoline hoses is
    a. nylon.
    b. neoprene.
    c. polyester.
    d. polyurethane.

12. Unlike other solids, glass atoms do not form
    a. molecules.
    b. fibers.
    c. crystals.
    d. polymers.

## Completion

On a separate sheet of paper, complete each statement by supplying the correct term.

1. Crude oil is another name for petroleum.

2. Coal is a solid formed from the remains of plants.

3. Nitrogen and hydrogen are combined at high pressures and temperatures to form ammonia.

4. In an oil refinery, crude oil is separated into different components called petrochemicals.

5. A process used to make rubber more elastic and less sticky is known as vulcanization.

6. At the high temperatures inside a blast furnace, iron ore reacts with oxygen to produce molten iron.

7. Coal is found underground in layers called beds or seams.

8. Porcelain is made from white clay, feldspar, and silica.

9. Any substance that helps plants grow is called a fertilizer.

10. When limestone is heated, it breaks down to form quicklime.

## Writing Critically Answers: see page T75.

1. Describe how gasoline is made from crude oil in an oil refinery.
2. Explain how a blast furnace is used to extract molten iron from iron ore.
3. Describe how polymers can be used in medicine as well as in everyday life.
4. **CHALLENGE** Compare the materials in a car made in the 1950s with those made in the 1980s.

## Skill Reinforcement

The Skill Activity on page 157 describes how to solve math problems. Use the method described in the Skill Activity to solve the following problem. If you wanted to stake out a mining area 800 m long and 200 m wide, how much would you have to pay if the land cost $0.50/m$^2$? $900

## Research Ideas

1. Find out what metals are important for modern technology. In what countries of the world are these metals found?
2. What chemical industries are active in your area? Find out why these industries are located in your neighborhood. Also find out what kinds of materials are manufactured by these companies and the processes involved in the manufacture.
3. If you live in a rural area, find out what materials farmers are using for chemical fertilizers. When do they apply the fertilizers to the soil? Where are the fertilizers made?
4. **CHALLENGE** Find out how optical fibers are made from glass. How are optical fibers used to transmit communications information? What advantages do optical fibers have over copper wires for transmitting signals? Find out what safety precautions must be taken in the manufacturing of their products? Why?

## For Further Reading

Bylinsky, Gene. "Where the U.S. Stands. (Special Report: The High-Tech Race)" *Fortune* (October 13, 1986). This comprehensive report discusses the latest developments in technology both in the United States and other countries.

Burkig, Valerie C. *Photonics: The New Science of Light.* Hillside, N.J.: Enslow, 1986. This short book gives an excellent overview of modern optical science and technology. The application of optical science to communication, computing, material processing, and medicine is clearly explained.

Corrick, James A. *Recent Revolutions in Chemistry.* New York: Franklin Watts Inc., 1986. This reference book provides an exciting and wide-ranging account of the practical applications of chemistry in modern technology.

Cotterill, R. *The Cambridge Guide to the Material World.* New York: Cambridge University Press, 1985. This is a beautifully illustrated and comprehensive description of many different types of materials, including metals, polymers, ceramics, and glass, as well as all the naturally occurring minerals.

# BIOENGINEERED BODIES

Artificial hearts and limbs. Joints made of plastic and metal. And that's not all. Somebody somewhere is working on a replacement for nearly every part of the body.

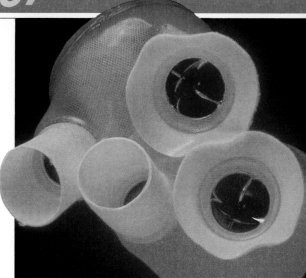

## Replacing Broken Hearts

Biomedical engineers have developed substitutes for many human parts. In doing so, they have had to use an extensive knowledge of chemistry. Knowing how certain elements and compounds combine has enabled these engineers to develop new substances for use in these replacement parts. In addition, biomedical engineers have used many new technologies, including computers, robotics, and electronics.

Probably the most spectacular product of biomedical engineering is the artificial heart. In 1982, the first artificial heart was implanted in a man whose own heart was failing. Two polyurethane pumps replaced the patient's right and left ventricles, or lower chambers of the heart. The heart was powered by an air compressor. Hoses connected the compressor with the pumps in the patient's chest. The device gave the patient several additional months of life, and has since been tested on others.

## Rearming

Until recent years, amputees resigned themselves to lives of restricted activity. Now, however, artificial arms have been developed that actually respond to messages from the brain, just as flesh-and-blood arms and legs do.

The artificial arm was developed by borrowing technology from robotics. The artificial arm is controlled by a microprocessor. Electrodes attached to muscles on the remnants of the amputee's arm send electrical signals down wires to motors that move the arm and hand.

Although not bionic, this arm can lift some heavy loads.

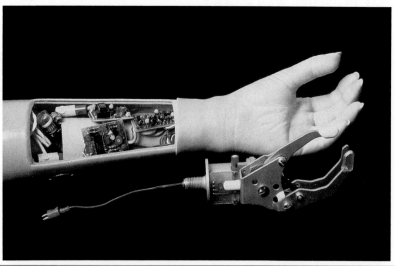

This artificial arm performs basic hand and arm movements. The hand opens and closes. The elbow bends and straightens. The wrist rotates clockwise and counterclockwise. The artificial limb is strong enough to allow the patient to perform even heavy manual labor.

## The Electrical Bypass

Spinal cord injuries often result in paralysis. When the cord is severed, messages from the brain can no longer reach the rest of the body.

Developments in computers and electronics are giving paralyzed patients a chance to move again. Electrodes implanted in unparalyzed muscles above the spinal-cord injury send signals to a computer. The computer analyzes the signals and sends messages to a device that electrically stimulates target muscles below the injury.

The system has allowed people who are paralyzed below

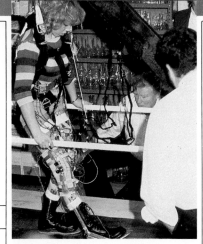

Walking with the aid of a computer.

the neck to grasp objects. The system has also allowed people who are paralyzed below the waist to take a few halting steps. Researchers are working on simple, portable systems that will permit paralyzed patients to live near-normal lives.

## All New Parts

People who have lost the use of joints because of disease or

injury can get replacements made of plastic and stainless steel. A new alloy made with the element titanium will soon take the place of metal and plastic in these artificial joints. This alloy has tiny spaces into which bone can grow. As bone grows into the spaces, a firm bond is created with the bones on both sides of the joint.

Biomedical engineers are working on a computer system that will custom design artificial joints for patients, using X-ray information and a 3-D software program.

Artificial blood, skin, and tendons are now in use. Researchers are working on an artificial pancreas, kidney, and lung. Electronic systems have been used experimentally to help the blind see and the deaf hear. The time may come when bioengineering can replace any part of the body.

Scientists use computers to design new body parts.

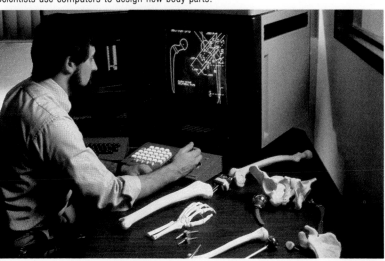

Computers imitate nature.

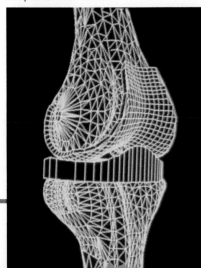

# 3

# How Things Work

Photograph right: the Brooklyn Bridge

Have you ever thought about what makes the world around you work in certain unchanging ways? *Physics* is the science that deals with how things work. The study of physics involves the properties, changes, and interactions of matter with energy. The principles of physics explain how everything works—from a light bulb to the most powerful supercomputer.

CHAPTER

**9**

For additional information,
see pages T78–T79.

# Motion

Using her senses of balance and timing, the
windsurfer in the photograph below captures the
force of the wind in the sail of her board to move
gracefully over the water. Many forces make it
possible for windsurfers to remain in motion.

# Motion in a Straight Line

**SECTION OBJECTIVES**

- **Define** *frame of reference*, *speed*, *velocity*, and *acceleration*.
- **Calculate** the average speed of an object.
- **Determine** the acceleration of an object.

Photograph left: windsurfing—Hawaii

NEW TERMS IN THIS SECTION
motion
distance
frame of reference
speed
average speed
instantaneous speed
velocity
acceleration

## 9.1 Distance

Walking along a path, riding in a car, and flying in an airplane are all examples of motion. **Motion** occurs when an object changes its position relative to its surroundings. The **distance** an object travels is the space between two points. Distance is measured in units of length, such as meters.

You have probably been in a car stopped at a traffic light and noticed that the car next to you was moving forward. But was it really? Maybe your car was moving backward. Unless you change your frame of reference, you cannot be sure which car is moving. A **frame of reference**—your car in this case—is the background against which motion is observed and measured. The most common frame of reference is the earth. How could you have changed your frame of reference in order to be sure which car was moving?

Other objects can be used as reference points for describing motion. Astronomers use distant stars as a frame of reference to study the motion of planets and comets. Passengers on a plane flying at a high speed are not aware of their motion because the inside of the plane is their frame of reference.

### ACTIVITY

**Determining a Frame of Reference**

Observe a friend tossing a ball in the air while running and catching it. Describe the motion of the ball using your friend as a frame of reference and then using yourself as a frame of reference.

Answers may include getting out of the car and looking at something else other than either car.

## 9.2 Speed

The **speed** of an object is the distance the object travels in a given time. Sometimes the speed of an object is constant—it does not change. For example, using the cruise-control device found on some cars keeps the speed nearly constant. However, the speed of most objects does not usually remain constant. Since most objects do not travel at a constant speed, the term *speed* usually means average speed. An object's **average speed** is the total distance traveled divided by the time it takes to cover that distance. The equation for average speed ($s$) is

$$\text{average speed} = \frac{\text{distance}}{\text{time}}$$

$$s = \frac{d}{t}$$

In this equation, $d$ is the distance and $t$ is the time. The metric unit of speed is meters per second (m/s).

**Example:** Determine the average speed ($s$) of a runner who runs 100 m in 20 s.

**Solution:**
- *Write* the equation for average speed.

$$\text{average speed} = \frac{\text{distance}}{\text{time}}$$

$$s = \frac{d}{t}$$

- *Substitute* the values for $d$ and $t$ in the equation.

$$s = \frac{100 \text{ m}}{20 \text{ s}}$$

- *Solve* by dividing.

$$s = 5 \text{ m/s}$$

**Figure 9–1.** Police officers use radar guns to measure the instantaneous speed of cars as they approach.

## 9.5 Newton's Second Law of Motion

The relationship between force, mass, and acceleration is explained by Newton's *second law of motion*. Newton's second law states that the acceleration of an object depends upon the net force acting on it and the mass of the object. The **net force** is the sum of the forces acting on an object. In the metric system, the unit by which force is measured is a newton (N). A newton is the force required to give a 1-kg object an acceleration of one meter per second squared, or $kg \cdot m/s^2$. Holding a small apple in your hand will give you an idea of the force of one newton. The equation for Newton's second law is

$$\text{net force} = \text{mass} \times \text{acceleration}$$
$$F = m \times a$$

In this equation, $F$ is the net force, $m$ is the mass, and $a$ is the acceleration.

For a given mass, the greater the force, the greater the acceleration. The greater the mass of an object, the greater the force required to accelerate it. For instance, a racehorse has a larger mass than a dog. Therefore, the horse must exert a greater force than the dog to accelerate at the same rate.

You may wish to tell the students that an object's mass can be thought of as how much inertia it has. A force changes matter's motion; it accelerates matter. Therefore, mass can be thought of as the magnitude of the force divided by the accerlation.

**Figure 9–6.** The horse requires a much greater force to accelerate at the same rate as the greyhound.

**Example:** A greyhound can accelerate up to 2 m/s². Calculate the force needed to give a 30-kg dog this acceleration.

**Solution:**
- *Write* the equation for Newton's second law.

  force = mass × acceleration
  $$F = m \times a$$

- *Substitute* the values for $m$ and $a$ in the equation.

  $$F = 30 \text{ kg} \times 2 \text{ m/s}^2$$

- *Solve* by multiplying.

  $$F = 30 \text{ kg} \times 2 \text{ m/s}^2$$
  $$F = 60 \text{ kg} \cdot \text{m/s}^2 = 60 \text{ N}$$

Now use the preceding example to calculate the force needed to give a 450-kg racehorse the same acceleration as the dog. You should find that the force required to accelerate the horse in Figure 9–6 is much greater than that for the dog. F = 450 kg × 2m/s²
F = 900 kg · m/s² = 900 N

## 9.6 Free Fall

When gravity is the only force acting on a falling object, the object is said to be in a state of **free fall**. Objects falling in the earth's atmosphere are not truly in a state of free fall. This is because a second force, air resistance, is acting on them. In the absence of air resistance, however, all freely falling objects have the same acceleration,

Two or more forces can act on an object without producing an acceleration. If the forces cancel each other out, the net force and the acceleration are equal to zero.

These sky divers are not experiencing free fall because they are encountering air resistance.

**Figure 9–7.** Explain why these sky divers are not really experiencing free fall.

regardless of their mass. This acceleration is called the **acceleration due to gravity** and is represented by the letter *g*.

To illustrate acceleration due to gravity, imagine dropping a bowling ball and a softball from the top of the World Trade Center in New York City. Which do you think would fall faster? Since the softball has a much smaller mass, it would seem that it would accelerate slower than the bowling ball. However, even though the bowling ball has a greater weight and mass than the softball, both balls would accelerate at the same rate. Newton's second law of motion helps explain why.

Remember that the acceleration of an object depends on the object's mass and on the net force acting on the object. In free fall, gravity is the only force acting on an object. Even though the masses of the bowling ball and softball are different, so is the force of gravity acting on each object. While the bowling ball is more massive than the softball, the force of gravity on the bowling ball is also greater. In other words, the ratio of the force of gravity on an object to its mass will always be the same. Therefore, the bowling ball and the softball would both accelerate at the same rate if there was no air resistance.

Near the earth's surface, the acceleration due to gravity is 9.8 m/s²; on the moon it is 1.6 m/s². On the moon, a feather and a hammer will accelerate at the same rate because there is no air resistance.

**Figure 9–8.** Astronauts have to adapt to weightlessness when in space.

A freely falling object is **weightless.** Weightlessness occurs when there are no forces supporting an object. You experience weightlessness whenever you jump off a diving board or step off a curb. A freely falling object is weightless only to the observer falling with the object. For instance, when you jump off a diving board, you feel as if you have no weight. To your friend in the water below, though, you certainly do have weight. Your friend sees you accelerating toward the water and swims out of the way.

**ACTIVITY**

**Testing Weightlessness**

Place two books on your desk. Put a sheet of paper between them with one end of the paper showing. Pull the paper out from between the books. Repeat the experiment, but this time remove the paper while a classmate drops the books from a small distance above your desk. Was it easier removing the paper the first time or the second time? Why?

the second time the books were weightless in relation to the paper

# COMPUTER APPLICATION

## Accelerated Motion

### 1. DESCRIPTION

This program shows the motion of an accelerated object. To change the acceleration, you can change the force, the mass, or both. Follow the instructions when you RUN the program.

### 2. PROGRAM

Input the following program. Key the computer to run the program. If the program does not run, check to make sure you have input correctly. If the program runs correctly, go on to steps 3 and 4.

### 3. HELPFUL HINTS

Remember to press ⟨RETURN⟩ after each input. An answer of N to both mass change and force change ends the program.

### 4. GOING FURTHER

- Change the program so that increasing the force doubles the acceleration.
- Decrease the force so that the acceleration is cut in half.
- If the mass is changed, what must be done to double the acceleration? to cut it in half?

```
100   HOME : PRINT "WATCH THE STAR ACCELERATE."
110   LET V = 5
120   PRINT : LET A = 10
130   FOR T = 1 TO 20
140   LET S = 0.5 * A * T * T / 10

150   ON (S > 39) GOTO 180: IF S < 1 THEN S = 1
160   VTAB V: HTAB S: PRINT "*";
170   FOR D = 1 TO 300: NEXT D
180   NEXT T
190   PRINT : LET V = V + 1: IF V = 13 THEN LET V = 5

200   VTAB 15: PRINT "CHANGE THE MASS? (TYPE Y OR N)"
210   INPUT M$
220   IF M$ = "N" THEN 270
230   PRINT "+ FOR MORE, - FOR LESS"
240   INPUT C$

250   IF C$ = "+" THEN LET A = A - 1
260   IF C$ = "-" THEN LET A = A + 1
270   PRINT "CHANGE THE FORCE? (TYPE Y OR N)"
280   INPUT F$
290   IF F$ = "Y" THEN 320

300   IF F$ = "N" AND M$ = "N" THEN END
310   GOTO 360
320   PRINT "+ FOR MORE, - FOR LESS"
330   INPUT C$
340   IF C$ = "+" THEN LET A = A + 1

350   IF C$ = "-" THEN LET A = A - 1
360   GOTO 130
999   END
```

Action-reaction forces always come in pairs and act on different objects.

# 9.7 Newton's Third Law of Motion

Push on your desk with your hand. Do you feel the desk pushing back on you? Now push a little harder. Does the desk push back even more? Whenever you push or pull on something, it will exert an equal but opposite force on you. This principle action-reaction is Newton's *third law of motion*. Newton's third law states that for every action there is an equal but opposite reaction. According to the third law, whenever one object exerts a force on a second object, the second object exerts an equal but opposite force on the first one.

If the action-reaction forces are equal but opposite, it might seem that the two forces should cancel each other out. This does not happen, because the forces are acting on different objects. For instance, when you use a mop to clean a floor, you are exerting a force on the mop. Your push moves it forward. At the same time, the mop is exerting an equal but opposite force on you and pushes you backward. Unlike the mop, however, you can resist the force because of your greater mass. Why does it hurt when you kick a massive object such as a large rock?

The rock has a large force due to its large mass.

# 9.8 Momentum

In addition to its velocity, a moving object also has momentum (moh MEHN tuhm). **Momentum** is equal to an object's mass multiplied by its velocity.

Momentum increases with an increase in mass or speed or both. A freight train traveling at 88 km/h has

*READING CRITICALLY*
Use the law of action and reaction to explain how a fish swims.

Fish push against water, water pushes against the fish.

Blow up a balloon. Let go of the open end. Use Newton's terms of action/reaction to describe what happens. Ask the students to explain how this relates to rocket propulsion. (Propulsion fuel pushes against the ground and the ground pushes back. The greater mass of the earth gets a smaller acceleration from the same amount of force as the rocket, so small that the earth does not move. The rocket lifts off due to its small mass and large acceleration.)

**Figure 9–9.** The woman's hand and the blocks are exerting equal pressure.

**SCIENCE FACT**
The human hand can easily withstand forces exceeding 25,000 N that often result from a karate chop.

more momentum than a motorcycle moving at the same speed. The train's larger mass gives it more momentum. A bullet traveling at a high speed has more momentum than a slowly moving arrow. Although the bullet has less mass than the arrow, its speed is much greater, so its momentum is greater.

The equation for momentum ($p$) is

$$momentum = mass \times velocity$$
$$p = m \times v$$

In this equation, $p$ is momentum, $m$ is mass, and $v$ is velocity. The unit of momentum is kg · m/s.

**Example:** Determine the momentum of a 2000-kg car moving with a velocity of 20 m/s.

**Solution:** • *Write* the equation for the object's momentum.

$$momentum = mass \times velocity$$
$$p = m \times v$$

• *Substitute* the values for $m$ and $v$ in the equation.

$$p = 2000 \text{ kg} \times 20 \text{ m/s}$$

• *Solve* by multiplying.

$$p = 40,000 \text{ kg} \cdot \text{m/s}$$

What happens to an object's momentum in a collision? If an object loses its momentum in a collision, the object with which it collides gains momentum. When a golf club strikes a golf ball, the golf club loses momentum and slows down. The golf ball gains momentum equal to that lost by the golf club and speeds up.

Momentum is always conserved. That is, the momentum of the first object is maintained and passed on to the second object. This basic principle is called the **law of conservation of momentum**. The law of conservation of momentum states that *when two or more objects collide, the total momentum of the objects is the same after the collision as it was before the collision.*

Figure 9–10 demonstrates the law of conservation of momentum. If the ball at one end is pulled out and allowed to swing, it falls back and hits the next one in the line. Almost immediately, the ball at the opposite end of the line flies out, as if by magic. The momentum of the first ball has been passed from one ball to the next until it reaches the end ball, which is free to move. What would happen if two balls at one end were pulled out and allowed to swing? Why?

Two balls at the other end would fly out because momentum is conserved.

Relate the relative size of members of the school football team, their positions, and their jobs on the team to momentum, force, mass, and acceleration.

**READING CRITICALLY**
Can a body be at rest and still have momentum? Explain.

No, because 0 velocity means 0 momentum.

In order to change the momentum of an object, a net force must be exerted on it. Both the strength of the net force and the time that net force acts on an object determine the change in momentum. For example, when a tennis player hits a ball, the goal is to give the ball the greatest momentum possible. To do this, the tennis player tries to follow through on his or her swing. Figure 9–11 shows how the follow-through extends the time of contact between the tennis racket and the ball, which increases the momentum of the ball.

**Figure 9–11.** When Chris Evert follows through on her backhand, she maximizes the momentum of the ball.

## Section Review

1. Describe two examples of Newton's first law of motion observed in everyday life.
2. Define inertia.
3. What is the force needed to give a 2-kg object an acceleration of 3 m/s$^2$?
4. Give two examples of free fall on Earth.
5. THINKING CRITICALLY Calculate the momentum of a 70-kg swimmer moving at 2 m/s; a 210-kg shark moving at 1 m/s; and a 1000-kg elephant standing still. Which has the the greatest momentum? Why?

1. Answers will vary but may include books or packages sliding off a car seat when the brakes are suddenly applied, snow sliding off a shovel when the shovel is abruptly brought to rest.
2. the tendency of an object to resist any change in motion
3. F = ma = 2 kg × 3 m/s$^2$ = 6 kg · m/s$^2$ = 6 N
4. riding a rollercoaster, stepping off a curb, jumping off a diving board, jumping on a trampoline (the top of the jump)
5. 140 kg · m/s, 210 kg · m/s, 0 the shark because its combination of weight and velocity results in the highest momentum

# SKILL ACTIVITY  Doing Library Research

## INTRODUCTION

Doing library research involves using books, magazines, encyclopedias, and other resource materials to find information on a subject. To locate information in the library, check the sources discussed below.

## PROCEDURE

Answers to Application
(a) 1969
(b) Neil Armstrong, Edwin Aldrin, Jr., Michael Collins
(c) Apollo 11
(d) second
(e) centripetal force
(f) Saturn
(g) 39,100 km/h
(h) decelerate
(i) third
(j) rocket
(k) *Eagle*
(l) Sea of Tranquility
(m) Neil Armstrong

1. For most assignments, start looking for information in a good encyclopedia. Encyclopedias often give references to other articles within the volume(s) where more information on a topic is available.

2. Use the many other reference books available at the library, such as atlases, almanacs, and specialized reference books.

3. Check the card catalog for books on a specific topic. The card catalog contains information on the title, author, and subject of each book in the library.

4. Use the *Readers' Guide to Periodical Literature* to research current subjects. Articles from 170 magazines are listed alphabetically by subject and by author. Many libraries store reduced copies of these magazines and newspapers on microfilm or microfiche.

## APPLICATION

Read the following passage. Do whatever research is necessary to correct the underlined information. Use any of the resource materials listed in Procedure, as well as the information in this chapter. Write your answers on a separate sheet of paper.

**The Apollo 11 Moon Landing**
On July 16, (a) 1960, (b) John Glenn, Alan Shepard, and John Young blasted off for the moon in the (c) Apollo 1 spacecraft. The force of the rocket engines caused the spacecraft to accelerate as it climbed into Earth orbit. This relationship between force, mass, and acceleration is explained by Newton's (d) first law of motion. Once in orbit, Earth's gravity supplied the (e) momentum needed to keep the spacecraft moving around the earth in a nearly circular path. At the right moment, (f) Atlas rockets were fired. Acting like a slingshot, the rockets hurled Apollo toward the moon at a speed of about (g) 200,000 km/h.

As Apollo traveled farther from the earth, the earth's gravity caused the spacecraft to (h) accelerate.

As Apollo neared the moon, rockets were fired to slow the spacecraft, sending it into lunar orbit. The action of the rocket gases and the reaction of the spacecraft are explained by Newton's (i) second law of motion.

A special lunar module called the (j) Hawk was lowered to the surface of the moon. It landed on a rocky plain called (k) the Sea of Storms. On July 20, 1969, astronaut (l) Michael Collins became the first human to step onto the moon.

# Motion Along a Curved Path

## SECTION OBJECTIVES

- **Identify** the basic characteristics of projectile motion.
- **Define** *trajectory*.
- **List** three factors that determine the amount of centripetal force needed to keep an object moving in a circle.

NEW TERMS IN THIS SECTION
projectile motion
trajectory
uniform circular motion
centripetal force

## 9.9 Projectile Motion

If you have ever watched a football game, then you have seen projectile (proh JEHK tuhl) motion. **Projectile motion** is the motion of an object that moves under the influence of gravity alone. Water sprayed from a squirt gun, a soccer ball kicked into the air, and a satellite orbiting Earth are all examples of projectiles.

A complicated motion such as projectile motion is made more understandable by viewing it as the combination of two independent motions—horizontal motion and vertical motion.

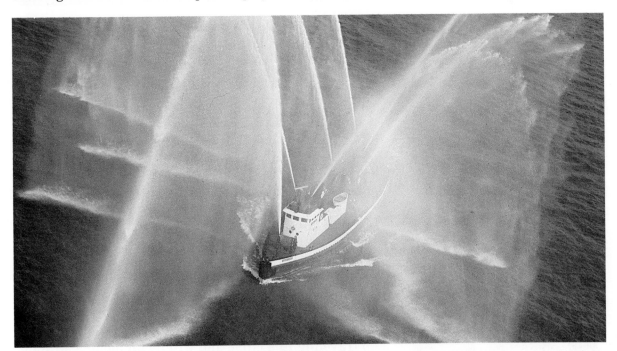

**Figure 9–12.** The streams of water from the hoses on this fireboat are an example of projectile motion.

To better understand projectile motion, imagine you are riding on a skateboard that is traveling at constant speed. You throw a ball straight up into the air. In your frame of reference, you see the ball rise and fall vertically. Your friend, who is watching the motion of the ball from the side of the road, observes something quite different. From your friend's point of view, the ball travels along a curved path. In addition to moving up and down, the ball also moves to the side with a constant velocity.

### READING CRITICALLY

Is there projectile motion in outer space? Why?

There is no projectile motion in outer space because there is no gravity.

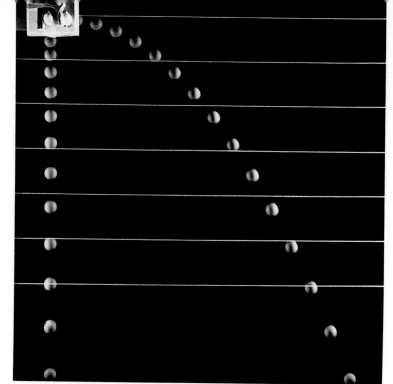

**Figure 9–13.** Difference in trajectory does not affect the time the ball hits the ground.

**Figure 9–14.** Banking the curves in this bicycle track allows the bikers to increase the centripetal force and stay on the track.

Projectile motion is a combination of both an accelerated vertical motion and a constant horizontal motion. The vertical and horizontal motions are independent—that is, they have no effect on each other. The curved path a projectile follows is called its **trajectory** (truh JEHK tuh ree).

The shape of a projectile's trajectory is described in mathematical terms as a parabola.

## 9.10 Circular Motion

A race car moving around a circular track, a child on a merry-go-round, and clothes being dried in a clothes dryer are all examples of objects undergoing uniform circular motion. **Uniform circular motion** refers to motion with constant speed around a circle.

A force is needed to keep an object moving in a circle. The force that causes an object to move in a circle is called the **centripetal** (sehn TRIHP uh tuhl) **force**. If the centripetal force is removed, the object will immediately stop traveling in a circle and will fly off along a straight line.

The amount of force needed to keep an object moving in a curved path depends on the object's mass, its speed, and the sharpness of the curve. If the speed of a bicycle moving through a curve on a track is doubled, the centripetal force required to keep it moving in its curved path is four times as great. If the speed is tripled, the centripetal force needed is nine times as great. To avoid sliding off the track, the cyclists in Figure 9–14 brake

Only one force acts on an object moving in a circle at constant speed: centripetal force. Centrifugal force exists only for an observer who is in an accelerating system but who is considered to be stationary. Therefore, centrifugal force does not actually exist.

sharply before entering the curves. Notice how the curves in Figure 9–14 are sloped upward, or banked. Race tracks and highways are also banked to increase the centripetal force acting on automobiles. <u>How does banking permit drivers to drive around curves more safely?</u> Banking creates centripetal force, causing the car to turn toward the center, thereby staying on the road.

## Section Review

1. State two characteristics of projectile motion.
2. What factors determine the shape of a projectile's trajectory?
3. A flare is dropped from a plane traveling in a straight line at constant speed. Describe the motion of the flare from the pilot's point of view and from the point of view of an observer on the ground.
4. THINKING CRITICALLY Explain why an object traveling in a circle at constant speed is accelerating.
5. THINKING CRITICALLY List two examples of uniform circular motion found in your home.

### ACTIVITY

**Understanding Centripetal Force**

A Hula Hoop® is kept in motion by swinging the hoop around your body and rotating your body in a circular motion. If possible, get a Hula Hoop and try to keep it moving around your body. <u>What forces do you think are involved in keeping the hoop in motion?</u>

centripetal force, your body

1. consists of two independent motions: vertical motion is accelerated and the horizontal motion is constant. The only force acting on a projectile after launch is gravity.
2. the speed of the projectile at launch, the angle at which it is launched, and the effects of air resistance
3. The pilot sees the flare falling straight down beneath the plane. An observer on the ground sees the flare moving in a curved trajectory.
4. because its direction of motion is constantly changing
5. a record turntable and a motor-driven lazy susan in a microwave oven

## CAREER

# Construction-Machinery Operator

**DESCRIPTION** A construction-machinery operator operates machinery capable of exerting enormous forces to move materials around a construction site. Construction-machinery operators run bulldozers, cranes, air compressors, trench excavators, and other heavy equipment.

**REQUIREMENTS** If you plan to be a construction-machinery operator, you should take high-school courses in automobile mechanics. A three-year trainee program, including additional classroom instruction, is usually required before you can become an operator. Some vocational schools may also offer courses that will prepare you for a job as a construction-machinery operator trainee.

**INFORMATION** Associated Builders and Contractors, 729 15th Street, N.W., Washington, DC 20036

# INVESTIGATION 9: Investigating Inertia

*How does the mass and the speed of an object affect inertia?*

## PURPOSE

To find the effect of mass and speed on the inertia of an object

## MATERIALS

string          ruler
set of masses   box

## PROCEDURE

1. Copy Table 1 onto a sheet of paper. Enter all data from this investigation onto your table.
2. Arrange a pendulum so that it will swing close to the surface of a table, as shown in Figure 1.
3. Make a loop at the end of the string so that different masses can be easily hung on it.
4. Place a box so that it is touching a freely hanging mass, as shown in Figure 1.
5. Hang different weights and swing them at different heights to determine how far they move the box.

## RESULTS

1. What effect did changing the height of the weight have on the distance the box moved? Doubling the height more than doubles the box's movement.
2. What effect did changing the mass have on the distance the box moved? The larger the mass the more the box is pushed.

## CONCLUSIONS

1. How does this experiment demonstrate Newton's first law of motion? The object tended to continue moving.
2. How would changing the mass of the box affect this experiment? It would have taken a larger mass on the pendulum to move the box.

## APPLICATIONS

1. Why is a person standing in a bus thrown to the rear of the bus when the bus suddenly starts to move?
2. Why does water spill out of a pan when a person carrying the pan stops suddenly?

| TABLE 1 | MASS AND HEIGHT OF BLOCKS | | |
|---|---|---|---|
| Trial | Mass (grams) | Height (cm) | Distance box moved (cm) |
| 1 | | | |
| 2 | | | |
| 3 | | | |
| 4 | | | |
| 5 | | | |

1. The passenger (not in motion) tends to stay at rest when the bus begins to move.
2. The water has a tendency to stay in motion according to Newton's first law.

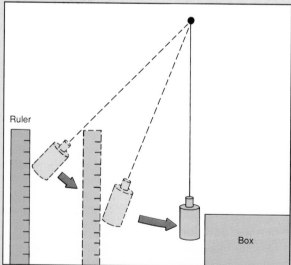

Ruler

Box

## Summary

1. The background against which motion is observed and measured is called a frame of reference. **(9.1)**

2. Average speed is the distance an object travels in a given time. **(9.2)**

3. Acceleration is the rate at which the velocity of an object changes. **(9.3)**

4. Newton's first law of motion states that an object at rest will remain at rest and an object in motion will remain in motion unless acted on by some outside force. **(9.4)**

5. Newton's second law of motion states that the acceleration of an object depends upon the net force acting on it and the mass of the object. **(9.5)**

6. When gravity is the only force acting on an object, the object is in a state of free fall. **(9.6)**

7. Newton's third law of motion states that for every action there is an equal but opposite reaction. **(9.7)**

8. Momentum equals an object's mass times its velocity. Momentum is conserved when two or more objects collide. **(9.8)**

9. Projectile motion is the combination of an accelerated vertical motion and a constant horizontal motion. **(9.9)**

10. An object will move in a circular path if acted on by a centripetal force. **(9.10)**

## Science Terms

On a separate sheet of paper, define each term in a sentence.

acceleration **(175)**
acceleration due to gravity **(181)**
average speed **(174)**
centripetal force **(188)**
distance **(173)**
frame of reference **(173)**

free fall **(180)**
inertia **(178)**
instantaneous speed **(175)**
law of conservation of momentum **(184)**
momentum **(183)**
motion **(173)**

net force **(179)**
projectile motion **(187)**
speed **(174)**
trajectory **(188)**
uniform circular motion **(188)**
velocity **(175)**
weightless **(181)**

## Modified True-False

On a separate sheet of paper, mark each true statement *TRUE* and each false statement *FALSE*. If false, change the underlined term to make the statement true.

1. A frame of reference is used to measure and observe motion. T

2. The speed of an object at a particular instant is called the average speed. F, instantaneous

3. The velocity of an object changes if either the speed or the direction of motion changes. T

4. Newton's second law of motion explains the relationship between momentum, acceleration, and mass. F, force

5. Force is measured in newtons. T

6. Free fall occurs when gravity is the only force acting on an object. T

7. Action and reaction forces act on different objects. T

8. When two cars collide, the total momentum decreases. F, stays the same

9. An object that moves under the influence of gravity is called a trajectory. F, projectile

10. Gravity causes objects to move in a circle. T

*(continues)*

## CHAPTER REVIEW

## Multiple Choice

On a separate sheet of paper, write the letter of the term that best answers the question or completes the statement.

1. 100 km/h due east is an example of a
   a. speed.
   c. force.
   b. velocity.
   d. trajectory.

2. The velocity of a body increases from 1 m/s to 5 m/s in 2 s. Therefore, the acceleration of the body is
   a. 4 m/s. b. −4 m/s². c. 2 m/s². d. 0 m/s².

3. A net force produces a change in
   a. mass.
   b. speed.
   c. direction of motion.
   d. acceleration.

4. A bowler follows through on his or her roll after releasing a bowling ball to increase the ball's
   a. velocity.
   c. momentum.
   b. speed.
   d. acceleration.

5. Whenever one object exerts a force on a second object, the second object exerts an _____ but opposite force on the first object.
   a. equal
   c. identical
   b. constant
   d. stronger

6. Which of the following is a unit of momentum?
   a. kg   b. m/s   c. kg · m/s²   d. kg · m/s

7. Action-reaction forces do not cancel each other out because they act on _____ objects.
   a. identical
   c. stationary
   b. moving
   d. different

8. When two or more objects collide, _____ is always conserved.
   a. force
   c. action
   b. velocity
   d. momentum

9. The centripetal force that keeps the moon orbiting the earth is supplied by
   a. friction.
   c. free fall.
   b. gravity.
   d. inertia.

10. A diver moving at 1 m/s walks off the end of a diving platform. If it takes 0.8 s for the diver to hit the water, how far away from the board does the diver land?
    a. 1 m   b. 0.8 m   c. 2 m   d. 3 m

## Completion

On a separate sheet of paper, complete each statement by supplying the correct term.

1. Average speed is the _distance_ divided by the time.

2. The _frame of reference_ is the background against which motion is observed and measured.

3. For two objects to have the same velocity, they must move with the same speed in the same _direction_ .

4. Newton's _first_ law of motion is based on the property of inertia.

5. The mass of an object and the net force exerted on it affect the object's _acceleration_ .

6. The sum of the forces acting on an object is the _net force_ .

7. Weightlessness occurs when an object is in a state of _free fall_ .

8. Chris Evert _follows through_ on her swing to increase the tennis ball's momentum.

9. Projectile motion is the combination of a horizontal motion and a _vertical_ motion.

10. An object moving in a circular motion is acted upon by a _centripetal_ force.

**192**   Chapter 9

# Writing Critically

1. Part of the thrill of going to an amusement park is experiencing the accelerations the rides provide. Describe your favorite ride and list the accelerations you experience as a passenger on the ride.

2. Weightlessness occurs when an object is in a state of free fall. Describe situations in everyday life in which weightlessness occurs, even if only for a short time.

3. **CHALLENGE** The performance and safety of automobiles are of great concern to car designers and consumers. Explain how Newton's laws of motion and the principles of momentum are related to the design of the following safety features in a car: collapsible bumpers, seat belts, antilock brakes, air bags, padded dashboards.

   1. up hills, going down hills, slowing down, stopping
   2. Answers will vary.
   3. All are examples of Newton's First Law of Motion in that they prevent the passenger from continuing in the same direction.

# Skill Reinforcement

The Skill Activity on page 186 describes how to do library research on a topic. Based on the information in this chapter, what subject areas in a card catalog could you use to find information on Sir Isaac Newton's research? Make a list of these subjects and take it to the library. Check your list of subjects against the subject cards in the card catalog. Does the card catalog include any areas other than the ones you noted? Choose one subject area and make a list of the books available on Newton. Select one book to read, and then write a report on Newton's research in that area.

# Research Ideas

1. Before going into space, astronauts must learn to live and work in a state of weightlessness. Investigate and report on the methods used to simulate this condition for astronaut trainees.

2. In the last few years, the principles of motion have been applied to improving the performance of athletes. Investigate the impact that sports science has had on athletic performance. In particular, report on any records that have been broken as the result of the application of the principles of motion.

3. As the space shuttle re-enters Earth's atmosphere, it acts very much like a projectile. Investigate and report on the procedures used to bring the shuttle back to Earth.

4. **CHALLENGE** The hammer throw is an Olympic sports event. Find out more about this sport. Using what you have learned from this chapter, explain how the concepts of motion, force, and momentum are put to use in this event.

# For Further Reading

Edgerton, Harold E., and James R. Killian. *Moments of Vision*. Cambridge, Massachusetts: The MIT Press, 1979. A visual history of the career of Harold Edgerton, the inventor of the strobe light, is presented through a collection of spectacular photographs of moving objects "frozen in time."

Hewitt, Paul G. *Conceptual Physics*. Boston: Little, Brown, 1985. Based on common, everyday experiences, the principles governing motion are presented in a clear and enjoyable manner.

# CHAPTER 10

# Work, Energy, and Machines

This book was printed on a printing press like the one shown below. This machine, which uses electrical energy to do the work, can print about one hundred books per hour. If you could copy this text by hand, it would take you about ten years to make one hundred copies of this book.

For additional information, see pages T80–T81.

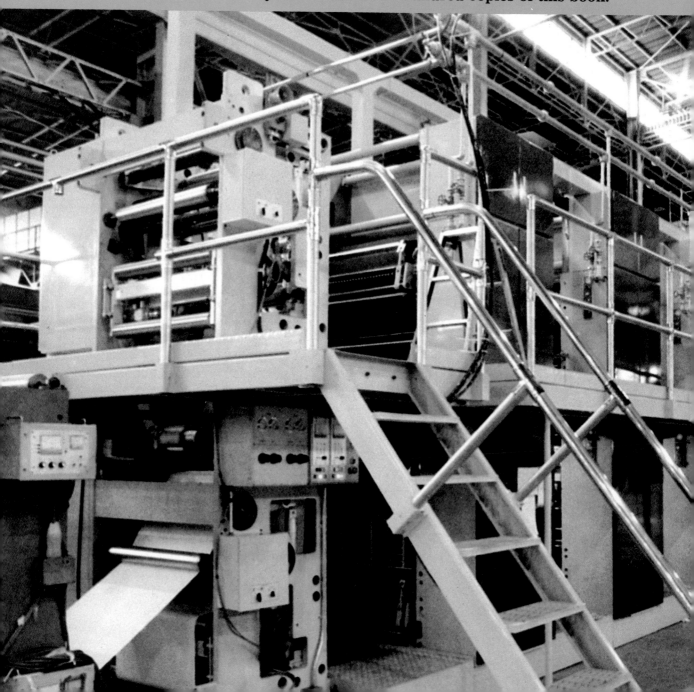

# Work and Energy

## SECTION OBJECTIVES

- **Define** *work*, *potential energy*, *kinetic energy*, and *power*.
- **List** several forms of energy.
- **Calculate** work, potential energy, kinetic energy, and power.
- **Describe** the law of conservation of energy.

Photograph left: automated printing press

NEW TERMS IN THIS SECTION
work
joule
energy
potential energy
gravitational potential energy
kinetic energy

## 10.1 Work

Whenever you swim, ride a bike, or swing a baseball bat, you are doing work. Even the smallest task, such as lifting a pencil or combing your hair, involves work. In science, **work** is done when a force moves an object over a distance.

The equation for work ($W$) is

$$\text{Work} = \text{force} \times \text{distance}$$
$$W = F \times d$$

In this equation, $F$ is the force acting on the object and $d$ is the distance the object moves in the direction of the force.

The unit of measurement for work in the metric system is the **joule** (JOOL). One joule (J) equals a force of 1 N moving an object a distance of 1 m. A joule is equal to a newton · meter (N · m). When you pick an apple up from the ground, you do approximately one joule of work because you lift an apple, which weighs about 1 newton, to a height of about 1 meter. The following example calculates the amount of work done by a student climbing a rope. The joule, the unit of work in the metric system, is named after James Prescott Joule, a nineteenth century English physicist who studied energy transformations.

Ask students if a horse standing still is doing work as it supports a rider on its back. (No. No force is acting over a distance.)

Work is done because a force is used to bend the wire. The work done in bending the wire is changed to heat, making the wire warm.

### ACTIVITY

**Doing Work**

Rapidly flex a piece of wire, such as a coat hanger, back and forth with your hands. Are you doing work? Why? Immediately after flexing it, touch the part of the wire being bent. How does the wire feel? What happened to the energy put into the wire?

**Figure 10–1.** It is easy to recognize that this swimmer doing the butterfly stroke is performing work as he moves his body through the water.

**Example:** Find the work done when a 500-N student climbs a rope to a height of 5 m.

**Solution:**
- *Write* the equation for work.
$$\text{Work} = \text{force} \times \text{distance}$$
$$W = F \times d$$
- *Substitute* the values for $F$ and $d$ in the equation.
$$W = 500\ \text{N} \times 5\ \text{m}$$
- *Solve* by multiplying.
$$W = 2500\ \text{N} \cdot \text{m} = 2500\ \text{J}$$

Once the student reaches the top of the rope, how much work do you think must be done to hold on? If you said "No work," then you were correct. No matter how much force the student uses to hold on, no work is done unless the student moves. Work is done only when a force moves an object over a distance. Similarly, a weight lifter holding a heavy barbell is not doing work. Even though the weight lifter exerts a large force on the barbell, there is no movement, so no work is done.

A second requirement for work to be done is that the force must act parallel to the direction that the object moves. For example, when you push a grocery cart in a food store, the force you apply to the cart's handle pushes the cart in the same direction you are moving. A force that acts at a right angle to the direction of motion, such as a centripetal force, cannot do work. Instead, such a force is used to change the direction in which an object moves.

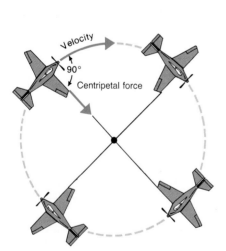

**Figure 10–2.** When this model airplane moves in a circle at the end of a wire, no work is done on the airplane by the force exerted by the wire. At each instant, the airplane is moving at right angles to the force exerted by the wire.

## 10.2 Potential Energy

When an alarm clock is wound, the work done in winding the spring is stored as energy. **Energy** can be defined as the ability to do work. When work is performed on an object, it is given energy. The energy an object has is, therefore, the work it can do. Like work, energy is measured in joules. Stored energy is called **potential** (puh TEHN shuhl) **energy**. The energy stored in the clock's spring is used to move the hands of the clock and cause the alarm to sound. Energy stored in food, fuels, and other chemicals is called *chemical potential energy*. Automobile batteries, gasoline, and coal are examples of things that have chemical potential energy. Nuclear energy is another form of potential energy.

Potential energy due to an object's position relative to the ground is called **gravitational potential energy**. The higher an object is above the earth's surface, the more potential energy it has. The equation for gravitational potential energy (*PE*) is

$$\text{gravitational potential energy} = \text{weight} \times \text{height}$$
$$PE = w \times h$$

In this equation, $w$ is the object's weight and $h$ is the object's height above the ground.

Because the kinetic energy of a body depends on the square of the body's speed, a car traveling at a speed of 80 km/hr will require four times the stopping distance as a car traveling 40 km/hr.

**Figure 10–3.** The water at the top of the Hoover Dam near Las Vegas, Nevada has a great deal of gravitational potential energy. When the water is released, the energy stored in the water can be used to generate electricity.

**Example:** Determine the potential energy of a diver weighing 500 N on a 3-m diving platform.

**Solution:** • *Write* the equation for potential energy.

potential energy = weight × height
$$PE = w \times h$$

• *Substitute* the values for $w$ and $h$ in the equation.
$$PE = 500 \text{ N} \times 3 \text{ m}$$

• *Solve* by multiplying.
$$PE = 1500 \text{ N} \cdot \text{m} = 1500 \text{ J}$$

Potential energy is converted to kinetic energy.

What happens to the diver's potential energy when he or she jumps off the platform? The energy of an object in motion is discussed in the next section.

**Figure 10–4.** A diver converts potential energy into kinetic energy when he performs a dive.

Heat energy is the kinetic energy associated with the random motion of molecules in a body.

## 10.3 Kinetic Energy

In Figure 10–4, as the diver falls, his potential energy is converted into kinetic energy. **Kinetic** (kuh NEHT ihk) **energy** is the energy of motion. The kinetic energy of an object depends on both the speed and mass of that object. The equation for kinetic energy ($KE$) is

kinetic energy = 1/2 mass × speed²
$$KE = 1/2 \ mv^2$$

In this equation, $m$ is the mass of the object and $v$ is the speed of the object.

## Summary

1. Work equals the product of the force acting on an object and the distance the object moves in the direction of the force. **(10.1)**
2. Energy is the ability to do work. **(10.2)**
3. Potential energy is stored energy. **(10.2)**
4. Kinetic energy is the energy of motion. **(10.3)**
5. The law of conservation of energy states that energy cannot be created or destroyed. **(10.4)**
6. Power is the rate at which work is done. **(10.5)**
7. A machine may be used to change the strength or direction of a force or the distance through which a force acts. **(10.6)**
8. The six simple machines are the lever, the inclined plane, the wedge, the pulley, the wheel and axle, and the screw. **(10.6)**
9. The mechanical advantage of a machine equals the resistance force divided by the effort force. **(10.7)**
10. The efficiency of a machine equals the useful energy output times 100 percent divided by the energy input. **(10.8)**
11. A complex machine is a combination of two or more simple machines. **(10.9)**

## Science Terms

On a separate sheet of paper, define each term in a sentence.

complex machine **(208)**
efficiency **(207)**
effort force **(203)**
energy **(197)**
fulcrum **(203)**
gravitational potential energy **(197)**
inclined plane **(205)**
joule (J) **(195)**

kinetic energy **(198)**
law of conservation of energy **(199)**
lever **(203)**
machine **(203)**
mechanical advantage **(206)**
potential energy **(197)**
power **(200)**
pulley **(204)**

resistance force **(203)**
screw **(206)**
simple machine **(203)**
watt (W) **(200)**
wedge **(205)**
wheel and axle **(205)**
work **(195)**

## Modified True-False

On a separate sheet of paper, mark each true statement *TRUE* and each false statement *FALSE*. If false, change the underlined term to make the statement true.

1. Work is defined as the product of the force acting on the object and the <u>time</u> the force acts. F, distance
2. In metric units, work is measured in <u>joules</u>. T
3. <u>Kinetic energy</u> is the energy an object has because of its position relative to the ground. F, gravitational potential energy
4. The <u>efficiency</u> of a simple machine equals the resistance force divided by the effort force. T
5. Power is determined by <u>multiplying</u> the work by the time it takes to do the work. F, dividing
6. One horsepower equals <u>1000</u> watts. F, 746
7. A wedge is an example of a <u>complex</u> machine. F, simple
8. A tightly wound spring is an example of an object that has <u>potential energy</u>. F, mechanical advantage
9. The efficiency of a real machine is always <u>greater</u> than 100 percent. F, less  *(continues)*

# CHAPTER REVIEW

## Multiple Choice

On a separate sheet of paper, write the letter of the term that best answers the question or completes the statement.

1. A book weighing 10 N sits on a shelf 1.5 m above the floor. The work done on the book by the shelf is
   a. 10 J.
   b. 15 J.
   c. 15 J.
   d. 0.0 J.

2. A tow truck pulls with a force of 5000 N on a car. The work done by the tractor to pull the car 40 m is
   a. 5000 J.
   b. 40 J.
   c. 200,000 J.
   d. 125 J.

3. The force applied to a lever is
   a. resistance force.
   b. effort force.
   c. mechanical advantage.
   d. efficiency.

4. As a sky diver falls toward the earth, the sky diver's potential energy
   a. increases.
   b. decreases.
   c. remains constant.
   d. increases then decreases.

5. The power developed by an electric motor that does 1000 J of work in 5 s is
   a. 200 W.
   b. 5000 W.
   c. 200 J.
   d. 746 W.

6. One kilowatt is equal to
   a. 746 W.
   b. 100 W.
   c. 1000 W.
   d. 0.746 W.

7. A lever is a rod or a bar that moves on a
   a. wedge.
   b. record.
   c. fulcrum.
   d. pulley.

8. A wheel and axle is an example of a
   a. frictionless machine.
   b. complex machine.
   c. compound machine.
   d. simple machine.

9. The efficiency of a pulley system is known to be 50 percent. When 200 J of work is done on the pulley system, the work done by the pulley system will equal
   a. 50 J.
   b. 100 J.
   c. 400 J.
   d. 0 J.

10. A frictionless machine would have an efficiency of
    a. 50%.
    b. 75%.
    c. 99%.
    d. 100%.

## Completion

On a separate sheet of paper, complete each statement by supplying the correct term.

1. Energy is defined as the ability to do __work__ .

2. A __newton meter__ is also called a joule.

3. The kinetic energy of an object depends on both the mass and the __speed__ of the object.

4. Fossil fuels possess __chemical potential__ energy.

5. Energy cannot be __created__ or destroyed.

6. The metric unit of __power__ is the watt.

7. Potential energy due to an object's position relative to the ground is __gravitational potential energy__ .

8. The mechanical advantage of a machine is a measure of how much the machine __increases__ the effort force.

9. Complex machines are combinations of __simple__ machines.

10. A knife blade, a chisel, and the pointed end of a nail are examples of a __wedge__ .

212     Chapter 10

## Writing Critically

1. Your family purchases electrical energy from the electric company. Appliances in your home convert this electrical energy into many different forms of energy. Select one of these forms of energy and explain how it is used in your home. List other ways you could accomplish the work done by that appliance.

2. Describe a procedure that would enable you to determine the rate at which you do work—that is, your power—when you walk up a flight of stairs. Be sure to list all the quantities that you must find and the necessary equations in your procedure.

3. Describe some complex machines in your home, in your family's car, or at school. Mention some simple machines that are contained in these complex machines.

4. **CHALLENGE** The human arm is an example of a lever. Describe two other parts of the human body that are used as levers. Explain how each of these parts is used as a first-, second-, or third-class lever.

## Skill Reinforcement

The Skill Activity on page 202 describes how to interpret diagrams. Look through your local newspaper or a weekly news magazine for different types of diagrams. Try to understand what the diagrams are explaining without reading the accompanying articles first. Then read the articles to see if the diagrams really helped make certain information clearer.

## Research Ideas

1. Investigate the origins of the six simple machines. In your research, try to determine when these devices were first used and by whom.

2. Many historians think that simple machines were used to construct one of the seven wonders of the ancient world, the Pyramids of Giza. Find out which simple machines are thought to have been used and how they might have been used.

3. Car makers have done much to increase the efficiency of automobiles. Investigate what changes have been made in automobile design to increase efficiency.

4. **CHALLENGE** The human body converts the energy that is stored in food into several forms. After researching the topic, make a list of these forms of energy and describe where the conversion to each form occurs in the body.

## For Further Reading

Bradner, John H. "Mammoth Machines." *Science Digest* (April 1981), 48-51. This article describes some of the world's largest machines, from dump trucks that stand 20 m high to supertankers that can carry the weight of 7.8 million people.

Gardner, Robert. *This Is the Way It Works: A Collection of Machines*. New York: Doubleday & Co., 1980. This book explains how many common machines, such as telephones, washing machines, and light switches, work. It also describes how more sophisticated machines such as artificial lungs, heart valves, and kidney machines help keep people alive.

Petre, Peter. "The High-Tech Car Hits the Road." *Fortune* (April 1985), 204-224. This article describes what car buyers can expect as standard equipment a few years down the road.

CHAPTER **11**

# Temperature and Heat

Early scientists recognized the importance of accurately measuring temperature and heat, but they had no accurate methods of measurement. A new, accurate method is *thermography,* as pictured below. This thermograph of a house indicates the hot spots by the colors pink, red, and yellow while the cool areas are shown in blue and green.

For additional information, see pages T82-T83.

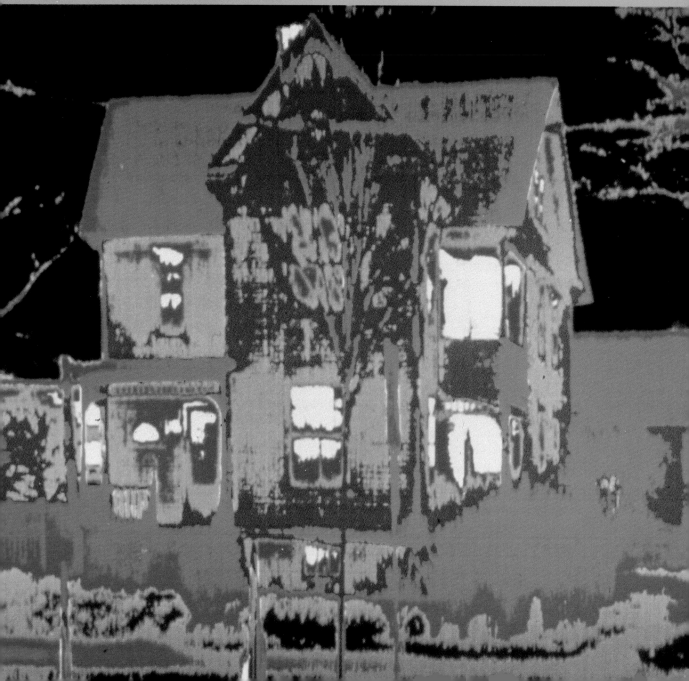

## Conduction

Heat transfer through **conduction** occurs when molecules collide with one another, transferring their kinetic energy from one molecule to the next. Substances whose molecules are close to one another are generally the best conductors of heat. The closeness of the molecules increases the number of collisions. The molecules in most solids are closer together than those in gases and liquids. For this reason, most solids are better conductors of heat than are gases and liquids. Metals are the best conductors of heat. In addition to the vibrations of molecules, some electrons in most metals are free to move. These free electrons are very good at transferring kinetic energy throughout the metal. Copper is used in quality cookware because it is a good conductor of heat.

**Figure 11–10.** This metal poker is too hot to touch because of heat transfer by conduction.

A substance that is a poor conductor of heat is called an **insulator** (IHN suh lay tuhr). Substances whose molecules are far apart are good insulators. Gases are poor conductors of heat, but they are good insulators because their molecules are separated by large distances. Nonmetallic solids, such as glass, wood, plastic, and ceramic materials, are also good insulators. The insulating properties of air and nonmetals are used in the design of clothing, cooking utensils, and building materials. The metal handles of pots and pans are usually covered with wood or plastic to prevent burns. Insulated plastic bottles keep liquids and foods hot or cold because heat is conducted out or in slowly.

**Figure 11–11.** The materials shown here are all examples of insulators. These materials help reduce the flow of heat out of an object.

**Figure 11–12.** Heat transfer through convection involves moving currents of air. As warm air expands, denser, cooler air moves in under it and pushes the warmer air upward. The cooler air is then warmed, and the cycle repeats itself.

Materials such as rock wool, fiberglass, and foam are used to insulate homes and other buildings. Insulation reduces the amount of heat loss to the outside in the winter. Insulation also reduces the amount of heat gain from the outside in the summer. The use of insulation improves the energy efficiency of buildings.

### Convection

The transfer of heat by moving currents in liquids and gases is called **convection**. The air above a hot heating element on an electric stove becomes warm and expands. Because of this expansion, the density of the warm air is reduced. The cooler air in the room, which is denser than the warmer air, pushes the warm air upward. This cooler air is then warmed, and the cycle continues. The currents of air, shown in Figure 11–12, are called *convection currents*. Convection currents may also be produced in a liquid. If a pan of water is placed on the heating element, the water near the bottom of the pan will become warm, expand, and rise just as air does. This results in convection currents in the water. Convection currents transfer heat energy by moving the heated gas or liquid from one place to another.

Radiators in homes are used to set up convection currents for heating purposes. The cooling element in a refrigerator creates convection currents that maintain a uniform temperature throughout the refrigerator compartment. Convection ovens use a fan to circulate the hot air in an oven. The circulating air keeps the temperature throughout the oven more uniform.

### Radiation

In both conduction and convection, the motion of matter is responsible for the transfer of heat. In the third process of heat transfer, energy is transferred from one place to another without passing through matter. This process is called **radiation**. Most of the energy on the earth arrives by way of radiation from the sun. Radiant energy reaches the earth in the form of rays. These rays pass through space where almost no matter exists. When this energy reaches the earth, it increases the energy of any material that absorbs it. How might radiation result in conduction and convection taking place?

Many devices use radiation as a method of heat transfer. Solar-energy devices, such as solar panels, use heat transferred from the sun to heat homes. Space heaters, such as the one in Figure 11–13, also use radiation to provide heat. Microwave ovens use radiation to cook food. The waves cause molecules in the food to vibrate rapidly. The high temperature caused by the increase in the kinetic energy of the molecules actually cooks the food. Heat lamps in many restaurants use radiation to keep food warm.

### READING CRITICALLY

Would the heating bills for an apartment on the top floor of a three-story building be more or less than the bills for an identical apartment on the first floor? Why or why not?

The heating bills for the third-floor apartment should be less because of heat transfer by convection. Other factors in heat transfer to the third floor might be the insulation of the building and the type of heating system.

Radiation transfers heat to matter. When matter absorbs heat, its temperature increases and heat can be transferred by conduction, convection, or both.

**Figure 11–13.** Many space heaters, such as the one pictured here, use radiation to provide heat.

## 11.7 Change of State

The molecules in all three states of matter are in constant motion, as illustrated in Figure 11–14. You may recall from Chapter 6 that the molecules in solids are held together by strong chemical bonds. The structure of these molecules limits the motion of solids to vibrational motion. That is, they shake back and forth around a fixed point within the solid. The molecules that make up a liquid have weaker chemical bonds between them and are not fixed around one spot. Molecules in liquids have more freedom of movement than those in solids. The molecules in a gas have almost no bonding between molecules, so they move very freely.

Solid          Liquid          Gas

**Figure 11–14.** This illustration shows the molecular motion in a solid, a liquid, and a gas.

Changes of state occur as a result of changes in a substance's internal energy. The **internal energy** of a substance is the sum of the internal kinetic and potential energies of the substance. When a solid is heated, the internal energy of the substance increases. Usually this results in an increase in the temperature of the substance. However, at a certain temperature the absorption of heat does not result in a further increase in temperature. The energy supplied to the substance does not increase the kinetic energy of the molecules in the substance. Instead the energy breaks the bonds between the molecules. The result is that the solid becomes a liquid.

Figure 11–15 shows a common example of the changes of state matter can go through. As ice melts, the heat it absorbs separates the tightly bound molecules. The amount of heat needed to change one gram of solid into one gram of liquid is called the **heat of fusion** (FYOO zhuhn).

A second type of change of state takes place when a liquid becomes a gas. When heat is added to a liquid, the molecules gain sufficient energy to move farther apart.

The movement of a molecule away from the rest of the molecules results in the change of state from a liquid to a gas for that molecule.

When water at room temperature is heated on a stove, its temperature increases to 100°C. At this temperature, the water will boil, but the temperature of the water will no longer increase. Heat added to the boiling water produces steam, which is a gas. The amount of heat needed to change one gram of a liquid into one gram of gas is called the **heat of vaporization**.

Another way a liquid may change into a gas is through a cooling process called *evaporation*. **Evaporation** (ih VAP oh ray shuhn) occurs when the most energetic molecules at the surface of a liquid escape from the liquid. As these molecules escape, the liquid's internal energy is reduced, which results in a lower temperature. If you leave a small dish of water out for a few days, you will see the results of evaporation.

Changes of state may also be reversed. When the internal energy of a liquid is reduced sufficiently, the liquid may again become a solid. When steam condenses, it changes from a gas back into a liquid.

**Figure 11–15.** The photographs here show the three changes of state water goes through: solid (left), as a liquid (middle), and as a gas (right).

When steam condenses, it releases energy. In fact, each gram of steam releases 2260 J of heat as it condenses. As a result, steam can produce severe burns if it comes in contact with human skin.

## SCIENCE FACT

Plastic surgeons are able to remove bags under peoples' eyes by evaporation. An electrically heated needle is inserted into the fat pad and vaporizes the fat cells, which are about 90% water.

## Section Review

1. List three ways that heat may be transferred from one place to another.
2. How does the specific heat capacity of water compare with the specific heat capacity of the other substances listed in Table 11-1?
3. What is the difference between convection and radiation?
4. What happens when heat continues to be supplied to an object whose temperature no longer increases?
5. THINKING CRITICALLY· Explain why a hot-water bottle is a more effective warming device than a block of wood having the same mass and the same temperature.

1. conduction, convection, or radiation
2. It is greater than that of any other substance.
3. Convection is the transfer of heat through matter; radiation may transfer heat without matter.
4. The material from which the object is made will change state from a solid to a liquid or from a liquid to a gas.
5. Water has a higher specific heat capacity than wood.

# Thermodynamics

## SECTION OBJECTIVES

- **State** the first law of thermodynamics.
- **Identify** the two factors involved in the second law of thermodynamics.
- **Define** *entropy*.

## 11.8 The First Law of Thermodynamics

There are two ways to light a match. You can strike it against the matchbook cover, or you can light it directly from a flame. If you strike it on the matchbook cover, you are increasing the match's internal energy by doing work on the match. If you light the match from another flame, you are increasing its internal energy by adding heat. The changes in energy that occur when work is done on an object or when heat is added to an object are governed by the laws of thermodynamics (thuhr moh dy NAM ihks). **Thermodynamics** is the study of the transformation of heat into other forms of energy.

The *first law of thermodynamics* states that the change in an object's internal energy equals the heat added to the object minus the work done by the object. This law is an extension of the law of conservation of energy. Whenever energy is changed from one form into another, the total amount of energy remains the same.

To illustrate the first law of thermodynamics, look at the container on the left in Figure 11–16. If heat is

### SCIENCE FACT

When humans consume food they are obeying the law of conservation of energy and the first law of thermodynamics. One hundred percent energy is consumed, and 100 percent energy is used. However, only 10 percent of the energy obtained from food is used to do work. The remaining 90 percent is used to generate heat.

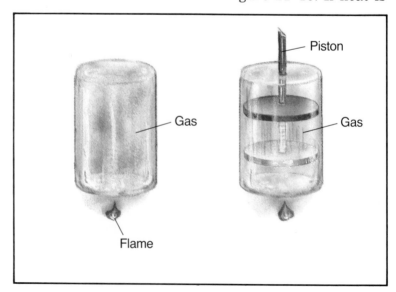

**Figure 11–16.** In the container on the left, heat is simply added to the gas. No work is done by the gas. When a piston is inserted into the container and heat is added (right), the gas does work by lifting the piston. The sum of the heat added to the gas and the work done by the gas illustrates the first law of thermodynamics.

added to the gas in the container, it increases the gas's internal energy, which increases the temperature of the gas. The gas's internal energy is changed by the addition of heat only. The gas itself is doing no work.

In the figure on the right, a piston is inserted into the container. When heat is added to the gas, the temperature of the gas increases and the gas expands, pushing the piston up. In other words, the gas does work on the piston. In this case, the heat added to the gas increases the internal energy of the gas and goes into the work done to lift the piston.

If the container in Figure 11–16 were well insulated, no heat could enter it or leave it. Similarly, if the piston were moved in or out very quickly, there would not be enough time for the heat to flow. Thus, any work done by the gas would result in a loss in the internal energy of the gas. If, on the other hand, work were done on the gas, its internal energy would increase. When work is done on a gas, as when it is compressed, the gas gets hotter. When a gas does work and is allowed to expand, the gas gets colder. When you use a bicycle pump, the increase in the temperature is partially due to the work done to compress the air inside the pump. As carbon dioxide gas is released from a fire extinguisher, it expands and the temperature drops. This drop in temperature is enough to condense the moisture in the air to snow.

**Figure 11–17.** As work is done on a gas, as when it is compressed in a bicycle pump, the internal energy, and thus the temperature of the gas, increases. When a gas does work and is allowed to expand, its temperature is reduced rapidly, as when carbon dioxide gas is released from a fire extinguisher.

## 11.9 The Second Law of Thermodynamics

The *second law of thermodynamics* states that internal energy can never be converted completely into useful energy output, or work. If this were not so, it would be possible to use heat from the air to run a car. Ships could use the energy from ocean water to run their engines.

**Figure 11–18.** All natural processes increase in entropy. As heat flows from the air and water into the ice, the ice melts and the entropy of the iceberg increases.

## READING CRITICALLY

A bathtub is filled with hot water. The water cools and the bathroom warms until both reach the same temperature. Explain what has happened in terms of conduction, convection, and entropy.

conduction: hot moved toward cold
convection: hot rose, cold sank
entropy: ability of hot water to do work is lost

The reason energy from the atmosphere and the oceans is not available to do work involves temperature. Remember that heat tends to flow from an object with a higher temperature to an object with a lower temperature. Although the atmosphere and ocean water have tremendous amounts of energy, their temperatures are lower than the temperatures in engines in cars or ships. There is no efficient way that heat can be transferred to an object at a higher temperature from an object at a lower temperature. As a result, this energy is not available to do work.

The second law of thermodynamics can also be explained in terms of *entropy*. **Entropy** (EN truh pee) is the measure of disorder in an object or substance. Work involves orderly motion. Internal energy can be thought of as disordered energy. That is, as heat is applied to an object and its internal energy increases, the motion of the object's molecules becomes more random and disorganized.

An increase in entropy is generally an irreversible process. Ordered energy easily becomes disordered energy, but it is impossible to completely convert disordered internal energy back into ordered motion, or work. For example, consider what happens when equal amounts of hot and cold water are mixed. As the hot and cold water mix, the entropy of the water increases. Once the hot and cold water are mixed and have come to a uniform temperature, the opportunity to convert a portion of the heat flowing out of the hot water to work is no longer available. The lukewarm water will never "unmix" itself. It will never separate back into a hotter portion and a colder portion. As entropy increases, what happens to the amount of energy available to do work? It decreases.

There is a tendency in all natural processes, such as heat flow, to bring about a uniformity of temperature. Scientists predict that as a result of these processes, the entire universe may reach a state of uniformity throughout. That is, the temperature would be the same throughout the universe. When and if such a state were reached, although there would have been no change in the energy of the universe, all physical, chemical, and biological processes would cease. This state of uniformity has been described as the "heat death" of the universe.

## Section Review

1. Define and give one example of the first law of thermodynamics.
2. Why is it impossible for heat to be converted completely to work?
3. THINKING CRITICALLY What two factors are involved in the second law of thermodynamics?
4. THINKING CRITICALLY In terms of entropy, explain what happens as ice melts and changes into water.

# CAREER

## Solar-Energy Systems Installer

**DESCRIPTION**  A solar-energy systems installer installs equipment that collects and circulates water or air that is heated by the sun. Installers make sure that equipment is properly connected. An understanding of the principles of heat, heat transfer, heat capacity, and pressure relationships is helpful to an installer.

**REQUIREMENTS**  If you plan to be a solar-energy systems installer, you may begin as an installer's helper after high-school graduation. Some solar-energy companies prefer to hire people who have had courses in solar-energy technology. These courses are offered at some high schools, vocational schools, and junior colleges.

**INFORMATION**  American Solar Energy Association, 910 17th Street, N.W., Suite 532, Washington, DC 20006

# INVESTIGATION 11: Heat Transfer During Mixing

*Can heat energy be transferred from cold water to hot water?*

## PURPOSE
To demonstrate that energy is conserved when two liquids are mixed

## MATERIALS
cold tap water
warm tap water
graduate (100 mL)
2 beakers (250 mL)
stirring rod
2 Celsius thermometers ($-10°$ to $110°$)

## PROCEDURE
1. Copy Table 1 onto a piece of paper. Enter all data from this investigation on your table.
2. **Trial I** Measure out 100 mL of cold tap water in the graduate, and pour it into a beaker. Measure and record its temperature and volume on your table.
3. Measure out 100 mL of warm tap water in the graduate, and pour it into the second beaker. Measure and record its temperature and volume.
4. Carefully pour the cold water into the container with the warm water. Mix the water gently with a stirring rod. The temperature will change rapidly at first. Try to measure the water's temperature as it begins to stabilize. Record the final temperature of the mixture on your table.
5. **Trial II** Measure out 50 mL of cold water in the graduate, and pour it into a beaker.

Measure and record its temperature and volume.
6. Repeat steps 3 and 4.

## RESULTS
1. Using the following equation for heat transfer, calculate the heat transferred from the warm water to the cold water in Trials I and II.

heat transfer = mass × specific heat × temperature change

$$Q = mc\,T$$

[Remember that the mass of one milliliter of water is .001 kg and the specific heat capacity of water is 4190 J/(kg ·(C°)]. Record these values on your table.

2. Using the equation for heat transfer, calculate the heat transferred from the cold water to the warm water in Trials I and II. Record this value on your table.

## CONCLUSIONS
1. How does the amount of heat gained by the cold water compare to the amount of heat lost by the warm water in both trials?
2. Which law of thermodynamics would you use to describe the results of this investigation?
   1. should be roughly equal
   2. the first law of thermodynamics

## APPLICATION
Explain why the ocean temperature is so much warmer in the fall than in the spring.

| TABLE 1 | CALCULATION OF HEAT FLOW | | | | | | |
|---|---|---|---|---|---|---|---|
| | Volume | | Temperature | | | Heat Transfer | |
| | Cold water | Warm water | Cold water | Warm water | Final temperature | To cold water | From warm water |
| Trial 1 | | | | | | | |
| Trial 2 | | | | | | | |

Ocean water in the fall has been warmed by the sun's radiation throughout the summer. The air is warmer than the water so heat flows to the water. During the winter, the air is colder than the water so heat is lost from the ocean. Therefore, in the spring, the ocean is colder.

## Summary

1. Temperature is a measure of the average kinetic energy of the molecules in a substance. **(11.1)**

2. Temperatures in the universe range from −273.15 to more than one billion degrees Celsius. **(11.2)**

3. The pressure exerted by a gas depends on both its temperature and its volume. **(11.3)**

4. Thermal expansion is the increase in size of an object or substance due to an increase in temperature. **(11.4)**

5. Heat is energy that is transferred from one object to another because of a difference in temperature. **(11.5)**

6. Heat can be transferred by conduction, convection, and radiation. **(11.6)**

7. A substance undergoes a change of state when it changes from a solid into a liquid or from a liquid into a gas. Such changes of state may also be reversed. **(11.7)**

8. The first law of thermodynamics states that the change in an object's internal energy equals the heat added to the object minus the work done by the object. **(11.8)**

9. The second law of thermodynamics states that internal energy can never be converted completely into useful energy. **(11.9)**

## Science Terms

On a separate sheet of paper, define each term in a sentence.

calorie **(223)**
Celsius (C) scale **(216)**
conduction **(225)**
convection **(226)**
entropy **(232)**
evaporation **(229)**
heat **(223)**

heat of fusion **(228)**
heat of vaporization **(229)**
insulator **(225)**
internal energy **(228)**
Kelvin (K) scale **(217)**
pascal (Pa) **(219)**
pressure **(219)**

radiation **(227)**
specific heat capacity **(224)**
temperature **(215)**
thermal expansion **(220)**
thermodynamics **(230)**
thermometer **(215)**

## Modified True-False

On a separate sheet of paper, mark each true statement *TRUE* and each false statement *FALSE*. If false, change the underlined term to make the statement true.

1. Temperature is a measure of the average <u>mass</u> of the molecules making up an object. F, kinetic energy

2. Some thermometers use the principle of <u>expansion and contraction</u> to measure the change in temperature of a substance. T

3. Cryogenics is the study of extremely <u>high</u> temperatures. F, low

4. The increase in the <u>mass</u> of a substance due to an increase in temperature is called thermal expansion. F, volume

5. The specific heat capacity of water is <u>less</u> than the specific heat capacity of iron. F, greater

6. Energy from the sun reaches the earth by a process known as <u>convection</u>. F, radiation

7. <u>Air</u> is a good thermal insulator. T

8. Evaporation <u>increases</u> the temperature of an object. F, decreases

9. When a substance changes from a liquid to a <u>solid</u>, it absorbs heat. F, gas

10. The second law of thermodynamics states that the order of a system has a tendency to <u>increase</u>. F, decrease

*(continues)*

## Multiple Choice

On a separate sheet of paper, write the letter of the term that best answers the question or completes the statement.

1. Absolute zero equals
   a. −273.15 K.
   (c.) 0 K.
   b. 0.000001 K.
   d. none of the above.

2. A plasma is a
   a. mixture of a gas and a liquid.
   (b.) gas made up of charged particles.
   c. gas under great pressure.
   d. liquid made up of charged particles.

3. The increase in the size of a substance due to an increase in temperature is
   a. temperature.
   b. internal energy.
   (c.) thermal expansion.
   d. specific heat capacity.

4. The pressure of a gas at a constant temperature _____ as its volume decreases.
   a. decreases
   b. remains constant
   (c.) increases
   d. levels off

5. Heat energy is transferred from one object to another because of a difference in
   a. pressure.
   b. specific heat capacity.
   (c.) temperature.
   d. internal energy.

6. The only means of heat transfer that does not require the presence of matter is
   (a.) radiation.
   c. convection.
   b. conduction.
   d. evaporation.

7. The specific heat capacity of a substance depends upon the nature of the substance and its
   a. temperature.
   c. pressure.
   (b.) mass.
   d. internal energy.

8. The first law of thermodynamics is another way of stating
   a. the law of conservation of momentum.
   b. Newton's second law of motion.
   c. the law of entropy.
   (d.) the law of conservation of energy.

9. The internal energy of a substance may change if
   a. its temperature changes.
   b. work is done on the substance.
   c. heat is added to the substance.
   (d.) all of the above.

10. A state of uniformity may cause
    (a.) the heat death of the universe.
    b. another ice age.
    c. entropy.
    d. conservation of energy.

## Completion

On a separate sheet of paper, complete each statement by supplying the correct term.

1. A ___thermometer___ is used to measure temperature.

2. The internal energy of a substance is the sum of the substance's molecular kinetic and ___potential___ energies.

3. The lowest possible temperature is ___absolute zero___.

4. The ___joule___ is the metric unit of heat.

5. Conventional ovens use the process of ___conduction___ to cook food.

6. The transfer of heat by moving currents in liquids or gases is ___convection___.

7. The heat of ___vaporization___ equals the amount of heat needed to change one gram of a substance from a liquid to a gas.

8. A calorie is the energy needed to increase the temperature of one ___gram___ of water one Celsius degree.

9. The ___second___ law of thermodynamics states that heat can never be completely converted to work.

10. Entropy is a measure of the ___disorder___ in a system.

## Writing Critically

1. List steps that have been taken to make the heating and cooling of your home more economical. For each energy-saving measure, describe the physical process that has been affected. For example, the use of storm windows reduces heat loss that occurs through the process of conduction. Also list suggestions for further improving your home's energy efficiency, and explain how these measures would work.

2. A vacuum bottle has two walls separated by a gap from which most of the air has been removed. Explain how this construction makes it possible for a vacuum bottle to keep both hot liquids hot and cold liquids cold.

3. **CHALLENGE** Some people believe that it is possible to cool a house by leaving the refrigerator door open. Would this makeshift air conditioner work? Explain your answer. If you do not think it would work, suggest how a refrigerator might be modified so that it could be used as an air conditioner.

1. Answers will vary but should reflect an understanding of the processes of heat flow.

2. Air is a good insulator, preventing flow of heat from a hot liquid and flow of heat to a cold liquid.

3. No. Since the refrigerator produces heat (from its motor), leaving the door open would actually increase the air temperature of the room. A large fan in the refrigerator cooling unit might help to distribute cool air.

## Skill Reinforcement

The Skill Activity on page 222 describes how to find the supporting details in an article. Choose an article from a recent scientific magazine such as *Omni* or from the science section of *Time* or *Newsweek*. Using the steps outlined in the Skill Activity, write down the topic of the article, the main idea of each paragraph, and the supporting details in each paragraph.

## Research Ideas

1. During flight, a space vehicle experiences a wide range of temperatures. The vehicle must be capable of withstanding both the bitter cold of outer space and the searing heat encountered during reentry into the earth's atmosphere. Investigate the methods used to protect the vehicle and the astronauts from these extreme conditions.

2. Thermography is a relatively new technology used to measure temperature. Find out what thermography is and how it is used in medicine, law enforcement, and construction.

3. Summarize the current applications of cryogenics. Propose possible future uses for this technology.

4. **CHALLENGE** Fire walkers can walk across hot coals without being burned. Some people can quickly stick their hands in molten lead without harm. Investigate how scientists explain these incredible phenomena.

## For Further Reading

Haines, Gail Kay. *Super Cold/Super Hot*. New York/London: Franklin Watts, 1976. The physics of both ends of the temperature spectrum are examined in this book. Possible future applications of cryogenics are discussed, and the challenge of achieving controlled thermonuclear fusion is explored.

Hillman, Howard. *Kitchen Science*. Boston: Houghton Mifflin Company, 1981. This book applies the basic principles relating to heat, temperature, heat transfer, and change of state to answer questions relating to cooking.

Stein, Kathleen. "Plasmas Under Glass." *Omni* (October 1984), 78–85. This picture essay captures the striking beauty of plasma. Various gases are shown in their plasma state.

# 12 Electricity and Magnetism

Can you imagine what life would be like without electricity? Almost everything, from flipping on a light switch in your home to the lightning-fast computations of supercomputers, is based on an understanding of the principles of electricity and magnetism.

For additional information, see pages T84–T85.

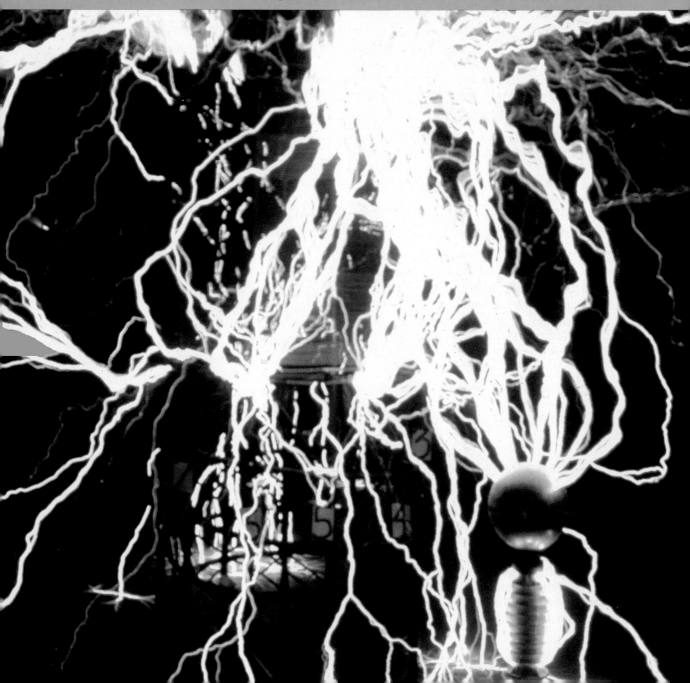

# SKILL ACTIVITY    Reading an Electric Meter

**INTRODUCTION** _____ Electric meters are placed in buildings to determine how much electricity is used by the occupants during each month. An electric bill is based upon the electric-meter reading. Electrical energy is measured in kilowatt-hours. A kilowatt-hour equals the work done by one kilowatt in one hour.

**PROCEDURE** _____

1. The five dials of an electric meter are read from right to left. The pointer on dial A must make one revolution before the pointer on dial B moves forward. The same applies to each of the other dials. Read dial A. This dial measures the kilowatt-hours in units of 1 to 10.

2. Read dial B. This dial measures the kilowatt-hours in units of tens to 100.

3. Read dial C. This dial measures the kilowatt-hours in units of hundreds to 1000.

4. Read dial D. This dial measures the kilowatt-hours in units of thousands to 10,000.

5. Read dial E. This dial measures the kilowatt-hours in units of ten thousands to 100,000.

**APPLICATION** _____

1. from the right
2. 64,592 − 64,213 = 379
   379 × 0.09700 = $37.14
3. 88,348
4. It will begin at zero again.

Examine the electric-meter readings below. Then answer the questions that follow.

1. Where do you start to read an electric meter?

2. Suppose the previous month's reading in the meter shown in Figure 1 was 64,213 kilowatt-hours. How many kilowatt-hours of electricity were used since then? At $0.09799 per kilowatt hour, what would the current month's electric bill be?

3. How many kilowatt-hours were measured on the meter in Figure 2?

4. What do you think will happen when the dial on the left reaches 100,000?

Figure 1

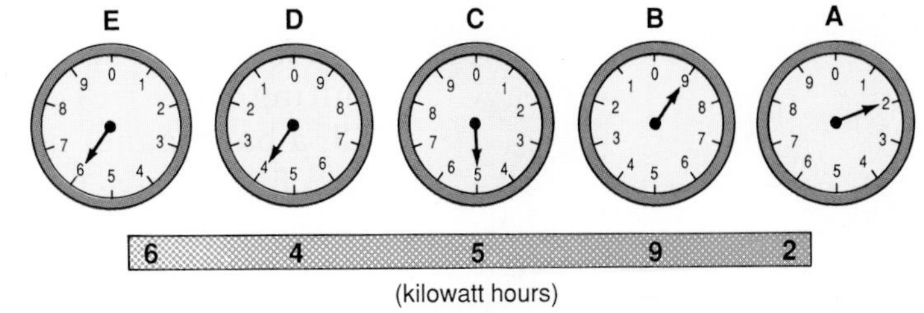

6    4    5    9    2
(kilowatt hours)

Figure 2

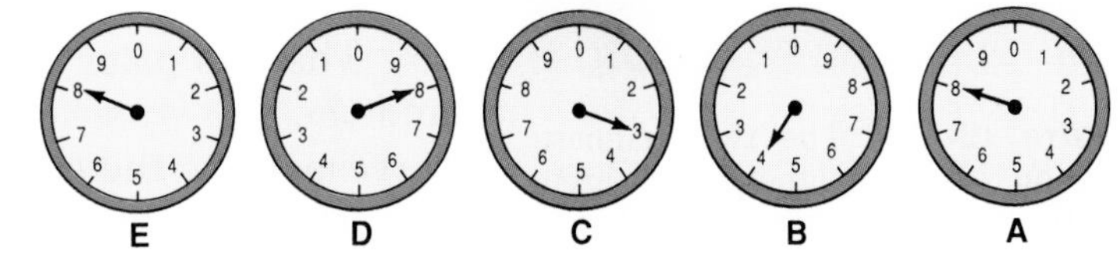

Electricity and Magnetism    **251**

# Magnetism

NEW TERMS IN THIS SECTION
magnet
magnetic pole
magnetic field
electromagnet
electromagnetic induction
domain

## SECTION OBJECTIVES

- **Define** *magnet*, *magnetic field*, *magnetic pole*, and *electromagnetic induction*.
- **Describe** interaction between magnetic poles.
- **Explain** how the principles of electromagnetic induction are used in generating electricity.

## 12.8 Magnets

Over 2000 years ago, the Greeks discovered that a material called *lodestone* was capable of attracting pieces of iron. The discovery of the attractive properties of lodestone occurred in a region of Greece known as *Magnesia*. As a result, the term **magnet** was given to any material that attracted iron and other metals. Scientists now know that lodestone is actually a very pure form of magnetic iron ore. Iron and other metals, such as cobalt and nickel, can be permanent magnets. That is, they contain natural magnetic properties.

**Figure 12–12.** The lodestone here is a natural magnet.

The early Chinese discovered that a piece of lodestone will always point in the same direction when allowed to move freely. As a result, lodestone became the first compass and was used by the Chinese for locating places on the earth's surface. The Chinese also found that other pieces of iron could become magnetized by rubbing the iron with lodestone.

### Magnetic Poles

All magnets have two magnetic poles. **Magnetic poles** are the areas where the magnetic attraction is the strongest. If a bar magnet is broken in two, each piece of the original magnet will still have two poles. If these pieces are broken into even smaller magnets, each resulting piece will always have two poles. In Figure 12–13, a bar magnet has been placed under a piece of glass. Iron filings have been sprinkled on the glass. The amount of iron filings indicates that the ends of the bar are the poles of this magnet because they have attracted more filings than the rest of the magnet.

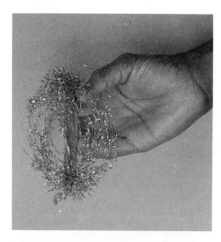

**Figure 12–13.** The two magnetic poles on this bar magnet are the areas where the most filings are located.

The two poles of a magnet are called the *north pole* and the *south pole*. Many people think a magnet's poles correspond to the earth's North and South poles, but just the opposite is true. If a magnet is allowed to hang freely

Some scientists continue to search for a magnet with only one pole (a magnetic monopole). So far, no such entity has been found.

on a string, the north pole of the magnet will point toward the earth's magnetic South Pole. The south pole of the magnet will point to the earth's magnetic north. Just as with negative and positive electric charges, like magnetic poles repel and unlike magnetic poles attract. In Figure 12–14, magnetic repulsion is being used to raise a train called a *MAGLEV* above the track. Instead of being supported by wheels, this train floats on a magnetic field, which reduces friction. The magnetic force is used to propel as well as to support the train.

## Magnetic Fields

As you bring a compass near a magnet, the compass needle, which is also a magnet, will respond by moving. Depending on the location of the compass relative to the magnet, the compass needle will point in a definite direction. The compass needle lines up with the magnetic field. A magnet does not have to be touching something for its pull to be felt. A **magnetic field** is the area around a magnet in which the magnet is exerting a force. As you bring a compass near a magnet, the direction of the compass needle indicates the direction of the magnetic field at that point. How might a natural deposit of lodestone result in a person getting lost if he or she were using a compass?

A useful way to picture a magnetic field is by using *magnetic lines of force*. The magnetic fields of several different magnets can be mapped out by iron filings that line up along each magnet's lines of force. The lines of magnetic force are continuous; they do not begin at one pole and end at the opposite pole. The number of lines is greatest where the magnetic field is strongest.

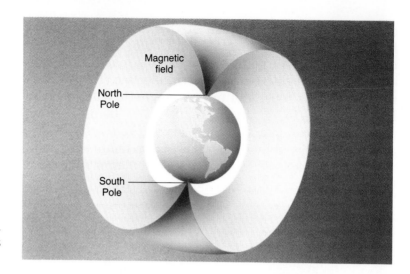

Figure 12–15. The earth is a magnet. The magnetic field is strongest at the poles.

The magnetic field surrounding the earth is very similar to that of a gigantic bar magnet. The cause of the earth's magnetism is still not completely understood. Some scientists believe that moving charges in the earth's molten core produce the magnetic field. Whatever the cause, scientists have discovered that the direction of the earth's magnetic field changes from time to time. Every 50,000 years or so, the magnetic field reverses itself. The reason for the reversal is a mystery.

## 12.9 The Source of Magnetism

The source of magnetism was discovered accidentally in 1820 by Hans Christian Oersted (UR stehd), a Danish physicist. Oersted observed that when a compass was brought near a wire carrying an electric current, the needle of the compass moved at right angles to the wire. When the current was turned off, the needle again lined up with the earth's magnetic field. Oersted's observations were important because they showed that electric currents produce magnetic fields.

Figure 12–16. The magnetic field depends on the shape of the magnet— a straight wire (below), a single turn of wire (middle), or a solenoid (right).

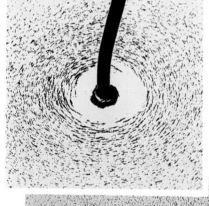

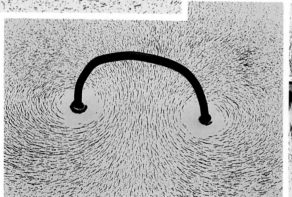

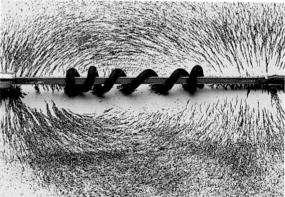

The magnetic field surrounding a current-carrying wire may be made visible by using iron filings. Figure 12–16 shows the magnetic field of a straight wire, a single turn of wire, and a coil of wire called a *solenoid*. Note that the magnetic field of a solenoid is very similar to that of the bar magnet in Figure 12–13.

When an iron core is placed inside a solenoid and a current is run through the solenoid, it becomes an **electromagnet**. Electromagnets differ from permanent magnets such as bar magnets and compass needles. When the electric current is turned off, electromagnets are no longer magnetic. However, when a permanent magnet is moved near a wire, the magnet induces a current in the wire. This effect is called **electromagnetic induction.**

Bring a horseshoe magnet close to a straight-line filament bulb such as a tubular bulb. The filament will vibrate because it acts as an electromagnet and is alternately attracted and repelled by the horseshoe magnet.

If electric currents are the source of magnetism, how can the permanent magnetic properties of certain materials, such as iron, be explained? When scientists unraveled the mystery of atomic structure, they learned that the movement of electrons in atoms is similar to tiny loops of electrical current.

**Figure 12–17.** Electromagnets have many applications—in heavy equipment (left), in television tubes (top, right), and in phonograph cartridges (bottom, right).

Electricity and Magnetism **255**

**Figure 12—18.** Magnetic domains are randomly arranged in most materials (top). The domains are aligned in magnets (bottom). This alignment produces a magnetic effect.

Bring a strong magnet near a cassette tape that does not contain any important material. Moving the magnet over the cassette will randomly arrange magnetic domains on the tape, erasing it.

In materials such as iron, each atom acts like a tiny bar magnet. The atoms form little clusters called *domains*. A **domain** is a group of atoms that are coupled and lined up in the same direction. Usually the domains themselves are not lined up. The result is that the magnetic fields of the domains cancel one another. When this happens, the material displays no magnetic effects.

If an iron bar is placed in a strong magnetic field, the domains tend to align with the external magnetic field. Iron and other metals often keep this domain alignment after they are removed from the external field. The overall effect of millions of domains pointing in the same direction is the large-scale magnetic field that exists around a permanent magnet.

## 12.10 Electromagnetic Technology

The principles of electricity and magnetism are important to methods of communication such as the telephone, radio, television, and tape recording. A television picture tube consists of an electron gun, a fluorescent screen, and two sets of magnetic coils. The electron gun at the rear of the tube sends a stream on high-speed electrons toward the front of the tube. Two sets of electromagnetic coils surrounding the tube are used to guide the electron beam so that the electrons strike the screen at the right place and time. As the electrons hit the screen, an image is produced. The strength of the electromagnets directing the electrons is controlled by the signal received from the television station.

Both audio and video recording tapes are made up of magnetic particles that are attached to a plastic tape.

**Figure 12–19.** When a videotape is made, light from the subject is changed to video signals in a video camera. The signals produce a magnetic field around the head that is on the drum. The magnetic field causes iron oxide particles to form patterns on the videotape. These patterns, when changed back to video signals, produce the picture seen on a television screen.

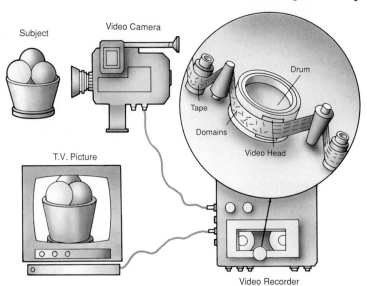

These particles may be thought of as little bar magnets that are arranged randomly on the tape. During the recording process, the tape passes over an electromagnetic recording head. The magnetic field of the recording head aligns the tiny magnets on the tape in a pattern controlled by the signal being recorded.

During the playback of the tape, the magnetized tape passes a coil of wire known as the playback head. A changing magnetic field caused by the moving tape induces a current in the coil. The current is then amplified and sent either to a loudspeaker or to a television picture tube.

## Section Review

1. How are magnetic poles like electric charges?
2. What is the difference between a magnet and an electromagnet?
3. Describe two properties of magnetic lines of force.
4. List two applications of electromagnetic induction.
5. THINKING CRITICALLY How does the existence of loops of electrical current explain why magnets always have two poles?

# CAREER

## Electrician

**DESCRIPTION** Electricians install, maintain, and repair electrical systems. Electricians follow blueprints to install wiring in buildings and other structures. They connect cables and wires to outlets, switch boxes, transformers, circuit breakers, and other devices.

**REQUIREMENTS** If you plan on a career as an electrician, you should take high-school courses in electronics, mechanical drawing, science, algebra, and shop. After graduation, you must complete a four-year apprenticeship program. This includes classroom instruction and on-the-job training. In most states, a person must pass a licensing examination to work as an electrician.

**INFORMATION** International Brotherhood of Electrical Workers, 1125 15th Street, N.W., Washington, DC 20005

# INVESTIGATION 12: Electric Circuits

*How could you determine if a circuit is series or parallel?*

## PURPOSE

To investigate the differences between series and parallel circuits

## MATERIALS

2 1.5-V D batteries
3 porcelain sockets with low-voltage bulbs

## PROCEDURE

1. Build a circuit as shown in Figure 1. When you have completed the circuit, the light bulb should glow.

2. Add a second battery to your circuit, as shown in Figure 2. Observe what happens to the brightness of the bulb. Record your observations on a separate sheet of paper. Using Ohm's law, explain the difference in the brightness of the bulb when the second battery is added.

3. Build a circuit as shown in Figure 3. Compare the brightness of the bulbs with that of the bulb in step 2. Record your observations.

4. Remove bulb 1 from its socket. Record your observations. Remove bulb 2, and record your observations.

5. Build a circuit as shown in Figure 5. Compare the brightness of the bulbs with that of the bulbs in the first three circuits. Record your observations.

6. Remove bulb 1 from its socket. Record your observations.

7. Repeat step 6 for bulbs 2 and 3.

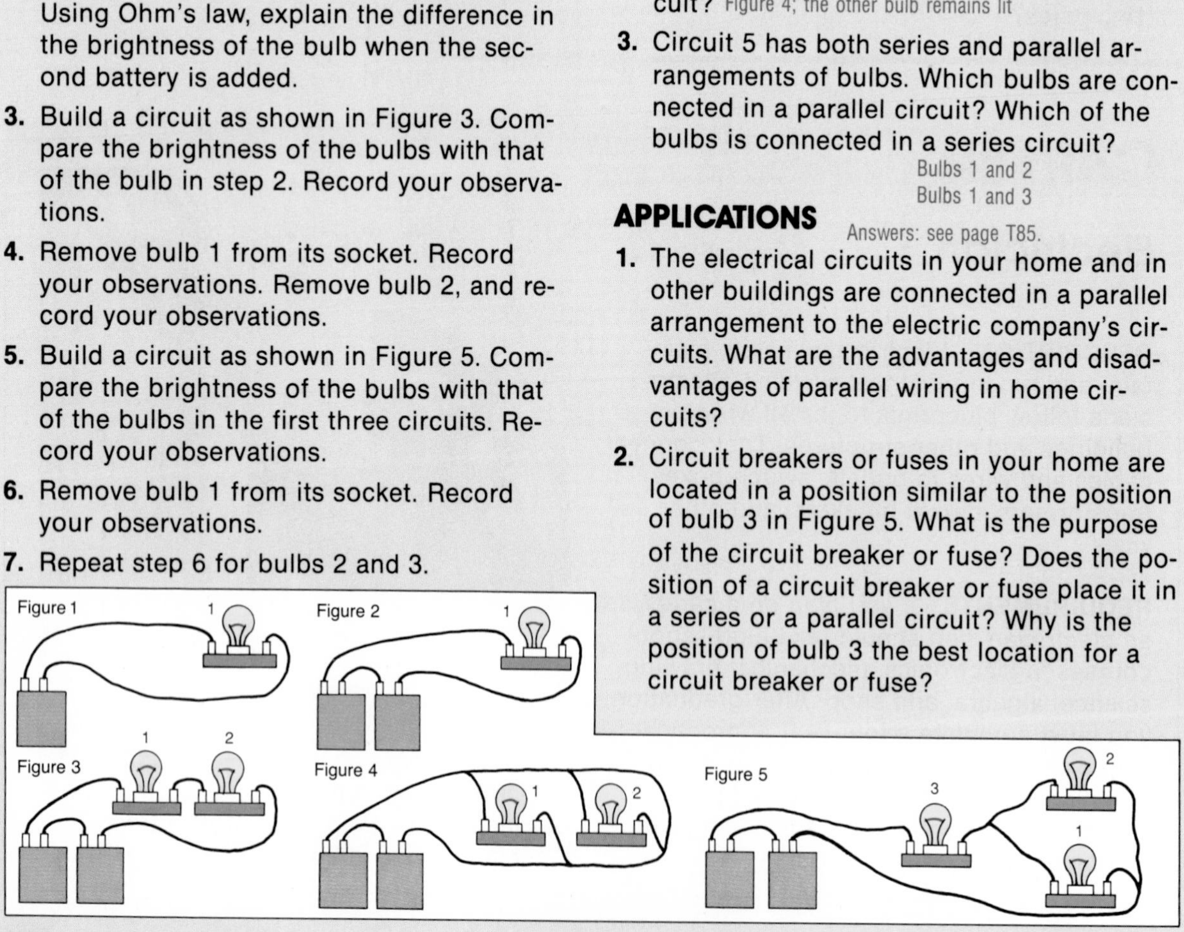

## RESULTS

1. What happened to the brightness of the bulb when you added the second battery to the circuit in step 2? brightness increased

2. Use Ohm's law to explain the differences between the brightness of the bulbs in each circuit you built. increase in voltage caused increase in current and therefore brightness

## CONCLUSIONS

1. Which circuit has bulbs only in series? What is the effect of removing one bulb of a set of bulbs connected in a series circuit? Figure 3; the other bulb goes out

2. Which circuit has bulbs only in parallel? What is the effect of removing one bulb of a set of bulbs connected in a parallel circuit? Figure 4; the other bulb remains lit

3. Circuit 5 has both series and parallel arrangements of bulbs. Which bulbs are connected in a parallel circuit? Which of the bulbs is connected in a series circuit? Bulbs 1 and 2 Bulbs 1 and 3

## APPLICATIONS

Answers: see page T85.

1. The electrical circuits in your home and in other buildings are connected in a parallel arrangement to the electric company's circuits. What are the advantages and disadvantages of parallel wiring in home circuits?

2. Circuit breakers or fuses in your home are located in a position similar to the position of bulb 3 in Figure 5. What is the purpose of the circuit breaker or fuse? Does the position of a circuit breaker or fuse place it in a series or a parallel circuit? Why is the position of bulb 3 the best location for a circuit breaker or fuse?

Figure 1    Figure 2    Figure 3    Figure 4    Figure 5

## Summary

1. Static electricity is a charge that an object has or that an object can produce. **(12.1)**

2. There are two types of charges: positive and negative. Like charges repel; unlike charges attract. **(12.1)**

3. There are many practical uses of electrostatics, such as xerography, electrostatic precipitators, and electrostatic particle accelerators. **(12.2)**

4. Conductors are materials in which electric charges are free to move. **(12.3)**

5. The flow of charge through a conductor is called an electric current. **(12.4)**

6. The potential difference between two points equals the work required to move a unit of charge between the points. **(12.4)**

7. Ohm's law states that electric current increases as voltage increases, and decreases as resistance increases. **(12.4)**

8. A circuit is a pathway for electric current. Circuits are connected in series or in parallel. **(12.5)**

9. Current does not always flow in the same direction. It may be direct or alternating. **(12.6)**

10. Electrical power is equal to the product of the voltage and the current. **(12.7)**

11. Magnets always have two poles—a north pole and a south pole. **(12.8)**

12. Electric currents are the source of all magnetism. **(12.9)**

## Science Terms

On a separate sheet of paper, define each term in a sentence.

alternating current **(248)**
ampere **(243)**
circuit **(246)**
conductor **(242)**
coulomb **(243)**
current **(243)**
direct current **(248)**
domain **(256)**

electromagnet **(255)**
electromagnetic induction **(255)**
insulator **(242)**
law of conservation of charge **(239)**
magnet **(252)**
magnetic field **(253)**
magnetic pole **(252)**
ohm **(245)**
Ohm's law **(245)**

parallel circuit **(247)**
potential difference **(243)**
resistance **(244)**
semiconductor **(242)**
series circuit **(247)**
static electricity **(239)**
volt **(243)**

## Modified True-False

On a separate sheet of paper, mark each true statement *TRUE* and each false statement *FALSE*. If false, change the underlined term to make the statement true.

1. An <u>electron</u> carries a positive charge. F, proton

2. In a metal, only <u>positive</u> charges are free to move. F, negative

3. Electricity can flow as direct current or <u>indirect</u> current. F, alternating

4. Ohm's law states that electric current is directly related to the <u>resistance</u> in a conductor. T

5. In a <u>series</u> circuit, the same current passes through each circuit element. T

6. Electrical power is measured in <u>volts</u>. F, watts

7. Batteries are used to produce <u>alternating</u> current. F, direct

8. Magnetic <u>poles</u> are the area where magnetic attraction is strongest. T

9. In electromagnetic induction, the magnet is a <u>permanent</u> magnet. F, temporary

10. All magnets have <u>two</u> poles. T

*(continues)*

## Multiple Choice

On a separate sheet of paper, write the letter of the term that best answers the question or completes the statement.

1. When an atom gains electrons, it has a
   a. positive charge.     c. neutral charge.
   b. negative charge.     d. no charge.

2. Xerography uses the principle of
   a. charge conservation.
   b. electrostatics.
   c. conduction.
   d. resistance.

3. The unit of potential difference is the
   a. volt.               c. ampere.
   b. ohm.                d. coulomb.

4. The resistance of a semiconductor is less than that of
   a. an insulator.        c. a conductor.
   b. most metals.         d. a superconductor.

5. A radio operates at 110V and 5A. What are the power requirements of this radio?
   a. 550 W               c. 0.04 W
   b. 22 W                d. 55 W

6. What are the power requirements for a stereo that operates at 120 V and 5 A?
   a. 600 W   b. 60 W   c. 6 W   d. 24 W

7. An 18-ohm resistor is placed across the terminals of a 9-volt battery. The current in the circuit equals
   a. 2 amperes.          c. 162 watts.
   b. 1/2 ampere.         d. 1/2 watt.

8. The flow of charge through a conductor is
   a. voltage.            c. current.
   b. power.              d. resistance.

9. A current passing through a wire produces
   a. an electric field.
   b. a magnetic field.
   c. a gravitational field.
   d. all the above.

10. By what process are photocopies made?
    a. xerography          c. particle acceleration
    b. induction           d. precipitation

11. The amount of work required to move a unit of charge is
    a. voltage.
    b. resistance.
    c. current.
    d. potential difference.

## Completion

On a separate sheet of paper, complete each statement by supplying the correct term.

1. A __proton__ has a positive charge.

2. Since electrical charges move easily through aluminum, it is considered an excellent __conductor__ .

3. Unlike charges __attract__ each other while like charges __repel__ each other.

4. A process known as __xerography__ uses static charges to produce photocopies.

5. An electric __curent__ is equal to the number of charges that flow past a point in a conductor each second.

6. Electrical outlets in homes are connected in __parallel__ .

7. Electrical power equals __voltage__ times current.

8. A flashlight battery produces __direct__ current.

9. The relationship between current, voltage, and __resistance__ is called Ohm's law.

10. The magnetic properties of permanent magnets are the result of the alignment of millions of __domains__ .

# Writing Critically

1. Electrical appliances generally have information regarding voltage, current, and power consumption on them. Explain what each of these quantities tells you about the electricity in your home.

2. A device that produces static electric charges is sold to help reduce record noise due to static charge buildup on records. Explain how such a device works.

3. Explain how the low resistance of metals accounts for their ability to conduct electrical current better than plastic or glass.

4. CHALLENGE Metal plates are often found installed at fixed intervals in hospital hallways. These plates are also seen at the entrances to intensive care units where pure oxygen is administered to patients. Suggest a reason for the use of these plates.

# Skill Reinforcement

The Skill Activity on page 251 describes how to read an electric meter. Look at your electric bill for last month. Notice how many kilowatt-hours were used. Then read your electric meter to determine how many kilowatt-hours have been used since then. Determine which electrical devices in your home use the most energy and how you can cut down on their use to save money.

# Research Ideas

1. There are three types of phonograph cartridges: ceramic, piezoelectric, and magnetic. Investigate how each of these devices converts mechanical energy into the electrical energy that you hear as sound.

2. Scientists have proposed that birds use the earth's magnetic field to navigate. Investigate the evidence for this theory and report on the mechanism that birds are believed to have that enables them to respond to a magnetic field.

3. CHALLENGE What is responsible for the large voltage produced by electric eels? Investigate the existence of other animals capable of producing external voltages.

4. CHALLENGE The earth has two magnetic poles. However, these poles are not located at one precise point. Find out how and why the magnetic poles are moving.

# For Further Reading

Reich, Leonard S. "From Edison's Wastebasket." *Science 84.* (November 1984), pp. 73–75. This article explains how American physicist Lee de Forest modified the light bulb to create the first vacuum tube amplifier.

Scott, John M. *Electricity, Electronics, and You.* Portland, Me.: J. Weston Walch, 1981. This book explains how to make a battery out of a lemon and why a car is the safest place to be during an electrical storm. It also provides answers to hundreds of other questions about electricity and magnetism.

Vowles, Andrew. *The EDC Book of Amazing Experiments You Can Do at Home.* Tulsa, Okla.: EDC Publishing, 1985. This book describes science activities that can be done in the home. Topics include static electricity, current electricity, electromagnets, and many others.

CHAPTER

# 13

# Light and Sound

Flashing strobes, laser blasts, giant television screens, electric guitars, synthesizers, and amplifiers—what would a rock concert be without these? These items use light and sound to stimulate the senses. In fact, everything you see and hear is transmitted by waves.

For additional informat,
see pages T86–T87.

# Waves

## SECTION OBJECTIVES

- **Compare** and **contrast** mechanical waves and electromagnetic waves.
- **Describe** the motion of a transverse and a longitudinal wave.
- **Define** *amplitude, frequency,* and *wavelength.*
- **Identify** the factors that determine the speed of a wave.

Photograph left: laser light

NEW TERMS IN THIS SECTION
mechanical waves
electromagnetic waves
transverse waves
longitudinal waves
frequency
hertz
amplitude
wavelength

## 13.1 Types of Waves

There are many types of waves, some you can see and some you cannot. Waves are all around you. Because of waves, you can see sunsets and hear music. You receive a large amount of information about your world through waves. In fact, most of the information you receive arrives through the use of two wave receptors—your eyes and your ears.

Waves transport, or carry, energy from one place to another. However, waves do not move matter from one place to another. For example, by shaking a long phone cord up and down you can produce waves. Energy is transmitted from one end to the other, but the points in the phone cord move up and down or back and forth only—they never actually travel along the cord. Consider the ocean waves you may have seen along a shoreline. What you have probably called "waves" were really breakers. The breakers come to shore and move the water in them away from the ocean. The waves in the ocean, however, only move the water up and down.

Different types of waves travel through different types of material. The material through which a wave

There are only two means by which energy and information may be carried from one point to another—by particles or by waves.

**Figure 13–1.** The waves shown here are the type people think of most often. However, the light from the sun and the sound coming from a stereo are two more examples of waves.

Light and Sound  **263**

## ACTIVITY

### Making Waves

Fill a sink about halfway with cool water. Touch the water with one finger. What kind of wave is produced? Next, touch the water with your finger three times in a row. Is the same kind of wave produced? Describe any similarities or differences between the two waves you made.

---

transverse waves, longitudinal waves; transverse waves move perpendicular to the direction of the wave, longitudinal move parallel to the direction of the wave.

The earth serves as a medium for earthquake, or seismic, waves. These waves may be longitudinal (P-waves) or transverse (S-waves).

**Figure 13–2.** In a longitudinal wave (top), the coils move in the same direction as the wave itself. The wave contains regions called *compressions*, where the coils are pushed closer together, and regions called *rarefactions*, where the coils are stretched farther apart. In a transverse wave (bottom), the particles move perpendicular to the direction of the wave itself.

passes is called the *medium* (plural, *media*). Waves may travel through solids, liquids, or gases.

Waves can be classified by the media through which they travel. Waves that travel through different types of matter are called **mechanical waves**. Sound waves and water waves are examples of mechanical waves. **Electromagnetic** (ih lehk troh mag NEHT ihk) **waves** can travel through matter and through empty space. Examples of electromagnetic waves include visible light, ultraviolet light, X rays, gamma rays, and radio waves.

Waves can also be described by the way they move. If the particles in the medium move perpendicular to the direction of wave motion, the wave is a **transverse wave**. When the particles in the medium move parallel to the direction of wave motion, the wave is a **longitudinal wave.** If you compress one end of an extended Slinky® and then release it, longitudinal waves are produced. As a wave moves along the Slinky®, some sections are compressed and some sections are pulled apart.

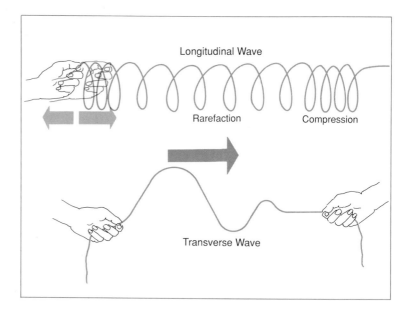

## 13.2 Characteristics of Waves

All waves have common characteristics. These characteristics include *wavelength*, *frequency*, *amplitude*, and *speed*. Look at the transverse wave shown in Figure 13–2. The wave consists of what appear to be peaks and valleys. The peaks are called *crests*, and the valleys are called *troughs* (TRAWFS). The distance between one crest and the next crest, or between any two successive troughs, is the **wavelength** of the wave.

The unit of frequency, the hertz (Hz) was named in honor of the German physicist Heinrich Hertz (1857–1894).

The number of waves that pass a particular point each second is the **frequency** of the wave. The frequency of a wave depends on how much energy the wave has. The more energy a wave has, the higher its frequency. The unit for frequency in the metric system is the **hertz (Hz).** One hertz equals one wave per second.

There is a direct relationship between the wavelength and the frequency of a wave. As the wavelength gets longer, the frequency gets lower. As the wavelength gets shorter, the frequency gets higher. The energy in a wave is related to both the wavelength and the frequency. The higher the energy, the higher the frequency and the shorter the wavelength.

In a wave, the **amplitude** is one half the distance from the bottom of the trough to the top of the crest. In the longitudinal waves that produce sound, an increase in amplitude will increase the volume you hear.

The distance that a wave travels in one second is the wave speed. Like all speeds, the speed of a wave is determined by the distance it travels divided by the time it takes to travel that distance. The speed of a wave depends on the type of wave and on the medium through which the wave is traveling. Wave speed is usually measured in meters per second.

Look at the bottle bobbing in the water in Figure 13–3. The distance the bottle bobs—the wave height—is 0.5 m. Since the wave height is 0.5 m, the wave amplitude is 0.25 m and the wavelength is 1 m. If it takes the bottle one second to bob up and down, then the wave frequency is 1 hertz. Another way to determine wave speed is to multiply the frequency of the wave times the wavelength. In this case the speed is one wave per second times 1 m per wave, which equals 1 m per second. If the amplitude of a wave was very small, but the speed was very high, what would the frequency of the wave be?

The frequency would be very high.

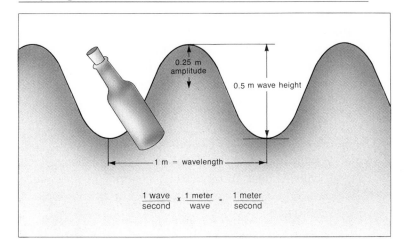

**Figure 13–3.** To calculate the speed of these water waves, multiply the wave frequency by the wavelength.

**Figure 13–4.** You see the flash of light from a rocket launch before you hear the sound of takeoff. List some experiences you have had in which the light reached you before the sound did.

Answers will vary, but may include lightning and thunder and fireworks.

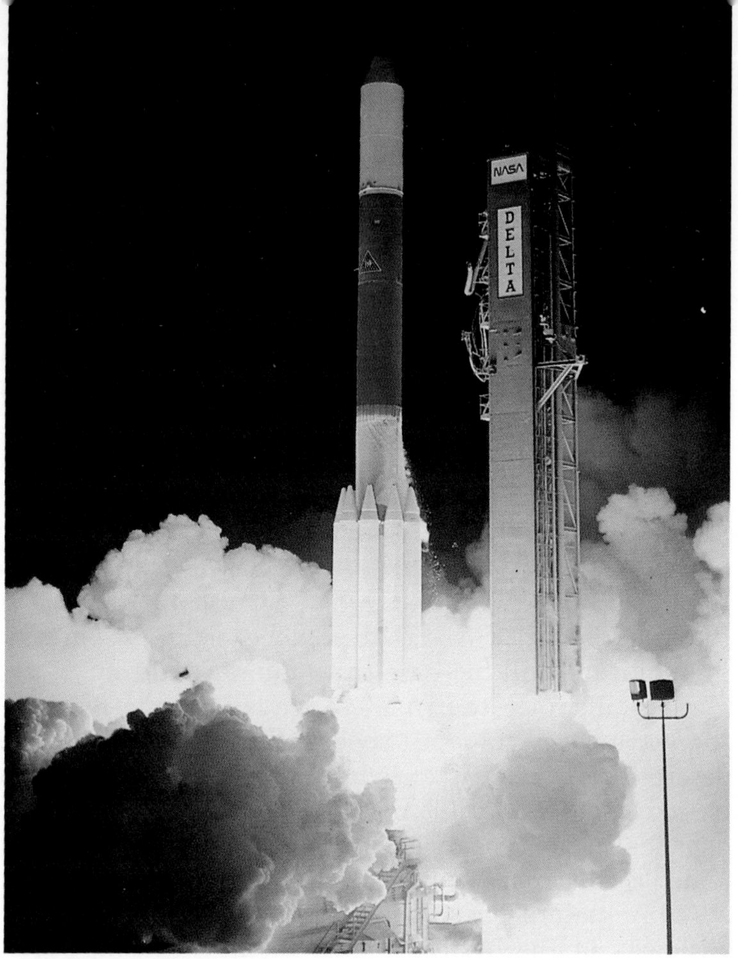


## READING CRITICALLY

Why do you see a flash of lightning and *then* hear the roll of thunder?

The speed of light is faster than the speed of sound.

Wave speeds range from a fraction of a meter per second for waves traveling across water, to 300 million m/s—the speed of light. The speed of sound (about 344 m/s) is slow compared to the speed of light. That is why you see the flash of light from a rocket launch before you hear the sound of the takeoff explosion.

## Section Review

1. What types of waves can pass through matter?
2. What is the only type of wave that can travel through empty space?
3. If the particles of the medium move perpendicular to the direction of wave motion, what kind of wave is produced?
4. Sketch a transverse wave and label the amplitude, wavelength, crests, and troughs.
5. THINKING CRITICALLY Sound travels at about 0.3 km/s. Assuming that the light from a lightning flash reaches you almost immediately, describe a procedure that you might use to determine how far away a bolt of lightning strikes.

1. both mechanical and electromagnetic waves
2. electromagnetic waves
3. a transverse wave
4. See Figure 13–3.
5. When observing a lightning flash, use a watch to determine the time between seeing the flash and hearing the thunder. By multiplying this time in seconds by the speed of sound (344 m/sec), you will be able to determine how far away the lightning struck.

# Light

## SECTION OBJECTIVES

- **Name** the primary components of the electromagnetic spectrum.
- **Define** *refraction* and *reflection*.
- **Contrast** laser light and the light produced by a light bulb.

NEW TERMS IN THIS SECTION
microwaves
infrared radiation
visible light
ultraviolet light
X rays
focal point
refraction
lens
laser

## 13.3 The Electromagnetic Spectrum

Light is made of little bundles of energy called *photons*. The characteristics of light can be described in terms of waves. Light is an electromagnetic wave. All electromagnetic waves are produced by vibrating electric charges. Electromagnetic waves differ only in frequency and wavelength. The different types of electromagnetic waves form the electromagnetic spectrum. Figure 13–5 shows the range of frequencies in the electromagnetic spectrum.

At the low-frequency end of the spectrum, there are waves produced by alternating electric current. With a frequency of 60 Hz, these electromagnetic waves have wavelengths of 5 million m. This is about the distance from New York City to Sacramento, California. The frequencies used in radio and television transmissions range between 500,000 and 500 million Hz.

Use Figure 13-5 to introduce the wide range of electromagnetic radiation that exists. Emphasize that the radiation that is visible to humans occupies only a tiny part of the spectrum.

**Figure 13–5.** The frequency for the electromagnetic spectrum ranges from $10^{23}$ hertz to $10^3$ hertz.

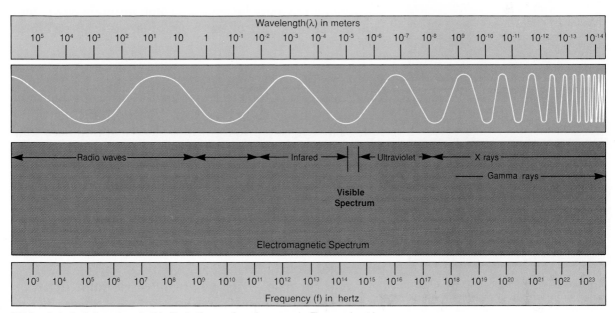

Tell the students that numbers in this illustration are for reference only. They need not be memorized and should not be tested.

**Figure 13–6.** Air-traffic controllers use radar to track hundreds of aircraft in the sky.

**Figure 13–7.** The photograph on top was taken with an ordinary camera. The photograph on the bottom was taken through infrared binoculars.

## Microwaves

Radio waves with the highest frequency (and the smallest wavelength) are **microwaves.** Microwaves have frequencies of about a billion Hz. They have wavelengths of 1 cm to about 100 cm. Radar devices use microwaves to track and detect ships and planes. Microwaves are used to send telephone, television, and radio transmissions around the world. They are also used to study the weather and to detect speeding automobiles.

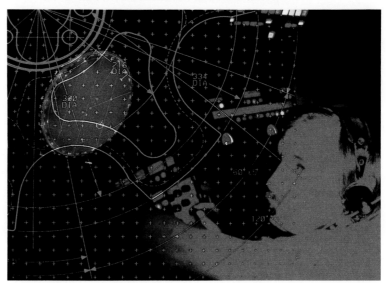

Molecules vibrating at frequencies higher than those of radio waves are the source of **infrared radiation.** Infrared waves are sometimes called *heat waves* and are given off by all hot objects. Infrared waves are not visible to humans but may be seen by some animals. Owls and snakes use this part of the electromagnetic spectrum to "see in the dark."

## Visible Light

The small part of the electromagnetic spectrum that may be seen by humans is known as **visible light**, or white light. The eye converts light into electrical impulses that are translated by the brain into images. Visible light waves have frequencies of between 400 and 700 trillion Hz. The visible spectrum is bounded at one end by red light with a wavelength of 0.00000075 m. Violet light is at the other end of the visible spectrum and has a wavelength of 0.0000004 m.

## Ultraviolet Light

Just beyond visible violet light is **ultraviolet light**, or ultraviolet radiation. Ultraviolet light has more energy and, therefore, a higher frequency than visible light. The ultraviolet rays from the sun cause some people to tan. However, it has been shown that ultraviolet radiation can also cause skin cancer in humans.

### X Rays

Having even more energy than ultraviolet light, **X rays** can pass through some solid matter. However, X rays do not pass through very dense matter such as bone or metal. Dentists and physicians use X rays to view bones and teeth.

___

***READING CRITICALLY***
Why do physicians recommend that people limit the number of X rays they have in a year?

X rays can cause cancer.
___

# 13.4 Reflection and Refraction of Light

How do you actually "see" light? All waves have certain properties, including reflection and refraction. Light waves can be reflected or refracted to make objects visible. Ask your students why the words on the front of some vehicles are written backward. (Right-to-left reversal occurs when an image is formed by a plane mirror,

### Reflection
making the words readable in a car's rear view mirror.)

When light waves are *reflected,* or bounced off an object, you see an image of the object. You are able to read this book because of reflected light. In fact, most of the light that enters your eyes is reflected light. Your friends, your clothing, and even the moon are made visible by reflected light. In Figure 13–8 a light ray is shown being reflected off a flat, or *plane*, mirror. For convenience, light rays can be drawn as straight lines that have a direction. The reference line drawn perpendicular to the mirror is called the *normal*. Look at the angle between the incoming ray, or *incident*, and the normal. This angle is equal to the angle formed by the normal and the reflected ray. The angle of incidence equals the angle of reflection. This principle is called the *law of reflection*.

To understand how an image is formed in a plane mirror, look at Figure 13–9. When you look at yourself in a plane mirror, rays from a light source are reflected from you and strike the mirror. The rays are then reflected into your eyes. The reflected light rays seem to form an image of you behind the mirror. The image formed by a plane mirror is called a *virtual image*.

A *concave* mirror is a special mirror that is curved inward. A concave mirror may be thought of as a large number of small plane mirrors, with each mirror positioned to reflect a single ray of light to a point called the **focal point**. This means that a concave mirror can take hundreds of light rays and focus them on a single point.

**Figure 13–8.** Because the light rays are hitting this plane mirror at a 90° angle, it is easy to see that the angle of incidence equals the angle of reflection.

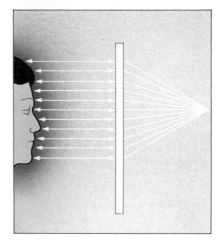

**Figure 13–9.** The image in this plane mirror is formed by extending reflected rays behind the reflecting surface (the mirror). This image cannot be projected.

## Comparing Concave and Convex Mirrors

Look at yourself in the concave side of a spoon while the spoon is close to your face. Describe the image you see. Now slowly move the spoon away from your face. What happens to the image? To see your image in a convex mirror, turn the spoon over. Describe your image for various distances of your face from the spoon.

Light rays reflected from a concave mirror intersect in front of the mirror and form a *real image*. Images such as those from movie projectors and cameras use concave mirrors to produce real images. Concave mirrors have a variety of uses. They are used in telescopes to collect light from objects in space. They are used in solar collectors to focus the sun's energy. Concave mirrors are also used in flashlights and searchlights.

A third type of mirror, called a *convex* mirror, curves outward. This type of mirror is capable of only spreading light rays. Convex mirrors form virtual images. Because convex mirrors collect light from a large area, they are often used for security purposes in stores. Many vehicles are also equipped with convex mirrors to provide a wider field of view, making backing up safer.

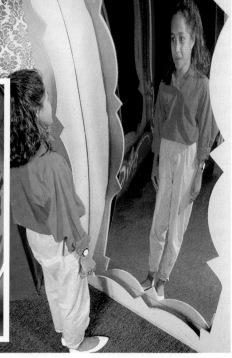

**Figure 13–10.** The security mirror in this store (left) is a convex mirror forming only a virtual image. A concave mirror, such as those found in a fun house (right) forms a real image.

A converging lens will form a right-side-up, enlarged, virtual image if the object is placed between the lens and its focal point. A magnifying glass is nothing but a converging lens used in this way.

### Refraction

When light passes from one transparent medium into another, such as from air into glass, the light may change direction, or bend. Bending of light is called **refraction.** Refraction occurs because waves travel at different speeds through different media. When a wave enters a new medium at an angle, its change in speed will result in a change in its direction.

The principle of refraction is applied in the construction of lenses. A **lens** is a curved piece of glass or plastic that refracts light to form images. Depending on its shape, a lens can form either a real or a virtual image.

When parallel rays pass through a lens and meet at a single point, the rays are said to *converge*. A lens that causes light rays to converge is called a *converging lens*. Converging lenses form real images. As with mirrors, the intersection of two light rays determines the image position. This time, however, the rays are refracted, rather than reflected.

A *diverging lens* can form only virtual images. A diverging lens spreads out parallel rays of light, as shown in Figure 13–12.

Lenses have many applications both in science and in everyday life. Microscopes and some telescopes use two or more lenses to make very small or very distant objects appear larger. A simple camera uses a single lens to form an image on film. More complex cameras use a series of lenses to form images of higher quality. Eyeglasses and contact lenses can be either converging or diverging, depending on the eye defect.

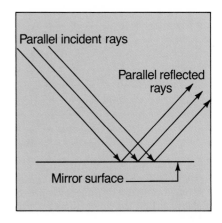

**Figure 13–11.** When parallel incident rays strike a reflective surface, the reflected rays are also parallel.

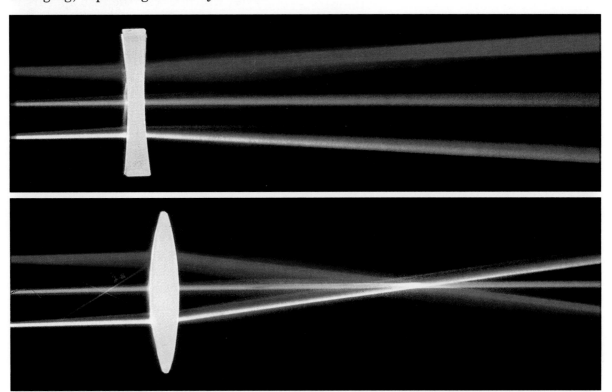

**Figure 13–12.** A concave lens (top) will refract parallel rays so that they diverge. A convex lens (bottom) will refract parallel rays so that they converge, crossing at the focus of the lens.

Refraction may be demonstrated quite simply by putting a ruler in a large beaker of water. The ruler will appear bent. An extension of this demonstration is to bend a coat hanger in such a way that it appears straight when placed in the water.

# 13.5 Color

Although sunlight appears to be simply white light, sunlight is actually a mixture of colors. White light is separated into different colors when it is passed through a prism. Similarly, under certain conditions, the atmosphere acts like a giant prism to produce a rainbow.

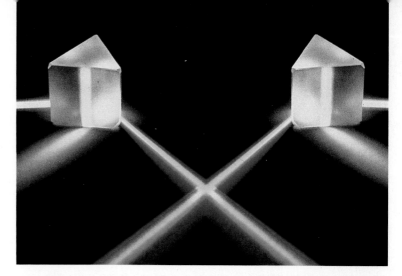

**Figure 13–13.** When white light enters the face of a prism at an angle, it separates into the rainbow spread of colors called the spectrum of white light.

Why is grass green but a rose red? Objects that do not give off light have color because they reflect light. When white light strikes a rose, all the colors of the spectrum except red are absorbed by the rose. The red is reflected to our eyes, which is why the rose appears to be red.

Objects that appear to be black absorb nearly all of the colors in the spectrum. Black objects reflect almost no light. On the other hand, white objects reflect nearly all colors. When light is absorbed, the light is changed into heat energy. <u>Why would it be more painful to sit on a black car seat on a hot day than on a white car seat?</u>

The black car seat will have absorbed all the light waves, making it very hot.

## 13.6 Lasers

The technological advances made in the study and uses of light in the last 30 years go far beyond the wildest science fiction stories. One device, the laser, has almost single-handedly made these advances possible.

**Laser** stands for *L*ight *A*mplification by *S*timulated *E*mission of *R*adiation. Light waves from a laser are *monochromatic,* which means they have only a single wavelength. They are also *coherent,* meaning that the wavelengths are perfectly lined up. Although gases are often used to produce the light in a laser, solids and liquids may also be used. For example, a helium-neon laser consists of a gas-filled tube with mirrors located at each end.

The laser has hundreds of applications. A laser beam can travel in a straight line for thousands of miles with minimal spreading. Laser light has been bounced off the moon to determine the distance from the earth to the moon. This measurement was accurate to within less than a meter. The laser is now commonly used as a surveying instrument.

**Figure 13–14.** Lasers have applications in society: in performing delicate eye surgery (left), in measuring the distances to satellites (middle), and in research (bottom).

Lasers are frequently used in operating rooms to cut through tissue. Due to the high temperatures the laser produces, it seals opened blood vessels at the same time it cuts. Delicate operations, such as reattaching retinas, are now done routinely through the process of "laser welding."

The applications of the laser in communications seem endless. Compact disc (CD) players use lasers to read tiny information-carrying indentations on the surface of small plastic disks. CDs produce a very high-quality sound. Since they are read with light and nothing touches the surface of the disk, they never wear out. In addition, the amount of information that can be placed on a single disk is quite large. An entire encyclopedia can now be reproduced on just one disk!

Finally, amazing three-dimensional pictures, called *holograms*, may be produced with a laser. A hologram is a recording of an interference pattern on conventional film. When illuminated with laser light, a hologram provides a lifelike, three-dimensional reproduction of the original object.

## Section Review

1. Which portion of the electromagnetic spectrum contains the most energetic radiation? The least energetic?

2. List the types of light in order of increasing frequency.

3. Sketch a ray of light reflecting off a plane mirror. In the sketch, label the incident ray, the reflected ray, the angle of incidence, and the angle of reflection.

4. THINKING CRITICALLY Describe the difference between laser light and the light from a light bulb.

Show your class an example of a hologram. If your school does not own a hologram, one may be found on the cover of the March 1984 issue of the *National Geographic*.

**Figure 13–15.** To produce a hologram, a laser is used to obtain hundreds of views of an object. When those images are reflected on a curved mirror, they overlap, creating a floating image.

1. Gamma rays are the most energetic. Waves produced by ordinary alternating current have the lowest energy.
2. microwaves, infrared radiation, visible light, UV, and X rays
3. See Figure 13–8.
4. A laser is a single coherent wave, incandescent light reflects in all directions.

# SKILL ACTIVITY  Writing a Summary

**INTRODUCTION**

After you read something, it often helps to summarize what you have read. Summarizing helps you understand and remember important facts.

**PROCEDURE**

1. A good summary should be brief. It should include only the most important information.
2. Start by writing down the main idea of the paragraph or article.
3. Write down any important facts. Unless the order in which they were presented is essential, it is not necessary to list them in order.
4. In your summary, include only the information given in the material you have read. Do not include your own opinion or what you think should have been included.
5. Depending on what you are reading, it is sometimes a good idea to begin with the writer's conclusion and work backward to pick out important points that lead to that conclusion.

**APPLICATION**

Read the article below. Then answer the questions that follow.

### Colors in the Sky

You have probably wondered at times, what makes the sky blue. When sunlight passes through the earth's atmosphere, it strikes the nitrogen and oxygen molecules in the air. These molecules scatter sunlight in all directions, but about ten times more molecules scatter at the blue end of the light spectrum. When you look up at the sky, you see mostly scattered blue light, which makes the sky look blue.

Flaming red sunsets are also caused by small particles in the atmosphere. Red sunsets occur most often when a high-pressure air mass is present. Concentrated in these air masses are millions of dust particles. These particles scatter light from the setting sun primarily from the red end of the light spectrum. The scattered red light produces a spectacular sunset.

1. What is the main idea of this article? 1. The sky is blue due to the scattering of blue light.
2. What important details would you include in a summary of this article? 2. Answers will vary, but should include mention of nitrogen and oxygen molecules, the scattering of light, and the relationship of pressure fronts to red sunsets.
3. Write a summary of this article. 3. Summaries will vary but should reflect an understanding of the summarizing process.
4. How does summarizing help you retain information? 4. Summarizing helps you understand the material by putting it in your own words.

# Sound

## SECTION OBJECTIVES

● **Describe** the source of all sound waves.
● **Define** *pitch* and *decibel*.
● **Explain** why motion affects the pitch of a sound.

NEW TERMS IN THIS SECTION
pitch
decibel
diffraction
interference
Doppler effect

## 13.7 The Nature of Sound

All sound waves are longitudinal waves produced by vibrating objects. Like all waves, sound waves transport energy but do not carry matter with them. Because sound waves are mechanical waves, sound can travel only through matter. Although most people think of sound as traveling through air, liquids and solids also carry sound waves.

The prongs of the tuning fork in Figure 13–16 are vibrating back and forth. This vibration results in a disturbance that is passed on from molecule to molecule. For as long as the tuning fork continues to vibrate, the disturbance will move out in all directions from the source.

### SCIENCE FACT

Without a medium through which to travel, sound waves cannot exist. For this reason, there is no sound on the moon.

Place the tips of a vibrating tuning fork in a glass of water to show how they are capable of disturbing a medium. The vibrating prongs will produce an impressive spray of water.

**Figure 13–16.** By striking a tuning fork and placing it in water, the waves formed by the sound vibrations can be seen.

The speed of sound depends on the medium through which it is traveling and on the temperature of the medium. Sound travels slowest through gases and fastest through solids. In air at room temperature, sound has a speed of about 344 m/s. The higher the temperature, the faster sound will travel.

| TABLE 13–1 SPEED OF SOUND THROUGH DIFFERENT MEDIA | |
| --- | --- |
| **Medium** | **Speed (m/s)** |
| Air (0°C) | 331 |
| Aluminum | 5000 |
| Brick | 3650 |
| Distilled water (25°C) | 1496 |
| Glass | 45400 |
| Sea water (25°C) | 1531 |
| Steel | 5200 |
| Wood | 4110 |

The highness or lowness of a sound is determined by a wave's frequency and is called **pitch.** A low-frequency sound wave has a low pitch, and a high-frequency sound wave has a high pitch. The range of frequencies heard by a healthy young person is roughly 20 to 20,000 Hz. As people age, their ability to hear higher frequencies is reduced because cells in the ear become less sensitive.

The greater the amplitude, or intensity, of a sound wave, the louder it is. A sound's loudness is called *volume.* Intensity is measured in **decibels** (dB). Table 13–2 indicates the decibel level of some common sounds. Sound levels exceeding 120 dB can cause physical pain. Long exposure to loud sounds can result in permanent hearing loss.

| TABLE 13–2 DECIBEL LEVELS OF SOME NOISES | |
|---|---|
| **Noise** | **Loudness (dB)** |
| Jet plane taking off | 135 |
| Thunder | 130 |
| Rock concert | 115 |
| Motorcycle | 110 |
| Police siren | 95 |
| Heavy traffic | 80 |
| Vacuum cleaner | 75 |
| Car accelerating | 70 |
| Normal conversation | 65 |
| Average home | 50 |
| Faint whisper | 20 |

**Figure 13–17.** Airport ground personnel are required to wear ear protection to prevent severe hearing loss due to the high decibels produced by jet engines.

A room that is virtually nonreflecting is called an *anechoic chamber.*

# 13.8 Reflection and Diffraction of Sound

Like light waves, sound waves have certain properties that make it possible for sound to be heard. These properties include reflection and diffraction.

### Reflection

Sound waves are reflected off of most objects in much the same way as light waves are. A common example of the reflection of sound waves is an *echo.* Echoes generally occur when sound reflects off buildings, hills, or mountains. Sound is constantly reflecting off objects in a room as you speak or listen to the radio.

By using special sound-absorbing materials, scientists can make a room almost totally nonreflecting. Such rooms are used to test stereo equipment, musical instruments, and the noise level of machinery.

The reflection of sound waves is used in sonar devices aboard ships to determine water depth. Sonar stands for *So*und *Na*vigation and *R*anging. The time

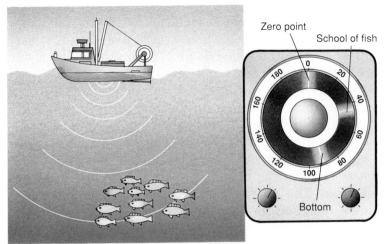

Zero point

School of fish

180 0 20 40 60 80 100 120 140 160

Bottom

**Figure 13–18.** A fishing boat uses sonar to detect schools of fish. Pulses of sound are sent out by the sonar. Echoes from the fish and the ocean bottom are returned. The depth of the fish is recorded on a meter (right).

Some cameras now use the reflection of ultrasonic sound to automatically determine the distance to a subject for focusing purposes.

required for a pulse of sound to reach the bottom of the water and to return to the ship is measured automatically. By using this time and the speed of sound in water, the sonar device calculates the distance to the bottom. How do submarines use sonar to determine if it is safe for the vehicle to surface? By sending pulses up, the submarine can determine if there is anything above it.

### Diffraction

Like light waves, sound waves can be bent. Unlike light waves, sound waves can move around corners in a process called **diffraction.** Diffraction makes hearing around corners possible. For example, you can hear the television set in the living room when you are doing your homework in the kitchen because of diffraction.

Have a student leave the classroom while talking to the class. Due, in part, to the diffraction of sound waves around corners, the class will be able to hear the student even when they can no longer see him or her. Note: Some of the sound will reach the students by reflection.

## 13.9 Interference

The interaction of waves in the same space is called **interference**. As two crests approaching each other meet, the amplitudes of the two waves are added together. This type of interference is called *constructive interference*. When the crest of one wave meets the trough of another wave, the result is called *destructive interference*.

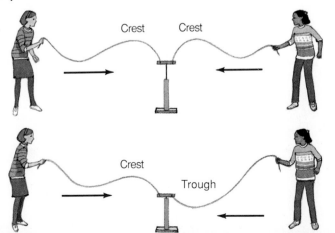

Crest    Crest

Crest

Trough

**Figure 13–19.** When the two wave crests arrive at the same time (top), constructive interference results and the bicycle pump handle will rise. When one crest and one trough arrive at the same time (bottom), destructive interference results and the bicycle pump handle will not move at all.

## ACTIVITY

### Tuning In to Sound Waves

Strike the prongs of a tuning fork against a rubber hammer. Listen carefully for the sound produced by the vibrating prongs. Strike the prongs again, but this time touch the fork's handle to the table top. What happens?

The fork stopped vibrating because the vibration passed on through the table.

Where interference is constructive, the sound is very loud. Where interference is destructive, the sound is very soft or there is no sound at all. These areas of no sound are called *dead spots*. Dead spots produced by the interference of direct and reflected sound waves can cause serious problems in auditoriums and concert halls. Such structures are carefully designed to prevent areas of destructive interference.

The interference of sound waves may also occur when two sources of sound have slightly different frequencies. The resulting interference can be heard at a single location because the intensity of the sound changes with time. When the vibrations from two tuning forks arrive at the listener's ear at the same time, constructive interference is heard. Since the frequencies of the two tuning forks are different, eventually the two waves will not arrive at the listener's ear at the same time. When the waves do not arrive at the same time, destructive interference occurs, and a soft sound is heard. After a short time, the two vibrations will again arrive at the same time, and again a loud sound is heard. The overall effect is a series of loud and soft sounds called *beats*.

Piano tuners listen for beats between a tuning fork of known frequency and a string on a piano. By adjusting the tension in the string, the tuner can make the beats disappear. Once this type of interference is gone, the string is in tune.

**Figure 13–20.** The Doppler effect is an apparent change in pitch produced by moving objects. The pitch of a train whistle seems to get higher as the train comes closer and lower as the train moves away. People at the crossing will hear a change in pitch as the train goes by; the people on the train will hear a uniform pitch.

Johann Doppler was said to have first demonstrated the Doppler effect by placing a brass band on a flat car of a moving train. He showed that when a sound source approaches an observer, the pitch of the sound increases. When the source of sound moves away from the observer, however, the pitch decreases.

A change in pitch caused by the motion of the source of a sound or of the listener is called the **Doppler effect.** Figure 13–20 shows a source of sound moving toward an observer. As the source moves forward, the sound waves in front of the source become crowded. When sound waves are moved closer together, the frequency of the sound is increased. An increase in frequency sounds like a higher pitch to the listener. When the sound source moves away from the observer, the sound waves are spread farther apart and arrive with lower frequency. This time, the observer hears a lower pitch.

## Section Review

1. How does the temperature of the medium affect the speed of sound waves traveling through the medium?
2. List two everyday examples of the Doppler effect.
3. Explain the difference between pitch and decibel.
4. Describe how sonar works.
5. THINKING CRITICALLY Why does sound travel faster in liquids and solids than in gases?

5. In liquids and solids the molecules are closer together than they are in gases. Thus, the time required for one moving molecule to interact with a neighboring molecule is reduced in a solid or a liquid. A disturbance will therefore travel much more quickly through solids and liquids.

*READING CRITICALLY*
How could you use the Doppler effect to determine whether a fire engine is coming toward you or moving away from you?

By listening to hear if the pitch is becoming higher or lower. If the pitch gets higher, then the vehicle is approaching; if the pitch gets lower, then it is moving away.

1. Higher temperature results in a faster speed of sound.
2. the change in pitch of a police car siren as it passes you and the shift in pitch of a railroad crossing warning bell as heard by passengers on a moving train
3. Pitch is the frequency, or highness and lowness of sound; decibel is the amplitude, or intensity of sound.
4. Sonar measures the time it takes for the reflection of sound to come back to the source of the sound. By knowing the speed of sound in a medium you can calculate the distance the object is from the source of the sound.

## CAREER

# Recording Studio Sound Mixer

**DESCRIPTION**  A sound mixer, or studio technician, controls the volume and quality of sound produced on records and tapes. Sound mixers direct the placement of microphones, adjust amplifiers, and make sure recording equipment is in good condition. They edit and copy recordings to create the finished product.

**REQUIREMENTS**  The student who plans to be a sound mixer should take as many high-school mathematics courses as possible. Courses in mechanical drawing are also valuable. After graduation, four years of technical training are required.

**INFORMATION**  Audio Engineering Society, 60 East 42nd Street, Room 2520, New York, NY 10065

# INVESTIGATION 13: Properties of Waves

*How would you describe the movement of waves?*

## OBJECTIVE

To demonstrate the properties of waves

## MATERIALS

strong wire (the length of the room)
triple-length Slinky®
string (4 m)
rubber tubing (3 m)
masking tape
stopwatch (or use second hand on watch)

## PROCEDURE

1. Attach a strong wire to the front and rear walls of the room, and stretch it tight.

2. To every tenth turn of the Slinky®, tie a string about 1 m long.

3. Loop the other end of each string around the horizontal wire and tie a knot. The attachment to the wire should be a loop so that its position can be changed.

4. Stretch the Slinky® out. Fasten the Slinky® to a fixed support at each end of the room.

5. Attach the rubber tubing to one end of the Slinky®, and let the rest of the tubing trail out on the floor.

6. Mark one turn of the Slinky® with a piece of tape. Shake one end of the Slinky® back and forth to generate a transverse wave.

7. Now generate a longitudinal wave by moving one end of the Slinky® back and forth parallel to itself.

8. Determine the speed of the transverse wave by measuring the time it takes for a crest to get from one end of the Slinky® to the other.

9. Change the frequency of the transverse wave by changing the rate at which the end is shaken.

## RESULTS

1. How would you describe the motion of the transverse and longitudinal waves? Answers will vary.

2. What was the speed of your transverse wave? Answers will vary.

3. How were frequency, wavelength, and velocity affected by speeding up or slowing down the rate at which the end was shaken? All changed accordingly.

## CONCLUSIONS

1. When the Slinky® is shaken back and forth, which way does the tape move? back and forth

2. Which kind of wave shows alternate compressions and rarefactions? longitudinal

## APPLICATION

A boat is floating unanchored in a lake 25 m from shore. There is little or no current. However, waves are moving toward shore at a rate of 5 m/s. How soon will the boat reach shore? It will not reach shore if there is no current. Waves do not move matter.

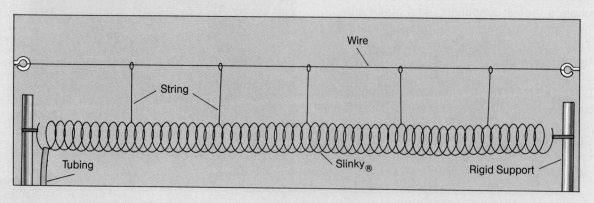

Wire

String

Tubing

Slinky®

Rigid Support

## Summary

1. In a transverse wave, particles in the medium move perpendicular to the direction of motion of the wave. **(13.1)**

2. In a longitudinal wave, particles in the medium move parallel to the direction of motion of the wave. **(13.1)**

3. All waves have four characteristics: wavelength, frequency, amplitude, and speed. **(13.2)**

4. Light is an electromagnetic wave. **(13.3)**

5. In reflection, the angle of incidence equals the angle of reflection. **(13.4)**

6. The bending of light as it passes from one medium into another is called refraction. **(13.4)**

7. Objects that do not give off light have color because they reflect light. **(13.5)**

8. Light waves from lasers have only one wavelength. **(13.6)**

9. Sound waves are longitudinal waves. **(13.7)**

10. Sound waves exhibit reflection, diffraction, and interference. **(13.8, 13.9)**

## Science Terms

On a separate sheet of paper, define each term in a sentence.

amplitude **(265)**
decibels **(276)**
diffraction **(277)**
Doppler effect **(279)**
electromagnetic wave **(264)**
focal point **(269)**
frequency **(265)**
hertz **(265)**

infrared radiation **(268)**
interference **(277)**
laser **(272)**
lens **(270)**
longitudinal wave **(264)**
mechanical wave **(264)**
microwave **(268)**

pitch **(276)**
refraction **(270)**
transverse wave **(264)**
ultraviolet light **(268)**
visible light **(268)**
wavelength **(264)**
X rays **(269)**

## Modified True-False

On a separate sheet of paper, mark each true statement *TRUE* and each false statement *FALSE*. If false, change the underlined term to make the statement true.

1. In a transverse wave, the particles in the medium move <u>parallel</u> to the direction of motion of the wave. F, perpendicular

2. Waves transport <u>energy</u>. T

3. <u>Electromagnetic waves</u> can travel through an empty space. T

4. The part of the electromagnetic spectrum that can be seen by humans is known as <u>visible light</u>. T

5. Infrared radiation has a higher frequency than <u>ultraviolet light</u>. F, microwaves

6. A <u>concave</u> mirror brings rays of light to a focal point. T

7. When a crest of one wave meets a trough of another wave, <u>constructive</u> interference occurs. F, destructive

8. You hear <u>frequency</u> as pitch. T

9. A wavelength is the distance between a crest and the next <u>trough</u>. F, crest

10. Sonar uses the <u>reflection</u> of sound waves to determine underwater distances. T

*(continues)*

## Multiple Choice

On a separate sheet of paper, write the letter of the term that best answers the question or completes the statement.

1. The height of a wave is called the
   a. frequency.
   c. wavelength.
   b. wave speed.
   d.) amplitude.

2. Light is an example of _____ wave.
   a. a mechanical
   c. a transverse
   b. a longitudinal
   d.) an electromagnetic

3. The origin of any sound wave is
   a. a condensation.
   c. velocity.
   b.) a vibrating object.
   d. energy.

4. The amplitude of a sound wave determines its
   a. pitch.
   c.) loudness.
   b. quality.
   d. frequency.

5. Lenses use _____ to form images.
   a. reflection
   c. diffraction
   b.) refraction
   d. interference

6. The speed of a wave depends on
   a. the shape of the wave.
   b. the amplitude of the wave.
   c. the frequency of the wave.
   d.) the medium in which it is traveling.

7. Lasers are used in
   a. communications.
   b. surgery.
   c. manufacturing.
   d.) all of the above.

8. Which of the following types of waves may exhibit interference?
   a. longitudinal waves
   b. mechanical waves
   c. transverse waves
   d.) all of the above

9. The type of image formed by a plane mirror is a
   a.) virtual image.
   c. refraction.
   b. real image.
   d. reflection.

10. Which form of light has the most energy?
    a. microwaves
    c. infrared radiation
    b.) X rays
    d. ultraviolet light

## Completion

On a separate sheet of paper, complete each statement by supplying the correct term.

1. The number of waves passing a given point each second is called the _frequency_.

2. White light is separated into different colors when it passes through a _prism_.

3. Waves that cannot travel through empty space are called _mechanical_ waves.

4. The phenomenon of _diffraction_ is responsible for the bending of sound waves around corners.

5. Two waves combining to produce a wave that is larger than either beginning wave are an example of _constructive_ interference.

6. Lasers produce light having a single _wavelength_.

7. Sound travels slowest through _gases_ and fastest through solids.

8. The _Doppler Effect_ may be heard when a police car with its siren on passes a stationary observer.

9. The reflection of a sound wave is commonly called an _echo_.

10. Wavelengths of light that are perfectly lined up are _coherent_.

## Writing Critically

1. Every home has several mirrors of various shapes and sizes. Describe as many of these in your own home as you can, stating the use of each mirror. Identify the mirrors as plane, concave, or convex. Also describe the nature of the image formed by each mirror.

2. Sound is produced by vibrating objects. Make a list of musical instruments with which you are familiar and describe which part of each instrument vibrates to create the sound.

3. **CHALLENGE** After examining a stereo system, describe what makes a stereo sound system different from a mono system. What advantage does stereo sound have over one-channel sound?

1. Answers will vary but should reflect an understanding of the three types of mirrors and the images they produce.
2. Answers will vary but can include any string instrument.
3. The use of constructive interference makes stereo sound fuller and more dimensional.

## Skill Reinforcement

The Skill Activity on page 274 describes how to write a summary. Reread any sections in this chapter that you have had trouble with. Then write summaries of those sections, using the steps outlined in the Skill Activity. Compare your summary with the summary at the end of the chapter. Which type of summary is more helpful?

## Research Ideas

1. Investigate how phonograph records and compact disks are made and how sound recorded on these devices is reproduced. Make a list of their similarities and differences.

2. Many medical procedures have been made simpler, safer, and more effective through the use of the laser. Report on some of the advances in medical techniques made possible by the laser.

3. **CHALLENGE** Investigate the process of holography. What makes a holographic image appear three-dimensional? List uses of holography in the sciences, technology, and the arts.

## For Further Reading

Berry, Richard. *Build Your Own Telescope: Complete Plans for Five High-Quality Telescopes That Anyone Can Build.* New York: Scribner's, 1985. This book explains how to make five different telescopes, from simple to complex. The book even includes practical observing tips to get the most out of your telescope once it is built.

Burkig, Valerie C. *Photonics: The New Science of Light.* Hillside, NJ: Enslow, 1986. This short book gives an excellent overview of modern optical science and technology and its applications in communication, computing, medicine, and other areas.

Heckman, Philip. *The Magic of Holography.* New York: Atheneum, 1986. This book, with more than 100 diagrams and photographs, gives a history of the science of optics.

CHAPTER

**14**

# Computer Technology and Robotics

The use of integrated circuits has revolutionized the use of computers. These circuits reduced the cost, size, and energy requirements of computers. Integrated circuits are made of thin discs of silicon, like those shown below. Such circuits are used for most of the operations performed inside computers today.

For additional information, see pages T88–T89.

# What Is a Computer?

### SECTION OBJECTIVES

- **Identify** the three main parts in a computer system and the three units in the central processing unit.
- **Define** *sequential programming*, *machine language*, *assembly language*, and *high-level language*.
- **Compare** the size and power of mainframes, minicomputers, and microcomputers.

NEW TERMS IN THIS SECTION

| | | |
|---|---|---|
| computer | input devices | microprocessor | high-level language |
| hardware | output devices | software | mainframe |
| | central processing unit | sequential programming | supercomputer |
| | | machine language | minicomputer |
| | | assembly language | microcomputer |

## 14.1 Hardware

As defined in Chapter 2, a **computer** is an electronic device that can store and process information. The earliest computers were mechanical calculators. These machines were invented to help mathematicians with their calculations. Today, with the help of transistors and integrated circuits, computers do everything from helping you with your math homework to sending astronauts to the moon.

A computer system has three main parts—input, the central processing unit, and output. The physical components, or machinery, that perform these functions are the computer **hardware**. What parts of the human body do you think might compare to the three main parts of a computer system? input = senses, CPU = brain, output = muscles, arms, legs

Information is put into a computer through **input devices**. Input devices include keyboards, tape machines, disk drives, and many other devices. **Output devices** are used to send information out of a computer. Video screens and printers are two examples of output devices.

**Figure 14–1.** The success of the early space program hinged on the use of highly complex computers that could perform all the necessary calculations for the astronauts' flight path and experiments in space. A "spinoff" of space technology is that computers and calculators are now commonplace.

Photograph left: silicon discs containing integrated circuits

Computer Technology and Robotics  **285**

Input → Processing → Output

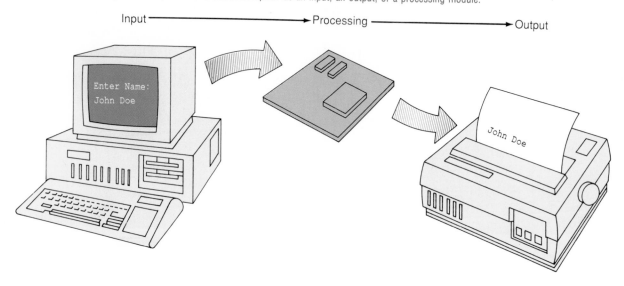

**Figure 14–2.** The basic computer processing cycle is shown in this illustration.

**Figure 14–3.** Mainframe computers (left) have all the subassemblies mounted in one cabinet. The microprocessor chip (right) used in microcomputers contains all the information on one tiny chip.

The actual computing, or information processing, is done in the computer's **central processing unit**, or CPU. The CPU is sometimes called the "brain" of the computer. The CPU receives all the information input to the computer, processes the information (does the work

Compare vacuum-tube hardware, a transistor radio, and integrated circuit equipment. Older vacuum-tube public address equipment is still in use and may be available in your school. Bring in a true transistor radio for the students to examine. A computer relies entirely on integrated circuits.

necessary to complete a task), and sends the information out through an output device.

In early computers, the CPU, or *processor*, was made up of many separate parts mounted on a printed circuit board. Today, a CPU is usually contained on a single chip called a **microprocessor**. Compare the sizes of the two processors shown in Figure 14–3. Believe it or not, more information may be stored on one tiny chip than on a circuit board many times its size.

Each chip carries one integrated circuit containing thousands of transistors. As shown in Figure 14–4, each chip is enclosed in a plastic case and placed on a carrier. The carrier's "legs" are the electric wires that connect the chip to the rest of the computer.

The CPU has three units—the arithmetic and logic unit (ALU); main storage, or memory; and the control unit. The ALU performs mathematical operations—addition, subtraction, multiplication, and division. It can also make logical "decisions" by comparing numbers, letters, or special characters. Computers "decide" whether there are any empty seats on an airplane or whether charge-card customers have gone over their credit limits by comparing letters or characters.

The main storage, or memory, unit stores the information and instructions the computer needs to perform different tasks. A computer's power is often defined by how much information it can hold in its memory. The larger the storage capacity of a computer, the more powerful it is.

The control unit of the CPU coordinates the operations of the ALU and the memory unit. How quickly the control unit coordinates these functions determines the computer's speed. How fast a computer operates also determines the computer's power.

**Figure 14–4.** For protection, each chip is bonded to a chip carrier. Without the carrier, the chip would crumble if dropped. The chip is connected to the electrodes of the carrier by gold wires.

## 14.2 Software

How does a computer know what to do with information that it receives? A computer must follow a different set of instructions for each task it performs. These instructions are called *programs*. The set of programs for a given computer system is called computer **software**.

Computers perform a task one step at a time. Therefore, computer programs must be written in the order in which each operation is to be performed. **Sequential programming** instructs the computer to perform specific steps in a specific order. Sequential programming is common to all computers.

Discuss with students the various computer programs they have encountered. Emphasize their experiences with programs that had fast-moving screen images (likely machine language) and programs that required them to wait for a period of time before the computer responded.

**Figure 14–5.** As this girl is discovering, everything is black and white to a computer. The language best understood by the computer is a series of yes or no commands.

Up to 20 or 30 machine languages can be combined into an assembly-language instruction. The assembly language is different for each model of computer and cannot be changed.

Programs must also be converted to a language a computer will understand. Computer programs are written in numerical codes that the CPU can translate. The codes are based on just two numbers, the digits one and zero. Computer operation is based on turning the transistors, which contain information, on and off at different times. Therefore, the computer's instructions are written in a series of "turn-on" and "turn-off" commands. A one turns a transistor on, and a zero turns it off. Commands in this form are called **machine language.** Machine language instructions can be built into the computer. Computers that are programmed in machine language perform their operations very quickly and accurately.

Because computers work electronically, they can complete millions and even billions of operations per second. Many computer functions are standard, often-repeated operations. To avoid repeating the commands for such steps, some computers are programmed with assembly language instructions. **Assembly language** instructions are made up of machine language instructions assembled, or grouped, into sets. Up to twenty or thirty machine language operations can be combined into an assembly language instruction. The assembly language used by each model of computer is different and cannot be changed.

Computers programmed with machine language or assembly language instructions can also follow programs written in high-level languages. **High-level languages** are program codes that look like everyday English. High-level languages are much easier to learn and to use than machine and assembly languages. These languages are made up of words or symbols that the computer translates into machine language instructions. Most high-level languages are used to write programs in specialized areas. Unlike machine or assembly language, high-level languages are not a permanent part of the computer's structure. They are stored in the computer memory. The same computer can use many different high-level languages.

## 14.3 Mainframes, Minis, and Micros

The word *size* is often applied to computers. In the computer field, *size* has two meanings. It can mean the physical size of a computer—its height and length. Size can also mean the memory capacity of the computer. Thus, the larger the computer, the more information it can store. Usually, when you hear of a "big" computer, it is in reference to a fast, powerful machine.

## Mainframes

Machines that are big in physical size and in power are **mainframe** computers. Mainframes are used to do large computing jobs, such as controlling a telephone switching network or holding data for a governmental agency. Mainframe computers are often so large that they fill entire rooms. Mainframes may be connected to several hundred terminals, or work stations, in different locations.

Lead the class to speculate on the difference in complexity of various computer jobs that might be performed within a school system: building attendance records, district property records, and transcripts. Discuss the complexity of each job, and attempt to arrange them in a comparative ranking. Divide the jobs into simple, intermediate, and complex groups as a way of utilizing more or less powerful computers.

**Figure 14–6.** The parts of the main section of the machines are mounted on metal racks, or frames, which is why these computers are called mainframes.

The largest, most powerful mainframes are known as **supercomputers**. Supercomputers work extremely fast—about twenty times faster than regular mainframes. Some supercomputers can perform one billion operations per second. Supercomputers perform such huge tasks as analyzing data from thousands of weather stations around the world. Using this information, a supercomputer does millions of mathematical calculations to prepare local weather forecasts for an area.

## READING CRITICALLY

What types of industry might need the services of a supercomputer?

Answers will vary, but may include NASA, the census bureau, and a telephone company.

**Figure 14–7.** This *Cray II* is a supercomputer. It can perform over 1 billion operations per second.

**Figure 14–8.** Computers are now part of everyday life. Your dentist may have your dental history (left) stored on a computer. These students (right) have portable computers that can easily be carried.

## Minis & Micros

Computers that perform less complex tasks than mainframes are called **minicomputers**. Minicomputers have less memory, cost less money, and occupy less space than mainframes, but they use similar technology. They are often used by medium-sized businesses, hospitals, libraries, and school-district offices.

The most familiar desk-top computer—the personal or home computer—is called a *microcomputer*. The **microcomputer** is the smallest and least expensive type of computer. Microcomputers were made possible by the invention of the microprocessor, the complete "computer on a chip." Microcomputers are used in education for individual student use, in business when great power is not needed, and by individuals for personal records and entertainment.

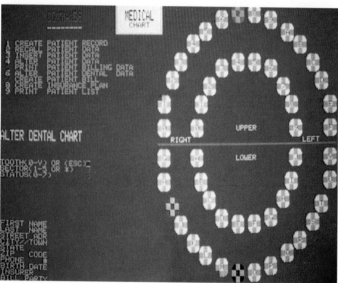

## Section Review

1. Which part of a computer system involves the use of computer programs?

2. What are the three units of the CPU? Explain why some people call the CPU the "brain" of the computer.

3. What is the difference between machine language and assembly language?

4. How does a minicomputer differ from a mainframe? From a microcomputer?

5. THINKING CRITICALLY List the types of languages found in a computer program and describe how each is used.

The use of artificial intelligence raises some controversial issues. Should a truly thinking computer be built? Could a computer reason effectively in unfamiliar situations? Could a computer make value judgments and come up with ideas? Should a computer be programmed to have human feelings? How could the decisions made by a computer be reviewed?

## ACTIVITY

**Using a Thinking Computer**

Divide your class into two groups and debate the pros and cons of developing a truly thinking computer.

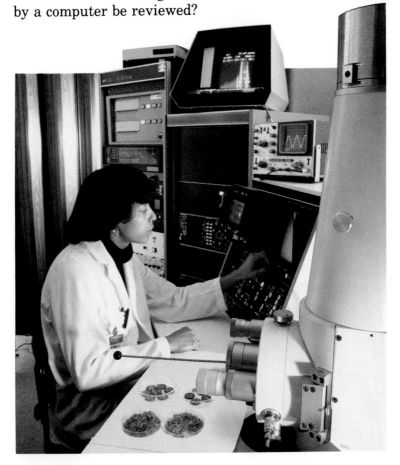

**Figure 14–12.** Computers can monitor the performance of other computers. This technician is using a computerized infrared scanner to detect hot spots in a supercomputer that is used in car design.

## Section Review

1. What are some ways computers can be used in business?

2. Explain how a data base management system can help a company keep its files up-to-date. List examples of information that might be stored in a data base other than those mentioned in this section.

3. What are the advantages of a CAD/CAM system, compared to pencil-and-paper sketches?

4. What is the difference between data processing and artificial intelligence?

5. THINKING CRITICALLY Is it possible for a computer to have true intelligence? Why or why not?

1. Possible examples: word processing, data base management (i.e., keep inventory and records, write letters, and maintain files).
2. Answers will vary. Instead of having mountains of paper for each file, a data base can keep all the information in a small section, and it can be updated without creating new paper.
3. Modifications may be made quickly and easily; experimentation with design is easier.
4. Data processing organizes and files information; artificial intelligence can make decisions based on data.
5. Answers will vary.

**Figure 14–13.** Robots can perform many functions.

# Robotics

**SECTION OBJECTIVES**
- **Describe** the characteristics of a robot.
- **Explain** the types and purpose of robotic sensors.
- **List** some uses of robots.

NEW TERM IN THIS SECTION
robot

## 14.7 How a Robot Works

A **robot** is a programmed, computer-controlled device that can sense and respond to changes in its environment. A robot is not defined by its shape or structure. As Figure 14–13 shows, robots come in all shapes and sizes. A robot can be thought of as a mobile computer. However, instead of a person typing in information, a robot receives information from sensors. The robot then sends commands to mechanical devices, rather than to a video screen or printer.

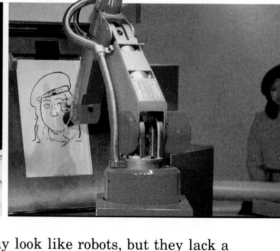

Many devices may look like robots, but they lack a true robot's ability to operate independently and to be reprogrammed. True robots are equipped with sensors. These sensors can be designed to detect almost any kind of change in the robot's environment. Such changes might include the presence of physical obstacles, differences in temperature, and the presence of odorless gases and fumes that may be harmful to humans. Signals from the sensors go to the computer that controls the robot. In turn, the computer responds to these signals according to its program. The responses are sent as electrical signals to the robot's wheels, arms, grippers, speech synthesizer, or other devices that allow the robot to respond.

Ask each student to write a short description of a potential robot job and to justify the use of a robot rather than a human worker to do the job.

Robots are often able to move in some way. Some robots stay in one place because their movement is restricted to one or two robotic arms. However, some robots use tracks or wheels to move from place to place while doing their jobs. A few experimental robots use four or more moving legs and "walk" from place to place, as shown in Figure 14–14. What uses can you think of for mobile robots in the home? housecleaning, cooking, security

Programming is the key to the effectiveness of any robot. As in other computer programming, the programs must provide for all of the types of information that the robot will receive through its sensors. The programs must also include the actions that the robot must take in response to input information. Robot programs are often stored on disks, as are computer programs. They are installed or changed in the robot as necessary.

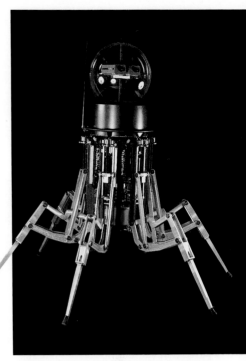

**Figure 14–14.** This experimental walking robot is used to study the problems of robot mobility. In this picture, *Odex I* is in its squat position.

# 14.8 Uses of Robots

There are several advantages to using robots in industry. Since robots can be used twenty-four hours a day, companies can increase the rate of production of certain goods or items. Since robots are not paid, production costs can be kept low. Manufacturers can pass along the savings to consumers by way of lower prices.

## Advantages of Robots

Robots are being used in places where people might be injured. For example, robots can operate in metal foundries, steel mills, and other environments where it is too hot for humans to work in comfort and safety. In some industries, dangerous chemicals, such as acids, are used in the manufacturing process. Robots can work in places where an accident involving such chemicals could be harmful to people. In mines, where workers are in constant danger of cave-ins, robots are being used to remove large quantities of solid materials and to operate huge machines.

**SCIENCE FACT**

One of the most common types of sensors used in robots is the sonar device. A robot can be programmed to use sonar to detect moving objects or to prevent it from running into an obstacle.

**Figure 14–15.** This robot has been nicknamed "Felix." The Los Angeles Police Department uses Felix to help in its bomb disposal unit.

**297**

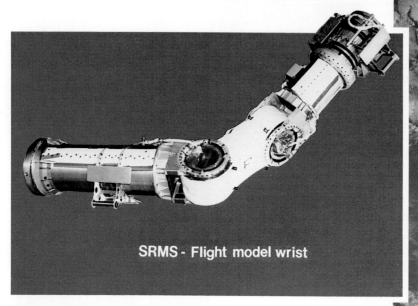

SRMS - Flight model wrist

**Figure 14-16.** Robots are used in space to help astronauts with dangerous tasks. The shuttle remote manipulator system is shown on the right. The flight model wrist (left) is one portion of the manipulator system.

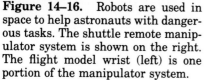

*READING CRITICALLY*

Why is NASA exploring the greater use of robots in the exploration of planets?

Many dangers are involved in space exploration; robots can do some of the dangerous jobs for humans.

## Types of Robots

One class of robots includes remote-control devices. These devices are used when risk to humans is high but moment-by-moment control by the operator is necessary. Remote-control robots are used in firefighting, in handling explosives, and in handling nuclear materials. Robots can also do most of the outside work on space stations while astronauts remain inside.

Another class of robots includes "robotic arms." These are probably the most common of all robots. These stationary arms put together machine parts, install parts on printed circuit boards, and operate paint sprayers and welding guns. Assembly lines in the automobile industry are being modernized with robotic arms that are able to weld together body panels for cars and paint the finished product.

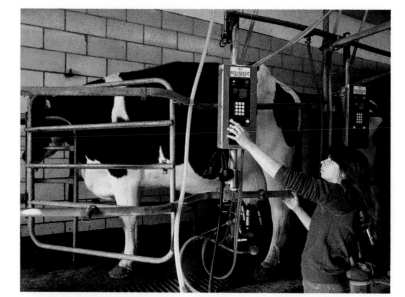

**Figure 14-17.** This milk production robot helps the farmer monitor the milk output of the cows and maintain more sanitary conditions.

Other robots actually move from one place to another. For example, in warehouses robots move products from receiving dock to storage location. They can also fill customers' orders by bringing items from storage to packing counters. A central computer is often used to control several robots at a time. The central computer tells the robots which paths to take to avoid collisions.

Many robot-related sensors are being incorporated into agricultural machines. The sensors send information to the person operating the machinery. Research is being done on how to combine sensors, computers, and machines into robotic farm equipment. An example of robotic farm equipment is shown in Figure 14–17.

## ACTIVITY

**Reading About Robots**

Read Isaac Asimov's book, *I Robot,* and list the "Three Laws of Robotics" described by the author. Discuss the application of these laws to the use of robots in today's world.

## Section Review

1. What determines whether or not a machine or device is a true robot?
2. Name some things that robotic sensors can detect.
3. How is the way in which robots are programmed similar to the way in which other computer programs are developed?
4. THINKING CRITICALLY How will the increasing use of robots in manufacturing affect people in the future?

1. True robots can operate independently and can be reprogrammed.
2. temperature changes, detection of different gases, physical obstacles
3. They must be given information on how to handle data because they cannot collect it themselves. They have only a series of programmed responses.
4. Answers will vary but may include putting people out of jobs and providing more leisure time.

# CAREER

## Computer Operator

**DESCRIPTION**  Computer operators are responsible for maintaining computer equipment. They respond to problems with the computer system and record use and problems in a log. They may also help programmers test-run new programs.

**REQUIREMENTS**  A student who plans to become a computer operator should take computer courses in high school. Computer operators must then complete several months of on-the-job training to learn how to run an operating system and to handle all problems.

**INFORMATION**  Data Processing Management Association, 505 Busse Highway, Park Ridge, IL 60068

# INVESTIGATION 14: Building a Better Mousetrap

*Can a computer catch a mouse more quickly than a cat can?*

## PURPOSE

To design and program a robotic mousetrap

## MATERIALS

pencil and paper

## PROCEDURE

1. Design a robot that catches mice. Decide what type of robot you need for the job and how it will operate.
2. Make a diagram of each part of the robot and of how all the parts will fit together.
3. Decide what materials you will need to build your robot. Make a list of these materials and possible sources from which you might be able to obtain them.
4. Draw a blueprint of how your robot would be constructed. (You may want to review the Skill Activity in Chapter 8 before beginning this step.)
5. Write a computer program (in English) that will instruct the robot on how to catch a mouse. Be sure to include all the operations, or steps, necessary to perform this task, based on how your robot operates.

## RESULTS

1. Compare your design with the designs of some of your classmates. Ask others to analyze your diagrams and make suggestions for improvements.
2. Review the programs written by other students for their robots. Determine whether or not your program includes enough instructions in order for the robot to perform.

## CONCLUSIONS Answers will vary.

1. What type of robot did you decide to build?
2. How would a flowchart help you program your robot?
3. How many different operations did you have to program your robot to perform in order to catch a mouse?

## APPLICATIONS

1. Revise your robot's computer program so that it can perform additional functions, such as disposing of the mouse once it is caught.
2. Suppose you could build a robot to go to school for you. In addition to mobility, what other capability would you want the robot to have? Why? How do you think you would respond to a robot as your teacher? Answers will vary.

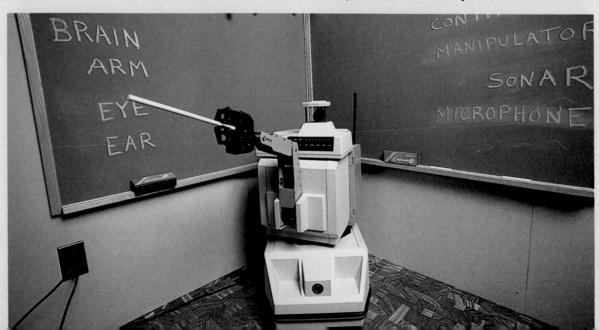

## Summary

1. The three main parts in a computer system are input, central processing, and output. All information processing is done by the central processing unit, or CPU. **(14.1)**

2. Computer software is the set of programs, or instructions, a computer follows in order to perform different operations. Programs may be written in several different computer languages. **(14.2)**

3. Computers are grouped into three types, based on size —mainframes, minicomputers, and microcomputers. **(14.3)**

4. Word processing, data base management systems, and CAD/CAM are three types of computer technology used in business. **(14.4, 14.5)**

5. Expert computer systems using artificial intelligence are used when the data concerning a given problem are incomplete or hard to understand. **(14.6)**

6. Robots are used in many environments and for many tasks. Robots may be used in some situations that may be dangerous to humans. **(14.7, 14.8)**

## Science Terms

On a separate piece of paper, define each term in a sentence.

artificial intelligence **(294)**
assembly language **(288)**
CAD/CAM **(293)**
central processing unit (CPU) **(286)**
computer **(285)**
data base management system **(292)**
hardware **(285)**

high-level language **(288)**
input devices **(285)**
machine language **(288)**
mainframe **(289)**
microcomputers **(290)**
microprocessor **(287)**
minicomputers **(290)**

output devices **(285)**
robot **(296)**
sequential programming **(287)**
software **(287)**
supercomputers **(289)**
word processing **(293)**

## Modified True-False

On a separate sheet of paper, mark each true statement *TRUE* and each false statement *FALSE*. If false, change the underlined term to make the statement true.

1. A computer is a mechanical device that can store and process information. F, an electronic

2. The physical components of a computer are called its hardware. T

3. Information and instructions necessary for the computer to perform different tasks are stored in the ALU. F, main storage

4. Assembly languages are not a permanent part of the computer's structures. F, high-level

5. Sequential programming allows the computer to perform certain steps in random order. F, certain

6. In many computers the CPU is contained on a single chip called a microprocessor. T

7. Computer hardware is the programs the computer uses to carry out different tasks. F, software

8. A computer works by turning transistors off and on. T

9. Data base management systems help businesses keep their files organized and up-to-date. T

10. Drawing machines that work with CAD/CAM are called plotters. T

*(continues)*

## Multiple Choice

On a separate sheet of paper, write the letter of the term that best completes the statement.

1. Which of the following is NOT part of the CPU?
   - **a.** ALU
   - **b.** control unit
   - **c.** main storage
   - **(d.)** printer

2. What type of programming is common to all computers?
   - **(a.)** sequential
   - **b.** linear
   - **c.** high-level languages
   - **d.** assembly

3. Which type of computer operates the fastest?
   - **a.** minicomputer
   - **b.** microcomputer
   - **(c.)** supercomputer
   - **d.** mainframe

4. The ALU is part of the
   - **(a.)** central processing unit.
   - **b.** main storage.
   - **c.** integrated circuit.
   - **d.** control unit.

5. One definition of a computer's power is in relation to its
   - **a.** size and shape.
   - **(b.)** storage capacity and speed.
   - **c.** CPU.
   - **d.** artificial intelligence.

6. Typewriters are rapidly being replaced by _____ in most offices.
   - **a.** data base systems
   - **b.** expert systems
   - **(c.)** word processors
   - **d.** CAD/CAM

7. Computers programmed to interpret information and to draw conclusions from that information use
   - **a.** human thought.
   - **b.** high-level language.
   - **(c.)** artificial intelligence.
   - **d.** data processing.

8. True robots are equipped with
   - **a.** wheels.
   - **b.** sonar.
   - **c.** arms.
   - **(d.)** sensors.

9. CAD/CAM systems use _____ to produce drawings.
   - **a.** pencil and paper
   - **b.** laser technology
   - **(c.)** computer graphics
   - **d.** robotics

10. A _____ is a programmed, computer-controlled device that can sense and respond to changes in its environment.
   - **a.** transistor
   - **b.** chip
   - **(c.)** robot
   - **d.** CAD/CAM

## Completion

On a separate sheet of paper, complete each statement by supplying the correct term.

1. The largest and most powerful mainframe computers are called <u>supercomputers</u>.

2. Computer systems that use artificial intelligence are called <u>expert systems</u>.

3. A video screen is an example of an <u>output device</u>.

4. ALU stands for <u>arithmetic and logic unit</u>.

5. Keyboards, tape machines, and disk drives are examples of <u>input</u> devices.

6. The three parts of the CPU are the ALU, memory, and <u>control</u> unit.

7. Machine language uses a series of ones and <u>zeros</u> to command the computer to perform different operations.

8. A computer's "size" can depend on its physical size and its <u>memory capacity</u>.

9. Many <u>terminals</u> at different locations may be connected to mainframes and minicomputers.

10. Information used in a data base system is stored on <u>discs</u> or tapes.

## Writing Critically

1. Compare and contrast the speed and abilities of supercomputers, mainframe computers, minicomputers, and microcomputers. Include in your comparisons some examples of what each type of computer is used for.

2. Many technological advances have made the development of the computer possible. Summarize these advances and the events that led to them. Be sure to mention the names of the people responsible for these advances and the dates important scientific breakthroughs were made.

3. **CHALLENGE** Artificial intelligence is a very controversial issue. Make arguments for and against the use of this technology in computers. **1.** Speed ranges from the fastest (supercomputers) to the slowest (microcomputers). **2.** Answers will vary, but may include examples taken from the text. **3.** Answers will vary.

## Skill Reinforcement

The Skill Activity on page 291 describes how to make a flowchart. Using the steps outlined in the activity, make a flowchart for the following problem. Imagine you are an editor. You have twenty-four weeks to edit a book that is 720 pages long. How many pages must you edit per week in order to meet your deadline? (*Hint*: Work through the calculations yourself to make sure that what you would enter into the program is correct. Be sure to include a step in your program to check your calculations.)

## Research Ideas

1. Through the use of artificial walking technology, some people who are paralyzed below the waist have been able to walk again. Using computer-controlled electrical stimulation, Jerrold Petrofsky at Wright State University in Dayton, Ohio, has made great progress in enabling paralyzed people to walk again. Investigate Petrofsky's program and the progress he has made with paraplegics. Discuss other possible applications of his research in this area.

2. The next time you are in a shopping mall, notice the different ways in which computer technology is used. Make a list of all the computers or computerized devices you find (not including those for sale in electronics or computer stores) and how they affect the way you shop.

3. **CHALLENGE** The idea of owning a personal household robot has fascinated people for years. What would you want your own robot to be able to do? What sources could you check to find out how to get a robot? If possible, contact a robot manufacturer to determine what kinds of robots or robotic devices they make and how much they cost. Discuss your findings with your classmates.

## For Further Reading

Baron, Naomi S. *Computer Languages: A Guide for the Perplexed*. New York: Doubleday, 1986. This book explains in simple English the basis for computer languages, what they are, how they evolved, and how they are still evolving.

Kassab, Vincent. *Apple IIe: BASIC Programming with Technical Applications*. Englewood Cliffs, NJ: Prentice-Hall, 1985. This book is a well-written guide for the beginning programmer. Graphics sections are also included, as well as data base and inventory programs.

Schultzer, Daniel. *Artificial Intelligence: An Applications-oriented Approach*. New York: Van Nostrand Reinhold, 1987. This book discusses the ideas that make artificial intelligence possible and how they are being used with today's computer technology.

# MADE IN SPACE

In July 1985, the first product manufactured in space went on sale. For $385, a company could buy a 25-gram container of tiny plastic beads that had been manufactured on the space shuttle. These beads are used to calibrate delicate measuring instruments. A knowledge of the effects of gravity and temperature on the formation of these beads make possible their manufacture. The special environment of space makes the manufacture of many products possible.

## The Low-Gravity Advantage

Why make plastic beads in space? The fact is, space is the only place where they can be made. The low-gravity environment of the space shuttle affects the physical and chemical processes in several remarkable ways.

- Metals that will not mix on Earth can be mixed in space to form alloys.

- Crystals—solids whose atoms are arranged in an orderly pattern—grow larger and purer in space than they do on Earth.

- Lasers and optics require extremely pure glass. This purity is attainable only in space.

## Space Beads

In the case of the beads, the near-zero gravity of space yields a product that is rounder and more uniform than that produced on Earth. Their uniform size and shape make the beads invaluable in producing tools that measure microscopic particles, from face power to air pollutants. The beads are made by a pro-

cess similar to making a large sponge from a small one by soaking it in water. The beads are made from bits of polystyrene, the same kind of plastic used in coffee cups. The beads are increased in size by adding molecules of styrene to them. When the beads have attained the right size, the process is stopped by heating the liquid in which the beads have been forming.

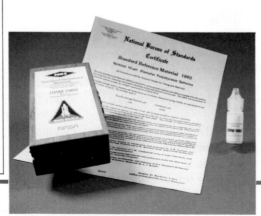

These polystyrene beads are certified as made in space.

When made on Earth, the beads float as they get larger and then sink when the liquid is heated to stop their growth. The result is that, either floating or sinking, they clump together. As a result, they are less round and less uniform in size than is desirable.

In space, where everything is weightless, differences in density do not cause floating or sinking. The beads made aboard the shuttle are perfectly round, and all are exactly the same size.

### Crystal Growth

In June of 1983, astronauts on the space shuttle used a furnace to heat a compound called *mercuric iodide.* The compound was contained in one end of a test tube. When heated, mercuric iodide produces a gas that forms crystals as it cools. The experiment was designed to find out how long it would take the gas to go to the other end of the tube and form crystals.

Surprise! The crystals were up to 100 times larger than crystals grown on Earth. Why? In space, the tiny crystals that formed first were weightless and floated in the tube. Because the crystals did not stick to the walls of the test tube, they could grow in all directions.

The discovery that large crystals could be produced in space was quickly applied in the field of protein study. The molecular structure of proteins can be determined using a special technique called X-ray diffraction analysis. However, this technique requires fairly large crystals.

In space, protein crystals have been produced that are up to 1000 times larger than those grown on Earth. These crys-

A large crystal of mercuric iodide made on Spacelab III

tals make X-ray examination of some kinds of proteins possible for the first time.

### Space Factories

By the end of the century, Space Industries, Inc., of Houston, Texas, will place the first of many space factories in orbit. The Industrial Space Facility (ISF) will be launched from a space shuttle. Once the ISF starts manufacturing space products, it is likely that other firms will follow suit. In the future, many products may bear the label "Made In Space."

A prototype of the first space factory

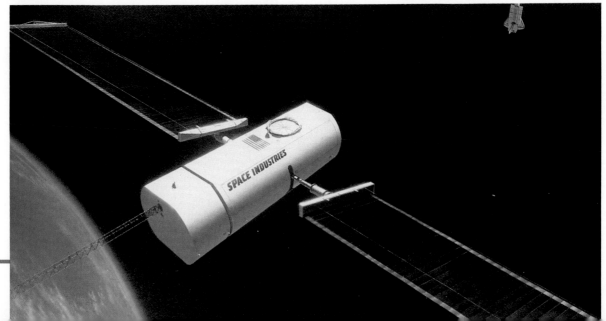

# UNIT 4

# Exploring the Universe

Photograph right: moonrise over Blue Mesa, Painted Desert, Petrified Forest National Monument, Arizona

How vast is our universe? *Astronomy* is the science that deals with stars, planets, and all other heavenly bodies. The study of one of those planets, Earth, is called *geology*. This unit explores the formation of and the history of the earth and of the universe. It also describes some of the changes that have occurred on Earth and the forces that are still changing our planet.

For additional information,
see pages T92–T93.

# CHAPTER 15

# Planet Earth

A spaceship moves through space, bathed by the
sun. The spaceship carries enough air, water, and
food to support more than four billion people. The
spaceship is Earth. The earth was formed from a
giant star that exploded billions of years ago.
Every atom in your body was once part of that
long-dead star.

# Locating Places on Earth

## SECTION OBJECTIVES

- **Describe** the shape of the earth.
- **Discuss** how directions are determined on Earth.
- **Summarize** how latitude and longitude are used to locate places on Earth.

Photograph left: Sunrise at Toroweap overlook—Grand Canyon, Arizona

NEW TERMS IN THIS SECTION
poles
equator
latitude
parallels
longitude
meridians
great circle

## 15.1 Size and Shape of the Earth

Three thousand years ago, the Greeks believed that the earth was flat. Greece and the Mediterranean Sea were believed to be in the center of this flat world. The Greeks thought that the ocean was the boundary for the edge of the world. Figure 15–1 shows a Greek map of the world made in about 500 B.C.

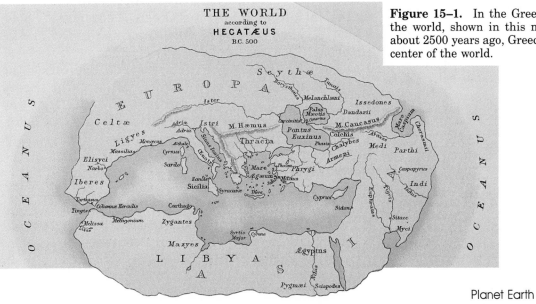

**Figure 15–1.** In the Greek view of the world, shown in this map made about 2500 years ago, Greece was the center of the world.

Planet Earth **309**

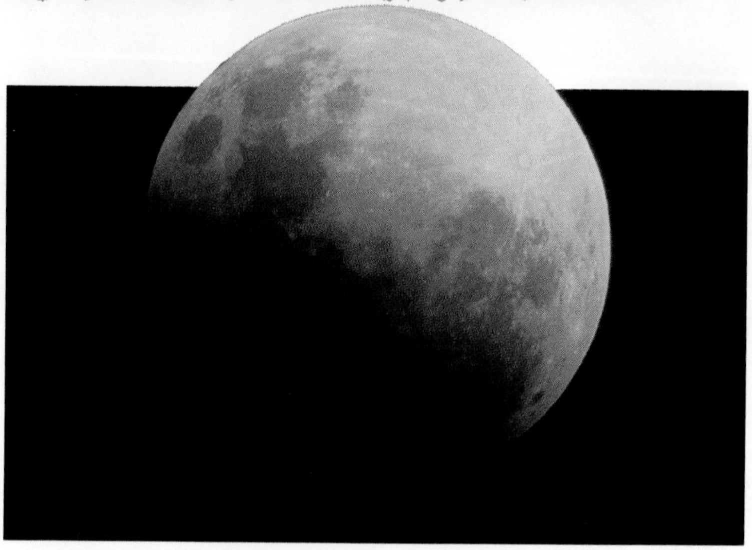

**Figure 15–2.** During a lunar eclipse, the shadow of the earth on the moon is curved. When Pythagoras saw this, he determined that the earth itself must be curved, or round.

## SCIENCE FACT

The average position of the magnetic pole, when measured in May 1984, was 77°N and 102.3°W. However, the pole does wander and has been known to stray by as much as 80 km a day.

The Greek philosopher Anaximander (uh nak sih MAN duhr) concluded that the flat earth must be suspended in space like a floating sheet of paper. This conclusion was based on the observation that the sun seemed to pass under the earth each night. However, another Greek, Pythagoras (pih THAG uhr uhs), noticed that during eclipses of the moon, or lunar eclipses, the shadow made by the earth on the moon was curved. Pythagoras knew that a curved shadow had to be made by a curved object. He concluded, therefore, that the earth must be round.

Modern scientists have proven that the earth is not perfectly round. The earth bulges very slightly in the middle and is flattened very slightly at the top and bottom. The flattening at the top and bottom and the bulge at the middle are caused by the earth's rotation. The two points at the top and the bottom of Earth are called **poles**. The poles are on an imaginary line called the earth's *axis* about which the earth rotates. The pole facing the North Star is called the *North Pole* and is located in the middle of the Arctic Ocean. The opposite pole, which is called the *South Pole*, is located in the middle of the continent Antarctica.

Halfway between the two poles, on the surface of the earth, is an imaginary line called the **equator.** Every point along the equator is the same distance from the two poles. The equator divides the earth into two hemispheres—the Northern Hemisphere and the Southern Hemisphere. The United States, which is part of the North American continent, is in the Northern Hemisphere.

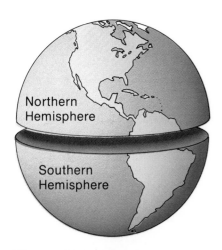

**Figure 15–3.** The equator marks the halfway point between the North Pole and the South Pole, dividing the Earth into the Northern and Southern hemispheres. It also marks the circumference of the earth.

If you live in the Northern Hemisphere and you stand outside at noon on a sunny day, your shadow will point toward the north. If you turn your back to the sun, you will be facing toward the north. When you stretch

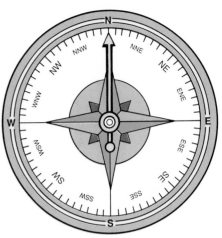

out your arms, your right arm will point toward the east and your left arm will point toward the west. The directions are shown in Figure 15–4.

If the sun is not shining, you cannot find north by your shadow. Another way to find your direction is to look at a compass. Directions are marked on the face of a compass and may also be expressed in degrees. The degrees increase in a clockwise direction around the compass. North is 0°; east is 90°; south is 180°; and west is 270°. Compass directions are shown in Figure 15–4.

You may wish to point out to students that the terms north, south, east, and west are known as cardinal points.

## 15.2 Latitude and Longitude

Locating a specific place on Earth requires using imaginary lines to represent the north-south and east-west location of the place. The location of a place north or south of the equator is called **latitude.** Imaginary circles are drawn around the earth parallel to the equator and are called **parallels.** The parallels become smaller the closer they are to a pole. Boston and Rome lie on the same parallel. New Orleans and Cairo also lie on the same parallel.

Parallels of latitude are numbered in degrees north or south of the equator. Each degree is further divided into smaller units called *minutes.* There are 60 minutes (60′) in a degree. Each minute is divided into 60 seconds (60″).

The east-west location of a place is found by using lines of **longitude.** The imaginary lines that mark the east-west location of a place are called **meridians** (muh RIHD ee uhns). Meridians run north-south from pole to pole. Meridians are numbered in degrees east or west of a starting point. The meridian that passes through

The latitude of the equator is 0 degrees. The distance from the equator to the North Pole or the South Pole is 90 degrees. The lines of longitude are numbered up to 180 degrees east or west of the prime meridian.

**Figure 15–5.** The earth is divided into meridians and parallels.

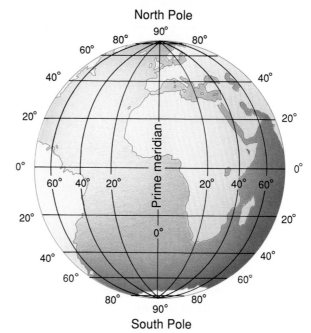

The prime meridian actually passes through the Royal Astronomical Observatory in Greenwich, England.

South Pole

Any great circle will be the greatest possible circle around the globe, as well as the circumference of the globe. The globe can have an infinite number of great circles. To get from *A* to *B* on any sphere, the shortest distance is a great circle. Great circles are used in aviation and in sailing.

## *ACTIVITY*

### Using a Map

Locate the city you live in or the large city nearest to you. Using its longitude and latitude, make a list of other cities located on the same parallel as your city.

Greenwich, England, is called the *prime meridian* and is the starting point of measurement for all meridians. Meridians and parallels are shown in Figure 15–5.

Two opposite meridians divide the earth's surface into two equal halves. Any line that divides the earth in half is called a **great circle**. Therefore, two opposite meridians are one great circle. Great circles are important because the shortest distance between any two places on a sphere is along a great circle. What is the only parallel that is also a great circle because it is the only parallel that divides the earth into two equal halves? the equator

To locate any place on the earth's surface, its latitude and longitude must be known. Honolulu, Hawaii, for instance, is located at latitude 21°18′N and longitude 157°50′W. Detroit, Michigan, is located at latitude 42°50′N and longitude 83°00′W.

## Section Review

1. How did Pythagoras determine that the earth was not flat?
2. What information is needed to locate any place on Earth?
3. What is the shortest distance between any two locations on the earth?
4. Why is the earth slightly flattened at the poles?
5. THINKING CRITICALLY  If you were lost on a sunny day and you knew that home was due south, how could you get your bearings?

1. He knew the curved shadow he saw during an eclipse was made by a curved object; therefore, he determined the earth was not flat.
2. latitude and longitude
3. along the great circle between the two points
4. The earth's rotation flattens the earth slightly.
5. On a sunny day, the person need only turn his or her back to the sun. Then turn around and the person will be facing south.

# Earth in Space

## SECTION OBJECTIVES

- **Explain** the relationship between the earth's rotation and time zones.
- **Describe** the rotation and revolution of the earth.
- **Relate** the seasons to the tilt of the earth's axis.

## 15.3 Earth's Rotation and Time Zones

If you look at the stars in the Northern Hemisphere for a few hours, you will notice that they appear to move in a circle around a certain star. Within 24 hours the stars appear to have made a complete circle. Figure 15–6 shows a time exposure of the northern sky. The star closest to the center in the figure is called *Polaris,* or the *North Star*. Since Polaris stays directly over the earth's North Pole, sailors in the Northern Hemisphere can use this star as a reference point.

Although the stars appear to move in the sky, they do not. It is actually the earth that is rotating. You could compare the rotation of the earth to being on a merry-go-round. Everything seems to fly by while you stand still. Actually, you are moving and all the objects are standing still. The earth rotates once in 24 hours. This time interval is called a **mean solar day**. The apparent motion of the sun across the sky is also due to the rotation of the earth. The earth rotates from west to east. Therefore, the sun "rises" in the east and "sets" in the west. Figure 15–7 shows the direction in which the earth rotates.

**Figure 15–6.** A time-exposure photograph of the northern sky reveals that the North Star appears not to move at all.

The earth travels faster when it is closer to the sun. Therefore, the actual length of a day varies from season to season.

North Pole

South Pole

**Figure 15–7.** Because the earth rotates from west to east, the sun rises in the east and sets in the west.

The time of day depends on the position of the sun in the sky. All places on earth that have the same longitude have noon at the same time. For example, when it is noon in New York City, it is also noon in Quebec City, Canada, and in Bogotá, Colombia. Every city in a longitude east or west of another city has noon at a different time. Because of the rotation of the earth, the noon position moves from east to west. When it is noon in New York City, it is 11 A.M. in Chicago, 10 A.M. in Denver. 9 A.M. in San Francisco, and 1 A.M. in Perth, Australia. However, when it is noon in New York City, it is 5 P.M. in London, because England is farther east than New York City.

The earth has been divided into twenty-four geographical regions. All places within the same geographic region have the same time. These regions are called **time zones.** The official time zones are shown in Figure 15–8. The sun moves 15 degrees every hour. Therefore, each time zone covers 15 degrees of longitude. The boundaries of time zones are usually adjusted to follow state or national boundaries. This adjustment avoids having time zones cut through a town or city. Imagine how awkward it would be if it was noon in one side of Denver while it was one o'clock across the street. The continental United States is divided into four time zones, called *Eastern*, *Central*, *Mountain*, and *Pacific*.

The system of time zones used today was established in 1883. Prior to that time, a person crossing the United States could encounter 53 different local times.

**Figure 15–8.** Twenty-four time zones, each covering 15° of longitude, make up a 360° circle.

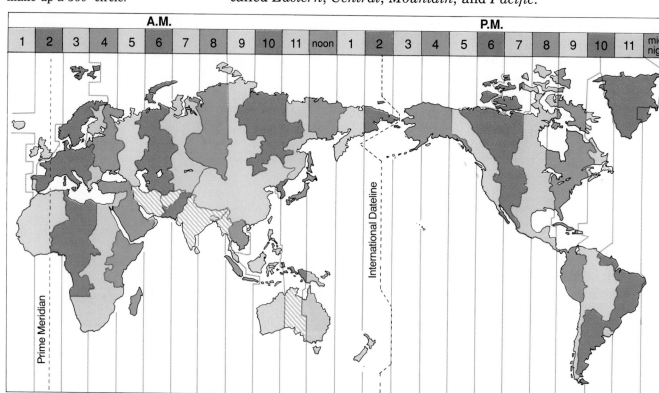

# 15.4 The Seasons

The earth not only rotates about its own axis, but it also moves around the sun. The earth's axis is like the center pole of the merry-go-round. Everything turns around the pole. The axis of the earth then moves around the sun. As seen from the north, the earth moves around the sun in a counterclockwise direction. The earth makes one turn, or *revolution*, around the sun every 365 days, 5 hours, 48 minutes, and 45 seconds.

The orbits of all planets and satellites are actually ellipses. An **ellipse** is a flattened circle. Because the earth's orbit is an ellipse, the distance from the earth to the sun varies during the year. For example, the earth is closest to the sun in late December.

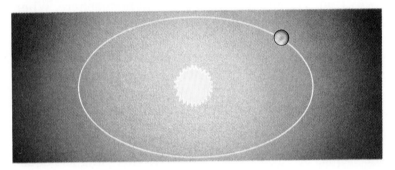

**Figure 15–9.** The earth follows an elliptical orbit rather than a perfectly circular orbit.

The days of the year when the noonday sun stands highest or lowest on the horizon at noon are called **solstices.** On a solstice the sun stops reaching higher and higher at noon and retraces its position downward. The day that the sun is at the highest point in the sky usually occurs on June 21 and is called the summer solstice. On this day, the Northern Hemisphere has the maximum number of hours of daylight. The winter solstice, when the sun is at the lowest point in the sky at noon, usually occurs on December 21. On this day, the Northern Hemisphere has the fewest hours of daylight. The days when night and day are equal in length are called **equinoxes** (EE kwuh nahks ihz). There are two equinoxes each year. The spring equinox usually occurs on March 21. The fall equinox usually occurs on September 22.

When the noonday sun is highest in the Northern Hemisphere, it is lowest in the Southern Hemisphere. The seasons are, therefore, opposite in the two hemispheres. When it is summer in the Northern Hemisphere, it is winter in the Southern Hemisphere. When it is spring in the Northern Hemisphere, it is fall in the Southern Hemisphere. In South America, southern Africa, and Australia, is December 25 a summer day or a winter day? a summer day

Use a light bulb as the sun and move a globe around it. Stop at each solstice and equinox location and discuss: location of the vertical rays, where the earth's axis is pointing, and the amount of daylight each part of the world is getting.

## ACTIVITY

**Comparing Seasons**

Make a table listing three cities in the Northern Hemisphere and three cities in the Southern Hemisphere. Find out the average temperature of these cities for January 15, March 15, July 15, and October 15. List these temperatures in your table.

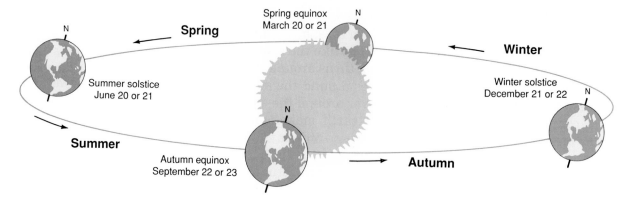

Figure 15–10. The earth's axis is tilted 23°28'. This tilt is one of the determining factors of the seasons. If the axis were perpendicular to the plane of the earth's orbit, there would be only one season.

Only the area between the Tropics of Cancer and Capricorn view the sun directly over head. For this reason, this region experiences little seasonal change.

1. day and night, and the apparent motion of the sun across the sky
2. 1 P.M.
3. It is not directly overhead anywhere in the Northern Hemisphere. It is directly overhead on 23°28'S.
4. The earth would have to reverse itself and rotate from west to east.
5. A day would be a year long, because it takes a year for the earth to revolve around the sun.

When a hemisphere is tilted toward the sun, it is summer in that hemisphere. When a hemisphere is tilted away from the sun, it is winter in that hemisphere. When the two hemispheres are equally exposed to the sun, it is spring or fall.

The noonday sun is directly overhead at the latitude of 23°28'N during the northern summer solstice. The noonday sun is directly overhead at the latitude of 23°28'S during the southern summer solstice. These two latitudes are called, respectively, the **Tropic of Cancer** and the **Tropic of Capricorn.** The latitudes between the tropics of Cancer and Capricorn, including the equator, are called the *tropics.*

Figure 15–10 shows that north of latitude 66°32'N, there are 24 hours of daylight during the northern summer solstice. In this region, the sun never sets on that day. When the part of the earth north of latitude 66°32'N experiences 24 hours of daylight, the earth south of latitude 66°32'S has 24 hours of darkness. The latitudes of 66°32'N and 66°32' are called, respectively, the **Arctic Circle** and the **Antarctic Circle.** They are also called *polar circles.*

## Section Review

1. Describe two effects of the earth's rotation.
2. If it is 3 P.M. in New York City, what time is it in Denver?
3. Where in the Northern Hemisphere is the noonday sun directly overhead on the shortest day of the year?
4. THINKING CRITICALLY In order for a person in California to see the sun rise over the Pacific Ocean, how would the earth's rotation have to change?
5. THINKING CRITICALLY If the earth did not rotate, how long would a day be?

# SKILL ACTIVITY     Calculating Time Zones

**INTRODUCTION** _____ Understanding time zones requires developing a sense of direction and movement. By understanding and reading the time-zone map, you will be able to calculate the time of day anywhere in the world.

**PROCEDURE** _____
1. Look at the time-zone map on page 314.
2. Count the number of time zones between New York City and Honolulu, Hawaii.
3. By locating the boundaries on the map, you can establish information about each area and its time zone.

**APPLICATION** _____ The cheapest telephone rates from Monday through Friday are between 11 P.M. and 8 A.M. for each time zone. However, you do not want to call someone at an inconvenient hour. With the help of the time-zone map below, what would be the best times for the following people to call each other during the week, considering rates and the time-zone advantage?

1. At 7:00 A.M. in San Francisco, it is 9:00 A.M. in Des Moines.
2. At 10:00 P.M. in Des Moines, it is only 8:00 P.M. in San Francisco.
3. At 7:45 A.M. it is 8:45 A.M. in Houston.
4. At 10:00 P.M. it is only 9:00 P.M. in El Paso.

1. Samantha lives in San Francisco and her aunt lives in Des Moines, Iowa. Should Samantha call at 10:00 P.M., 7:00 A.M., or 5 P.M.?
2. Should Samantha's aunt call Samantha at 10:00 P.M., 7:00 A.M., or 8 A.M.?
3. Carl lives in El Paso and his daughter lives in Houston. Should Carl call at 7:45 A.M., 10:30 P.M., or 9:30 P.M.?
4. Should Carl's daughter in Houston call him at 6:00 A.M., 10:00 P.M., or 11:00 P.M.?

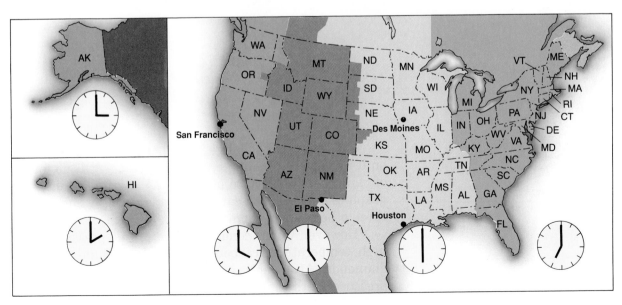

# Solid Earth

## ACTIVITY

### Investigating Minerals

Use references in the library or contact the state Department of Natural Resources to investigate which important minerals are found within your state. You might also obtain samples of these minerals for display in your class.

## SECTION OBJECTIVES

- **List** and **describe** some common minerals.
- **Distinguish** between igneous, metamorphic, and sedimentary rocks.
- **Describe** the internal structure of the earth.

## 15.5 Minerals

Eighty-nine elements are found naturally on Earth. Of these elements, iron, oxygen, and silicon are the most abundant. Many of these natural elements combine to form minerals. **Minerals** are natural substances with specific chemical compositions. For example, petroleum, coal, quartz, and iron are minerals.

Nearly all minerals that make up the solid earth are crystals. A **crystal** is a structure in which the atoms are arranged in a regular order. Common table salt, for instance, consists of sodium and chlorine atoms arranged in a regular, cubic pattern. There are six major crystal structures, which are shown in Figure 15–11.

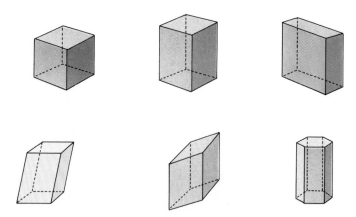

**Figure 15–11.** There are six major crystal structures.

A mineral may change its structure if the pressures on it change. For example, the common crystalline form of carbon at the surface of the earth is graphite. In the graphite crystal, each carbon atom is strongly bonded to three other carbon atoms.

However, under conditions of extreme pressure and high temperature, carbon atoms can combine to form diamonds. At a depth of 100 km inside the earth, the pressure on the carbon atoms is so high that the atoms

## Summary

1. The spherical shape of the earth is slightly flattened due to the speed of the earth's rotation. **(15.1)**

2. The lines of longitude and latitude can be used to locate places on the earth. **(15.2)**

3. The earth is divided into 24 time zones based on the earth's rotation. **(15.3)**

4. The combination of the earth's tilt and revolution around the sun results in the four seasons. **(15.4)**

5. The eighty-nine elements found naturally on Earth combine to form minerals. **(15.5)**

6. Rocks are classified by the way in which they are formed. The three categories of rocks are igneous, sedimentary, and metamorphic. **(15.6)**

7. The earth is composed of four layers—the inner core, the outer core, the mantle, and the crust. **(15.7)**

## Science Terms

On a separate sheet of paper, define each term in a sentence.

Antarctic Circle **(316)**　　great circle **(312)**　　magma **(320)**　　parallels **(311)**
Arctic Circle **(316)**　　igneous rock **(320)**　　mantle **(322)**　　poles **(310)**
core **(322)**　　isostasy **(323)**　　mean solar day **(313)**　　rocks **(319)**
crust **(322)**　　latitude **(311)**　　meridians **(311)**　　sedimentary rock **(320)**
crystal **(318)**　　lava **(320)**　　metamorphic rock **(321)**　　solstices **(315)**
ellipse **(315)**　　longitude **(311)**　　minerals **(318)**　　time zones **(314)**
equator **(310)**　　　　　　Tropic of Cancer **(316)**
equinoxes **(315)**　　　　　　Tropic of Capricorn **(316)**

## Modified True-False

On a separate sheet of paper, mark each true statement *TRUE* and each false statement *FALSE*. If false, change the underlined term to make the statement true.

1. The curved shadow of the earth on the moon during a lunar eclipse is evidence that the earth is <u>hot</u>. F, round

2. The slight flattening of the earth's poles is due to the earth's <u>revolution</u>. F, rotation

3. A person in the Southern Hemisphere would travel <u>north</u> to reach the equator. T

4. Liquid rock inside the earth is <u>extrusive</u>. F, magma

5. <u>Meridians</u> run east to west. T

6. The shortest distance between points on the earth is along a <u>great circle</u>. T

7. The apparent rotation of the stars is due to the earth's <u>rotation</u>. T

8. At the summer solstice, the noonday sun is directly overhead at the <u>equator</u>. T

9. When it is summer in Chicago, it is <u>fall</u> in Buenos Aires. F, winter

10. The arrangement of carbon atoms in diamonds and in graphite is <u>different</u>. T

*(continues)*

## Multiple Choice

On a separate sheet of paper, write the letter of the term that best answers the question or completes the statement.

1. The direction east on a compass is
   a. 45°.
   b. 90°.
   c. 270°.
   d. 180°.

2. Meridians are used to determine
   a. latitude.
   b. longitude.
   c. parallels.
   d. great circles.

3. The heat inside the earth is due in part to
   a. rotation.
   b. revolution.
   c. radioactivity.
   d. magnetism.

4. Which of the following is *not* an imaginary line halfway between the two poles?
   a. a great circle
   b. a meridian
   c. a parallel
   d. the equator

5. The orbit of the earth around the sun is
   a. parabolic.
   b. square.
   c. elliptical.
   d. circular.

6. In the Northern Hemisphere, the longest night occurs during the
   a. spring equinox.
   b. winter solstice.
   c. summer solstice.
   d. fall equinox.

7. Which of the following is *not* a metamorphic rock?
   a. marble
   b. slate
   c. schist
   d. limestone

8. The principle of _____ says that the thicker and less dense a body is, the higher it floats.
   a. magnetism
   b. orientation
   c. radioactivity
   d. isostasy

9. The earth has been divided into _____ time zones.
   a. 20
   b. 24
   c. 36
   d. 28

10. The average thickness of the continental crust is about _____ km.
   a. 7
   b. 35
   c. 100
   d. 2900

## Completion

On a separate sheet of paper, complete each statement by supplying the correct term.

1. The movement of the earth in a 24-hour period is a _mean solar day_

2. Any location on Earth can be specified by its _longitude_ and longitude.

3. The earth rotates from _west to east_ on its axis, as seen from the North Pole.

4. The seasons are due to the _tilt_ of the earth's axis.

5. The noonday sun is directly overhead at the _Tropic of Capricorn_ on December 21.

6. Both graphite and _diamond_ are forms of carbon.

7. The layer of the earth between the core and the crust is called the _mantle_ .

8. Molten rock inside the earth is called _intrusive_ .

9. The earth's _inner_ core is solid.

10. The crust is composed mainly of _sedimentary_ rock.

11. The earth's time zones are divided into twenty-four _geographic_ regions.

12. The Arctic Circle and the Antarctic Circle are also called _polar circles_ .

## Writing Critically

1. Summarize how time and geographical location are determined on Earth.

2. Explain why the Northern Hemisphere is having winter while the Southern Hemisphere is having summer.

3. Why do we have winter when the earth is closest to the sun?

1. Answers should include linking time zones to longitude. Geographic regions within 15° longitude have the same time. Some zones are altered due to geographic location.

2. The hemispheres have different seasons due to the tilt of the earth in relation to the sun.

3. because our hemisphere is tilted away from the sun, and therefore gets indirect rays

4. CHALLENGE  Which items in the following list are minerals and which are not? In each case give a reason for your answer. Salt, an oyster shell, ice cubes from the freezer, liquid water, oxygen, a diamond in a piece of jewelry, a pearl. 4. Are: salt, diamond.
Are not: oyster shell, ice cubes from freezer, pearl, oxygen, liquid water.

## Skill Reinforcement

The Skill Activity on page 317 describes how to determine time changes between time zones. You have just arrived in Tokyo, Japan, and you want to let your parents back in Boise, Idaho, know that you arrived safely.

However, your parents are at home only from 8 A.M. to 5 P.M. It is 6 A.M. in Tokyo. Should you wait until later to phone? Explain when you should phone and why you chose that time. It is 1 P.M. in Boise and okay to call.

## Research Ideas

1. Today most of the salt used in the United States is mined from salt domes underground, but salt can also be harvested from the sea. If you wanted to corner the market on sea salt, how and where would you do it?

2. Find out where the International Date Line is and explain how and why the date changes across the line.

3. CHALLENGE  Certain animals, called corals, use minerals from sea water to build coral reefs. Coral reefs are a very special environment that humans can help create. Suppose you wanted to build a vacation resort near an artificial coral reef. How and where would you build the reef?

## For Further Reading

McClintock, Jack and David Helgren. *Everything Is Somewhere: The Geography Quiz Book.* New York: William Morrow & Co., 1986. This book contains hundreds of questions about about geography. It will challenge even the most knowledgeable trivia buffs.

Makower, J. and L. Bergheim. *The Map Catalog.* New York: Random House, 1986. The authors describe many of the types of maps that are available, as well as give information about how maps are made.

Parfit, Michael. *South Light: A Journey to the Last Continent.* NY: Macmillan, 1985. Antarctica is the world's largest natural laboratory. In this personal diary, the author discusses the unusual conditions under which scientific programs are conducted.

For additional information,
see pages T94–T95.

# CHAPTER 16

# The Solar System

Nine planets circle the sun. On one of these planets, life is known to exist. Astronomers are using radio telescopes like the one shown in the photograph to search for signals from outer space. Perhaps during your lifetime, contact will be made with a civilization beyond our solar system.

# The Sun

NEW TERMS IN THIS SECTION

| | |
|---|---|
| core | chromosphere |
| radiative layer | sunspot |
| convective layer | corona |
| photosphere | solar prominence |
| granules | solar wind |

Photograph left: eclipse of sun over tracking antenna, Virginia

## 16.1 Structure of the Sun

Many ancient people believed the sun was a god. Today, astronomers view the sun as a rather ordinary star. The radius of the sun is 696,000 km, about 109 times greater than the radius of the earth. Its volume is more than a million times greater than Earth's volume. In fact, the sun's mass is 745 times greater than the combined mass of all the planets and their satellites. These figures mean that over 99 percent of the mass in the entire solar system is in the sun.

The surface of the sun has a temperature of about 6000 K. At this temperature, all matter is a gas. At the center of the sun, temperatures reach an incredible 15,000,000 K. Because of these high temperatures, the sun is in a gaseous state and has an average density of 1.4 g/cm³—much less than that of Earth.

At the sun's center is its **core**, which is 38 percent hydrogen and 62 percent helium. The core extends from the center to about one-fourth of the way to the surface. The intense pressure and temperature found in the core causes atoms to crash into each other at very high speeds. The collisions knock electrons from their orbits around atoms, leaving bare nuclei and free electrons. As a result, the hydrogen atoms in the sun's core exist as single protons.

## SCIENCE FACT

The sun consumes about 4 million tons of matter every second. This amount is equal to the matter that would be contained in 11.5 Empire State Buildings.

In the core of the sun, the pressure is so great that the density of hydrogen and helium is about 160 g/cm³, more than 14 times the density of lead.

## ACTIVITY

### Making a Camera Obscura

Get a large cardboard box. In one end of the box, punch a small hole. At the other end of the box (inside) attach a white sheet of paper. With your back to the sun, and holding the box with the hole facing the sun, observe the focused image of the sun on the white sheet of paper. Write down your observations.

Convection is the same type of motion seen in boiling water. Have the students compare the action of boiling water with the rising and falling of gases in the convective layer of the sun.

At a temperature of 6000 K, the photosphere is the coolest layer of the sun.

Around the core of the sun is the **radiative** (RAY dee ay tihv) **layer,** which reaches to more than three-fourths of the way to the surface. Radiation produced in the core moves slowly through this layer, taking more than a million years to pass all the way through.

After making its way through the radiative layer, radiation enters the **convective** (kuhn VEHK tihv) **layer,** which is 105,000 km thick. In the convective layer, hotter matter from below rises, while cooler matter from above sinks. Convection is the same type of motion seen in boiling water. Why do the hotter gases rise and the cooler gases sink? hotter gases are less dense than the cooler gases

Above the connective layer lies the 500-km-thick **photosphere.** The photosphere is called the sun's surface because it is the part of the sun that is normally visible from Earth. The surface of the photosphere is boiling and is marked by granules (GRAN yoolz). The **granules** are the tops of rising columns of hot gases. The dark boundaries between granules are cooler gases, which are sinking.

Although the photosphere is the sun's surface, there are other layers above it. Above the photosphere is a 2500-km-thick layer of low-density gases called the **chromosphere** (KROH muh sfihr). In this layer, the temperature increases with altitude, reaching 50,000 K at the top.

**Figure 16–1.** This computer-generated photograph of the sun clearly shows the three outer layers. The first thin layer surrounding the sun is the photosphere, the intense color in the middle is the chromosphere, and the thin outer layer of gases is the corona. Remember: never look at the sun without using special filters to protect your eyes. Invisible radiation from the sun can cause permanent damage to your eyes in only a few seconds.

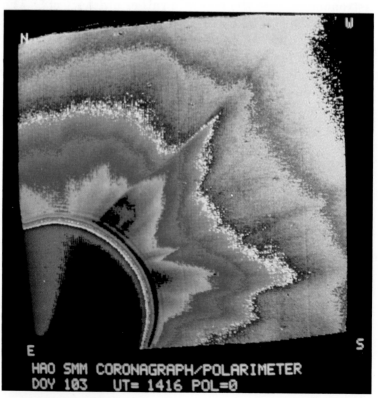

The chromosphere, the photosphere, and the convective and radiative layers all have the same composition. They consist of 72 percent hydrogen, 27 percent helium, and one percent other elements.

Above the chromosphere lies the **corona** (kuh ROH nuh), or "crown." The corona is a layer of extremely thin solar gases. Both the chromosphere and the corona are normally visible only during a total eclipse, when the moon blocks the face of the sun. The temperature in the corona is very high—over 1,000,000 K.

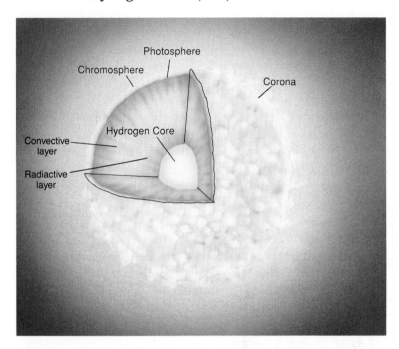

**Figure 16–2.** This diagram shows the interior of the sun and the parts of the solar atmosphere. The pressure is so great at the core of the sun that the density of the hydrogen and helium found there is fourteen times the density of lead.

# 16.2 Motions and Activity of the Sun

The sun, like the earth, rotates counterclockwise on its axis as seen from the north. However, because the sun is made of gas, not all parts of the sun rotate at the same speed. The sun's equator takes 25.5 days to make one rotation. However, the poles take 36.6 days.

### Sunspots and Solar Prominences

A common feature of the solar photosphere is sunspots. **Sunspots** are giant areas of hot gases created by very strong magnetic fields. Sunspots appear dark because the gases trapped within them are cooler than the surrounding gases.

Groups of sunspots form at about 40 degrees of latitude north or south of the solar equator and last from a few weeks to a few months. As they grow in size, sunspots move toward the equator in groups. A group of sunspots is shown in Figure 16–3.

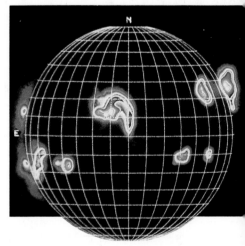

**Figure 16–3.** This computer-generated photograph of the sun shows the location of several sunspots on its surface. During a regular cycle of sunspot activity, the area of formation of sunspots moves toward the sun's equator.

**Figure 16–4.** This photograph of a large prominence was taken in ultraviolet light. The gas that forms a prominence is much cooler (between 20,000 and 70,000 K) than the corona (1,000,000 K).

Sunspot formation seems to follow an 11-year cycle. When there is a minimum of sunspot activity, the surface of the sun may be completely free of sunspots. During an intense period of sunspot activity, several groups of sunspots may dot the surface of the sun at once.

Although the sunspot cycle averages 11 years, it actually varies from as short as 7.5 years to as long as 17 years. Some astronomers think that the sunspot cycle is caused by Jupiter's close approach to the sun every 11.86 years. However, there have been long periods in which there was hardly any sunspot activity. The last time this happened was between 1645 and 1715.

Another feature of the solar surface is solar prominences, which are shown in Figure 16–4. **Solar prominences** are streams of hot gases that form in the corona and arc downward toward the surface of the sun. The gases follow the curved paths of the magnetic fields created by sunspots. Solar prominences are very common during intense sunspot activity and are one of the most spectacular displays of the sun. In 1946, the largest solar prominence ever observed extended more than one-and-a-half million kilometers into space.

### The Solar Wind

Charged particles such as protons, electrons, and ions are accelerated to high speeds by the magnetic fields of the sunspots. Some of these particles escape from the sun and form a stream of particles called the **solar wind**. After leaving the sun, solar wind particles take about 2.5 days to reach the earth.

One effect of the solar wind is the appearance of rays of light in the sky at night. The light is given off by air molecules that have been charged by the solar wind. In the Northern Hemisphere, this phenomenon is called the *aurora borealis*, or northern lights. In the Southern Hemisphere, it is called the *aurora australis*, or southern lights.

1. the photosphere, because it is the part normally visible from Earth
2. See Figure 16–2.
3. All three involve activity of the hot gases coming off the surface of the sun and reacting with magnetic fields.
4. because there is no oxygen on the sun; oxygen is necessary for flame

## Section Review

1. Which layer of the sun is usually called the sun's surface? Why?
2. Sketch the layers of the sun and describe each layer.
3. Explain how sunspots, solar prominences, and solar wind are related.
4. THINKING CRITICALLY Why is a solar prominence not actually a flame?

# SKILL ACTIVITY   Determining the Scale of a Graph

**INTRODUCTION** _____  Both tables and graphs can show the same information. However, a graph shows patterns more clearly than a table does. To make a graph, a suitable scale must be chosen.

**PROCEDURE** _____

1. To make the scale for a graph, you need to know the range of the data and the length of your graph.

2. To determine the range of a set of data, subtract the smallest value from the largest value. In Table 1, the range is 142,700 km − 3000 km = 139,700 km.

3. To calculate the scale, divide the range by the length of the graph. Assuming that your graph is 15 cm long, you can find the scale by dividing:
$$\frac{139{,}700}{15} = 9313$$

4. Round off the scale either up or down. For example, 9313 might be rounded off to 9000. Then each centimeter division of your graph will represent 9000. In the graph that follows, the number was rounded off to 10,000 since multiples of 10 are easy to work with.

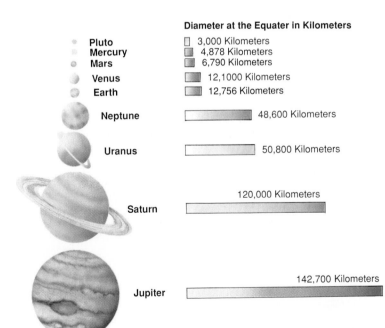

**Diameter at the Equater in Kilometers**

Pluto — 3,000 Kilometers
Mercury — 4,878 Kilometers
Mars — 6,790 Kilometers
Venus — 12,1000 Kilometers
Earth — 12,756 Kilometers
Neptune — 48,600 Kilometers
Uranus — 50,800 Kilometers
Saturn — 120,000 Kilometers
Jupiter — 142,700 Kilometers

| TABLE 1 PLANETARY DIAMETERS | |
| --- | --- |
| **Planet** | **Diameter at the Equator (km)** |
| Pluto | 3,000 |
| Mercury | 4,878 |
| Mars | 6,790 |
| Venus | 12,100 |
| Earth | 12,756 |
| Neptune | 48,600 |
| Uranus | 50,800 |
| Saturn | 120,000 |
| Jupiter | 142,700 |

**APPLICATIONS** _____

1. Jupiter
2. 47.5 times larger
3. Graphs will vary but should show an understanding of relative scale.

Using the information in Table 1 and the graph above, answer the following questions.

1. Which planet has the largest diameter?

2. How much larger is Jupiter than Pluto?

3. Redraw the graph above using a different scale.

# The Planetary System

## SECTION OBJECTIVES

- **Compare** and **contrast** the planets.
- **Contrast** Pluto with the other outer planets
- **Distinguish** between an asteroid and a comet.

## 16.3 The Inner Planets

The planetary system, which is shown in Figure 16–5, consists of nine planets, at least 54 satellites (or moons), and a large number of asteroids and comets. Mercury, Venus, Earth, and Mars are called the **inner planets**. Jupiter, Saturn, Uranus, Neptune, and Pluto are called the **outer planets**. Table 16–1 lists some characteristics of the planets.

| TABLE 16–1 | CHARACTERISTICS OF THE PLANETS | | | | | |
|---|---|---|---|---|---|---|
| Planet | Distance from Sun (AU) | Revo-lution (years) | Equatorial Radius (km) | Mass Compared to Earth | Density (g/cm³) | Average Surface Temperature (°C) |
| Mercury | 0.39 | 0.24 | 2,439 | 0.05 | 5.4 | 170 |
| Venus | 0.72 | 0.61 | 6,051 | 0.82 | 5.2 | 460 |
| Earth | 1.00 | 1.00 | 6,378 | 1.00 | 5.5 | 15 |
| Mars | 1.5 | 1.9 | 3,398 | 0.11 | 4.0 | −55 |
| Jupiter | 5.2 | 11.9 | 71,492 | 318.0 | 1.3 | −108 |
| Saturn | 9.6 | 29.5 | 60,268 | 95.2 | 0.67 | −133 |
| Uranus | 19.2 | 84.0 | 25,400 | 14.5 | 1.3 | −216 |
| Neptune | 30.1 | 164.8 | 24,750 | 17.2 | 1.7 | −216 |
| Pluto | 39.4 | 248.5 | 1,250 | 0.002 | 0.9 | −231 |

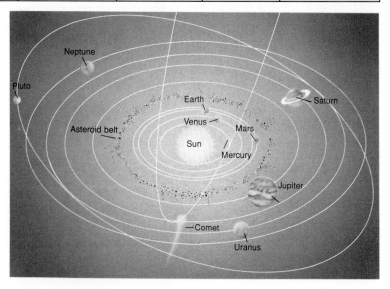

**Figure 16–5.** The orbits of the nine planets in the solar system are shown here.

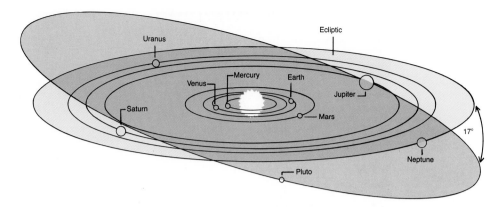

All the planets revolve counterclockwise around the sun in elliptical orbits. Similarly, all the planets except Pluto revolve around the sun in nearly the same plane as the earth. This plane of revolution, shown in Figure 16–6, is called the **ecliptic** (ih KLIHP tihk).

Although illustrations, such as Figure 16–5, make the planets appear to be close together, they are really very far apart. Distances between planets in the solar system are so large that astronomers measure them with a unit called an *astronomical unit* (AU). One **astronomical unit** is equal to the average distance of the earth from the sun—149,597,871 km. Referring to Table 16–1, you will notice that Pluto is 39.4 AU from the sun—5,894,156,117 km. Another unit of measurement used in astronomy is the light-year. A **light-year** is the distance light travels in one year. If light from the sun takes 8 minutes to reach Earth, how long does it take light from the sun to reach Pluto? 315.2 minutes

### Mercury

Mercury, the planet closest to the sun, is the second-smallest planet in the solar system. Only Pluto is smaller. Mercury can usually be seen lying low over the earth's horizon just after sunset or just before sunrise. Because of its low gravity and high temperature and the effect of solar wind, Mercury has no atmosphere.

A picture of Mercury's surface is shown in Figure 16–7. This picture shows that the surface of Mercury is covered with a large number of impact craters. An **impact crater** is a crater caused by a collision with an asteroid or a meteor. Without an atmosphere or water to wear away the craters, the surface of Mercury has probably changed little in the last 4 billion years.

Mercury has a density similar to that of Earth. This similarity has lead astronomers to believe that Mercury has an iron-nickel core that may reach halfway to the planet's surface. Although Mercury's core is similar to

**Figure 16–6.** The ecliptic is an imaginary circle on the celestial sphere and represents the plane of the earth's orbit around the sun. All the planets revolve around the sun on the ecliptic, except for Pluto, which orbits the sun inclined 17° to the ecliptic.

Any gases near the surface of the planet would rise and blow away.

READING CRITICALLY
Why would low gravity, high temperature, and solar wind cause Mercury to lack an atmosphere?

**Figure 16–7.** The surface of Mercury, photographed by *Mariner 10*, shows a similarity to that of the moon. The craters tend to appear in pairs, groups, or lines and to have some central peaks.

Earth's, its magnetic field is very weak. The weak magnetic field is probably due to the planet's slow rotation rate of once every 58.6 Earth days. At this slow rate of rotation, the electrical currents necessary for a magnetic field would not be created.

### Venus

Venus's thick clouds hide its surface from direct view. Space probes that have landed on the planet have shown that the surface is like a rocky desert.

Like Mercury, Venus is visible just after sunset or just before sunrise. The planet is sometimes called Earth's sister planet because of its similarity in size to Earth. Venus also has a density similar to that of Earth. Like Earth, Venus probably has an iron-nickel core. However, Venus rotates too slowly to have a magnetic field.

**Figure 16–8.** This computer-generated photograph of Venus reveals extensive cratering, which may be due to meteors and volcanic activity. Lava flow has been detected by radar.

Unlike most of the other planets, Venus rotates in a clockwise direction as seen from the north. Venus rotates very slowly, making one rotation every 243 days. Uranus is the only other planet that rotates in a clockwise direction. Venus has the highest surface temperature of any planet—460°C. The temperature on Venus is even hotter than that on Mercury, which is closer to the sun. This is because the atmosphere of Venus traps the heat energy it receives from the sun.

## The Earth-Moon System

Earth, the third planet from the sun, is the largest of the inner planets and is the only one of the four that has a significant magnetic field. Earth is also the only planet in the solar system to have liquid water. No other planet has lakes, rivers, or oceans. Earth is the only planet that is known to have life. Other features of Earth are discussed more fully in Chapter 18.

The moon, which is Earth's only natural satellite, orbits at an average distance of 384,401 km from Earth. With a radius of 1738 km, the moon is one of the largest satellites in the solar system. However, the moon's mass is only 1/81 that of the earth, and its density is 3.3 g/cm³. Unlike Earth, the moon has no magnetic field and its gravitational pull is only one-sixth that of Earth.

The surface of the moon has two major features—highlands and plains. The highlands, which are older than the plains, are lighter in color. The highlands consist of rocks ranging in age from 3.7 billion to 4.6 billion years. The plains, or **maria,** appear as darker areas on the moon's surface. The maria, shown in Figure 16–9, range in age from 3.1 billion to 3.8 billion years. The

Fragments of astroids that fall to Earth are called *meteorites*. Meteorites may also be fragments of comets. Over three thousand meteorites have been collected. However, only about one thousand of these were actually seen falling.

**Figure 16–9.** The terrain of the moon is stark. It is nearly colorless, rugged, and covered with craters, vast dusty maria, and mountainous highlands.

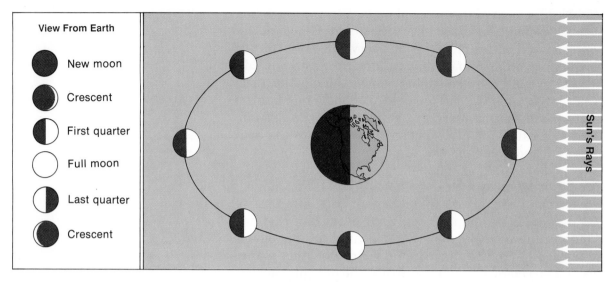

**Figure 16–10.** The moon can be seen in different phases as it orbits the earth. It is invisible in the new-moon phase and fully visible at full moon.

**View From Earth**

● New moon

◐ Crescent

◖ First quarter

○ Full moon

◗ Last quarter

◑ Crescent

Sun's Rays

## SCIENCE FACT

Although much smaller than the sun, the moon can still block the face of the sun. An eclipse is possible because the moon is so much closer to Earth than to the sun.

surface of the moon is also pockmarked with impact craters from asteroids. The moon's layer of fine rock also includes meteoroids. **Meteoroids** are fine mineral grains left over from passing comets. Meteoroids constantly bombard the surface of the moon.

The moon revolves around the earth in 27.3 days. However, since the earth is also moving, the time between each full moon is 29.5 days. As the moon revolves around the earth, its orbital plane is not perfectly in line with that of the earth around the sun. For this reason, the moon is only occasionally in line with the earth and sun. When the earth, moon, and sun are directly in line, an eclipse occurs. The two types of eclipses are shown in Figure 16–11.

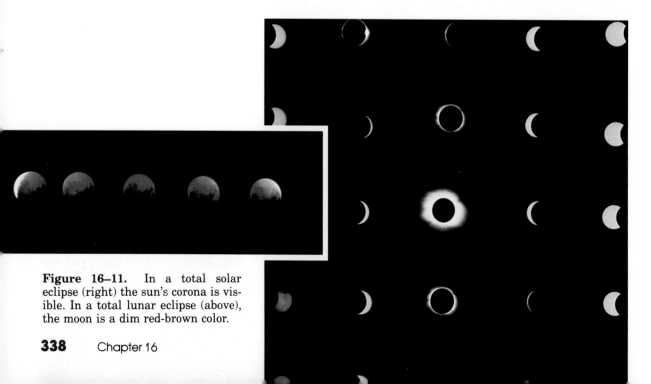

**Figure 16–11.** In a total solar eclipse (right) the sun's corona is visible. In a total lunar eclipse (above), the moon is a dim red-brown color.

The average density of Mars suggests that it has a small iron-nickel core. The planet's magnetic field, like that of Mercury and Venus, is very weak.

## Mars

Mars, the fourth planet from the sun, orbits the sun in 687 days. Mars has a radius of 3398 km, a little more than half of Earth. Mars is a dry planet with a thin atmosphere. Earth's atmospheric pressure is more than one hundred times greater than that of Mars. The Martian atmosphere is composed mainly of carbon dioxide, nitrogen, and argon, with traces of oxygen, carbon monoxide, water, and rare gases. Although the Martian atmosphere is thin, it is quite violent. Huge dust storms continuously reshape the Martian surface. Mars has two satellites, Phobos and Deimos.

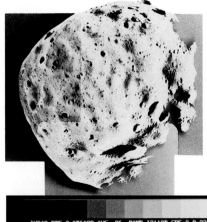

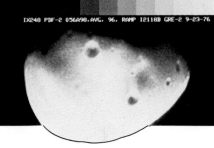

**Figure 16–12.** Rocks of various sizes litter the vivid orange-red landscape of Mars (left). Phobos (top) is the larger of the two satellites of Mars, having a diameter of 23 km. Deimos (above) has a diameter of only 10 km.

There is evidence that an asteroid 10 km in diameter hit Earth 65 million years ago. According to some scientists, this asteroid may have thrown so much dust and water into the atmosphere that Earth's climate was temporarily, but drastically, changed. This change in climate may have killed the dinosaurs and a large number of other animals and plants.

Scientists believe that water was once abundant on Mars. Evidence of dry riverbeds and flood plains support this theory. Some scientists also believe that life could have existed on Mars in the past when the planet had liquid water. In 1976, two *Viking* spacecraft landed on Mars to conduct experiments that could detect the presence of life. Although not conclusive, the results of those experiments indicate that there is no life on Mars today.

Between the inner and outer planets is a band of small planetary bodies, called **asteroids**, that orbit the sun. Scientists believe that the asteroids are bodies that failed to form into planets. For this reason, the asteroids are sometimes called the *minor planets* or *planetoids*.

**Figure 16–13.** The Barringer Crater in Winslow, Arizona, was formed 50,000 years ago when an asteroid weighing 484,000,000 kg struck the earth. This asteroid had the mass of a medium-sized office building.

# 16.4 The Outer Planets and Comets

### Jupiter

Jupiter, which is shown in Figure 16–14, is the largest of all the planets. Jupiter has a mass 2.5 times greater than the combined mass of all the other planets.

**Figure 16–14.** The colored bands on Jupiter's "surface" are the top layers of its atmosphere. The four largest of Jupiter's 16 satellites are shown here.

Beneath Jupiter's atmosphere lies its mantle, which extends down to the core. The mantle consists of solid hydrogen with helium dissolved in it. Scientists estimate the temperature at the center of Jupiter's core to be 25,000 K.

Jupiter rotates faster than any other planet, completing one turn about its axis in 9 hours and 50 minutes. However, Jupiter is so far from the sun that it takes 11.86 years for Jupiter to complete one orbit.

Jupiter's 1000-km-thick atmosphere is made up of brightly colored bands of gases. The lighter-colored bands are warmer, rising gases; the darker bands are cooler, sinking gases. The Great Red Spot, which is many times larger than Earth, consists of a mass of warm gases rising 8 km above the surrounding clouds.

Jupiter is the only planet that radiates almost twice as much energy as it receives from the sun. Most of this energy is in the form of infrared and radio waves. The source of this energy is the decay of radioactive elements in Jupiter's core. Heat left over from the planet's formation also contributes to this radiation.

Jupiter has 16 satellites. Four of Jupiter's largest satellites were discovered and named by Galileo. These satellites, Io, Europa, Ganymede, and Callisto, were

## READING CRITICALLY

Why, do you think, does Jupiter have a strong magnetic field?

because it rotates so fast

closely studied using the *Voyager 1* and *Voyager 2* space probes. As a result, scientists have learned that these four satellites, which are shown in Figure 16–14, are very different from one another.

### Saturn

Saturn, which is shown in Figure 16–15, has the lowest density of all of the planets. The density of Saturn is so low that the planet would actually float on water. The planet is composed mainly of ice surrounding the core. It is the solar system's largest "snowball."

Saturn's rings, as well as the rings of Jupiter, Uranus, and Neptune, may be composed of debris from passing comets.

Saturn has a complex ring structure that circles the planet's equator. The rings of Saturn are made of particles ranging in size from less than a centimeter to 10 meters across. The ring system consists of hundreds of rings separated by gaps of varying widths. The widest gap is 4500 km across. Saturn has 23 satellites, the largest of which is Titan. Titan is larger than the planet Mercury, but not as large as Jupiter's Ganymede.

**Figure 16–15.** This computer-enhanced photograph shows Saturn and some of its 23 satellites (left). The rings of Saturn (above) are composed of particles of water-ice. Space photographs have revealed that the rings are made up of hundreds of separate smaller ringlets.

### Uranus and Neptune

Uranus was discovered in 1781 by the English astronomer William Herschel. Uranus, like Saturn, has a ring system. The rings are thin and extend to twice the radius of the planet. In addition, Uranus has 15 satellites, five of which are larger than 400 km in diameter.

Uranus has a volume about fifty times greater than Earth's but a much smaller density.

Like the other three giant planets, Neptune has a rocky core. Neptune has two known satellites, one of which, Triton, has a radius of 1200 km. Little is known about Neptune because of its distance from Earth.

| TABLE 16–2 TRAVEL TIMES TO PLANETS | |
| --- | --- |
| **Planet** | **One-Way Time** (speed = 30,000 km/h) |
| Mercury | 4 months |
| Venus | 2 months |
| Mars | 3 months |
| Jupiter | 2 years, 4 months |
| Saturn | 5 years |
| Uranus | 10 years |
| Nep- | 16 years |
| Pluto | 22 years |

## SCIENCE FACT

Scientists believe that comets are the remains of matter left over when the planetary system was beginning to form. They may be the oldest objects in the solar system.

A comet loses several cubic meters of material from its surface each time it nears the sun. Scientists believe that most comets last for about a dozen orbits around the sun.

**Figure 16–16.** A comet consists of a nucleus, a coma, and a tail. The nucleus is usually less than 16 km in diameter and is a mixture of gas, dust, ice, and snow. It vaporizes as it approaches the sun to form the coma and eventually the tail. The tail always points away from the sun.

## Pluto

Pluto is usually the farthest planet from the sun. However, because Pluto's orbit is more elliptical than the orbits of the other planets, Pluto's orbit sometimes passes inside the orbit of Neptune. From April 1979 to May 1999, Neptune is actually the most distant planet. The existence of Pluto was predicted by astronomers. During the early 1900s, astronomers searched the night sky for this mysterious "planet X." Finally, in 1930, Pluto was observed. Little is known about this distant planet. Even the most powerful telescope cannot reveal much about Pluto. Pluto has one known satellite, Charon, discovered in 1978.

## Comets and Meteors

**Comets** are the outermost members of the solar system. When Halley's comet passed near Earth in 1986, data showed that it was made up of dark mineral matter embedded in ice. Comets form an envelope around the sun called the *Oort cloud.* There may be 100 million comets embedded in ice in the Oort cloud. Most of the comets never leave the cloud.

Comets occasionally enter the earth's atmosphere. At 7:15 A.M. on June 30, 1908, a small comet, or possibly a fragment of the comet Encke, plunged into the earth's atmosphere. The comet traveled at a speed of 30–40 km/s and had a mass of about 220,000,000 kg. The comet exploded at an altitude of 8.5 km above northeastern Siberia. Trees were flattened up to a distance of 15 km away from the blast. Since the comet exploded in the atmosphere and not on the earth, no crater was formed. However, iron-nickel and silicate particles were found in the soil at the site.

Nobody lived at the site of the explosion in 1908.

However, people living in a village 60 km away were knocked off their feet. Windows were broken and ceilings collapsed. Shock waves generated by the explosion were recorded around the world.

Meteoroids are particles of asteroids and comets. These usually small bodies are constantly pulled into the earth's atmosphere by gravity. As the meteoroids plunge through the atmosphere, friction causes the particles to begin to burn. These burning particles are called **meteors**, or *shooting stars*. Most meteors burn up entirely before they reach Earth's surface. Those that do not burn up strike the Earth and are called *meteorites*.

## Section Review

1. List three ways in which Earth is different from other planets.
2. Why is Saturn sometimes referred to as a snowball?
3. Why does Jupiter radiate energy?
4. Why are meteors called shooting stars?
5. THINKING CRITICALLY How do you think ancient people might have reacted to seeing Halley's comet appear in the night sky?

# CAREER

## Aerospace Engineer

**DESCRIPTION** An aerospace engineer designs and develops aircraft or spacecraft. Most aerospace engineers specialize by working mainly on either navigational instruments or structural design. More than half of all aerospace engineers work for private industry. The rest are employed by the federal government, consulting firms, manufacturers of communications equipment, and commercial airlines.

**REQUIREMENTS** A student planning to be an aerospace engineer should take high school courses in mathematics, physics, and chemistry. A bachelor's degree in aerospace engineering from a four-year college or university is required for engineering jobs.

**INFORMATION** American Institute of Aeronautics and Astronautics, Inc., 1633 Broadway, New York, NY 10019

# INVESTIGATION 16: Diameter of the Sun

*How can you measure the sun's diameter?*

## PURPOSE
To measure the diameter of the sun

## MATERIALS

| | | |
|---|---|---|
| ring stand | convex lens | card holder |
| test tube clamp | lens holder | metric ruler |
| meter stick | index card | |

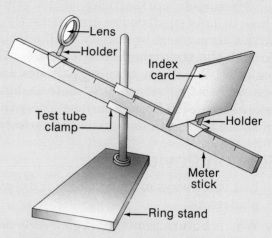

## PROCEDURE

1. Copy Table 1 onto a sheet of paper. Enter all data from this investigation onto your table.

2. Set up the materials as shown in the figure. Carefully move the entire setup next to a window that faces the sun. Position the setup so that the meter stick is directly lined up with the sun. **CAUTION: Do not look directly at the sun to position the meter stick. Never look at the sun without using special filters.**

3. Move the index card toward or away from the lens until the circular image of the sun appears on the card. Measure in millimeters the distance between the lens and the index card. Carefully draw a circle around the sun's image on the index card.

4. Move the lens 5 to 10 cm closer to the index card. Move the index card about 3 cm to the right; then move it away from the lens until the sun's image on the card is sharp and clear.

5. Measure the distance between the lens and the index card. Draw a circle around the sun's image on the card.

6. Repeat this procedure once more, again moving the lens 5 to 10 cm closer to the index card.

## RESULTS

1. Calculate the diameter of the sun.

## CONCLUSIONS

1. What is the average distance between the lens and the index card? Answers will vary.

2. What is the average diameter of the sun's image on the index card? Answers will vary.

3. The actual distance between the sun and the earth is approximately 150,000,000 km. Use this figure and the following ratio to determine the diameter of the sun. Answers will vary.

$$\frac{\text{actual distance}}{\text{average distance}} : \frac{\text{actual diameter}}{\text{average diameter}}$$
$$\text{to the sun} \qquad \text{of the sun}$$
$$\text{from lens to card} \qquad \text{of image on card}$$

## APPLICATION

1. Suppose astronomers have just discovered a new planet. They have determined its diameter but not its distance away from Earth. How could the distance from Earth of the new planet be determined?

Answers: see page T95.

| TABLE 1 | MEASUREMENTS OF DISTANCE AND DIAMETER | | | |
|---|---|---|---|---|
| | Distance Between Lens and Card | Avg. Dist. | Diameter of Sun's Image | Avg. Diam. |
| 1 | | | | |
| 2 | | | | |
| 3 | | | | |

# CHAPTER 16 REVIEW

## Summary

1. The sun consists of the core, the radiative layer, the convective layer, the photosphere, the chromosphere, and the corona. **(16.1)**

2. Sunspots, solar prominences, and the solar wind are activities that take place on the surface of the sun. **(16.2)**

3. The planetary system consists of the inner planets—Mercury, Venus, Earth, and Mars; and the outer planets—Jupiter, Saturn, Uranus, Neptune, and Pluto. **(16.3)**

4. Mercury is the second smallest planet in the solar system, and the planet closest to the sun. Earth is the only planet known to have liquid water and to have life. **(16.3)**

5. The surface of Mars shows evidence of the existence of water. **(16.3)**

6. Jupiter, the largest of all the planets, is the only planet that radiates almost twice as much energy as it receives from the sun. **(16.4)**

7. The rings of Saturn each consist of hundreds of rings. Saturn is made mainly of ice. **(16.4)**

8. Uranus, Neptune, and Pluto can be seen only with a telescope. Pluto is usually the farthest planet from the sun. **(16.4)**

9. Comets are mixtures of mineral matter embedded in ice. They may be the oldest objects in the solar system. **(16.4)**

## Science Terms

On a separate sheet of paper, define each term in a sentence.

asteroid **(339)**
astronomical unit (AU) **(335)**
chromosphere **(330)**
comet **(342)**
convective layer **(330)**
core **(329)**
corona **(331)**
ecliptic **(335)**

granules **(330)**
impact crater **(335)**
inner planets **(334)**
light-year **(335)**
maria **(337)**
meteor **(343)**
meteoroid **(338)**
outer planets **(334)**

photosphere **(330)**
radiative layer **(330)**
solar prominence **(332)**
solar wind **(332)**
sunspot **(331)**

## Modified True-False

On a separate sheet of paper, mark each true statement *TRUE* and each false statement *FALSE*. If false, change the underlined term to make the statement true.

1. Most <u>inner</u> planets have rings and numerous satellites. F, outer

2. The <u>solar wind</u> is responsible for the phenomena known as auroras. T

3. The surface of the sun has a temperature of about <u>6000</u> K. T

4. Mercury has a <u>surface</u> similar to that of Earth's moon. T

5. The moon revolves around the earth in <u>27.3</u> days. T

6. Mars has <u>three</u> satellites. F, two

7. <u>Saturn</u> is the largest of all the planets. F, Jupiter

8. Debris from passing comets makes up the rings of <u>Saturn</u>. T

9. The three planets farthest from <u>Earth</u> are Uranus, Neptune, and Pluto. T

10. Unlike most of the planets, Venus rotates in a <u>clockwise</u> direction. T

*(continues)*

The Solar System **345**

## Multiple Choice

On a separate sheet of paper, write the letter of the term that best answers the question or completes the statement.

1. Which planet is *not* an outer planet?
   a. Pluto
   b. Neptune
   c. Uranus
   d. Mercury ✓

2. The _____ is not part of the sun's structure.
   a. core
   b. corona
   c. ecliptic ✓
   d. photosphere

3. The solar photosphere contains giant areas of hot gases called _____ , which are created by strong magnetic fields.
   a. sunspots ✓
   b. solar winds
   c. prominences
   d. coronas

4. The sun is mainly made up of
   a. carbon and oxygen.
   b. hydrogen and helium. ✓
   c. oxygen and hydrogen.
   d. carbon and helium.

5. Which planet is sometimes called Earth's sister planet because of its similarity to Earth in size?
   a. Mars
   b. Venus ✓
   c. Uranus
   d. Neptune

6. Fragments of asteroids that fall to Earth are called
   a. meteorites. ✓
   b. planetoids.
   c. comets.
   d. meteoroids.

7. The largest of all the planets is
   a. Earth.
   b. Jupiter. ✓
   c. Saturn.
   d. Uranus.

8. Because it is composed mainly of ice, which planet is the solar system's largest snowball?
   a. Pluto
   b. Venus
   c. Saturn ✓
   d. Jupiter

9. What forms the Oort cloud found around the sun?
   a. meteoroids
   b. comas
   c. asteroids
   d. comets ✓

10. What material makes up the core of the earth and of several other planets?
    a. iron-nickel ✓
    b. hydrogen
    c. water
    d. carbon dioxide

## Completion

On a separate sheet of paper, complete each statement by supplying the correct term.

1. The only inner planet that has no atmosphere is Mercury .

2. The photosphere. _____ is the coolest layer of the sun.

3. The orbit of Pluto sometimes passes within the orbit of Neptune.

4. The only planet that radiates twice as much energy as it receives from the sun is Jupiter .

5. Earth's only natural satellite is the Moon .

6. Asteroids are sometimes called planetoids or minor planets .

7. The Great Red Spot is found on Jupiter .

8. Scientists believe that water was once abundant on Mars .

9. When the earth, moon, and sun are directly in line, an eclipse occurs.

10. A depression caused by a collision with an asteroid or meteor is called an impact crater .

## Writing Critically

1. Describe the factors that make each of the following planets unsuitable for life: Mercury, Venus, and Mars.
2. Explain why making a trip to another planet might mean travelling longer than just the distance indicated in Table 16–2. Why do scientists very carefully choose the best time to launch a space probe to a planet?
3. **CHALLENGE** Write a science-fiction story about life on Earth 4.5 billion years from now when the sun begins to get hotter and to expand toward Earth.

1. Mercury: no atmosphere, no water, and high temperature make it uninhabitable; Venus: high temperatures make it uninhabitable; Mars: violent atmosphere and no water make it uninhabitable.

2. You must take into account the speed and orbit of the planet in order to ensure that your path will connect you with that planet.

## Skill Reinforcement

The Skill Activity on page 333 describes how to determine a range for a graph. From the first two columns in Table 16–1, draw a scale for a graph showing the relationship between the distance of each planet from the sun and the number of years it takes each planet to revolve around the sun. Then plot the values from each column on the graph. What does the pattern that emerges tell you about the relationship between distance from the sun and the length of time it takes a planet to revolve?

The farther the planet is from the sun, the longer it takes to make one rotation.

## Research Ideas

1. The aurora borealis and aurora australis are two of the wonders of nature. Read more about these phenomena and write a report on how they are formed and where they can be seen.
2. Research the three major hypotheses about the origin of the moon. Based on your research, decide which theory seems the most probable. Write a paper contrasting this theory with the other two theories.
3. **CHALLENGE** Investigate the possibility of the existence of a planet beyond Pluto. If there is one, how big would you expect it to be? Give reasons to support your opinion.

## For Further Reading

Joels, Kerry Mark. *The Mars One Crew Manual.* NY: Ballantine Books, 1985. The author shows how modern technology will be used to make the first trip to Mars. The book is your crew member's manual, describing ship systems, crew's duties, flight time, and experiments to be conducted.

Todd, Robert T. *Thunderstones and Shooting Stars: The Meaning of Meteorites.* Boston: Harvard University Press, 1986. The author summarizes the history of meteorites. He also describes how huge meteorites that struck Earth in the past may have affected the evolution of life on Earth.

# The Universe

How did the universe begin? Will the universe ever end? Astronomers are using the latest technology to develop theories that help answer such questions. This computer-enhanced photograph shows a galaxy with a giant center surrounded by relatively cool red stars. The blue regions containing hotter stars give off radio waves.

For additional information, see pages T96–T97.

# CHAPTER OUTLINE

# Stars

## SECTION OBJECTIVES

- **Discuss** ways in which stars are different from one another.
- **Explain** how the different types of stars are formed.
- **List** the stages a star goes through as it ages.

Photograph left: Milky Way Galaxy

## 17.1 Stars and Constellations

When you look at the starlit sky, you may notice that stars differ in color and brightness. Some stars, such as Antares and Betelgeuse, are red. Other stars, such as Sirius and Rigel, are blue. You can find these stars on the star chart in Figure 17–1.

### Brightness of Stars

The brightness of stars varies a great deal. In about 150 B.C., the Greek astronomer Hipparchus (hih PAHR kuhs) grouped, or ordered, stars into six classes of brightness, which he called **magnitude.** First-magnitude stars were the brightest. The second, third, fourth, and fifth magnitudes included stars of decreasing brightness. The sixth magnitude included stars that are barely visible to the naked eye.

This method of grouping stars is still used today. However, the use of modern telescopes has made many more stars visible from Earth. Six magnitudes of brightness can no longer cover the range of stars now visible. Orders of magnitude now extend to 25. The orders of magnitude have also been expanded to include brighter objects. Negative numbers are used to order stars with a magnitude brighter than 1. The sun, for example, has a magnitude of −27.

NEW TERMS IN THIS SECTION

| | |
|---|---|
| magnitude | nova |
| binary system | supernova |
| constellations | neutron star |
| zodiac | pulsars |
| red giant | nebula |
| white dwarf | bursters |
| black dwarf | black hole |
| | quasars |

Tell students that how bright a star appears when seen from Earth is called its *apparent brightness*. The actual amount of light a star gives off is its *absolute brightness*.

## SCIENCE FACT

The number of stars in the universe is only one-third the number of copper atoms contained in a copper penny.

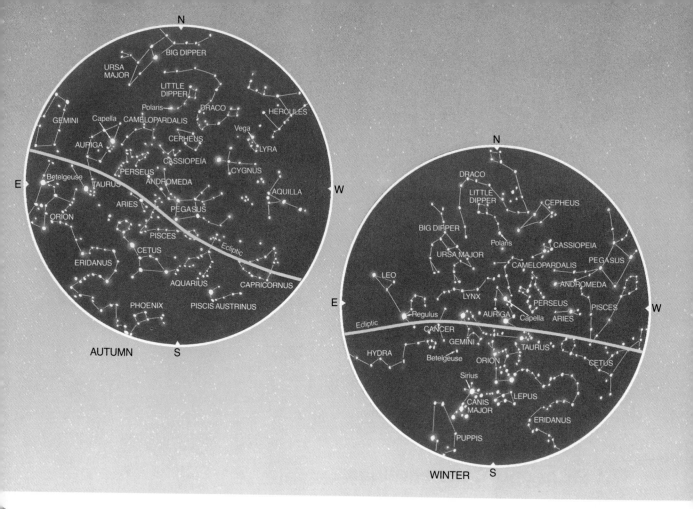

**Figure 17–1.** This star chart indicates the location of stars as seen from the Northern Hemisphere during the different seasons.

Colors of stars from coolest to hottest are red, orange, yellow, green, blue.

There is a great difference in the energy output of stars. Some stars give off 1/100,000th of the energy given off by the sun. Other stars give off 100,000 times more energy than the sun. The cooler stars are red, and the hottest stars are blue. The color of a star can be compared to the color of a burner on an electric stove. As the burner's temperature rises, its color changes from dull red to bright orange. If the burner could be heated even more, it would turn blue.

About 60 percent of all stars are members of pairs. A pair of stars in which each star revolves around the other is called a **binary system**. One star in a pair is usually bigger than the other. Sometimes the two stars are so close that they have a common atmosphere.

Scientists believe that most of the single stars are accompanied by planetary systems.

## Constellations

When you look at stars, you might notice that some seem to form groups. Ancient astronomers saw patterns in these groups of stars. When the groups were outlined, they seemed to form the figures of animals, people, and objects. These groups of stars are called **constellations** (kahn stuh LAY shuhnz).

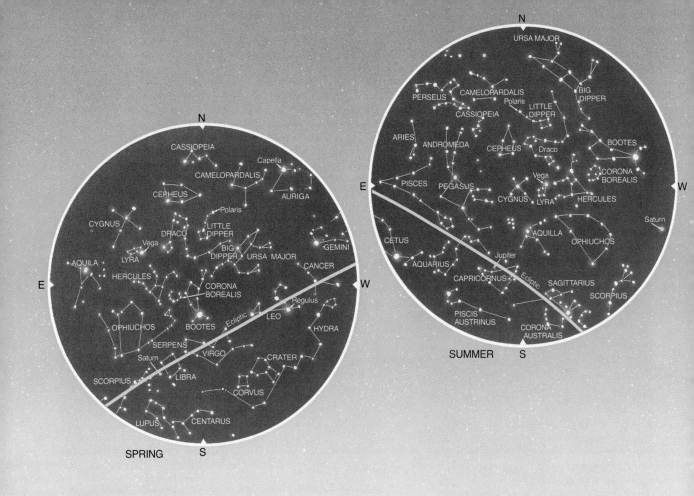

SPRING

SUMMER

Figure 17–2 is a star chart that shows various stars and constellations. Notice that some constellations fall along the *ecliptic*. The twelve constellations found along the ecliptic form the **zodiac**. This name comes from the Greek word *zoon* (ZOH uhn), which means "animal," and is used because seven of the twelve constellations represent animals. What are the seven animals found in the zodiac? fish, lion, ram, crab, horse, scorpion, dog

## 17.2 The Life History of a Star

The length of a star's life depends on its mass. The most massive stars live only a few million years. A star the size of the sun may live 10 billion years. Smaller, less massive stars may live for many more billions of years. Figure 17–3 shows the life history of stars.

Most stars are *main sequence stars*. White stars and yellow stars such as the sun fall into this category. These stars are made mostly of a core of hydrogen and helium. The nuclear reactions that take place within the core are the source of a star's power. The bigger a star is, the faster it uses up hydrogen and the shorter its life is.

The life history of a star depends on its mass and gravity. The greater the mass and gravity, the faster the star's atoms move. Nuclear reactions occur more quickly, shortening the star's life.

**Figure 17–2.** This star chart shows the twelve constellations that make up the zodiac.

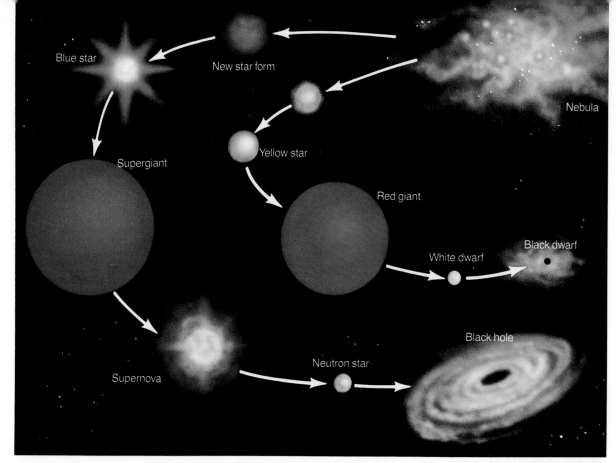

**Figure 17–3.** Some scientists believe the life of a star begins in a nebula. From there, its "life style" depends on its mass and what it is made of. Although the sun, a yellow star, may appear to be the largest star we can see, it is small compared to the size of a red giant. Some red giants become so large that they are called supergiants.

Astronomers use the term solar mass to describe the mass of a star compared with the mass of the sun. A few stars have masses 20 to 50 times that of the sun.

## ACTIVITY

### Identifying Constellations

On a clear night, go outside and look at the sky. Try to locate and identify as many of the constellations as you can. View the sky at different times during the evening. Record the constellations you see and the time they are most visible.

When a star begins to run out of hydrogen and begins to cool, it goes through many changes. The remaining hydrogen continues to react and to release energy around the hot core. The heat from the core causes the outer layers of gases to be pushed outward. As these changes take place, a red giant forms. A **red giant** is a star that has used up most of its hydrogen and has expanded. As helium replaces hydrogen, the red giant grows to tremendous size.

The sun is about 4.6 billion years old. In about another 5 billion years, the sun will become a red giant. When the sun becomes a red giant, it will expand outward until it reaches beyond the orbit of Venus. The earth will be completely burned up.

### Dwarf Stars

Millions of years after the sun has become a red giant, it will begin to collapse in on itself. The sun will shrink until it is about the size of Earth and will shine with an intense, white light. This type of star is called a **white dwarf**. The white dwarf will continue radiating light for billions of years, cooling down slowly. At the end of its life, when the white dwarf stops radiating light, it will become nothing more than a black cinder, or **black dwarf**.

## Novas

If a white dwarf is part of a binary system, it may take hydrogen gas away from the second star in the system. As more hydrogen moves to the dying star's surface, the hydrogen layer becomes thicker. The layer also becomes hotter because it is absorbing heat from the star. When the temperature reaches ten million degrees Celsius, a fusion reaction begins, changing the hydrogen into helium. As a result, the star flares up and may become about ten thousand times brighter. This flare of light is called a **nova**, which means "new star." A nova reaches peak brightness in a day or two, and then it slowly fades. Over a period of months or years, the nova returns to its original brightness.

*READING CRITICALLY*

How do astronomers know that a nova is a member of a binary system?

A nova can occur only when a hydrogen layer builds up on the surface of a white dwarf. This hydrogen must be captured from a companion star.

**Figure 17–4.** Nova Cygni (V1500 Cyg) exploded in 1975 and is now surrounded by an expanding shell of gas that was released during the explosion. Novas occur in binary star systems containing a white dwarf star.

## Supernovas

When the hydrogen in the core of a red giant is used up, the star explodes in a tremendous burst called a *supernova*. A **supernova** is a two-way explosion: the core *implodes,* or is blown inward, and the rest of the star explodes.

## Neutron Stars

When a supernova explodes, 90 percent of the mass of the star spreads out into space, forming a huge cloud of gas. However, in the star's core, the implosion causes protons and electrons to combine into neutrons. The core of the exploded star becomes a **neutron star**. This type of star has a radius of only about 15 km and spins at a very high speed. Because of the rapid spinning, a neutron star has a very strong magnetic field.

**SCIENCE FACT**

Astronomers recently observed a supernova in the Large Magellanic Cloud. It is apparently the first supernova to be visible to the naked eye in 400 years.

Pulsars are rapidly rotating neutron stars with strong magnetic fields. They send out short, regular radio waves that change in intensity very quickly. When they were first discovered, the waves seemed to be twinkling. At first these objects were not associated with stars because they did not give off any light. A radio source was later discovered in the Crab Nebula. At the same location, a very dim star flashed on and off with the radio pulses.

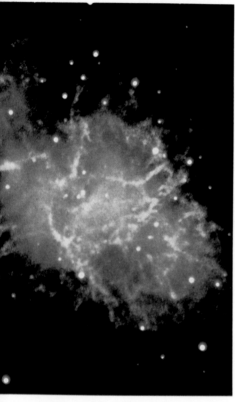

**Figure 17–5.** The Crab Nebula is made up of the expanding gas remains of a supernova.

A neutron star is also very dense. If the Great Pyramid of Cheops in Egypt had the density of a neutron star, the pyramid would be the size of a pinhead. However, the pyramid would still weigh 13 million kg.

## Pulsars

A neutron star is so dense and its gravitational field is so strong that it easily captures matter from space or from a companion star. As matter falls into the neutron star, radiation is given off. Because the star is rotating, the radiation is seen as pulses of light. Rapidly pulsating stars are called **pulsars**.

The famous Crab Nebula, shown in Figure 17–5, is the remains of a supernova. A **nebula** (plural, nebulae) is a gas cloud. The Crab Nebula is an expanding shell of gas that formed when a supernova exploded. At the center of the Crab Nebula is a pulsar that spins 30.3 times a second.

## Bursters

If a neutron star is part of a binary system, it can pull large amounts of hydrogen from the other star in the system. The temperature at the surface of a neutron star is high enough for the hydrogen to be fused into helium. As helium builds up on the surface of the neutron star, the temperature of the star rises to 100 million degrees Celsius. At that temperature, helium nuclei fuse into carbon nuclei. This nuclear reaction lasts only about 20 seconds and causes a powerful burst of X rays. Neutron stars that give off powerful X-ray bursts are called **bursters**.

## Black Holes

If a star becomes a supernova, it may implode with such force that the core compresses into an extremely dense point. Because all the mass is concentrated into a single point, both space and time are distorted at that point. Not even light can escape from the gravitational field. The collapsed star is called a **black hole**, which is illustrated in Figure 17–6. Since light cannot escape, a black hole is invisible. The only way to detect a black hole is by its gravitational effect on a nearby star or by the X rays produced by gases falling into the black hole.

Only one object in the sky, Cygnus X-1, has been tentatively identified as a black hole. Cygnus X-1 has a strong gravitational effect on the other star in its binary system. X rays are given off when matter from the second star is pulled into the black hole.

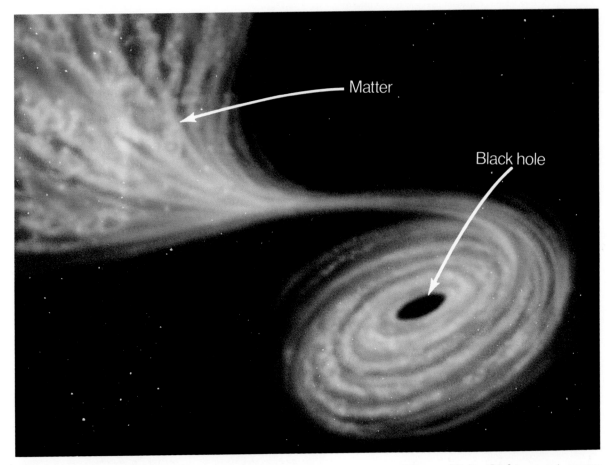

Matter

Black hole

## Quasars

Some very distant, compact objects look like stars but give off 100 times more energy than an ordinary system of stars. These objects are called **quasars.** A quasar probably consists of a giant black hole. Scientists have calculated that each second a quasar consumes about the same amount of matter as the amount of water in the Caribbean and the Gulf of Mexico combined.

**Figure 17–6.** Light cannot escape from a black hole. Black holes may be detected by their gravitational effect on nearby stars. Only one object, Cygnus X-1, has been tentatively identified as a black hole.

*Quasar* is an acronym for Quasi-stellar object. Quasars were first discovered because they emit large amounts of radio waves. Quasars are probably black holes having a mass of at least a billion solar masses and a radius of at least 3 million km.

## Section Review

1. Why have the orders of magnitude of stars been extended from 6 to 25 and from 1 to −27?

2. What does a star's color reveal?

3. What type of star will the sun become in 5 billion years?

4. Summarize the stages in the life of a typical star such as the sun.

5. THINKING CRITICALLY Scientists have discovered an extremely dense object at the center of a nebula. How can they determine if it is a pulsar or a black hole?

1. Modern telescopes have made many more stars visible, so six categories no longer cover the range of stars. As brighter objects such as the sun were identified, a scale of greater brightness was needed.
2. the amount of energy (heat) given off
3. a red giant
4. yellow star, red giant, white dwarf, black dwarf
5. Pulsars emit radiation in regular pulses; black holes can be detected by their gravitational effect on nearby stars or by the X rays produced by gases being pulled into the black hole.

# SKILL *ACTIVITY*   Reading a Star Map

**INTRODUCTION**

Reading a star map involves learning to recognize some of the stars and constellations in the sky. Star maps show the positions of the stars during certain months of the year.

**PROCEDURE**

1. Check the magnitude key. Usually the zero-magnitude and first-magnitude stars are grouped together as "first-magnitude stars."
2. The map shown includes the horizon at latitudes 30°N, 40°N, and 50°N. Find the latitude closest to where you live to locate stars at the horizon.

Instruct the students in the proper use of the star chart. Locate North, South, East, and West on the chart. While keeping the textbook right side up, hold the chart above your head and look up. Make sure that North and South on the chart are aligned with North and South on a compass. The other compass points will now be aligned. The various stars and constellations will be aligned with the chart.

Without turning the chart, turn and face South. The stars in the southern portion of the sky can now be located. Again without turning the chart, turn and face North. The stars in the northern portion of the sky can now be located.

A transparency and a copying master of the chart are included in the separate box of overhead transparencies that accompany this program.

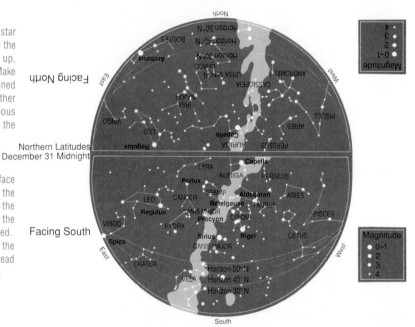

**APPLICATION**

Prepare a table like the one below.

| Brightest Stars | Constellation | Direction to Look |
|---|---|---|
|  |  |  |
|  |  |  |
|  |  |  |

1. Locate the following stars on the map: Sirius, Capella, Arcturus, Rigel, Procyon, Betelgeuse, Aldebaran, Pollux, Spica, and Regulus. On the table you prepared, write the name of the star, the constellation, and the direction in which the star can be found.

2. How can a star map help you locate the constellations?
A star map provides a frame of reference.

# Galaxies

NEW TERMS IN THIS SECTION
galaxy
spiral galaxies
barred spiral galaxies
elliptical galaxy
irregular galaxy
galactic clusters

## SECTION OBJECTIVES

● **Describe** the different types of galaxies.

● **Identify** ways in which galaxies interact with one another.

## 17.3 Types of Galaxies

If you are out on a moonless night, without the interference of city lights, you may notice a band of stars called the *Milky Way Galaxy*. A **galaxy** is a group of billions of stars. The sun and all other stars that you see in the sky belong to our Galaxy, the Milky Way. However, the Milky Way is only one of billions of galaxies in the universe. The billions of galaxies in the universe can be classified as four major types. The four types are spiral galaxies, barred spiral galaxies, elliptical galaxies, and irregular galaxies.

### Spiral Galaxies and Barred Spiral Galaxies

The **spiral galaxies** are usually large galaxies with 100 billion or more stars. As Figure 17–7 shows, spiral galaxies have well-developed spiral arms and much interstellar dust and gas. *Interstellar* means "between stars."

The Milky Way Galaxy contains about 180 billion stars and large amounts of interstellar gas and dust.

## SCIENCE FACT

The Egyptians thought that the Milky Way was a river Nile flowing through the heavens where dead Egyptians happily lived forever.

**Figure 17–7.** This spiral galaxy has well-developed arms extending from the center of the galaxy. Compare this galaxy to the galaxies in Figure 17–8.

## ACTIVITY

**Visualizing Galaxies**

Sketch a diagram of the Milky Way and indicate where the sun and solar system would be located.

The Milky Way is a spiral galaxy that is 100,000 light-years across. It is 10,000 light-years thick at the center and decreases to a thickness of 1000 light-years toward the edge. The sun is on the inner rim of one of the spiral arms, about 30,000 light-years from the center of the Galaxy.

A **barred spiral galaxy** is a spiral galaxy in which the stars are aligned along a bar crossing the center. Barred spiral galaxies also have much interstellar dust and gas. Figure 17–8 shows a barred spiral galaxy. The average age of stars in spiral and barred spiral galaxies is about 5 billion years.

**Elliptical Galaxies** Elliptical galaxies have no dust or interstellar gas.

An **elliptical galaxy**, shown on the right in Figure 17–8, is very different from the other types of galaxies. Elliptical galaxies are disk-shaped but thicker than the spiral and barred spiral galaxies. The average age of older stars is an elliptical galaxy is about 10 billion years. There is no gas or interstellar dust because it has all been captured by the stars. These galaxies rotate very slowly, if at all. Elliptical galaxies are the most common type of galaxy. What evidence is there that elliptical galaxies may be some of the oldest galaxies?

**Figure 17–8.** A barred spiral galaxy (*left*) has stars that are aligned along a bar crossing the center of the galaxy. An elliptical galaxy (*right*) is a much older galaxy in which all the interstellar dust and gas have already been captured by the stars.

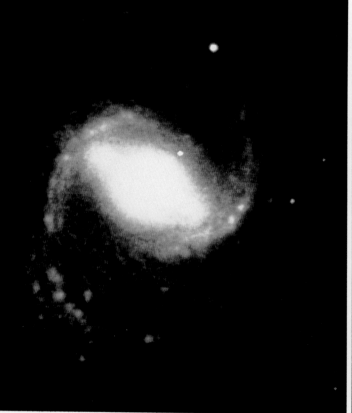

# The Changing Universe

**SECTION OBJECTIVES**

● **Explain** how scientists know that the universe is expanding.

● **Describe** the Big Bang theory and **explain** how the solar system may have been formed.

● **Compare** and **contrast** two possible futures for the universe.

● **List** and **describe** some instruments used in the study of the universe.

NEW TERMS IN THIS SECTION
Big Bang theory
refractors
reflector telescopes

## 17.5 The Expanding Universe

At one time, scientists believed that the universe never changed. However, in 1929 the astronomer Edwin Hubble made the startling announcement that the universe was expanding. Hubble based his theory on his knowledge of the Doppler effect.

The Doppler effect for sound is explained in Chapter 13. The Doppler effect can indicate if an object is moving toward or away from an observer. A similar Doppler effect exists for light. As Figure 17–11 shows, the light from a star approaching Earth is shifted toward shorter wavelengths, or *blue shifted*. Similarly, the light from a star moving away from Earth is shifted toward the red end of the spectrum, or *red shifted*. The amount of the shift depends on the speed of the star.

The greater the speed of the star, the greater the red shift. Some stars have shifted from the blue end of the spectrum all the way to the red end.

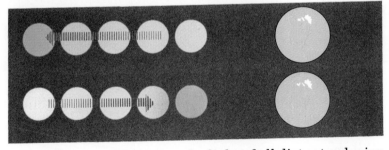

**Figure 17–11.** The light from a star is blue shifted as it approaches Earth. As a star moves away from Earth, it is red shifted. This shift in color is evidence that the universe is expanding.

Hubble observed that the light of all distant galaxies was shifted toward the red end of the spectrum. He also noticed that the amount of red shift increased regularly with distance. Hubble concluded that the universe must be expanding at a constant rate. Astronomers have now shown that a galaxy at a distance of one million light-years from Earth moves away at the speed of 18 km/s. A galaxy at a distance of three million light-years moves away at the speed of 48 km/s. A galaxy at a distance of one billion light-years moves away at the speed of 18,000 km/s. At this speed a rocket could travel between the earth and the moon in 30 seconds.

## 17.6 The Origin of the Universe

If the universe is expanding, then it must have once been much smaller. If you could run the life of the universe in reverse, like a film, you would see the universe contracting until it disappeared in a flash of light, leaving nothing.

In the realm of the universe, *nothing* really means *nothing*. Not only matter and energy would disappear, but also space and time. However, physicists theorize that from this state of nothingness the universe began in a gigantic explosion about 16.5 billion years ago. This theory of the origin of the universe is called the **Big Bang theory**. The Big Bang theory does not explain how the universe began. The theory only explains how the existing universe could have developed.

Point out to students that the model of the universe from Big Bang to implosion is called a *cycloid*. In the cycloid model, universes follow each other in periods of 80 billion years.

**Figure 17–12.** The explosion of a supernova is one possible explanation of the Big Bang theory. The photos here show a supernova before it has exploded (*left*) and after it has exploded (*right*). If the remains of a supernova expand and meet an interstellar dust cloud, a shock wave is produced that may cause the cloud to collapse. Some astronomers believe that such a compression may have triggered the formation of our solar system.

About 4.6 billion years ago, a supernova exploded, and the resulting gas cloud began to contract. Within a few million years, matter had condensed into a central body, a system of ten rings, and millions of bodies about a kilometer in diameter.

As the cloud continued to contract, the temperature began to rise. In a short time, the temperature rose to more than a million degrees Celsius in the center of the cloud. At this temperature, nuclear fusion began and the central body began to shine. The sun was formed.

Under the influence of gravity, the matter in the various rings began to clump together and also to spin. In about 400 million years, all these rings except one had become planets. The one ring that did not form into a planet was between Mars and Jupiter. What did the ring between Mars and Jupiter become? asteroids

# 17.7 The Future of the Universe

If everything that goes up must come down, must everything that expands also contract? The universe is expanding. Will the universe continue to expand forever, or at some time in the future will it begin to contract? There are two theories about the future of the universe. One states that the universe will continue to expand indefinitely. The other theory states that the universe will contract and collapse on itself.

To determine whether the universe will contract, scientists must know the density of the universe. Astronomers have counted stars and galaxies and have measured gas clouds, trying to estimate the density of the universe. At present, scientists estimate that the density is about one-sixth of what is needed to make the universe contract. However, there is evidence that the universe may contain much invisible matter that scientists have been unable to measure. Black holes, for example, may contain large amounts of matter. In addition, any future discovery will add to the known mass of the universe rather than subtract from it.

The night sky is dark because the Doppler effect makes distant galaxies invisible to the human eye. However, if the universe were to stop expanding, the night sky would become as bright as the sun. If the universe then started contracting, the earth's temperature would begin to rise. The end of the universe would come in an implosion that would return the universe to a state similar to the one that existed just prior to the Big Bang.

**Figure 17–13.** Most astronomers believe that the universe will continue expanding (A–E) and become increasingly less active as more and more stars die. Other astronomers believe in the *pulsating universe theory* (F–K). They think there is enough matter in the universe to make it stop expanding and collapse back on itself, leading to a second Big Bang. They believe that this cycle will repeat itself endlessly, and that the universe will exist forever.

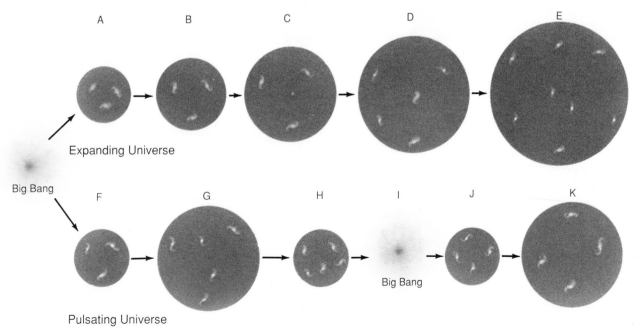

A    B    C    D    E

Expanding Universe

Big Bang

F    G    H    I    J    K

Big Bang

Pulsating Universe

The second largest reflector telescope is the Hale reflector at the Palomar Observatory in Southern California. Motors on a telescope mount can keep the telescope focused on a faint object for days, giving enough time for the object to leave an image on the plate.

## SCIENCE FACT

The mirror in the world's second largest reflector telescope took over a year to make. Most of that time was needed to cool the molten glass from which the mirror is made.

# 17.8 Using Technology to Study the Universe

Stars, gas clouds, novas, supernovas, neutron stars, pulsars, and black holes all give off energy. Electromagnetic radiation from the universe ranges from long-wavelength radio waves to very short-wavelength gamma rays. Astronomers have developed a number of instruments to study these different wavelengths.

Since its invention in 1609, the optical telescope has been the basic tool of scientists. The simplest telescopes are made of just two lenses, an *objective* and an *ocular,* as shown in Figure 17–14. Telescopes made with lenses are called **refractors.** The largest refractor telescope has an objective lens that is 101.6 cm in diameter.

The largest telescopes in the world are **reflector telescopes,** which consist of two mirrors. The *primary mirror* is a large concave mirror. The *secondary mirror* is a much smaller concave mirror. The largest reflector has a primary mirror 6 m across. This telescope is located in the Soviet Union.

**Figure 17–14.** The simple telescope shown above has just two lenses—an objective lens and an ocular lens. This type of telescope is called a refractor. The radio telescope on the right is used to study radio waves from space. This radio telescope, found in Puerto Rico, is the largest in the world.

Radio telescopes, which were developed in the 1940s, have been used to study radio waves from space. The largest of all radio telescopes is near Arecibo in Puerto Rico. This telescope, shown on the right in Figure 17–14, is 305 m across. It cannot be moved. The rotation of the earth serves to point it in different directions.

Infrared radiation, like visible light from stars, is studied using reflecting telescopes. The only difference is that the ground, the surrounding buildings, and the material of which the telescope itself is made are warm and radiate infrared radiation. A photographic plate in a normal observatory would absorb more infrared radiation given off by the mirror itself than reflected from space. To reduce this problem, infrared telescopes are placed on top of remote mountains and cooled with liquid nitrogen or liquid helium.

## ACTIVITY

**Understanding a Telescope**

Sketch the major components of a reflecting telescope.

The atmosphere stops ultraviolet, X-ray, and gamma radiation. Instruments designed to study these types of radiation are operated from spacecraft or satellites above the atmosphere. Although visible light passes through the atmosphere, the light is distorted. This distortion is the reason why stars seem to twinkle, or flicker. As a result, star images produced by ground-based optical telescopes are always a bit fuzzy. A telescope operating from outside the atmosphere can produce much sharper images and allow astronomers to study the universe in much greater detail. What kinds of everyday information can satellite photographs provide us with here on Earth?

Answers may vary but could include weather information and topographical information.

## Section Review

1. How does the red shift of the stars help explain the Big Bang theory?
2. Would the density of the universe have to increase or decrease to cause it to begin contracting?
3. Why are all pictures of the stars taken from Earth fuzzy?
4. What are three instruments used to study the stars?
5. THINKING CRITICALLY Where could scientists take the most accurate photographs of the stars? What kind of instruments should they use?

1. Red shift means movement away from Earth. This means the universe is expanding.
2. increase
3. Earth's atmosphere distorts light.
4. refractor, reflector, and radio telescopes
5. in space with reflector telescopes where the atmosphere cannot distort the image

## CAREER

### Astronomer

**DESCRIPTION** Astronomers use mathematics and physics to study the universe. They study the movements of planets and stars, the composition of bodies in space, and the formation of galaxies. Astronomers work for colleges and universities or the federal government.

**REQUIREMENTS** An advanced degree is necessary for most jobs in astronomy. A high-school student who plans to be an astronomer should take courses in physics, chemistry, and mathematics. After graduation, the student earns a bachelor of science degree at a four-year college or university, and then continues his or her education to obtain an advanced degree, preferably a Ph.D.

**INFORMATION** American Astronomical Society, 1816 Jefferson Place N.W., Washington, DC 20036

# INVESTIGATION 17: Distance of Stars

*How can you tell if one star is farther away than another star?*

## PURPOSE

To demonstrate how the distance of stars is measured

## MATERIALS

metric ruler    straight pin
index card    modeling clay
graph paper    tape

## PROCEDURE

1. Copy Table 1 onto a sheet of paper. Enter all data from this investigation on your table.

2. With the ruler, draw a line 2 cm from the long edge of the index card. Mark the line at one centimeter intervals from 0 to 20 cm. Fold the card in half lengthwise so that it will stand up as shown in Figure 1.

3. With the ruler, draw a straight line lengthwise down the center of the graph paper. Tape the paper to the edge of a table. Position the folded index card as shown.

4. Measure and mark the line on the graph paper at 5 cm, 10 cm, 15 cm, and 20 cm away from the edge of the index card.

5. Place a small amount of clay onto the point of the pin. Place the pin at the 5-cm mark on the graph paper. Bend down at the table edge. Close your right eye. Look at the pin with your left eye. Record the position of the pin along the marked line on the index card on Table 1. Repeat this step, looking at the pin with your right eye.

6. Repeat step 6 with the pin at the 10-cm, 15-cm, and 20-cm marks on the graph paper.

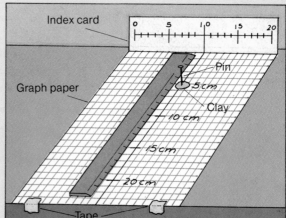

## RESULTS

| TABLE 1 | OBSERVATIONS | | |
|---|---|---|---|
| **Distance of Pin** | **Left Eye** | **Right Eye** | **Shift** |
| 5 cm | | | |
| 10 cm | | | |
| 15 cm | | | |
| 20 cm | | | |

Calculate the distance between the positions of the pin as viewed with the left and right eyes. This apparent shift in position of the pin is called the *parallax effect*. Record these distances in Table 1.

## CONCLUSIONS

1. At which distance away from the index card was the shift between the pins the least? the greatest?    20 cm; 5 cm

2. Predict how the shift of the pin would be affected if you viewed the pin from 2 m away from the edge of the table.
   amount of shift would decrease

## APPLICATION

1. Astronomers use a background of stars for measurement instead of the index card. Suppose the astronomers were observing two stars, one directly in front of the other. How would the astronomers be able to tell which star was farther away?
   The closer star would have a greater shift.

# CHAPTER 17 REVIEW

## Summary

1. The ancient Greeks classified the stars according to magnitude and grouped them in constellations. **(17.1)**

2. As stars age, they change from red giants to white dwarfs and then to black dwarfs. **(17.2)**

3. Supernovas, which are exploding red giants, develop into neutron stars and pulsars. Exploding stars can develop into black holes. **(17.2)**

4. There are billions of galaxies in the universe that can be categorized according to four basic shapes. **(17.3–17.4)**

5. The fact that the universe is expanding can be shown through the shift in the color of distant galaxies. **(17.5)**

6. The Big Bang theory is an explanation of how the universe came into existence. **(17.6)**

7. Scientists must determine the density of the universe to know if it is contracting. **(17.7)**

8. Telescopes placed both in and outside the earth's atmosphere are the key to learning more about the universe. **(17.8)**

## Science Terms

On a separate sheet of paper, define each term in a sentence.

barred spiral galaxy **(358)**
Big Bang theory **(362)**
binary system **(350)**
black dwarf **(352)**
black hole **(354)**
bursters **(354)**
constellation **(350)**
elliptical galaxy **(358)**

galactic clusters **(359)**
galaxy **(357)**
irregular galaxy **(359)**
magnitude **(349)**
nebula **(354)**
neutron star **(353)**
nova **(353)**
pulsars **(354)**

quasars **(355)**
red giant **(352)**
reflector telescopes **(364)**
refractors **(364)**
spiral galaxies **(357)**
supernova **(353)**
white dwarf **(352)**
zodiac **(351)**

## Modified True-False

On a separate sheet of paper, mark each true statement *TRUE* and each false statement *FALSE*. If false, change the underlined term to make the statement true.

1. The brightness of a star is known as its <u>magnitude</u>. T

2. About 60 percent of all stars are part of a <u>binary system</u>. T

3. Ancient astronomers called the patterns of stars <u>zodiacs</u>. F, constellations

4. <u>Spiral galaxies</u> are the most common type of galaxy. F, Elliptical galaxies

5. The Milky Way belongs to a <u>galactic cluster</u> known as the Local Group. T

6. Scientists determined that the universe is expanding by observing the changes in <u>light</u>. T

7. The Big Bang theory explains how the universe <u>will end</u>. F, began

8. The hottest stars are <u>red</u>. F, blue

9. When the sun begins to shrink in size, it will first become a <u>white dwarf</u>. T

10. Because a neutron star rotates at high speeds, it has a <u>weak</u> magnetic field. F, strong

*(continues)*

## Multiple Choice

On a separate sheet of paper, write the letter of the term that best answers the question or completes the statement.

1. A star that has used up most of its hydrogen and has expanded is a
   a. neutron star.
   **b.** red giant.
   c. white dwarf.
   d. black dwarf.

2. The bigger a star is, the faster it uses up hydrogen and
   **a.** the shorter its life.
   b. the longer its life.
   c. the higher its magnitude.
   d. the lower its magnitude.

3. Galactic clusters are groups of _____ distributed all around the universe.
   **a.** galaxies
   b. stars
   c. gravity waves
   d. white dwarfs

4. Nebulae are
   a. star clusters.
   b. galaxies.
   c. Local Groups.
   **d.** gas clouds.

5. A neutron star is very
   a. large.
   b. old.
   c. weak.
   **d.** dense.

6. What type of galaxy is the Milky Way?
   a. elliptical
   b. irregular
   **c.** spiral
   d. barred spiral

7. The Large Magellanic Cloud is
   a. an elliptical galaxy.
   **b.** an irregular galaxy.
   c. a spiral galaxy.
   d. a barred spiral galaxy.

8. Stars twinkle in the sky because of
   a. temperature change.
   **b.** distortion of light by the atmosphere.
   c. the speed of the stars.
   d. the interference of radio waves.

9. The largest telescopes are
   **a.** reflectors.
   b. refractors.
   c. radio telescopes.
   d. observatories.

10. When a red giant explodes, it becomes a
    **a.** supernova.
    b. burster.
    c. black hole.
    d. pulsar.

## Completion

On a separate sheet of paper, complete each statement by supplying the correct term.

1. The twelve constellations grouped along the ecliptic form the _zodiac_ .

2. When a white dwarf stops radiating light it becomes a _black dwarf_.

3. When a supernova occurs, the core implodes, resulting in a _neutron star_.

4. An expanding cloud of gas is a _nebula_ .

5. Not even light can escape from a _black hole_ .

6. The sun and planets in this solar system are located on a _spiral arm_ of the Milky Way Galaxy.

7. In _elliptical galaxies_, all the gas and dust have been captured by the stars.

8. A star that is moving away from Earth is red shifted, meaning that the light shifts to _longer_ wavelengths.

9. The current explanation of how the universe could have developed is called the _Big Bang_ .

10. The density of the universe would have to _increase_ for the universe to contract.

## Writing Critically

1. Summarize the ways in which astronomers describe and classify stars.
2. How does red shift help to support the Big Bang theory?
3. CHALLENGE Compressing the life of a star like the sun into 24 hours, describe the various stages a star may pass through.
4. CHALLENGE Discuss some ways in which scientists could increase the use of telescopes for research.

## Skill Reinforcement

The Skill Activity on page 356 describes how to read star maps. Refer once again to the star map on page 350, and find all twelve constellations of the zodiac.

## Research Ideas

1. Investigate the constellations of the zodiac, and find out to which galaxies they belong.
2. Find out if there are any stars the size of the sun in the galaxy nearest to the Milky Way. Find out if they have been named and list them.
3. CHALLENGE The Big Bang theory is not the only proposed explanation for the origin of the universe. Investigate other theories and report on how they compare with the Big Bang theory.

## For Further Reading

Berry, Richard. *Build Your Own Telescope: Complete Plans for Five High-Quality Telescopes That Anyone Can Build*. New York: Scribner's, 1985. This is a step-by-step manual that shows anyone with basic carpentry skills how to build a telescope.

Kerrod, Robin. *The All Color Book of Space*. New York: Arco, 1985. This is a series of essays that relates astronomy to space exploration. The author describes early telescopes, space exploration technology, and space pioneers.

Liller, William and Ben Mayer. *The Cambridge Astronomy Guide: An Introduction to Practical Astronomy*. London: Cambridge University Press, 1987. This practical guide explains how to progress from being a stargazer to an amateur astronomer. The authors explain how to take photographs of the night sky.

Mitton, Simon and Jaqueline Mitton. *Invitation to Astronomy*. New York: Basil Blackwell, 1986. The authors explain what astronomy is all about and what astronomers do. It is an excellent book for anyone who is considering a career in astronomy.

Answers to Writing Critically
1. brightness, color, distance, size, age
2. Big Bang states that the universe is expanding; red shift has shown that many stars are moving rapidly away from Earth.
3. 1 A.M.—star formed; 12 noon—star becomes red giant; 6 P.M.—star collapses on itself and becomes white dwarf; 12 midnight—star becomes black dwarf
4. Answers will vary, but may include: place telescopes in Earth orbit or on the moon; possibly place telescopes in solar orbit.

# CHAPTER 18

# Earth's History

Locked together by the force of gravity, the earth
and the moon circle each other once every 27.3
days. As the photo shows, the earth and the moon
are very different. Unlike the moon, the earth has
an atmosphere, oceans, and life. The origin and
development of life are intimately tied to the
history of the earth.

For additional information,
see pages T98–T99.

# The Earth's Past

**SECTION OBJECTIVES**

● **Explain** a theory that describes how the earth was formed.

● **Describe** how scientists believe the earth's atmosphere and ocean formed.

● **Review** how fossils can be used to learn about the earth's origin, including the development of living things.

Photograph left: Earth rising over the moon

NEW TERMS IN THIS SECTION
geologic time
eras
periods
evolution
fossils

## 18.1 The Formation of the Earth

In Chapter 17, the origin of the solar system was discussed. You may recall that the sun and the planets condensed from a huge gas cloud, or nebula. As the cloud shrank, gravitational energy was changed into heat. In addition, the newly formed planets were probably rich in radioactive elements, which would also have released large amounts of heat.

When the earth formed, most of the denser elements such as iron and nickel sank toward the center, forming the planet's core. Less dense elements and minerals floated on top of the dense elements. As Figure 18–1 shows, silicate rocks and other less dense minerals form the earth's mantle and crust.

The young earth's mantle and crust probably resembled the moon as it looks today. One major difference changed the earth. Earth had an atmosphere. Since water was able to form inside the atmosphere, many of the earth's craters soon filled with water. The action of the atmosphere and water continuously changes the surface of the earth. Earthquakes, volcanoes, and earth movements also change the earth's surface.

The average density of surface rocks is only 2.8 g/cm$^3$, the average density of Earth is 5.5 g/cm$^3$. Therefore, material inside Earth must be denser than 5.5 g/cm$^3$.

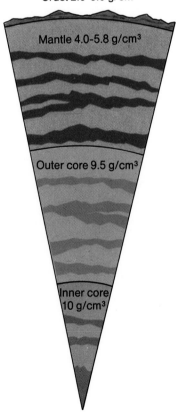

Crust 2.6-3.0 g/cm$^3$

Mantle 4.0-5.8 g/cm$^3$

Outer core 9.5 g/cm$^3$

Inner core 10 g/cm$^3$

**Figure 18–1.** The layers of the earth are shown in this illustration.

Earth's History **371**

**Crystallizing Minerals**

**CAUTION: Put on safety goggles for this activity.** Place a small amount of phenyl salicylate on a watch glass. Then place the watch glass on a beaker of water, that is heated by a burner. Once the chemical melts, shut off the burner and allow the chemical to cool. As the chemical cools, observe how the denser material settles out and forms crystals.

*Have the students list the major changes in the atmosphere. Discuss how most of the carbon dioxide disappeared. (used by plants for photosynthesis)*

## SCIENCE FACT

Today, scientists divide the earth's great body of water into four oceans: the Pacific Ocean, Atlantic Ocean, Indian Ocean, and Arctic Ocean.

# 18.2 The Origin of the Atmosphere and Ocean

When the earth first formed, its atmosphere may have been very like the atmosphere found on the planet Jupiter today. As the earth formed, its gravity kept many gases from escaping from the planet. These gases formed the earth's early atmosphere. At first, the earth's atmosphere was mostly carbon dioxide and water. Since there were no plants, any oxygen in the early atmosphere came from water molecules. The water molecules in the atmosphere were broken down into hydrogen and oxygen by ultraviolet radiation. However, this first oxygen immediately combined with iron in the warm rocks. As a result, the earth's surface began slowly to turn reddish. On what other planet did oxygen combine with iron in the surface rocks? Mars

Over time, water vapor and other gases trapped inside the earth escaped into the atmosphere from volcanoes. Hydrogen and helium, the two lightest gases, escaped from the earth's atmosphere. All other gases remained. Table 18–1 compares the composition of the early atmosphere with the modern atmosphere.

| TABLE 18–1 | EARLY AND MODERN ATMOSPHERES | |
|---|---|---|
| Gas | Early Atmosphere (% by volume) | Modern Atmosphere (% by volume) |
| Carbon dioxide | 92.2 | 0.03 |
| Nitrogen | 5.1 | 78.1 |
| Sulfur dioxide | 2.3 | 0.0 |
| Hydrogen sulfide | 0.2 | 0.0 |
| Methane | 0.1 | 0.0 |
| Ammonia | 0.1 | 0.0 |
| Oxygen | 0.0 | 20.9 |
| Argon | 0.0 | 0.9 |

As the earth cooled, water vapor in the atmosphere cooled. Eventually it began to rain. The water collected in low places on the earth's surface and the early ocean was formed. This ocean was very different from today's oceans. The water in the early ocean was not only hot but also fresh. Over millions of years, the rain dissolved salts from rocks and carried these salts to the ocean. Within one billion years after the earth formed, enough salt had been dissolved from the rocks that the ocean water became salty. It was in this early ocean that the first life on Earth appeared. Today, more than 70 percent of the earth's surface is covered by water. Of this amount, 97 percent is made up by oceans.

# 18.3 Geologic Time

The time interval from the formation of the earth to the present is called **geologic time**. The total length of time is about 4.6 billion years. Geologic time is divided into large time units called **eras**. Eras are divided into smaller units of time called **periods**. Table 18–2 shows the *geologic time scale* and some important events that occurred during each unit of time.

Periods are divided into smaller units of time called *epochs*.

| TABLE 18–2 | GEOLOGIC TIME SCALE | | |
|---|---|---|---|
| **Era** | **Period** | **Began (Millions of Years Ago)** | **Major Events** |
| Cenozoic | Quarternary | 0.025 | Human societies arise. |
| | | 1.75 | The ice ages begin. |
| | Tertiary | 14 | Mammals, birds, modern sea life appear. |
| | | 30 | Primitive apes appear. |
| | | 65 | Small animals plentiful. |
| Mesozoic | Cretaceous | 130 | Dinosaurs die out. |
| | Jurassic | 180 | Dinosaurs abundant. First feathered birds and mammals appear. |
| | Triassic | 225 | Insects plentiful; giant reptiles appear. |
| Paleozoic | Permian | 275 | Fish, reptiles, and amphibians plentiful. |
| | Carboniferous | 310 | Age of amphibians; extensive land forests develop. |
| | Devonian | 405 | Fish plentiful; amphibians and insects appear. |
| | Silurian | 435 | First land plants appear. |
| | Ordovician | 480 | Algae and shelled animals are plentiful. |
| | Cambrian | 600 | Trilobites and mollusks appear. |
| Precambrian | | 590 | Multicellular animals appear. |
| | | 1,700 | Single-celled animals appear. |
| | | 4,600 | Formation of solar system. |

You might ask how anyone can really know how old the earth is. The answer is that the earth has a natural clock—radioactive elements. Radioactive elements decay at constant rates. These constant rates provide scientists with a precise clock for measuring geologic time. This clock started ticking when the earth's solid crust formed. Uranium decays into lead at a constant rate. By comparing the amounts of uranium and lead in rocks, scientists have been able to measure the age of the earth. Radioactive decay is discussed in detail in Chapter 7.

Lead a discussion in which students hypothesize why dinosaurs became extinct.

Since the formation of the earth 4.6 billion years ago, the earth's surface has changed dramatically. The changes in the earth's surface eventually resulted in the origin and evolution of living things. **Evolution** is the change in living things over time. Evolution is also discussed in Chapter 25. The record of evolution is found in the form of fossils. **Fossils** are the traces of plants and animals found in rocks. Scientists learn how and when various forms of life evolved on Earth by using radioactivity to determine the age of rocks containing fossils.

According to the fossil record, many different kinds of plants and animals have existed on Earth. The fossil record also shows that great numbers of these plants and animals died out, or became *extinct*. Some scientific theories as to why these plants and animals became extinct are discussed later in this chapter.

## READING CRITICALLY
Why is it important to know the age of a fossil?

To determine its place in the evolution of organisms

**Figure 18–2.** Scientists do not know why animals such as this saber-toothed cat suddenly disappeared.

1. Denser elements formed the core, lighter elements formed the mantle and crust, gravity helped keep gases in to form the atmosphere, gases cooled, it began to rain, both oceans and atmosphere were formed.
2. The atmosphere trapped the gases necessary for it to rain and form the oceans.
3. eras and periods
4. Fossils enable scientists to determine which forms of life are older than others, thereby evolving first. Fossils also enable scientists to study similarities and differences between early living things and those that exist today.
5. Lakes are younger. The ocean is salty due to millions of years of salt deposits; lakes have not been around long enough for the salt deposits to build up.

## Section Review

1. Describe the origin and development of the earth.
2. Why must the earth's ocean have formed after the earth's atmosphere?
3. Name the units of time that make up geologic time.
4. How have scientists used fossils to learn more about the earth's history and about the evolution of living things?
5. THINKING CRITICALLY Lakes have fresh water, but oceans are salty. Based upon this information, what conclusion can you make about the age of lakes compared with that of oceans? Explain.

# The Precambrian and Paleozoic Eras

## SECTION OBJECTIVES

- **Compare** and **contrast** the Precambrian and Paleozoic eras.
- **Trace** the development of plants and animals during the Precambrian and Paleozoic eras.
- **Explain** the relationship between fossil fuels and ice ages.

NEW TERMS IN THIS SECTION
mollusks
ice ages

## 18.4 The Precambrian Era

The first era of geologic time is the Precambrian, which lasted about 4 billion years. Life evolved during the first half billion years. During that time, all chemical compounds basic to life were formed in the early ocean and atmosphere. Combinations of these chemicals eventually resulted in living organisms. The earliest organisms were bacteria. Point out that life originated in the ocean, not on land.

Slowly the composition of the atmosphere changed to that of the modern atmosphere. Eventually, animals appeared. About 590 million years ago the animals began to develop hard body coverings. These hard coverings are what most fossils are formed from. There was no life on dry land during this era.

### ACTIVITY

**Making Fossils**

Locate a human or animal footprint. Then mix plaster of Paris with water until it has the thickness of pancake batter. Pour the mixture into the footprint. When the plaster hardens, remove the cast and study the imprint.

The earliest fossils date to the Precambrian era, but few are found because they were soft-bodied animals. In order to form a fossil, a hard body part, such as a stem, a shell, or a bone, must be embedded in mud or the like. If the mud becomes rock, the organic matter is replaced by minerals, leaving a cast or imprint of the once-living thing.

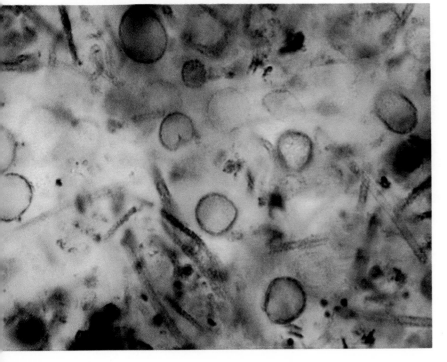

**Figure 18–3.** Precambrian fossils, such as those shown in this photograph, are very difficult to locate. These fossils are of blue-green bacteria. Because these organisms have no hard body parts, very few fossils ever formed.

## 18.5 The Paleozoic Era

The Paleozoic era began 600 million years ago and lasted for about 375 million years. At the beginning of the Paleozoic era, the concentration of oxygen in the atmosphere was about 10 percent of the present amount. However, as plants became abundant, they added more oxygen to the atmosphere. The first land animals and plants appeared during this era.

It is easy to remember these eras when the roots are known: -zoic is "life," paleo- is "old," meso- is "middle," and ceno- is "present."

### The Cambrian and Ordovician Periods

During the Cambrian and Ordovician (awr duh VIHSH uhn) periods there were no plants or animals on dry land. Tiny, snail-like animals called **mollusks** first evolved during the Cambrian period. Figure 18–4 shows the coiled shells of these early mollusks.

Present-day mollusks include clams, oysters, squid, octopus, snails, and slugs.

**Figure 18–4.** The shells of these Paleozoic animals are clearly visible. The mollusk above is an ammonite, while the arthropod on the right is a trilobite.

The most abundant animals during this period were the crablike *trilobites* (TRY luh byts). Trilobites were exclusively marine, or saltwater, animals that lived in shallow water. They existed from 570 million years ago to the end of the Paleozoic era, about 225 million years ago. By 500 million years ago, during the beginning of the Ordovician period, only a few kinds of trilobites remained.

Although many marine plants and animals became extinct during the Ordovician period, the fossil record shows that the first fishes appeared late in this period. These early fishes, however, were poor swimmers because their bodies were covered with protective bony plates.

More than 10,000 varieties of trilobites have been identified. Trilobites were arthropods with highly complex, segmented bodies protected by a hard shell. They used their legs for crawling or for swimming.

because there were more animals with hard shells during the Ordovician

## READING CRITICALLY
Why are there more fossils from the Ordovician period than from the Cambrian period?

**Figure 18–5.** Unlike fishes with bony plates, the fossils of these fishes show the remains of bone structures that enabled them to swim faster.

## The Silurian and Devonian Periods

During the Silurian period, which lasted from 435 to 405 million years ago, all major types of fishes evolved. The earliest known land animals also evolved during the Silurian period.

The Devonian period covers from 405 to 345 million years ago. By the late Devonian period, large seed-bearing trees had developed and forests became abundant. Over the same time period, amphibians evolved from fish. Amphibians are animals that can live both on the land and in the water.

Seven million years before the end of the Devonian period another extinction occurred. Plankton, which are tiny marine plants and animals, became extinct. As a result, all tropical reefs were wiped out. Scientists think that this mass extinction was caused by a rise in the temperature of the tropical oceans. Even a small temperature rise may be fatal to marine organisms.

## SCIENCE FACT

Young amphibians breathe with gills and live in water, like fish. As adults, amphibians breathe with lungs and live on land. Like reptiles, amphibians are cold-blooded.

Whatever the cause, there was a global temperature increase. This temperature increase caused a mass extinction of a great many plants and animals. However, within a few million years, new tropical animals and plants had evolved, replacing those that had become extinct.

### The Carboniferous and Permian Periods

The variety of land plants increased greatly during the Carboniferous and Permian periods—the last two periods of the Paleozoic era. Vast forests, as shown in Figure 18–6, came into existence. Reptiles, such as snakes, lizards, and turtles, evolved toward the end of the Carboniferous period. The number and types of reptiles quickly increased during the Permian period.

**Figure 18–6.** The vast forests that first covered the land during the Carboniferous period may have looked something like the one shown here.

Reptiles increased very quickly for a simple reason. Amphibians, the first land animals, laid their unprotected eggs in water. If the water dried up, the eggs died. Reptile eggs, however, have a protective outer layer and also contain a yolk, which is a food supply. You might think of such an egg as being like a space capsule that protects the developing animal. The ability of reptile eggs to survive under harsh conditions enabled the reptiles to thrive during the Carboniferous and Permian periods.

During the Carboniferous period, the global temperature dropped. A huge ice sheet formed over eastern South America, southern Africa, western Australia, Antarctica, and parts of India. The size of the ice sheet is shown in Figure 18–7. Intervals of time when the earth's temperature drops and ice sheets spread over parts of the earth are called **ice ages**.

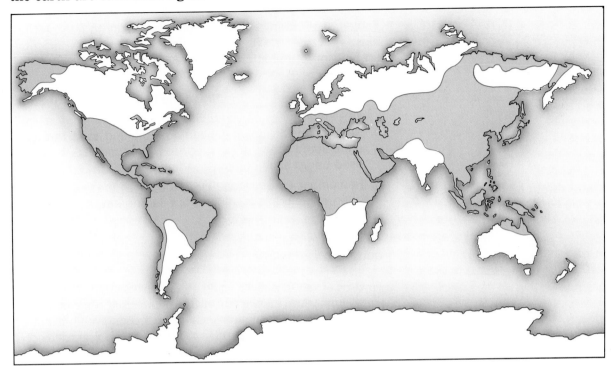

**Figure 18–7.** Sheets of ice covered most of the continents during the ice ages. The areas shown in white in this illustration were covered by ice sheets.

Ice ages came and went every 400,000 years during the Carboniferous and Permian periods. Each time the ice advanced, sea level dropped; each time the ice retreated, sea level rose. When sea level rose, the water covered the low-lying land and killed the forests. Marine sediments were deposited on top of the wood remains. When the ocean retreated, new forests grew. In time, the forests killed by the Paleozoic ice ages formed the major coal resources of the world today.

At the end of the Permian period, much of the world's water was locked up as ice. Sea level dropped, and shallow seas were greatly reduced. This change caused over 90 percent of the marine plants and animals to become extinct. How did this change cause extinction?

Marine animals could not survive without water.

## Section Review

1. Give two reasons why there are few fossils from the Precambrian era.

2. List the following according to the order in which they evolved: amphibian, fish, mollusk, reptile.

3. Describe how coal is related to ice ages.

4. THINKING CRITICALLY  Explain how life began on Earth.

1. Organisms of this era were soft-bodied and did not form fossils.
2. mollusk, fish, amphibian, reptile
3. Ice ages killed all the forests that were then turned into coal.
4. formation of atmosphere that allowed water to form, leading to chemical reactions that resulted in life.

# SKILL ACTIVITY   Interpreting Tables

**INTRODUCTION**

Tables help organize information. The ability to interpret tables is a valuable skill that can help you improve your comprehension of the information presented.

**PROCEDURE**

1. To interpret a table, first read the title and make sure that you understand its meaning.
2. Next, scan the column headings, making sure that you understand these. It is important to recognize the units used under each column heading.
3. Remember that a reference to a table in the textbook will often contain information about its content.

**APPLICATION**

Read the following paragraph and table. Then answer the questions that follow.

Gases from volcanoes made up the early earth's atmosphere. Ultraviolet light from the sun caused some of these gases to break down and to recombine with other gases in the atmosphere. By about 3.5 billion years ago, algae began adding oxygen to the atmosphere. However, it took an additional two billion years for a significant amount of free oxygen to build up in the atmosphere. Table 1 lists the stages in the development of Earth's atmosphere.

### TABLE 1   EARTH'S ATMOSPHERE

| Time Period | Stage 1 4–4.5 Billion Years Ago | Stage 2 2.5–4 Billion Years Ago | Stage 3 Present Day |
|---|---|---|---|
| Major components | Methane | Nitrogen | Nitrogen Oxygen |
| Minor components | Water Nitrogen Hydrogen sulfide Ammonia Argon | Sulfur dioxide Water Carbon dioxide Argon | Argon Water Carbon dioxide |
| Trace | | Neon Helium Methane Ammonia | Neon Helium Methane Krypton |

1. sulfur dioxide, carbon dioxide, neon, and helium
2. oxygen and krypton
3. methane, argon, nitrogen, and water

1. What substances present in the atmosphere during stage 2 were not present during stage 1?
2. What substances are present only in stage 3?
3. What substances are found in all three stages?

# The Mesozoic and Cenozoic Eras

## SECTION OBJECTIVES

- **Describe** how animals evolved during the Mesozoic and Cenozoic eras.
- **Explain** one theory about why the dinosaurs became extinct.
- **Discuss** how ice ages affected plants and animals.

NEW TERMS IN THIS SECTION
Pangaea
primate
interglacial age

## 18.6 The Mesozoic Era

There is evidence that during the Precambrian era there was only one land mass, or supercontinent. This supercontinent is called **Pangaea.** At the beginning of the Mesozoic era, hot rocks from the earth's mantle began to rise through cracks in the earth's crust. The pressure created by this movement began to break Pangaea apart. Deep basins began to form between what are now the east coast of the United States and the west coast of Europe. Over a period of 50 million years, the crack broadened to form the Atlantic Ocean.

The young Atlantic Ocean opened three times before it became permanent.

**Figure 18–8.** When the continent Pangaea (left) split apart, dramatic cliffs such as the Palisades (right) in New Jersey and New York were formed.

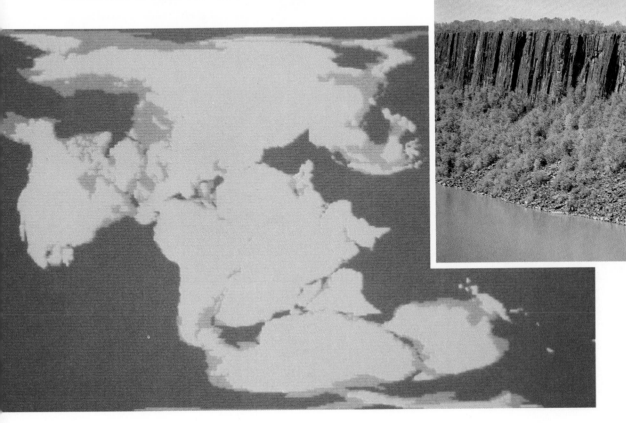

**Depositing Layers of Sediment**

Place soil, sand, and gravel in a large jar of water. Shake the mixture and then allow the jar to stand for 24 hours. Describe the layers of sediment that form.

At this time sediments rich in organic matter accumulated on the bottom of the Atlantic. These sediments were black in color and eventually formed rocks called *black shales*. In time the organic matter in black shales was transformed into oil.

## The Age of Reptiles

Although reptiles first appeared during the Carboniferous period of the Paleozoic era, they increased in number and size during the Mesozoic era. During this era, reptiles spread to all parts of the earth's surface. As a result, the Mesozoic era is called the *Age of Reptiles*.

Mammals and dinosaurs evolved at the same time. At first, both were small animals. However, as the dinosaurs increased in number and in size, they crowded the mammals out. By the end of the Triassic period, some dinosaurs were as long as 6 m. By the late Jurassic period, the dinosaur *diplodocus* (dih PLAHD uh kuhs) had reached a length of 26 m.

**Figure 18–9.** Scientists have been able to create mechanical devices that resemble flying reptiles of the Mesozoic period.

The period between one ice age and the next, when the ice melts and sea level rises, is called an **interglacial age**. We are now in the middle of an interglacial age. If the past is an indication of the future, the earth should be entering a new ice age within a few thousand years. Humans, however, are interfering with weather. Industrial and agricultural activities are adding carbon dioxide, other gases, and dust to the atmosphere. The addition of these gases may cause global temperatures to rise, changing the cycle of ice ages. Scientists are trying to determine how seriously these activities influence the weather.

## Section Review

1. Which animals evolved during the Mesozoic and Cenozoic eras?
2. What relationship exists between dinosaurs and asteroids?
3. Discuss the effects of the ice ages on the environment.
4. When did primates appear on Earth?
5. THINKING CRITICALLY In what ways might the earth's history be different if the ice ages had not occurred?

1. Mesozoic: giant reptiles (dinosaurs) and small mammals; Cenozoic: large mammals including primates
2. An asteroid striking Earth may have caused the extinction of the dinosaurs.
3. Ice ages caused periodic flooding and draining of various parts of the earth, resulting in the extinction of many species of plants and animals.
4. soon after the dinosaurs became extinct
5. Many extinct species might now exist. This may have changed evolutionary patterns that resulted in present-day life forms.

# CAREER

## Petroleum Technician

**DESCRIPTION** A petroleum technician works in natural gas and oil production. Technicians help geologists look for new oil and gas sources. The technicians test rock samples or study geological data. Petroleum technicians called *scouts* gather information on prospecting reports and drilling operations.

**REQUIREMENTS** A student planning to be a petroleum technician should take science and mathematics courses in high school. Junior colleges and community colleges offer two-year associate degrees, and most employers prefer to hire people who have had at least two years of training or on-the-job experience. However, some companies offer on-the-job training.

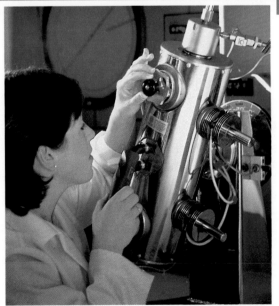

**INFORMATION** American Petroleum Institute, 1220 L Street N.W., Washington, DC 20037

For teacher information about this Investigation, see page T99.

# INVESTIGATION 18: Creating a Time Line

*What method could you use to list events in Earth's history?*

## PURPOSE
To develop a method of comparing the times when events took place in Earth's history

## MATERIALS
adding machine tape    scissors
meter stick         pencil

## PROCEDURE
1. Establish a scale for your time line. (1 mm = 10,000,000 years will work.)
2. Calculate the length of paper you will need to create your time line. You can make this calculation by dividing the age of the earth (4,600,000,000 years) by 1,000,000 years. The answer will be the length of the paper in millimeters. Convert the millimeters to meters to make measurement easier.
3. Cut a length of adding machine tape equal to your calculation. You may wish to add several centimeters so you do not have to work on the ends of the paper.
4. Mark the right-hand end of the tape "The Present."
5. Using Table 18–2 on page 373, measure back from the present and mark the points on the tape representing the beginning of the eras and periods.
6. Mark your time line in divisions of 100,000,000 years.

## RESULTS
Using Table 1 (right), plot the events on your time line. 1. The time after the Precambrian is only a small percentage (about 10%) of the total time line.

## CONCLUSIONS
1. Compare the total amount of time that was Precambrian to the total amount after Precambrian. How do these times compare?
2. Why was the discovery of fossils important to developing a time line like this?
   2. Fossils allowed scientists to accurately date and place
## APPLICATION  animals on the geologic time line.
Make a list of scientific advances that have occurred since 1800. Create a time line to reflect these advances.

**388**    Chapter 18

| TABLE 1 | EVENTS IN TIME |
| --- | --- |
| **Historical Event** | **Years Before Present** |
| Titanic discovered | 5 |
| Astronauts land on the moon | 20 |
| Sputnik launched | 30 |
| World War II began | 50 |
| World War I began | 75 |
| Civil War began | 128 |
| Declaration of Independence signed | 215 |
| Fall of the Roman Empire | 1,500 |
| Last ice age ends | 10,000 |
| Complex human societies start | 25,000 |
| Last ice age begins | 1,000,000 |
| Mammals dominate the earth | 1,750,000 |
| Primitive apes appear | 40,000,000 |
| First large mammals appear | 55,000,000 |
| Small mammals begin to dominate as dinosaurs become extinct | 65,000,000 |
| Flowering plants and trees appear | 130,000,000 |
| Dinosaurs dominate; first mammals and feathered birds appear | 180,000,000 |
| Insects and cone-bearing trees abound | 225,000,000 |
| First seed plants appear | 275,000,000 |
| Age of Amphibians | 310,000,000 |
| Coral reefs form | 345,000,000 |
| Fish become common | 405,000,000 |
| First land plants | 435,000,000 |
| First vertebrates in sea | 480,000,000 |
| Clams and snails appear | 600,000,000 |
| Few fossils; bacteria and algae | 3,500,000,000 |
| Origin of the earth | 4,600,000,000 |

## Summary

1. When the earth formed, dense elements sank to the core, while less dense nonmetals rose to the surface. **(18.1)**

2. The early atmosphere was mostly carbon dioxide and water. As the atmosphere cooled, rains began, forming the ocean. **(18.2)**

3. Geologic time is divided into eras and periods. **(18.3)**

4. The Precambrian era covers 90 percent of Earth's history. Life evolved more than 3 billion years ago during the Precambrian era. **(18.4)**

5. Early in the Paleozoic era, fish evolved. Later in this era land plants, amphibians, and reptiles evolved. A large variety of plants and animals became extinct at the end of this era. **(18.5)**

6. Dinosaurs and other reptiles were the most successful animals during the Mesozoic era. **(18.6)**

7. A mass extinction of the dinosaurs and many other animals and plants occurred about 66 million years ago. **(18.6)**

8. The mammals replaced the reptiles as the most successful form of life on Earth during the Cenozoic era. However, modern humans date from only about 125,000 years ago. **(18.7)**

9. Ice ages have occurred repeatedly during the past three million years, separated by interglacial ages having temperatures as warm as the present time. **(18.7)**

## Science Terms

On a separate sheet of paper, define each term in a sentence.

era **(373)**
evolution **(374)**
fossil **(374)**
geologic time **(373)**

ice age **(379)**
interglacial age **(387)**
mollusks **(376)**
Pangaea **(381)**

period **(373)**
primate **(385)**

## Modified True-False

On a separate sheet of paper, mark each true statement *TRUE* and each false statement *FALSE*. If false, change the underlined term to make the statement true.

1. The early atmosphere and surface of the earth looked similar to the moon. T

2. Rocks of similar densities form the earth's core and mantle. F, crust

3. The earth formed 4.6 million years ago. F, billion

4. The first oxygen in the atmosphere was produced by plants. F, water molecules

5. Today's oceans are hotter and saltier than the early ocean. F, cooler

6. Geologic time is divided into periods. T

7. The Cenozoic is the earliest era. F, Precambrian

8. Dinosaurs evolved at about the same time as mammals. T

9. Coal deposits are closely linked to ice ages. T

10. The earliest shelled organisms were tiny, snail-like animals called mollusks. T

*(continues)*

# CHAPTER REVIEW

## Multiple Choice

On a separate sheet of paper, write the letter of the term that best answers the question or completes the statement.

1. Trilobites were exclusively _____ animals.
   a. land
   b. freshwater
   c. marine
   d. marsh

2. Which of the following represents the largest unit of time?
   a. geologic time
   b. era
   c. ice age
   d. period

3. Life did not appear until the earth was almost a billion years old because the earth was initially too
   a. hot.
   b. cold.
   c. dry.
   d. wet.

4. Ice ages have occurred several times during the last _____ million years.
   a. 3
   b. 30
   c. 300
   d. 3000

5. In what period did fishes first appear?
   a. Cambrian
   b. Ordovician
   c. Silurian
   d. Devonian

6. Primates have existed on Earth for approximately _____ years.
   a. 125,000
   b. 350,000
   c. 3,000,000,000
   d. 650,000,000

7. The time between one ice age and the next is called
   a. an interglacial age.
   b. an epoch.
   c. an era.
   d. a geologic age.

8. The earliest land animals appeared during the _____ period.
   a. Cambian
   b. Ordovician
   c. Silurian
   d. Devonian

9. The most abundant animals in the Cambrian period were
   a. fishes.
   b. mollusks.
   c. trilobites.
   d. dinosaurs.

10. During an ice age, which of the following would be least affected?
    a. mammals
    b. deep-sea fishes
    c. shallow-water fishes
    d. amphibians

## Completion

On a separate sheet of paper, complete each statement by supplying the correct term.

1. Traces of plants and animals in rocks are called _fossils_.

2. Fishes evolved during the _Ordovician_ era.

3. There was only one ocean during the early _Precambrian_ era.

4. Intervals of time when ice sheets spread out are called _ice ages_.

5. Forests of the Paleozoic ice ages are the _coal_ resources of today.

6. In most _mammals_, young develop inside the mother.

7. Mammals that can grasp objects with their fingers or toes are called _primates_.

8. The single continent of the Precambrian era is called _Pangaea_.

9. The extinction of the _dinosaurs_ led to the increase in the number of mammals.

10. One of the largest dinosaurs, the _diplodocus_, grew to a length of 26 m.

**390** Chapter 18

## Writing Critically

1. Mars has a composition similar to Earth. Explain why Mars and Earth are so different today.
2. Plants grow best within a narrow range of temperature. Using this information, discuss how periodic cooling and warming of the earth beyond this range would affect humans.
3. CHALLENGE Dinosaurs became extinct, and so may humans. Write an article that agrees with or opposes this statement.

1. Answers should include a discussion of the atmosphere and water that are missing on Mars.
2. If all the plants died, which would happen in an extreme change of temperature, humans would also die.
3. Answers will vary, but should include sufficient evidence for the student's position.

## Skill Reinforcement

The Skill Activity on page 380 describes how to interpret tables. Referring to Table 18–1, form a hypothesis to explain why the composition of the atmosphere changed during geologic time. For example, one hypothesis might be that carbon dioxide in the atmosphere decreased because carbon dioxide is soluble in water.

## Research Ideas

1. Investigate how radioactive carbon is used to determine the age of plant and animal remains.
2. CHALLENGE One theory about sharks is that they stopped evolving because they are perfectly adapted for their environment. Research what makes sharks so successful.
3. CHALLENGE Investigate how the eruption of Mt. St. Helens affected global temperatures in a parallel way to a meteor hitting Earth.

## For Further Reading

Cairne-Smith, A. G. *Seven Clues to the Origin of Life: A Scientific Detective Story*. New York: Cambridge University Press, 1985. The author uses a Sherlock Holmes approach to develop a possible scenario for the origin of life during the early history of Earth.

Halliday, Tim R., and Kraig Adler. *The Encyclopedia of Reptiles and Amphibians*. New York: Facts on File, 1986. This book tells everything you could ever want to know about snakes, lizards, frogs, turtles, and related animals.

Sattler, Helen Roney. *Pterosaurs, The Flying Reptiles*. New York: Lothrop, Lee & Shepard, 1985. The author describes pterosaurs, which were flying reptiles that ruled the skies during the age of the dinosaurs.

# CHAPTER 19

# The Changing Earth

The surface of the earth can be compared to a giant jigsaw puzzle. Composed of 13 individual pieces, these parts push and slide against one another, causing many of nature's most powerful displays: earthquakes and volcanoes. The San Andreas Fault, shown here via high-altitude aerial photograph, is the result of two pieces of the jigsaw puzzle pushing against one another.

For additional information, see pages T100–T101.

# Earthquakes and Volcanoes

## SECTION OBJECTIVES

- **Describe** the causes and effects of earthquakes.
- **Identify** some methods of predicting earthquakes.
- **Explain** the causes and effects of volcanic eruptions.

Photograph left: San Andreas fault running diagonally bottom left to top right

NEW TERMS IN THIS SECTION

| | |
|---|---|
| earthquake | Richter scale |
| focus | seismograph |
| epicenter | seismogram |
| faults | volcano |
| seismic waves | magma |
| tsunami | lava |

## 19.1 Earthquakes

At 5:36 P.M. on Friday, March 27, 1964, the ground began shaking along a 500-km-long path in southern Alaska. The violent shaking lasted only a few minutes. When the shaking stopped, 75 percent of the homes, industries, and businesses in Anchorage lay in ruins. During the next three days, almost 300 minor earthquakes, or *aftershocks*, rattled the buildings that were left standing. Over the next eighteen months, there were 10,000 more aftershocks of decreasing intensity.

The Alaskan earthquake released 214 megatons of energy. At least one earthquake of similar magnitude has occurred about every five years during the past 80 years.

**Figure 19–1.** In spite of the great destruction caused by the Alaskan earthquake, only 131 people were killed. Thousands of people have been killed in less violent earthquakes.

The disaster in Alaska was caused when rocks far below the earth's surface began to shift and then break. The result was an earthquake. An **earthquake** is a violent shaking of the ground, caused by the sudden shifting and breaking of deep rocks. The place where the rocks break deep below the surface is called the **focus** (plural, *foci*). The place on the surface directly above the focus is called the **epicenter.**

The Alaskan earthquake of 1964 was caused by rocks breaking at a depth of 20 to 30 km. The epicenter was 150 km east of Anchorage. A strip of land, 100 km wide and running northeast from Kodiak Island, sank an average of almost 2 m. The sinking caused the crust to break into long blocks separated by deep cracks, or **faults**. Part of an oceanfront suburb of Anchorage was destroyed in this process. Offshore, a 100-km-wide stretch of the sea floor was pushed up by about 2 m.

Rock fractures that cause earthquakes do not occur in a single instant. As strain accumulates, the rocks start moving and eventually break.

**Damage From Seismic Activity**

- [ ] None
- Minor
- Moderate
- Major

**Figure 19–2.** Based on seismic data, this map pinpoints those areas in the United States that have the greatest risk of experiencing an earthquake.

The energy produced by an earthquake travels in waves. The ground moves up and down and back and forth in a rolling motion. Earthquake waves are called **seismic** (SYZ mihk) **waves.** Seismic waves, often called shock waves, can travel deep within the earth or along the surface. There are two types of deep seismic waves—*primary,* or *P, waves,* and *secondary,* or *S, waves. Surface waves* are also called *L waves.* Earthquakes that occur beneath the sea floor can also cause huge sea waves called **tsunamis** (su NAHM eez). Tsunamis are discussed in Chapter 22.

L waves are also called *love waves*.

## Measuring Earthquakes

Earthquake intensity is measured by the **Richter** (RIHK tuhr) **scale**, which was named after the American seismologist Charles Richter. On this scale, the magnitude of earthquakes is measured on a series of graded steps. Each step is ten times greater than the previous step. So, the difference between 5 and 6 on the Richter scale is greater than it seems. Earthquakes of magnitude 2 or less on this scale are felt only by instruments. Those earthquakes with magnitudes between 2 and 5 may be felt by people but usually produce no damage to structures. As the magnitude increases beyond 5, the damage also increases. The Alaskan earthquake, the most powerful ever recorded, had a magnitude of 8.5. The famous San Francisco earthquake of 1906 had a magnitude of 8.3. By comparison, the Los Angeles earthquake of October 1, 1987 had a magnitude of 6.1.

| TABLE 19–1 | MAGNITUDE OF EARTHQUAKES |
|---|---|
| **Richter Magnitude** | **Destructive Effect** |
| 0 to 2 | Almost none |
| 2 to 4 | Localized damage |
| 4 to 6 | Moderate damage in populated areas |
| 6 to 8 | Serious damage |
| 8 to 9 | Total destruction |

A large earthquake can release strain along a strip 200 km long and 50 km wide. Once the strain is relieved, another large earthquake may not occur in that place for several decades.

## Predicting Earthquakes

Seismic waves are recorded by an instrument called a **seismograph.** The two basic types of seismographs are shown in Figure 19–3. One type records the vertical motion of the ground. The other type records the horizontal motion. The record of an earthquake is called a **seismogram.**

The first waves to arrive during an earthquake are the P waves. The S waves, which travel more slowly than P waves, arrive next. Last to arrive are the surface waves. Notice that the first S waves and the surface

**Figure 19–3.** These scientists (right) are using both vertical and horizontal seismographs to record seismic waves. The measurement is recorded as a seismogram (left).

## ACTIVITY

**Hearing Wave Sounds**

Place your ear on your desk. Then scratch the end of the desk. The sound you hear is a wave that travels through the solid. Earthquake waves travel in the same way.

waves are the strongest and therefore the most destructive. By comparison, P waves are weak. The arrival of P waves provides a warning that more destructive waves will soon follow. Unfortunately, the warning is very short. Even halfway around the earth from an earthquake, the time between the arrival of the first P waves and the first destructive waves is only about 20 minutes.

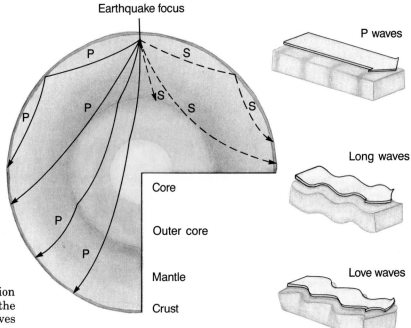

**Figure 19–4.** As this illustration shows, S waves enter the core of the earth and stop at that point. P waves travel through the earth's core.

The possibility of earthquakes can be predicted using a *strain meter*. A strain meter consists of a quartz tube that is anchored to the rock at one end and is free to move at the other end. A strain meter measures the strain as it accumulates in the earth's crust and deforms the rocks.

Another instrument, a *tilt meter,* determines the possibility of an earthquake by measuring the tilting of the ground. Two containers of water are connected by a tube. If the ground tilts, the water level drops in one container and rises in the other.

A *creep meter* is used to measure changes in distance between two points. A creep meter consists of a wire anchored to the rock at one end and attached to a weight at the other. If the distance between the two points changes, the weight rises or falls.

*Lasers* are used to measure changes in distance between two points. A laser source produces a powerful light beam. A mirror 10 km away reflects the light back

to the source. The time it takes for the laser beam to travel to the mirror and back is measured. A change in the time indicates a change in distance between the two points.

**Figure 19–5.** Laser beams are highly sensitive to changes in distance. A laser similar to the one shown here may be used to detect slight changes in distances on the earth's surface.

## 19.2 Volcanoes

Earthquakes release energy from the interior of the earth. Another way in which internal energy is released is through the action of volcanoes. A **volcano** is a vent in the earth's crust through which ash, gases, and molten rock erupt. A volcano usually consists of a volcanic *vent*; a *chimney,* or *pipe*; a volcanic *cone*; and a *crater*. Figure 19–6 is a diagram showing the structure of a volcano.

Volcanoes alternate periods of activity with periods of quiet. Mount Vesuvius (vuh SOO vee uhs), in Italy, remained dormant for a very long time. The inhabitants of the area did not even know it was a volcano. Suddenly, in A.D. 79, Mount Vesuvius erupted. Ash falling from the volcano buried the city of Pompeii (pahm PAY). Archeologists have dug up the city and found many works of art perfectly preserved. They have also found the mummified bodies of people and animals. The most recent eruption of Mt. Vesuvius took place in 1944.

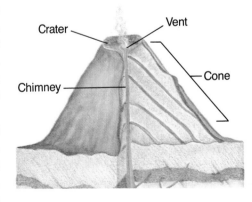

**Figure 19–6.** A cross section of a volcano

**Figure 19–7.** The eruption of Mount St. Helens vastly changed the appearance of the environment. Life is already returning in the form of young trees and plants.

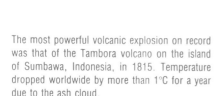
The most powerful volcanic explosion on record was that of the Tambora volcano on the island of Sumbawa, Indonesia, in 1815. Temperature dropped worldwide by more than 1°C for a year due to the ash cloud.

SCIENCE FACT

Mt. Vesuvius also erupted in the years 472, 1631, 1794, 1822, 1855, 1872, 1880, 1895, 1906, and 1929. The 1631 eruption killed an estimated 18,000 people.

Mount St. Helens, in Washington State, erupted in 1980 after remaining totally dormant for over 100 years. Sixty people who had refused to leave the area were killed. The top 400 m of the cone was destroyed in the eruption, which shot an enormous cloud of ash 22 km into the atmosphere. Most of the ash formed a cloud that raced down the side of the volcano. When all the ash had settled, it covered 600 km² of land. The layer of volcanic matter was 2 km deep.

Volcanoes erupt when **magma**, or molten rock inside the earth, rises from the mantle through the crust. As the magma rises, it thickens. If the magma reaches the surface, it is called **lava**. If magma cools inside the volcano, it may form a plug in the neck of the volcano. The plug bottles up gases and vapors from below. When the pressure becomes too high, the plug blows out. Pressure is suddenly reduced, the gases bubble up, and the magma becomes a froth. A cloud of water vapor, other gases, and tiny rock fragments erupts. The tiny rock fragments form volcanic ash.

The temperature in the ash cloud is several hundred degrees Celsius. The cloud is denser than the surrounding air because of the ash it contains. Being denser, it rolls down the slope at high speed, clinging to the ground. The gas cloud moves with the force of a hurricane. Everything in its path is flattened, burned, and buried.

A rolling, hot, volcanic ash cloud is called a *nuée ardente,* which is French for "burning cloud."

Volcanic eruptions in the ocean are quieter and less spectacular than those on land. However, even an underwater volcano produces great amounts of lava during eruptions. The islands of Hawaii contain the tallest volcanic system on Earth. The tallest volcano, Mauna Kea, rises about 10 km above the base of the island of Hawaii on the floor of the Pacific. Figure 19–8 shows a recent eruption of another volcano, Mount Kilauea on the island of Hawaii.

**READING CRITICALLY**
What causes the eruption of a volcano to be so intense?

build up of pressure over the years

**Figure 19–8.** Hawaii is a very fertile island, due in part to rich mineral deposits in the soil from volcanic ash and lava.

Volcanic eruptions can cause destruction, but they may also be beneficial. Volcanic soils contain many minerals and are therefore very fertile. The slopes of Mount Vesuvius have been densely inhabited since before Roman times because crops grow better there than anywhere else in the region. Why is this fact probably related to the great loss of life that resulted from the A.D. 79 eruption of Mount Vesuvius? Because the volcanic ash on Vesuvius caused the soil to be fertile, more people were drawn to the area.

## Section Review

1. How are earthquakes produced?

2. Compare the effects of earthquakes with magnitudes of 2, 5, and 9 on the Richter scale.

3. Explain the functions of four instruments used to predict earthquakes.

4. What causes volcanic eruptions?

5. THINKING CRITICALLY  In what ways might earthquakes and volcanoes be related?

1. by the sudden shifting and breaking of deep rocks
2. 2, local damage; 5, moderate damage; 9, total destruction
3. Strain meter measures strain in rocks; tilt meter measures tilt of the ground; creep meter measures changes in distance between two points; and laser beams also measure distance between two points.
4. Magma rises to the surface, where it flows out, or the pressure of hot gases in the volcano causes the plug to blow, bubbling up the magma.
5. Both are caused by pressure building within the earth; both cause immense destruction.

# SKILL ACTIVITY   Revising a Paper

_____ INTRODUCTION
While you are in school, you will be asked to write many reports and term papers. Writing a rough draft helps you to get your ideas on paper. Then you can refine and revise what you have written. The purpose of revising what you have written is to improve your writing.

_____ PROCEDURE
1. The first step in revising is to reread your paper several times. As you read, consider how each sentence fits in each paragraph and in the writing as a whole. Ask yourself the following questions: Is the main idea well developed? Is the development of the main idea clear and logical?

2. The next step is to review each sentence. Does it say exactly what you intended to say? Examine each word to see if it is necessary. Unnecessary words should be taken out.

3. An important part of revising is to check your writing in terms of its purpose and the audience. Purpose and audience affect both the content of the writing and the style of the language.

_____ APPLICATION
The following article was written for a group of geologists. Revise the article with the purpose of encouraging people to move to California.

Geologists feel that California is a prime target for a major earthquake in the near future. Because of movements of the Pacific and North American plates, a major earthquake can be expected in California every 50 to 100 years. The last great earthquake struck San Francisco in 1906.

Instruments have been placed throughout California to measure movements in the earth's crust. Scientists hope that the information collected from these instruments can be used to predict earthquakes. Early prediction would enable people to be safely evacuated prior to an actual earthquake.

Since the Los Angeles earthquake of October 1987 was only 6.1 in magnitude it is not considered a major earthquake (8.0 and above).

# Moving Continents

- **Describe** the work of Alfred Wegener.
- **Describe** how continents have moved during the past 250 million years.
- **Summarize** the evidence for continental drift.

NEW TERM IN THIS SECTION
continental drift

## 19.3 Continental Drift

In 1912, Alfred Wegener (VEHG uhn uhr), a German meteorologist, first proposed an idea that startled scientists around the world. While looking at maps of the world, Wegener noticed something interesting about the coastlines of certain continents. Based upon his observations, Wegener proposed that the continents had moved to their present locations from other locations on the earth.

Have students look at a world map and figure out what continents could fit together like the pieces of a jigsaw puzzle.

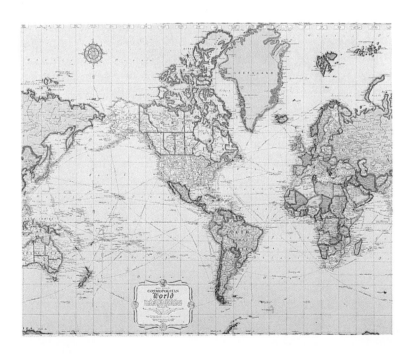

**Figure 19–9.** It is clear from this map that certain continents, such as South America and Africa, fit together like the pieces of a jigsaw puzzle.

Wegener attempted to prove his idea in several ways. Observations made during his explorations showed that warm-weather plants once grew in Greenland. He also found that glaciers once covered areas of continents located near the equator. He believed that the climates in these areas had changed because the continents on which they were located had moved. Other scientists

## SCIENCE FACT

In 1801 Alexander von Humboldt also noticed that the continents appeared to fit together. However, he thought that the continents had become separated by erosion.

ridiculed Wegener's theory. They were not convinced because no one could explain how the continents had moved such great distances. At the time of Wegener's death in 1930, most scientists considered his idea to be incorrect.

After Wegener's death, a few scientists continued to support his idea. During the 1950s, scientists collected evidence that showed that the continents do in fact move. Scientists now believe that continental drift has occurred. **Continental drift** is the theory that says the continents have moved, or drifted, from other positions on the earth's surface. Evidence indicates that the continents are still drifting. In the millions of years to come, continental drift will continue to alter the appearance of the earth's surface.

## 19.4 Evidence of Continental Drift

Although continents move slowly, they have moved a great deal throughout geologic time. According to the continental drift theory, two hundred million years ago the major continents were grouped together in a single supercontinent. This continent, called *Pangaea*, was surrounded by a single ocean called *Panthalassa*. When the supercontinent began to break up, new oceans began to form. The Atlantic Ocean is the result of a long crack in Pangaea. The Atlantic Ocean is still getting wider. The Americas are moving westward at the rate of about 3 cm per year.

As the Atlantic and Indian oceans opened and grew, Panthalassa shrank. The Pacific Ocean is what remains. About half of the oceanic crust of Panthalassa has slid underneath the various continents and has been destroyed. What has occurred at points where the oceanic crust has slid under the continental crust?

earthquakes and volcanoes

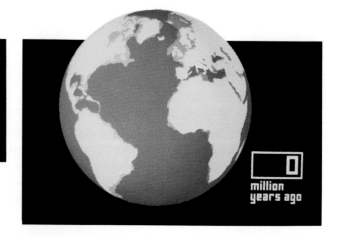

**Figure 19–10.** These computer-generated photographs illustrate the movement of the earth's plates from 200 million years ago to the present.

200 million years ago

150 million years ago

100 million years ago

50 million years ago

0 million years ago

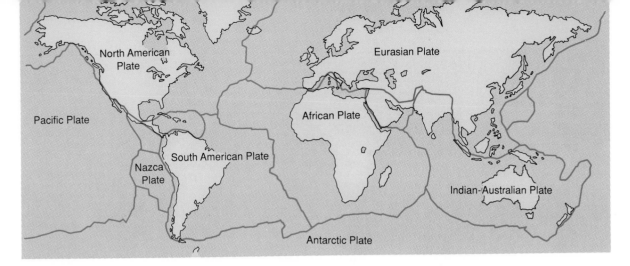

concentrated along plate margins. The movement of plates is called **plate tectonics.**

The plates of the lithosphere are constantly moving with respect to one another. This movement causes earthquakes and volcanoes and is responsible for the formation of continents, oceans, mountains, and islands. There are four types of plate movement—sea-floor spreading, subduction, collision, and sliding.

## Sea-Floor Spreading

When magma from below reaches the surface along faults between plates, **sea-floor spreading** occurs. The plates are pushed apart and new crustal rock is formed. Magma material continues to emerge along the middle of the Atlantic Ocean. It forms the Mid-Atlantic Ridge. Spreading also occurs between other plates, forming the Western and Eastern Indian Ocean Ridges and the East Pacific Rise. As shown in Figure 19–15, the oceanic ridges form a continuous mountain system that circles the globe.

**Figure 19–14.** The 13 major plates on the earth's surface are shown here.

In several places, mid-ocean ridges run into a continent. The continent is split apart here. The Western Indian Ocean Ridge is slowly separating Arabia from Africa and widening the Red Sea.

**Figure 19–15.** The sea floor deepens along subduction margins, forming deep-sea trenches. The deepest trench is the Marianas Trench in the western Pacific.

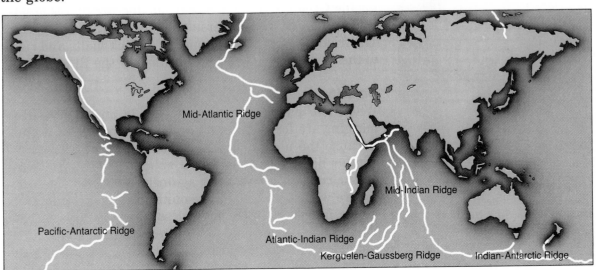

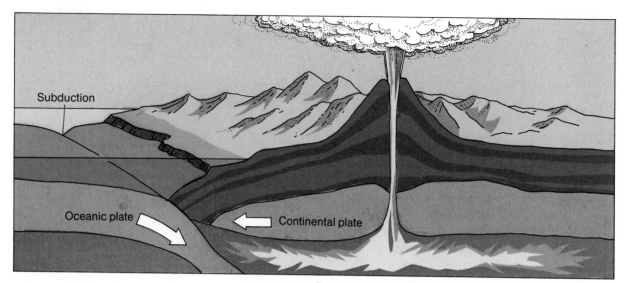

Figure 19–16. The action of one plate sliding over another can cause an earthquake.

READING CRITICALLY
Which plate is denser, the Pacific plate or the North American plate? Explain.

The Pacific plate is denser because it is subducting under the North Amerian plate; denser oceanic plates subduct under less dense continent plates.

Figure 19–17. Spectacular mountain landscapes, like the Himalayas shown here, are produced by plate collision.

## Subduction

The strongest earthquakes occur around the Pacific Ocean and along the Indonesian island arc.

The oceanic plates are thinner but denser than continental plates. As a result, if an oceanic plate is forced against a continental plate, the oceanic plate will slide under the continental plate. This motion, called **subduction**, is shown in Figure 19–16. Subduction occurs in a jerking motion, which produces earthquakes.

The Pacific plate subducts under the North American plate near the Aleutian Islands to the north and under the Eurasian, Philippine, and Indian plates to the west. The Philippine plate, in turn, subducts under the Eurasian plate. To the east, the Nazca and Cocos plates subduct under the South American plate. Why did Anchorage, Alaska, experience such a large earthquake in 1964? because it is at the edge of the Pacific plate, which is experiencing subduction

The result of this belt of subduction is a ring of volcanoes. This so-called "Ring of Fire" surrounds the Pacific Ocean on all sides. The subducting plates create friction against the undersides of the continental plates. The friction produces extreme heat. Rock melts and rises to the surface, forming the volcanoes of the Ring of Fire.

## Collision

When two plates carrying continents on their leading margins are forced against each other, **collision** occurs. Because the plates of the two colliding continents have similar densities, neither can subduct under the other. As the two continents push against each other, the lithosphere wrinkles and great mountain ranges are formed. Africa is now pushing against southern Europe. At the same time, Arabia and India are being pushed against central Asia. The resulting collisions have formed the Pyrenees, the Alps, the Caucasus, and the Himalayas.

### Sliding

When two plates pass each other along a common boundary, **sliding** occurs. The crack between two plates that slide by each other is called a *transform fault*. The San Andreas Fault is a transform fault. There, the Pacific plate, which carries southern California, is sliding northwestward with respect to the North American plate. Movement along the San Andreas Fault is responsible for the earthquakes that have occurred in parts of southern California.

## Section Review

1. Which layers of the earth are involved in plate tectonics?
2. Explain the four different types of plate movement.
3. How is plate tectonics related to continental drift?
4. THINKING CRITICALLY Why are there so few earthquakes along the east coast of the United States?

### ACTIVITY

**Using Friction to Produce Heat**

Rub two pencils together for 10 seconds. Then touch the side of one pencil to the palm of your hand. How does your observation relate to the movement of plates?

Friction causes buildup of heat on the plates, causing them to move.

1. lithosphere and asthenosphere
2. In sea-floor spreading, plates are pushed apart by volcanic activity on the ocean floor. In subduction, an oceanic plate slides underneath a continental plate. In collision, two plates push each other up to form mountains. In sliding, two plates pass each other along a common boundary to produce faults.
3. Plate tectonics explains how continental drift occurs.
4. It is spreading rather than subducting or sliding.

## CAREER

# Geologist

**DESCRIPTION** A geologist studies the earth. Most geologists specialize in a certain field. *Mineralogists* identify and classify rocks and minerals. *Seismologists* examine the movement of the earth's crust. *Paleontologists* study fossils to describe plants and animals of the earth's past. *Oceanographers* study the oceans. Many geologists are employed by firms involved in prospecting for oil and gas. Federal and state government agencies also employ geologists.

**REQUIREMENTS** A student who plans to become a geologist should take mathematics and science courses in high school. Computer science courses are also valuable. After graduation, the student will need to earn a bachelor of science degree from a four-year college or a university. For many jobs, a master's degree, or a doctoral degree is required.

**INFORMATION** American Geological Institute, 4220 King Street, Alexandria, VA 22302

# INVESTIGATION 19: Epicenter of an Earthquake

*How can geologists locate the epicenter of an earthquake?*

## PURPOSE

To locate the epicenter of an earthquake

## MATERIALS

map of the United States
drafting compass

## PROCEDURE

1. Copy Table 2 onto a sheet of paper. Enter all data from this investigation onto your table.

2. Study the seismogram shown on this page. The data from each location shows the arrival of the P wave and the S wave. By subtracting the arrival time of the P wave from the arrival time of the S wave, scientist can determine how far away from each location the earth quake occurred. This time difference is called *lag time.* Calculate the lag time for each of the three locations and record the data.

3. Refer to Table 1 to determine the distance from each location the earthquake occurred. Record the distances.

### TABLE 1 — TIME/DISTANCE RELATIONSHIPS

| Lag Time in Seconds | Distance (km) from Epicenter |
|---|---|
| 120 | 1000 |
| 180 | 1800 |
| 240 | 2500 |
| 300 | 3500 |
| 360 | 4500 |

4. Locate Seattle, Washington; Denver, Colorado; and Dallas, Texas on a map of the United States. Using the distance scale on the map, set the compass to equal the distance the earthquake occurred from Seattle. Draw a circle using Seattle as the center. Set the compass and draw two more cirlces using Denver and Dallas as

the centers. Where the circles intersect is the epicenter of the earthquake.

## RESULTS

### TABLE 2 — EARTHQUAKE DATA

| Location | Arrival Time of P Wave (in sec) | Arrival Time of S Wave (in sec) | Lag Time (in sec) | Distance (km) from Epicenter |
|---|---|---|---|---|
| Dallas | 160 | 360 | 200 | 2200 |
| Denver | 140 | 300 | 160 | 1500 |
| Seattle | 120 | 250 | 130 | 1200 |

## CONCLUSIONS

1. What is the epicenter of the earthquake?
2. Why might the circles not intersect at exactly the same point? 1. San Francisco, California 2. Human error

## APPLICATION

How might seismograph information from additional locations help scientists to determine the epicenter of an earthquake?
More measurements make for more accurate data.

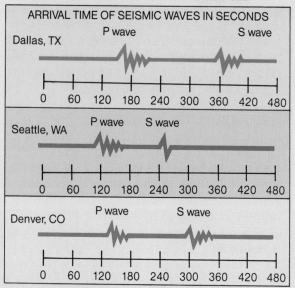

## Signals from the Stars

Quasars are very distant stars that generate huge amounts of energy for their size. They produce radio signals. These radio signals are used in a technique known as *Very Long Baseline Interferometry*, or VLBI, to measure continental drift. Receiving stations at different locations measure the arrival times for the same signal. These data can then be used to determine the distance between stations.

## Navstar

VLBI is exact, but it also requires large, expensive, immobile radio telescopes. Earth scientists have recently started to use a new military satellite system, the Navstar GPS (*Global Positioning System*) to measure the distances between continents. Navstar can take the place of a VLBI at a fraction of the cost and with far more mobility. The equipment is relatively inexpensive and extremely mobile. It can be carried in the back of a station wagon and set up virtually anywhere.

Orbiting Navstar satellites produce radio signals that serve as a navigational aid to pilots and ship captains. A satellite receiver can be used to fix latitude, longitude, and altitude within an error of 10 meters. However, earth scientists use the system by substituting the satellite signals for quasar signals. Using complicated surveying devices along with directional antennas, two temporary stations are placed at different locations. The antennas pick up the signal from one satellite and determine the distance between the sites.

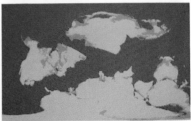

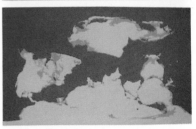

Computer-generated pictures of the earth's plates show their movement.

Satellites, stars, and lasers are providing answers to questions about the earth's shifting crust. They reveal, for example, that the North American and Eurasian plates are moving apart at a rate of about 2 cm a year. Yes, New York is moving away from London.

Navstar satellites (left) relay signals to radiotelescopes (right).

# UNIT 5

# Weather and the Oceans

Photograph right: Pobasana Beach, Venezuela

Have you ever seen it rain on one side of the street but not on the other? *Meteorology* is the science that deals with the atmosphere and weather. One important factor that affects weather patterns is the world's oceans. *Oceanography* is the science that deals with the environment in the oceans. This unit explains the effects of the oceans and weather on your life.

CHAPTER

# 20

# The Atmosphere

In the Alaskan spring and summer evenings, the sky lights up in vivid hues. Long, thin rays form curtains of light. Flickering and ever-changing, the lights move like a breeze in a dazzling display. Known as the aurora borealis, this natural light show is caused by solar wind striking the earth's atmosphere.

For additional information, see pages T104–T105.

## The Stratosphere

Above the tropopause lies the stratosphere (STRAT uh sfihr). The **stratosphere** is a layer of the atmosphere that begins at about 10 km to 16 km above the earth. It extends to 50 km above the earth. The ozone layer is contained in the stratosphere. Ozone absorbs not only ultraviolet radiation from the sun, but also some infrared and visible light. Maximum absorption is at about 50 km of altitude.

The temperature in the lower part of the stratosphere is a constant −50°C. The upper part of the stratosphere warms up to about −3°C. The warming is caused by the absorption of solar radiation in the ozone layer. Convection does not occur in the stratosphere because the less dense, warmer air lies above the denser, colder air.

Different surfaces absorb different amounts of solar radiation. A black surface becomes hot because it absorbs most of the solar radiation that falls on it. A white surface absorbs very little radiation and stays cool.

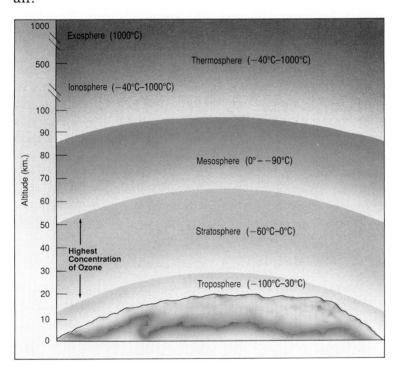

**Figure 20–4.** The earth's atmosphere is divided into four layers based on their temperatures.

## The Mesosphere

Above the stratosphere lies the mesosphere (MEHZ uh sfihr). The **mesosphere** is a layer of atmosphere that extends from 50 km to 85 km above the earth. Temperature drops from −3°C at the base of the mesosphere to −85°C at the top. This drop in temperature occurs for two reasons. First, the concentration of ozone decreases and very little solar radiation is absorbed. Second, because of the great distance from the ground, the heat absorbed by land and water has very little effect on this layer.

## The Thermosphere

Above the mesosphere lies the thermosphere (THUR muh sfihr). The **thermosphere** extends from 80 km above the earth to 650 km—the upper edge of the atmosphere. Temperature rises again through this layer. Atmospheric gases are thin at this altitude and are readily penetrated by protons from the sun. The atmospheric atoms and molecules are hit by the protons and made to move faster, causing the temperature to rise.

Within the thermosphere is the ionosphere. The **ionosphere** (eye AHN uh sfihr) is a layer of electrically charged particles that extends from 85 km to 650 km of altitude. When streams of particles from the sun hit the electrically charged particles in the ionosphere, the ions glow in different colors. This display of light is known as an **aurora** (aw RAWR uh). Auroras form most commonly between 100 and 200 km of altitude. The ionosphere is important to communications because it bounces certain radio waves back to Earth.

You may wish to refer to Chapter 22, which has a more detailed discusson of auroras.

Above the thermosphere, extending from 650 km above the earth to outer space, lies the **exosphere.** Atmospheric gases are so thin at this altitude that a gas molecule moving horizontally travels an average of 650 km before hitting another molecule. At sea level a molecule can travel only 1/100,000 mm before hitting another molecule.

The atmosphere as a whole is an important natural resource. Many gases from the atmosphere are obtained from the atmosphere by liquefying and separating air.

## Section Review

1. What are the two most abundant gases in the earth's atmosphere? How are these gases essential to life?

2. Explain the importance of ozone in the earth's atmosphere.

3. What two devices are used to measure air pressure? Explain how each device works.

4. What is convection, and what effect does it have on the atmosphere?

5. Compare the different layers of the atmosphere.

6. THINKING CRITICALLY  Water boils faster on top of a high mountain than it does at sea level. Explain why a liquid turns into a gas more quickly when the atmospheric pressure is lower. What would happen to the blood of an astronaut if he or she did not wear a pressure suit during a space walk?

1. nitrogen and oxygen; oxygen is needed by most animals for breathing; nitrogen is an important nutrient for plant growth.
2. Ozone prevents most of the ultraviolet radiation from the sun from reaching the earth.
3. Mercury barometer—as air pressure increases or decreases, the mercury in the tube rises or falls respectively. Aneroid barometer—as air pressure increases or decreases, the chamber is compressed or expands respectively.
4. Convection is the process by which warm air rises and cool air sinks. It serves to overturn the air in the troposphere.
5. Troposphere contains most of the atmosphere's gases and dust; stratosphere contains the ozone layer; mesosphere is a very cold layer; thermosphere contains the ionosphere and the exosphere.
6. Water boils faster at lower pressure because it is easier for the molecules to escape from the water. Without a pressure suit the astronaut's blood would form gas bubbles; and the astronaut would die.

# SKILL ACTIVITY    Reading for Comprehension

**INTRODUCTION** _____ Information is often presented by means of words and diagrams. Being able to use the two in combination is a skill that can help you more easily learn and remember certain information.

**PROCEDURE** _____

1. Read the following information about ozone.
2. Study the diagrams shown below.

Ozone Buildup

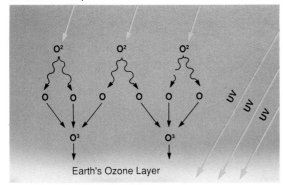

Ozone Breakdown

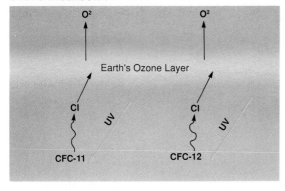

Ozone is a form of oxygen that has three atoms in each molecule, compared with oxygen's two atoms in a molecule. It is constantly being built up and broken down in the atmosphere. The sharp odor of ozone can be noticed after a thunderstorm.

The process of building up and breaking down ozone plays almost like a computer game. Notice in the diagram how one "side" tries to destroy ozone and the other "side" tries to build it up. On one side, ultraviolet (UV) rays strike molecules of oxygen. The oxygen molecules break apart. Some of the stray oxygen atoms combine with others to form ozone.

The ozone molecules line up to form an ozone layer about 15 to 30 kilometers above the earth. This is a barrier that shields the earth from strong UV rays. The ozone layer protects living things on the earth by absorbing harmful UV rays.

On the other hand, the ozone layer is under constant attack by the chlorofluorocarbons, called CFC-11 and CFC-12. These are sent into the air by refrigerants in air conditioners and refrigerators. They are also present in insulation products.

UV rays break up CFC-11 and CFC-12 in the atmosphere and release chlorine atoms. These chlorine atoms react with other chemicals that cause the ozone to break down. Scientists fear that with a reduced ozone layer the earth may become a dangerous place for people to live.

**APPLICATION** _____

1. ultraviolet radiation from the sun
2. It protects living things from dangerous ultraviolet radiation.
3. By not releasing CFC–11 and CFC–12 into the atmosphere.
4. chlorine

1. Where does the energy needed to form ozone come from?
2. In what way is the ozone layer useful to living things on earth?
3. How could industry help to preserve the ozone layer?
4. What element in CFC-11 and CFC-12 is responsible for breaking down ozone?

# Movement of the Atmosphere

NEW TERMS IN THIS SECTION
radiation balance
greenhouse effect
Coriolis effect
doldrums
trade winds
prevailing westerlies
polar easterlies
jet stream

## SECTION OBJECTIVES

- **Discuss** how the addition of carbon dioxide to the atmosphere affects the radiation balance of the earth.
- **Explain** the Coriolis effect.
- **Describe** the major circulation patterns of the earth's atmosphere.

## SCIENCE FACT

The earth receives only about 1/2,000,000,000th of the sun's energy.

## 20.4 Solar Radiation

Practically all the energy needed on Earth is received from the sun in the form of visible light. Light travels the 149,597,871 km from the sun to the earth in 8.3 minutes. In addition to visible light, the sun gives off energy of all wavelengths, ranging from long radio waves to short ultraviolet waves.

The solar radiation that hits the earth is 5.78 percent ultraviolet radiation, 45.65 percent infrared radiation, and 48.57 percent visible light. The most common wavelength of light, visible light, appears to the human eye as white light.

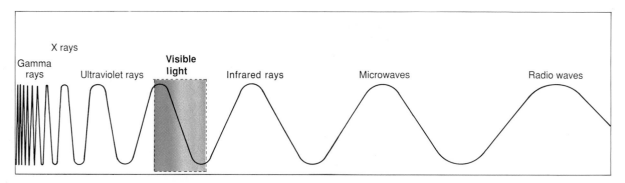

**Figure 20–5.** Radiation from the sun travels in waves. Waves with short wavelengths, such as gamma rays and X rays, have more energy than waves with long wavelengths. Ultraviolet rays cause sunburn. Infrared rays are felt as heat.

If the sun produces white light, why is the sky blue and why are sunsets red? The light given off by the sun is scattered by gas molecules and by tiny solid or liquid particles in the atmosphere. Dust, smoke, salt crystals from sea spray, and chemical pollutants are all examples of particles found in the atmosphere. As light passes through the atmosphere, these particles scatter the light. Light with a short wavelength is scattered more than light with a long wavelength.

The sky is blue because blue light has a shorter wavelength than the other colors. When the sun is high in the sky, its disk appears slightly yellow because it has lost some of its blue light through atmospheric scattering. As the sun sets, its rays have to cross more of the atmosphere to reach a viewer's eyes. More of the blue light is scattered, and the disk of the sun appears redder as it approaches the horizon. Why does this increased scattering of light result in a bright red and orange sunset? The blue wavelength of light is scattered.

The radiation from the sun is responsible for the earth's climate. However, the earth's climate is controlled not only by the incoming solar radiation, but also by the outgoing reflected radiation. This outgoing radiation is reflected off the ground and off the tops of clouds. The balance between incoming and outgoing solar radiation is called **radiation balance**. Radiation balance is affected by many physical and environmental factors.

Atmospheric gases let most solar radiation pass through. By comparison, clouds and particles absorb or reflect into space about 25 percent of the solar radiation entering the atmosphere. About 30 percent of the solar radiation that reaches the ground or the surface of the ocean is changed into infrared radiation.

Infrared radiation is reflected back up into the atmosphere. In the atmosphere, infrared radiation is absorbed by water vapor and carbon dioxide. The absorbed energy is shared with the molecules of nitrogen and oxygen. As a result, the air warms up. Air near the ground is closer to the source of infrared radiation. Therefore, it is generally warmer than the air above. This is why temperature decreases with altitude.

Different surfaces absorb different amounts of solar radiation. A black surface absorbs most of the solar radiation that falls on it and becomes very hot. A white surface absorbs very little radiation and stays cool. When the air is calm and the sun is directly overhead, the sea surface absorbs almost all the solar radiation that falls on it. This makes the deep ocean look almost black when observed from an airplane.

**Figure 20–6.** Why do people who live in desert environments wear light-colored clothing?

light colors reflect more light, resulting in less heat absorption

**Figure 20–7.** Of the radiant energy that reaches the earth, about 25 percent of the solar radiation is absorbed by clouds or reflected into space. Only about 30 percent is changed into infrared radiation. The surface of the earth absorbs the remaining 45 percent. It is the 75 percent that is changed into infrared radiation or absorbed by the earth that keeps the planet warm. Without this energy, life would have never developed on Earth.

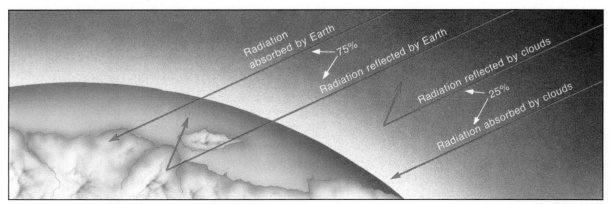

**Demonstrating the Greenhouse Effect**

Conduct your own greenhouse experiment by taking an air temperature reading outside and inside a closed car on a sunny day.

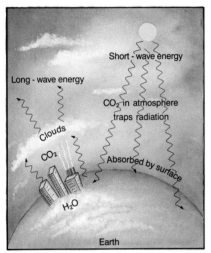

**Figure 20–8.** Because of the greenhouse effect, the atmosphere acts like a giant blanket to keep the earth warm.

You may wish to refer to Chapter 18 for a more detailed diagram of the greenhouse effect.

Unfortunately, the activities of humans now threaten to upset the radiation balance of the earth. Humans release chlorine-containing compounds, gases from spray cans, and carbon dioxide into the atmosphere. These substances break down the ozone, allowing more radiation into the atmosphere. If enough radiation is allowed in, it could affect human welfare.

The addition of these compounds to the atmosphere may cause the temperature of the earth to either increase or decrease. Carbon dioxide traps infrared radiation reflected from the ground and keeps it in the troposphere. Glass has the same effect on a greenhouse or on a car left in the sun. Glass lets sunlight through but traps the returning infrared radiation. As a result, the inside of a car or of a greenhouse warms up. The global temperature rise that may result from the addition of carbon dioxide to the atmosphere is called the **greenhouse effect.**

Many scientists fear that human activities may change the radiation balance enough to trigger another ice age or to melt the ice that covers Antarctica and Greenland. Either event would be disastrous. A new ice age would destroy much of the world's agriculture. The melting of polar ice would raise sea level by 70 m and destroy all coastal cities and lowlands.

# 20.5 Major Circulation Patterns

The circulation of air on Earth is affected by many factors. The rotation of the earth and differences in the heating and cooling rates of land and water are two factors that affect air circulation.

### The Coriolis Effect

The energy that circulates the atmosphere is provided by the sun. The light of the sun warms the earth more near the equator than it does near the poles. Hot air is less dense than cold air. You would expect hot air to rise at the equator, travel to the poles, sink there, and return to the equator along the ground. However, this does not happen. Hot air rising at the equator cannot travel all the way to the poles. Air circulation is influenced by the Coriolis (kawr ee OH lihs) effect. The **Coriolis effect** is a force that causes moving objects near the earth's surface to be turned from their original paths.

The Coriolis effect can be seen in the movement of air masses. Air masses moving north from the equator appear to veer eastward. Air masses moving south from the North Pole appear to veer westward. However, the

**Figure 20–9.** The Coriolis effect causes objects moving near the earth's surface to be turned westward from their original paths due to the Earth's eastward rotation.

surface of the earth is not perfectly smooth. Mountain ranges, valleys, plains, and large bodies of water affect the movement of these air masses. The Coriolis effect is seen in both the Northern and Southern Hemispheres. However, in the Southern Hemisphere, the movement is reversed from that in the Northern Hemisphere.

## Wind Systems

There are four major wind systems on the earth—the trade winds, the prevailing westerlies, the polar easterlies, and the jet streams. There is no wind system at the equator. This zone is called the **doldrums.** Although the air appears to be motionless, it is actually rising.

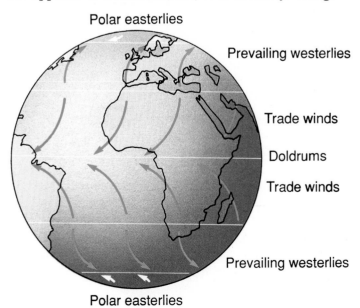

**Figure 20–10.** The major wind systems move from areas of high-density descending currents toward areas of low-density rising currents.

By the time hot air has reached 30° of latitude on either side of the equator, it has risen and moved eastward due to the Coriolis effect. The air cools off and sinks to ground level. As it sinks, the air spreads out. The air that blows toward the equator forms the **trade winds**. The air that blows toward the poles forms the winds called the **prevailing westerlies**.

The polar areas are very cold. As a result, cold, dense air sinks over the poles and streams out at ground level. The flow is clockwise as seen looking down over the Arctic. It is counterclockwise as seen looking down over Antarctica. As a result, the winds near the poles blow from east to west in both hemispheres, forming the **polar easterlies**.

As mentioned earlier, the tropopause lies at an altitude of between 10 and 16 km. Between latitudes 40° and 50°, the tropopause drops from 16 to 10 km of altitude. There is a strong pressure difference across this drop. As the wind rushes toward the poles to equalize the pressure, it is pushed eastward by the Coriolis effect. The result is a high wind circling both polar areas at 12 to 13 km of altitude. This high wind is called the **jet stream**.

The position of the jet stream in January is shown in Figure 20–11. Its speed averages 60 km/hour in the summer and 150 km/hour in the winter. The speed of the jet stream is greater in the winter because the temperature contrast between low latitudes and high latitudes

**Figure 20–11.** Jet streams form where warm air from the tropics meets cold air from the poles. Jet streams in the Northern Hemisphere flow from west to east in the tropopause, as shown in the figure.

is much stronger and steeper. The highest speed measured in the jet stream is 650 km/hour. The jet stream does not run around the poles in a smooth circle. It forms broad loops that may extend almost to the tropics. The jet stream strongly influences the weather at middle and high latitudes in both hemispheres.

## Section Review

1. What causes the sun to appear to change colors at sunrise and sunset?
2. What is the Coriolis effect and how does it affect moving winds in the Northern and Southern Hemisphere?
3. Name and describe the movement of the major wind patterns of the earth.
4. How might an increased level of carbon dioxide in the atmosphere cause a greenhouse effect?
5. THINKING CRITICALLY How might airline pilots use the jet stream to shorten flying time?

# CAREER

## Pilot

**DESCRIPTION**   Pilots fly airplanes and helicopters. Some pilots fly helicopters used in putting out forest fires; others fly aircraft used in the scientific investigation of weather and the atmosphere. Most pilots work for commercial airlines, moving passengers and cargo from one airport to another.

**REQUIREMENTS**   The student who plans to be a pilot should take mathematics courses in high school. After graduation, a future pilot learns how to fly in a military or civilian flying school. Pilots are licensed by the Federal Aviation Administration; helicopter pilots must have a special helicopter rating. Most airlines hire only applicants with two or more years of college training, and most prefer college graduates.

**INFORMATION**   Future Aviation Professionals of America, 4291 Memorial Drive, Decatur, GA 30032

# INVESTIGATION 20: Absorption of Radiant Energy

*How is the absorption of radiant energy affected by color?*

## PURPOSE

To demonstrate the rate of absorption of radiant energy by different substances

## MATERIALS

4 200-mL beakers
white paper
black paper
masking tape
water
dark-colored soil
light-colored sand
4 Celsius thermometers
desk lamp
timer

## PROCEDURE

1. Copy Table 1 onto a sheet of paper. Enter all data from this investigation onto your table.

2. Completely wrap the sides and bottom of one beaker with white paper. Use tape to hold the paper in place. Wrap the sides and bottom of a second beaker with black paper. Fill the paper-covered beakers with water to a depth of about 5 cm.

3. Fill one of the remaining beakers with the dark-colored soil to a depth of about 5 cm. Fill the remaining beaker with light-colored sand to a depth of about 5 cm.

4. Insert a thermometer into each beaker. Place the four beakers under the desk lamp, as shown in the figure. Read the temperature on each thermometer. Record the temperatures. Turn on the lamp.

5. Record the temperature on each thermometer every 2 minutes for 10 minutes.

6. Turn off the lamp. Record the temperature on each thermometer every 2 minutes for 10 minutes.

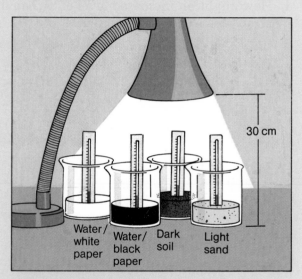

30 cm

Water/white paper　Water/black paper　Dark soil　Light sand

## RESULTS

| TABLE 1 | TEMPERATURE READINGS | | | | | | | | | | |
|---|---|---|---|---|---|---|---|---|---|---|---|
| | Warming | | | | | | Cooling | | | | |
| Time (min) | 0 | 2 | 4 | 6 | 8 | 10 | 12 | 14 | 16 | 18 | 20 |
| Water with white paper | | | | | | | | | | | |
| Water with black paper | | | | | | | | | | | |
| Light-colored sand | | | | | | | | | | | |
| Dark-colored soil | | | | | | | | | | | |

## CONCLUSIONS

1. Which beakers warmed faster? slower? Why? warmed faster: black paper, black sand; warmed slower: white paper, light sand; dark surfaces absorb more radiant energy

2. Which beakers cooled faster? slower? Why?

3. On a piece of graph paper, make a graph of your data comparing the rate of absorption of radiant energy of the beakers.

2. faster: white paper; white sand; slower: dark paper, dark soil; the lighter-colored materials absorbed less heat initially, therefore it takes less time to return to the starting temperature

## APPLICATIONS

1. Why is it more comfortable to wear light-colored clothing than dark-colored clothing on warm, sunny days? They reflect light and therefore help keep you cool.

2. What color should the floor be in a room that relies on solar radiation as its only source of heat? Explain your answer.
a dark floor; to absorb as much heat energy as possible

# CHAPTER 20 REVIEW

## Summary

1. Nitrogen and oxygen are the two most abundant gases in the earth's atmosphere. **(20.1)**
2. The weight of air on the earth's surface is known as air pressure. **(20.2)**
3. Barometers measure the amount of air pressure on a given area. **(20.2)**
4. The layer of atmosphere closest to the earth is the troposphere. **(20.3)**
5. The stratosphere is the layer of atmosphere containing the ozone. It lies above the tropopause. **(20.3)**
6. The layer of atmosphere in which temperature drops from −3°C to −85°C is the mesosphere. **(20.3)**
7. The layer of atmosphere that extends to outer space is the thermosphere. **(20.3)**
8. The balance between incoming and outgoing solar radiation is called radiation balance. **(20.4)**
9. The Coriolis effect causes air masses to move to the right in the Northern Hemisphere and to the left in the Southern Hemisphere. **(20.5)**
10. Major circulation patterns include the trade winds, the prevailing westerlies, the polar easterlies, and the jet streams. **(20.5)**

## Science Terms

On a separate sheet of paper, define each term in a sentence.

atmosphere **(419)**
atmospheric pressure **(420)**
aurora **(424)**
barometer **(421)**
convection **(422)**
Coriolis effect **(428)**
doldrums **(429)**

exosphere **(424)**
greenhouse effect **(428)**
ionosphere **(424)**
jet stream **(430)**
mesosphere **(423)**
ozone **(420)**
polar easterlies **(430)**

prevailing westerlies **(430)**
radiation balance **(427)**
stratosphere **(423)**
thermosphere **(424)**
trade winds **(430)**
troposphere **(422)**

## Modified True-False

On a separate sheet of paper, mark each true statement *TRUE* and each false statement *FALSE*. If false, change the underlined term to make the statement true.

1. Without chlorine plants would die. F, nitrogen
2. The jet stream occurs between 40° and 50° latitude in the troposphere. F, tropopause
3. The trade winds occur at the equator when there is no wind at all. F, doldrums
4. The Coriolis effect is the change in direction of air masses caused by the earth's rotation. T
5. A temperature rise that may result from trapped air and the formation of carbon dioxide in the atmosphere is called the greenhouse effect. T
6. The balance between incoming solar radiation and outgoing reflected radiation is radiation balance. T
7. The most common wavelength of light, visible light, appears to the human eye as blue light. F, white
8. Within the thermosphere is a layer of electrically charged particles called the mesosphere. F, ionosphere
9. The ozone layer in the stratosphere is cooler than the lower part of the stratosphere. F, warmer
10. Almost all weather occurs within the exosphere. F, troposphere *(continues)*

# CHAPTER REVIEW

## Multiple Choice

On a separate sheet of paper, write the letter of the term that best answers the question or completes the statement.

1. The most common gases in the atmosphere are
   a. nitrogen and oxygen.
   b. hydrogen and oxygen.
   c. nitrogen and hydrogen.
   d. hydrogen and argon.

2. Ozone is found in the
   a. mesosphere.
   b. stratosphere.
   c. thermosphere.
   d. ionosphere.

3. The _____ ranges from sea level to 16 km.
   a. stratosphere
   b. exosphere
   c. troposphere
   d. thermosphere

4. The overturning of the troposphere is due to
   a. atmospheric pressure.
   b. radiation balance.
   c. trade winds.
   d. convection.

5. The greenhouse effect might be caused by an increase of _____ in the atmosphere.
   a. nitrogen          c. oxygen
   b. carbon dioxide    d. hydrogen

6. A force that causes moving objects on Earth to turn from their original paths is the
   a. Coriolis effect.
   b. doldrums.
   c. greenhouse effect.
   d. prevailing westerlies.

7. A zone near the equator that has no winds is the
   a. polar easterlies.
   b. doldrums.
   c. trade winds.
   d. prevailing westerlies.

8. High winds circling both polar areas are known as the
   a. trade winds.          c. polar easterlies.
   b. prevailing westerlies. d. jet stream.

9. The layer of gases surrounding the planet is the
   a. atmosphere.       c. trade winds.
   b. jet stream.       d. doldrums.

10. A barometer measures the
    a. Coriolis effect.
    b. polar easterlies.
    c. atmospheric pressure.
    d. radiation balance.

## Completion

On a separate sheet of paper, complete each statement by supplying the correct term.

1. Nitrogen-fixing bacteria form <u>nitrogen</u> compounds that plants use.

2. Animals use <u>oygen</u> directly from the atmosphere.

3. The highest concentration of <u>ozone</u> is found at altitudes of 20 to 30 km.

4. Atmospheric pressure <u>decreases</u> outward from the earth.

5. The <u>tropopause</u> is a boundary for the troposphere.

6. The overturning of hot and cold air in the troposphere is known as <u>convection</u>.

7. Atmospheric pressure is affected by <u>temperature</u> and altitude.

8. The layer of electrically charged particles that extends from 85 to 650 km altitude is the <u>ionosphere</u>.

9. The outermost layer of the atmosphere is the <u>exosphere</u>.

10. Although the air at the <u>equator</u> appears to be motionless, it is actually rising.

# Writing Critically

1. Compare the greenhouse effect in a black car to that in a white car. How does it differ? What causes the difference?

2. Look at a globe of the earth. Compare the Coriolis effect in the Northern and Southern hemispheres. In which hemisphere might land masses have less influence on the Coriolis effect?

3. Explain how life on Earth would be affected if there were no stratosphere.

4. **CHALLENGE** Explain why the auroras occur more frequently in the polar regions.

1. The greenhouse effect would be more intense in a black car because black will absorb more heat than white.
2. Southern, because there are fewer continents and they are spaced farther apart.
3. There would be no ozone and eventually no life.
4. They are nearer magnetic poles where there are more charged particles.

# Skill Reinforcement

The Skill Activity on page 425 describes how to interpret diagrams. Refer to the diagrams in the Skill Activity. In a brief paragraph, explain how CFC-11 and CFC-12 break down the ozone layer.

# Research Ideas

1. Research recent articles on the condition of the ozone layer. Analyze the situation and tell whether you think the ozone is really in danger.

2. Research the most common routes for airplanes and determine how jet streams can affect the flying time of planes.

3. Research the composition of Earth's early atmosphere. How does the composition compare with that of the modern atmosphere? What might have caused the changes in the atmosphere?

4. **CHALLENGE** Research history texts for ships' logs that document the existence of the doldrums. Discover how the ships' captains resolved problems in dealing with the doldrums.

# For Further Reading

Barth, Michael C. and James G. Titus, eds. *Greenhouse Effect and Sea Level Rise: A Challenge for This Generation.* New York: Van Nostrand Reinhold, 1984. This book discusses the possible global warming that could result from increased concentrations of carbon dioxide and other gases in the atmosphere.

Linn, Alan. "The Earth Spins, So We Have the Coriolis Effect." *Smithsonian.* February, 1983. This article provides a thorough discussion of the Coriolis effect.

Watson, Lyall. *Heaven's Breath: A Natural History of the Wind.* New York: Morrow, 1985. This book is a comprehensive explanation of the impact of wind on the earth.

# CHAPTER 21

# Weather and Climate

Mighty weather systems roam the earth's atmosphere. Some bring rain or sunshine that support life. Others bring freezing temperatures or drought that destroy life. This satellite photograph of storms over the United States was taken by the *Landsat* weather satellite. Scientists use satellite photographs and other data to forecast weather.

For additional information, see pages T106–T107.

# Water Vapor in the Air

## SECTION OBJECTIVES

● **Define** *relative humidity*.

● **Identify** the major types of clouds.

● **Describe** the hydrologic cycle.

NEW TERMS IN THIS SECTION

| | |
|---|---|
| weather | fog |
| humidity | precipitation |
| evaporation | stratus clouds |
| relative humidity | cumulus clouds |
| condensation | cirrus clouds |
| dew point | hydrologic cycle |

Photograph left: Hurricane in Gulf of Mexico as seen from space

## 21.1 Humidity

The state of the atmosphere at a given time and place is called **weather.** Weather conditions on Earth are largely determined by the amount of moisture in the atmosphere. Sometimes in the summer it may feel as though the air is heavy with moisture. Moisture in the atmosphere is called **humidity**. The moisture enters the atmosphere mainly from large bodies of water and also from moist land, plant leaves, and animals through the process of evaporation. **Evaporation** is the process by which water changes into a gas, or *vapor,* at a temperature less than the boiling point of water.

When air is heated, gas molecules move farther apart. This distance allows more room for water vapor. When air cools, the gas molecules press together. Because the gas molecules are pressed closer together, there is less room for the water vapor. Therefore, warm air can hold more moisture than an equal volume of cold air.

The amount of water vapor in the atmosphere ranges from almost none above the deserts of the world and the ice caps of Greenland and Antarctica to 2.5 percent in humid areas near the equator. The amount of water vapor air can hold depends on the temperature. The higher the temperature the more water the air can hold.

Review the discussion of phase changes as described in Chapter 3. Remind students that water molecules are in constant motion. This motion causes molecules to escape from the surface. This escape, or evaporation of molecules, is aided and increased as the temperature of the water and air increases.

## READING CRITICALLY

Why do people tend to have dry skin in the winter?

Cold air contains less moisture, which dries out the skin.

## Relative Humidity

The amount of water vapor per cubic meter of air is called *absolute humidity*. However, air humidity is usually expressed as relative humidity. **Relative humidity** is the amount of water vapor in a given volume of air compared to the total amount that volume of air could hold at a given temperature. For example 1 cubic meter of air at 30°C can hold no more than 30 g of water vapor. When the air contains 30 g of water vapor, it has a relative humidity of 100 percent. If the same air held only 15 g of water vapor, its relative humidity would be 50 percent.

**Figure 21–1.** These areas all have different relative humidity. The rain forest at the bottom has the highest relative humidity, and the desert has the lowest. The polar region falls in between.

## Condensation

Warm, humid air is less dense than the cooler air above it. As the warm air rises, it expands and its temperature decreases. When enough heat is lost to the surrounding

Within a half hour, the downdraft slows and the rainstorm is replaced by a gentle rain that may last an hour or two.

Thunderstorms generally occur when a cold front moves quickly into an area. The warm moist air there is rapidly pushed up to high altitudes. Occluded fronts and very low pressure areas are also sometimes accompanied by severe thunderstorms.

### Tornadoes

Very violent weather disturbances can occur along cold fronts that lead into very low pressure areas. Such settings are perfect for tornadoes to develop. **Tornadoes** are violent, whirling funnels of wind that move over land. Warm air rising along the cold front condenses into a line of thunderclouds, as shown in Figure 21–10. This line of thunderclouds is called a *squall line*. The energy from the condensation of water vapor causes violent winds along the squall line. The warm air moves into a low-pressure system, following a counterclockwise path. As the air approaches minimum pressure, it rotates faster. The whirling mass of air is called a **vortex**.

A tornado develops when the vortex forms a funnel extending down from the bottom of the thundercloud. This extension is caused by the air below being drawn up. Pressure at the center of the vortex is estimated to be 10 to 15 percent less than on the outside of the funnel. This sudden pressure decrease causes the air drawn into

If you count the number of seconds between the time you see lightning and the time you hear the thunder, and then divide that number by three, you can tell the distance of the lightning in kilometers.

Discuss with the students what safety precautions they should take in the event of a tornado: open windows and seek shelter under a heavy piece of furniture, in a door frame, or in a basement. If out in the open, move away from the vortex in a direction perpendicular to its path and seek shelter under a bridge or in a culvert. Do not try to outrun a tornado.

**Figure 21–10.** Tornadoes are most common in the United States in the Midwest: Oklahoma, Kansas, and Nebraska. This group of states has been nicknamed "Tornado Alley" because of the number of tornadoes that occur there.

the vortex to become saturated. As a result, water vapor condenses, which makes the funnel visible. High winds and extremely low pressure concentrated in a small area make tornadoes very dangerous.

**Figure 21–11.** Although waterspouts often occur over the ocean, they can also occur over lakes or other bodies of water.

Other areas where planetary wind conditions favor the generation of hurricanes are off the west coast of Central America and off the Philippines during summer in the Northern Hemisphere. During summer in the Southern Hemisphere, conditions are favorable to hurricane development in the western Pacific and in the Indian Ocean south of the equator. Hurricanes are known by other names around the world—typhoons (Asia), cyclones (India), and willy-willies (Australia).

## ACTIVITY

### Measuring Rainfall

Set an empty soup can outside in the open, away from any roof runoff drain. At the same time each day, use a metric ruler to measure the amount of rain or other water that has accumulated in the can. Record your measurements. Keep a record of the rainfall in your area for a week. Listen to or read local weather reports to see if your measurements are close to those given in the reports.

A fully developed hurricane is an almost perfectly circular vortex, as much as 600 km in diameter. The pressure difference between the center and the outer boundary is 5 to 10 percent.

**Waterspouts,** such as the one shown in Figure 21–11, are tornadoes that develop over water. For example, sea water is sucked up from the ocean surface. Waterspouts are much less powerful than tornadoes because the temperature difference between neighboring air masses over sea is usually much less than over land. Wind speed within waterspouts is rarely more than 80 km per hour.

### Hurricanes

A dangerous type of weather disturbance is a hurricane. **Hurricanes** are cyclones that form over oceans in the tropics. These massive storms are formed in much the same way as tornadoes. The difference between tornadoes and hurricanes is that tornadoes involve only local air masses. Hurricanes, however, can involve the wind system of the entire planet. At the center of the vortex is the *eye,* a core of warm, descending air.

Condensation of water vapor is the source of the hurricane's energy. Hurricanes develop only in the tropics, where absolute humidity is high. Most hurricanes have winds of 100 to 120 km per hour. Turbulence within a hurricane produces tornadoes. These make a hurricane even more dangerous.

Hurricanes produce waves 10 to 12 m high on the open seas. When a hurricane crosses a coastline and moves over land, winds push the sea water inland. Sea level may rise as much as 5 m, causing severe flooding

There are several different types of weathering. *Chemical weathering* is caused by rainwater as it filters through the rocks. Rainwater contains carbon dioxide. More carbon dioxide is picked up as the water filters through soil. The carbon dioxide makes the rainwater slightly acidic, which causes a chemical reaction in minerals. Over time, these reactions break down the rocks and minerals completely.

*Mechanical weathering* results from the freezing and thawing of water flowing through rock. It also results from the impact of windblown mineral particles on rock surfaces. The action of wind-driven quartz sand on rock surfaces is much like sandblasting. Mechanical weathering of this type is limited to desert areas. The effects of weathering on soil are discussed in Chapter 29.

## Section Review

1. latitude, altitude, ocean currents, and topography

1. What are four factors that affect climate?
2. List and describe three types of climate in terms of temperature and three in terms of humidity.
3. Describe the difference between chemical weathering and mechanical weathering.
4. THINKING CRITICALLY Explain how two areas with different climates could have similar weather conditions?

Humidity increases the rate of weathering.

**READING CRITICALLY**
How does humidity affect the rate of weathering?

2. in terms of temperature: tropical (hot), temperate (warm), and polar (cold); in terms of humidity: humid (wet), semiarid (moderate moisture), and arid (dry)
3. Chemical weathering is caused by rain as it filters through rocks. Carbon dioxide in the water makes the water slightly acidic. The acid causes breakdown of the rocks. Mechanical weathering is caused by freezing and thawing of water causing expansion and contraction of the rocks.
4. Georgia and Vermont, for example, can have different climates but may have similar weather conditions if affected by similar types of air masses.

## CAREER

### Weather Technician

**DESCRIPTION** A weather technician observes weather conditions, including air pressure, temperature, wind speed and direction, humidity, cloud cover, and precipitation. In addition to visual observations, technicians use many different instruments to measure weather conditions. Weather technicians sometimes assist meteorologists in studying the weather and atmosphere.

**REQUIREMENTS** If you plan to be a weather technician, you should take mathematics courses in high school. Following graduation, you must complete one year of technical training in meteorology at a technical institute or community college or in the Armed Forces.

**INFORMATION** American Meteorological Society, 45 Beacon Street, Boston, MA 02008

# INVESTIGATION 21:  Relative Humidity

*How would you measure the amount of moisture in the air?*

## PURPOSE
To determine the relative humidity of the air

## MATERIALS
2 Celsius thermometers
cheesecloth (10 cm X 10 cm)
masking tape
2 pieces of string, each 10 cm in length
ring stand with ring
small beaker
water
fan or piece of cardboard

## PROCEDURE

1. Copy Table 1 onto a sheet of paper. Enter all data from this investigation onto your table.

2. Wrap the cheesecloth around the bulb of one thermometer so that about 2 cm of the cloth hang below the bulb. Hold the cheesecloth in place with the masking tape.

3. Tie a piece of string to each thermometer.

4. Hang the Thermometers from the ring, as shown in Figure 1. Hang the thermometer wrapped in cheesecloth into the beaker. Add water to the beaker until the water level just covers the cheesecloth. Be sure that the water does not cover the bulb of the thermometer.

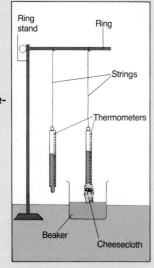

Ring stand
Ring
Strings
Thermometers
Beaker
Cheesecloth

5. Fan the two thermometers until the temperature on the thermometer wrapped in cheesecloth remains constant. Record both temperatures.

6. Repeat step 5 at the same time each day for five days. Record the temperatures. Check the water level each day to make sure the cheesecloth is hanging in the water.

## RESULTS

| TABLE 1 | | TEMPERATURE READINGS | | |
|---|---|---|---|---|
| Day | Dry Bulb | Wet Bulb | Temperature Difference | Relative Humidity |
| 1 | | | | |
| 2 | | | | |
| 3 | | | | |
| 4 | | | | |
| 5 | | | | |

## CONCLUSIONS

1. What does the dry thermometer measure?

2. What does the thermometer wrapped in cheesecloth measure?

3. Refer to the chart in Figure 2. Use the information on the chart to determine the relative humidity for each day. Record your results. Which day had the highest relative humidity? Which had the lowest relative humidity?

| Dry Bulb | Difference between wet and dry bulb readings (°) | | | | | | | | | |
|---|---|---|---|---|---|---|---|---|---|---|
| °C | 1 | 2 | 3 | 4 | 5 | 6 | 7 | 8 | 9 | 10 |
| 10 | 88 | 77 | 66 | 55 | 44 | 34 | 24 | 15 | 6 | |
| 11 | 89 | 78 | 67 | 56 | 46 | 36 | 27 | 18 | 9 | |
| 12 | 89 | 78 | 68 | 58 | 48 | 39 | 29 | 21 | 12 | |
| 13 | 89 | 79 | 69 | 59 | 50 | 41 | 32 | 22 | 15 | 7 |
| 14 | 90 | 79 | 70 | 60 | 51 | 42 | 34 | 26 | 18 | 10 |
| 15 | 90 | 80 | 71 | 61 | 53 | 44 | 36 | 27 | 20 | 13 |
| 16 | 90 | 81 | 71 | 63 | 54 | 46 | 38 | 30 | 23 | 15 |
| 17 | 90 | 81 | 72 | 64 | 55 | 47 | 40 | 32 | 25 | 18 |
| 18 | 91 | 82 | 73 | 65 | 57 | 49 | 41 | 34 | 27 | 20 |
| 19 | 91 | 82 | 74 | 65 | 58 | 50 | 43 | 36 | 29 | 22 |
| 20 | 91 | 83 | 74 | 67 | 59 | 53 | 46 | 39 | 32 | 26 |
| 21 | 91 | 83 | 75 | 67 | 60 | 53 | 46 | 39 | 32 | 26 |
| 22 | 92 | 83 | 76 | 68 | 61 | 54 | 47 | 40 | 34 | 28 |
| 23 | 92 | 84 | 76 | 69 | 62 | 55 | 48 | 42 | 36 | 30 |
| 24 | 92 | 84 | 77 | 69 | 62 | 56 | 49 | 43 | 37 | 31 |
| 25 | 92 | 84 | 77 | 70 | 63 | 57 | 50 | 44 | 39 | 33 |

1. air temperature
2. rate of evaporation; the combined wet and dry thermometer are used to determine relative humidity
3. Answers will vary.

## Summary

1. Weather is the state of the atmosphere at a given place and time. **(21.1)**
2. Relative humidity is the amount of water vapor in the air compared to the maximum amount of water vapor that the air at a given temperature can hold. **(21.1)**
3. Clouds are concentrations of water droplets. There are three basic types of clouds—cumulus, stratus, and cirrus. **(21.2)**
4. The hydrologic cycle is the cycle of evaporation, condensation, and precipitation. **(21.3)**
5. There are five types of fronts: cold, warm, stationary, occluded, and polar. **(21.4)**
6. Cyclones, thunderstorms, tornadoes, and hurricanes get their energy from the condensation of water vapor. **(21.5)**
7. Meteorologists use satellite photographs and measurements of temperature, humidity, barometric pressure, and wind conditions to forecast weather. **(21.6)**
8. Climate is affected by latitude, altitude, ocean currents, and topography. The three major climatic zones in terms of temperature are tropical, temperate, and polar. **(21.7)**
9. Weathering is the process by which rocks and minerals are broken down. **(21.8)**

## Science Terms

On a separate sheet of paper, define each term in a sentence.

air mass **(442)**
anticyclones **(444)**
cirrus clouds **(440)**
climate **(449)**
cloud **(439)**
condensation **(439)**
cumulus clouds **(440)**
cyclones **(444)**

dew point **(439)**
evaporation **(437)**
fog **(439)**
front **(442)**
humidity **(437)**
hurricane **(446)**
hydrologic cycle **(441)**
meteorology **(447)**

precipitation **(439)**
relative humidity **(438)**
stratus clouds **(440)**
tornadoes **(445)**
vortex **(445)**
waterspouts **(446)**
weather **(437)**
weathering **(450)**

## Modified True-False

On a separate sheet of paper, mark each true statement *TRUE* and each false statement *FALSE*. If false, change the underlined term to make the statement true.

1. During the process of <u>condensation</u>, liquid water changes into a gas. F, evaporation
2. The temperature at which a vapor begins to <u>evaporate</u> is known as the dew point. F, condense
3. <u>Nimbus</u> clouds produce precipitation. T
4. The cycle of evaporation and precipitation is known as the <u>hydrologic cycle</u>. T
5. A <u>front</u> is a large body of air with uniform temperature and humidity. T
6. A <u>stationary front</u> occurs when a front stops moving. T
7. The line of thunderclouds rising along a cold front is known as an <u>anticyclone</u>. F, squall line
8. <u>Waterspouts</u> are tornadoes that develop over water. T
9. The terms tropical and temperate, describe the <u>humidity</u> of a climate. F, temperature
10. The breakdown of rocks and minerals under natural conditions is <u>weathering</u>. T

*(continues)*

# CHAPTER REVIEW

## Multiple Choice

On a separate sheet of paper, write the letter of the term that best answers the question or completes the statement.

1. When no more molecules can evaporate into the air, the air is said to be
   a. condensed.          c. at dew point.
   b. humid.              **d.** saturated.

2. Thick, puffy-looking clouds are called _____ clouds.
   **a.** cumulus         c. stratus
   b. nimbus              d. cirrus

3. Precipitation that returns to the ocean is called
   a. saturation.         c. condensed.
   **b.** runoff.         d. marine.

4. Frozen rain is
   a. hailstones.         c. snow.
   **b.** sleet.          d. ice crystals.

5. Two cold air masses merging form
   a. a cold front.
   b. a stationary front.
   **c.** an occluded front.
   d. a polar front.

6. The process by which water vapor changes into a liquid is
   a. evaporation.        c. precipitation.
   **b.** condensation.   d. humidity.

7. High-pressure areas circulating in a clockwise motion are
   a. vortexes.           c. cyclones.
   **b.** anticyclones.   d. tornadoes.

8. Violent whirling funnels of wind moving over land are
   a. waterspouts.        c. cyclones.
   b. hurricanes.         **d.** tornadoes.

9. The science of the study of the atmosphere is known as
   **a.** meteorology.    c. weathering.
   b. climate.            d. astronomy.

10. Climates not affected by the ocean are called
   a. maritime.           c. arid.
   **b.** continental.    d. temperate.

11. Climate varies not only by latitude but also by
   a. longitude.          **c.** altitude.
   b. pressure.           d. time.

12. The air drawn down by the rain in a thunderstorm is called a
   a. squall line.        c. vortex.
   b. tornado.            **d.** downdraft.

## Completion

On a separate sheet of paper, complete each statement by supplying the correct term.

1. Climates are classified as humid, semiarid, and arid when referring to their _humidity_.

2. Moisture in the atmosphere is called _humidity_.

3. The center of the vortex of a hurricane is called the _eye_.

4. A cloud that hovers at ground level is _fog_.

5. Movement of water droplets in a cloud is called _turbulence_.

6. A _polar front_ separates polar air from tropical air.

7. Polar and tropical are terms used to describe _climate_.

8. The state of the atmosphere at a given time and place is referred to as _weather_.

9. The highest clouds in the troposphere are _cirrus_.

10. Clouds with extended cloud layers and even bases are called _stratus_.

**454**   Chapter 21

## Writing Critically

1. Discuss how the humidity of two climates can differ although the temperatures may be the same.

2. Describe the similarities and differences among tornadoes, hurricanes, waterspouts, and cyclones.

   1. Two climates can have the same temperature, but if the amount of moisture in the air is different, then the humidity will be different.
   2. Answers should include the size of weather disturbances, wind action, duration, and amount, if any, of precipitation.

3. Describe all of the types of clouds and rank them according to their altitude.

4. CHALLENGE  Why would you expect weathering to occur more rapidly in Boston than in Phoenix?

   3. Answers should include a summary of the information shown in Figure 21-4.
   4. Phoenix has little humidity; Boston has higher humidity. Humidity increases the rate of weathering.

## Skill Reinforcement

The Skill Activity on page 448 describes how to interpret weather maps. Using any other weather map, explain how you might predict changes in weather over the next few days.

## Research Ideas

1. In the current *Farmer's Almanac*, look up the weather predicted for your area for this year. Compare these predictions with the actual weather your area has been experiencing. How accurate is the almanac's prediction for your area? Research how people who develop the almanac go about making predictions for future weather.

2. Investigate the weather patterns over the continent of Africa. Explain how weather conditions have affected Africa's climate. What problems do many Africans face as a result of these conditions?

3. CHALLENGE  The world's weather patterns are cyclic. Currently, the world is in a warming trend. As the earth heats up, scientists are concerned over the effects melting glaciers and polar caps will have on the earth and its weather. Research weather cycles and, based on your findings, make a prediction as to how the weather will change in the future. Also predict how these changes might affect the face of the earth.

## For Further Reading

Gibrilisco, Stan. *Violent Weather: Hurricanes, Tornadoes, and Storms.* Blue Ridge Summit, Pennsylvania: TAB Books, 1984. This book explains the formation of each of these weather conditions, their similarities and differences, and the destructive power of each.

Ludlum, David M. *The Weather Factor.* Boston: Houghton-Mifflin, 1984. A meteorologist gives a fascinating account of how the weather has influenced American history and life from colonial times to the Space Age.

Weisbird, Stefi. "Stalking the Weather Bombs," *Science News,* Vol. 129, 5/17/86, pp. 314–317. This article explains how huge cyclones develop and discusses the extensive variety of instruments scientists use to track and study them.

CHAPTER

# 22

# The Oceans

The earth's oceans are a precious natural resource. Plants and animals from the sea provide food and oxygen for millions of people. Valuable petroleum, natural gas, and minerals are found beneath the ocean floor. Scientists are now working on ways to tap all these valuable resources.

For additional information, see pages T108-T109.

# The Structure and Composition of the Oceans

**SECTION OBJECTIVES**

- **Compare** active and passive continental margins.
- **Describe** the various properties of sea water.

Photograph left: tang fish on a coral reef

## 22.1 The Shoreline

Land and ocean meet at underwater areas that border the continents. These areas are called *continental margins*, or shorelines. When you think about the shoreline, what do you picture? One of two images usually comes to mind. High cliffs dropping to small beaches is one image of a shoreline. These shorelines form along active continental margins. An **active continental margin** occurs along a boundary where two plates of the earth collide or where one plate slides beneath another plate. The coastline of California is an active continental margin. The shoreline is usually high and rocky with strong wave action. Narrow, pebbly beaches are scattered between rocky points.

Another image of a shoreline is of land sloping to wide sandy beaches. These shorelines develop along passive continental margins. **Passive continental margins** are located where a continent ends some distance from a spreading plate edge. The east coast of North America is an example of a passive continental margin.

Large rivers empty into the oceans along passive continental margins. The rivers carry heavy loads of sediment. As the sediment is distributed by currents

NEW TERMS IN THIS SECTION
active continental margin
passive continental margin
delta
estuary
continental shelf
continental slope
oceanography
salinity
thermocline

Reintroduce the idea of plate tectonics, which was discussed in Chapter 19. Demonstrate how being near or far from the edge of a plate affects the type of beach found along the coast.

**Figure 22–1.** Atlantic coast beaches, like the one at Bald Head Island, North Carolina (right), are passive continental margins. Beaches on the Pacific coast, like the one at Point Reyes, California (left), are active continental margins.

**Figure 22–2.** A coral reef is made up of the external skeletons of corals, simple animals with fingerlike tentacles. The skeletons, and therefore the reef, are almost pure limestone. The reef supports a wide variety of marine life, including the corals themselves.

along the shore, a low coastline builds up and slowly advances toward the ocean. *Beaches* are deposits of sandy sediment pushed against the shore by sea waves. Beaches require a continuous supply of sediment because storms move some of the sand offshore. Sediments moving along a coastline tend to form sandbars offshore.

Coral reefs, which are composed of the skeletons of tiny sea animals, are found in areas where there is little sediment. Sediment tends to kill reef-building animals. Southern Florida and the Bahamas rest on a 5-km-thick bed built on a framework of coral.

Rivers carry 20 billion tons of sediment to the ocean each year. These sediments form triangular-shaped deposits called **deltas** at the mouth of many rivers. Well-known deltas are those of the Nile River in Egypt and the Mississippi River in the United States.

At the mouth of some rivers, the movement of the ocean is particularly strong. In these areas, sediment may be removed not only from the river mouth but also from regions far inland. Broad areas called **estuaries** are formed where river water and sea water mix. These estuaries are important breeding areas for wildlife and sealife.

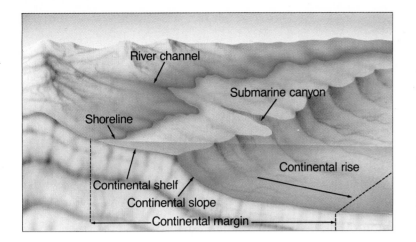

**Figure 22–3.** The continental margin forms the true base of the continent as it rises from the sea floor. The margin can be divided into two distinct areas: the continental shelf and the continental slope.

## 22.2 The Continental Shelf

Along many shorelines of the world, the land slopes gradually away from the exposed land, forming a shelf. The water above this shelf is relatively shallow, ranging from a few meters to about 130 m. The underwater shelf of land bordering a continent is called a **continental shelf.**

In some places, such as off the French Riviera, there is little or no continental shelf. The coast plunges directly into deep water. In other places, such as off Newfoundland, the continental shelf is hundreds of kilometers wide. At the edge of the continental shelf is the continental slope. The **continental slope** marks the place where the continental shelf drops off to the deep ocean floor below.

## 22.3 Deep Ocean Basins

About 71 percent of the earth's surface is covered by water. The study of the oceans is called **oceanography**. Oceanography includes the study of the physical features such as the ocean floor, oceanic ridges, and water temperature of the oceans. This science also includes the study of all living things in the oceans.

The Pacific Ocean is by far the largest and deepest ocean. It covers one-third of the earth's surface. Deep-sea trenches are found along the margins of the Pacific. These trenches trap sediment that flows out from the continents. The floor of the Pacific is deeper than those of the other oceans because sediment from land cannot reach it. The sediment becomes trapped in deep-sea trenches. Because the other oceans have fewer trenches, their ocean floors collect much more sediment. Therefore, the other oceans are shallower than the Pacific.

The movement of ocean water pulls sediments across the continental shelf and piles them up along the shelf edge. A storm, or even gravity alone, may cause the sediments to flow down the continental slope and out along the deep ocean floor. This flow of sediments is called a *turbidity current*.

### READING CRITICALLY
How would a large storm affect the continental slope?

The storm could move a great deal of sediment from the slope down to the ocean floor.

Have the students name the four major oceans. (Pacific, Atlantic, Indian, and Arctic)

### SCIENCE FACT
The Pacific Ocean is three times the size of Asia.

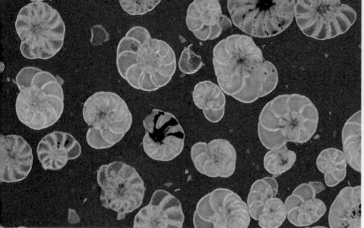
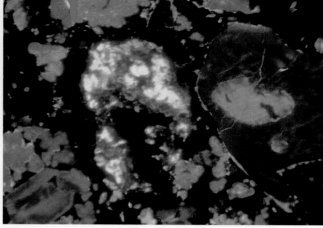

**Figure 22–4.** The ocean floor is covered by a layer of sediments composed mainly of two types—ooze and clay. Ooze consists mainly of the skeletal remains of marine plankton and other sea creatures (left). Clay (right) is a combination of ashes, particles, and rocks that have landed in the ocean.

## ACTIVITY

**Mapping the Ocean Floor**

Using a deep pan, make a model of the ocean floor from modeling clay. Include both types of beaches and shorelines. Fill the pan with colored water and make sketches of the ocean floor as it appears from above.

The total volume of seawater is enormous. Sea water also contains many valuable elements. For example, there are about 10 million tons of gold in seawater, but in very small concentrations. Only about one part gold is found in each million million parts of the water. Therefore, the gold is not easily removed from seawater.

The deep ocean floor is covered with deep-sea sediment. The sediment settles out of the water above. The two major types of deep-sea sediment are *ooze* and *red clay*. Ooze accumulates on the ocean floor to a depth of about 4 km. This sediment consists of clay mixed with the shells of tiny sea creatures. The clay portion of ooze comes from particles of rock, ash, and volcanic dust that the wind has blown over the oceans. Ooze accumulates at a rate of 1 to 3 cm per thousand years.

Red clay accumulates more slowly than ooze—about 1 mm per thousand years. In addition to minerals such as iron, red clay contains tiny quartz crystals and rare particles shed by meteorites. These particles are shown in Figure 22–4.

The thickness of deep-sea sediment increases with distance from the crests of the mid-ocean ridge. Only thin patches of recently deposited sediment cover the ridge crests. The sediment becomes thicker toward the ocean margins because the age of the sea floor increases. Therefore, there has been more time for sediment to accumulate. The maximum thickness of deep-sea sediment close to the ocean margins is about 1 km.

# 22.4 The Properties of Sea Water

If 1 kg of normal sea water is allowed to evaporate completely, about 34.5 g of various salt compounds are left behind (see Table 22–1). The most abundant compound is sodium chloride (NaCl), common table salt.

### Salinity

The total amount of salts dissolved in 1 kg of sea water is called **salinity.** The average salinity of the oceans is 34.5 g of salts per kilogram of water. In areas where evaporation is high, the salinity of the water is higher than average. The Mediterranean Sea and the Red Sea have higher-than-average salinity. Areas where evapo-

| TABLE 22–1 | SALTS DISSOLVED IN 1 KG OF SEA WATER | | |
|---|---|---|---|
| **Name** | **Chemical Formula** | **Concentration (g/kg)** | **Weight (percent)** |
| Sodium chloride | NaCl | 26.7 | 77.4 |
| Magnesium sulfate | $MgSO_4$ | 3.2 | 9.4 |
| Magnesium chloride | $MgCl_2$ | 2.2 | 6.4 |
| Calcium chloride | $CaCl_2$ | 1.1 | 3.2 |
| Potassium chloride | KCl | 0.7 | 2.0 |
| Sodium bicarbonate | $NaHCO_3$ | 0.2 | 0.6 |
| All others | | 0.4 | 1.0 |

ration is low and the supply of fresh river water is abundant have lower salinities. The Arctic Ocean, the Baltic Sea, and the Black Sea are areas of low salinity.

The water that formed the original ocean was fresh. Fresh water is not the same as pure water. Pure water contains only water molecules and no other materials. Fresh water contains a number of dissolved elements and compounds. These elements and compounds have been washed out of the rocks by rain and by water in the ground. Rivers eventually bring these elements and compounds to the oceans. Some of these materials remain in solution, and their concentration increases with time. Others form solids that accumulate on the ocean floors. The two elements found in sea water that are rarely found in fresh water are sodium and chlorine. These two elements remain in the ocean and make it salty.

**Figure 22–5.** Deriving usable salt from the sea is a major project in some parts of the world. These salt flats are used as giant evaporation dishes to obtain the salt from sea water.

In addition to salts, sea water contains gases from the atmosphere. Nitrogen, oxygen, and carbon dioxide are present in sea water. In fact, most of the carbon dioxide on Earth is dissolved in ocean water. Only a small fraction is in the atmosphere. The opposite is true for nitrogen and oxygen. Most of these two gases are in the atmosphere and very little is dissolved in ocean water. <u>What do you think happens to carbon dioxide in the oceans?</u> It is used by plants in the oceans for photosynthesis.

## Thermal Properties

Without the oceans, the temperature of the earth would rise above 100°C during the day and plunge below −100°C at night. In the polar regions, temperatures would drop to −200°C during the winter. The oceans function as temperature equalizers for the entire globe. Sea water absorbs heat energy, or thermal energy, when the atmosphere is warmer than the sea water. Sea water releases thermal energy when the atmosphere is cooler than the sea water.

Sea water freezes at −1.872°C instead of 0°C, the freezing point of pure water. *Brines,* which are salt solutions even saltier than sea water, freeze at even lower temperatures. <u>What is the purpose of spreading salt on icy streets?</u>

Although the oceans act as thermal regulators, ice does form on the oceans. Surface sea ice is generally no thicker than about 3 m. The ice itself protects the underlying sea water from the colder air above, preventing it from freezing. Sea ice does not form icebergs. Icebergs are slabs of ice several hundred meters thick. They form when pieces of land glaciers break off and float to sea. Antarctic icebergs reach a thickness of 1000 m.

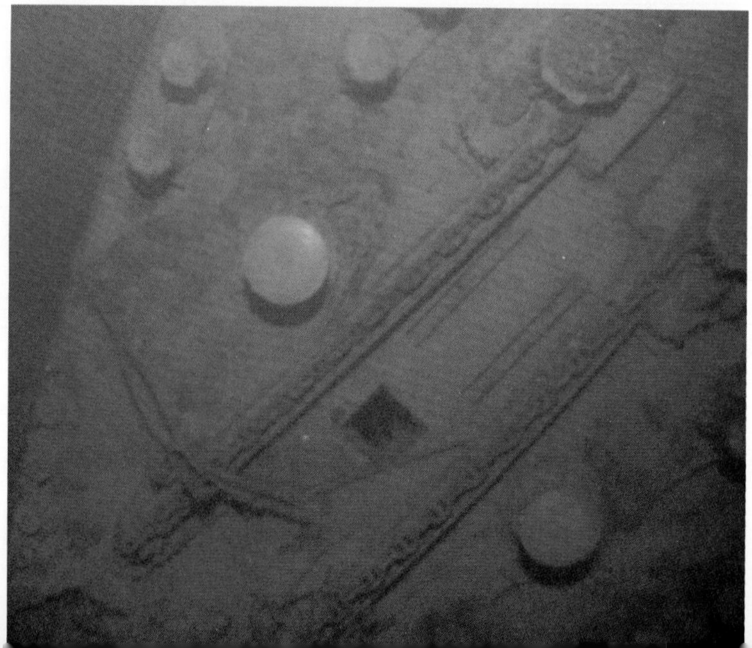

READING CRITICALLY

The water in Great Salt Lake freezes at −22°C. What does this tell you about the salinity of the lake?

The salinity is much much higher than that of sea water.

Salt on the street causes the ice to melt because salt water has a lower freezing point than fresh water.

**Figure 22–6.** Only ten percent of an iceberg sticks out above the water. The *Titanic* sank on April 15, 1912, when it struck the submerged portion of an iceberg. Of the 2224 people on board, 1513 were drowned or killed in the collision. Recent expeditions to the grave of the *Titanic* (below) have resulted in the retrieval of many artifacts.

**462**    Chapter 22

Although a large portion of the earth's water is in the form of ice, there is still a lot of water in the oceans. The ocean is warmed by the sun from above. The sun's rays reach 100 m into the oceans' depths. The water at the surface is warmer and less dense than the water below. Being less dense, it does not mix with the colder, denser water below. The layer between the warm water above and the colder water below is called the **thermocline** (THUHR muh klyn). Temperature decreases rapidly from the top to the bottom of the thermocline.

Over three quarters of the water in the oceans has a temperature less than 5°C. Ocean temperatures range from freezing to about 30°C at the surface of tropical seas.

### Pressure and Density

Gravity causes the atmosphere to press on the surface of the earth from all sides. In turn, the oceans press on the ocean floors, and the rock layers below press downward on each other. Pressure acts on the atoms and molecules that form the atmosphere, the oceans, and the rocks below. Pressure is measured in units called *atmospheres*. The pressure of the atmosphere at sea level is 1 atmosphere. At the deepest parts of the oceans, pressure is as great as 1000 atmospheres.

Like all liquids, water is not easily compressed. Therefore, density does not increase much with pressure. Density at the deepest part of the ocean is only 7 percent greater than at the surface.

**Figure 22-7.** The special steel cylinder emerging from the ocean is a bathyscaph. In this ship, Jacques-Ernst Piccard and Donald Walsh were able to descend to the Challenger Deep, the deepest portion of the Marianas Trench, on January 23, 1960. The descent took 4 hours and 48 minutes.

## Section Review

1. What is the difference between active and passive continental margins?
2. What are three properties of sea water?
3. Describe how pressure and density vary in the oceans.
4. THINKING CRITICALLY How do the oceans influence the temperature of the earth?

1. Active margins are found near plate boundaries and have high shorelines and narrow, pebbly beaches. Passive margins are far from plate boundaries and have wide, sandy beaches.
2. salinity, high thermal capacity, pressure, and density
3. Density varies very little; pressure increases greatly with depth.
4. The oceans absorb heat from a warm atmosphere and release it when the temperature drops below the oceans' temperature.

# SKILL ACTIVITY 22    Completing a Table

## INTRODUCTION

Scuba divers must plan how deep they will descend before they dive. They take into account how many cubic feet of air they will breathe per minute for every 33 feet they descend. As the pressure increases, the amount of air used by the diver also increases.

## PROCEDURE

1. The chart shows how much air a relaxed diver with a surface breathing rate of 0.6 cubic feet per minute will breathe at various depths.

2. To find out how long the air in a 70-cubic-foot tank will last for a diver at each level, divide 70 cubic feet of air by the number of cubic feet of air breathed per minute.

Customary measurements, rather than metric measurements, are used in this activity because they are the measurements commonly used in scuba diving.

| Depth | Amount of Air Breathed | Time 70 cu. ft. of Air Will Last |
|---|---|---|
| 33 feet | 1.2 cu. ft./min. | 58 minutes |
| 66 feet | 1.8 cu. ft./min. | 38 minutes |
| 99 feet | 2.4 cu. ft./min. | 29 minutes |
| 132 feet | 3.0 cu. ft./min. | 23 minutes |
| 165 feet | 3.6 cu. ft./min. | 19 minutes |
| 297 feet | 6.0 cu. ft./min. | 11 minutes |

## APPLICATION

1. Why would scuba divers need to know how deep they will go even before they dive?

2. How does pressure affect the amount of air used?

3. At sea level, the air pressure is said to be 1 atmosphere. For every 33 feet the diver descends, the pressure is said to increase by one atmosphere. How many atmospheres of pressure does a diver at 132 feet experience?

1. To make sure that the diver has enough air for the time and depth allotted.
2. Increased pressure means more air is used.
3. 4.

# Movement of Ocean Water

## SECTION OBJECTIVES

- **Explain** how ocean currents are produced.
- **Distinguish** among currents, waves, and tides.
- **Describe** how the moon and tides are related.

NEW TERMS IN THIS SECTION
ocean current
sea wave
swell
current
tide
spring tide
neap tide

## 22.5 Ocean Currents

On land, wind may move loose sediment and form dunes or loose deposits. At sea, winds are partly responsible for the movement of water in the oceans creating waves and surface currents. The movement of ocean water in riverlike ribbons through the oceans is called an **ocean current**.

Ocean currents are partly responsible for temperature changes on Earth. Heat is transported from the equator towards the poles by winds and ocean currents. Winds transport 80 percent of the heat, while ocean currents transport the remaining 20 percent. Heat transport across latitudes reduces extremes of climate. This movement of heat cools the latitudes closest to the equator and warms the latitudes farther from the equator.

Surface currents are driven by the wind, but density differences in ocean water cause a second type of current. Deep-water currents are formed when cold, dense water near the poles sinks and flows along the sea floor to the equator. Deep-ocean currents are responsible for bringing important nutrients nearer the surface, where they can be used by living things.

### READING CRITICALLY

How do ocean currents on one part of the earth affect temperatures on another part of the earth?

Currents transport heat from one area to another.

**Figure 22–8.** The major ocean surface currents of the earth are shown in this illustration.

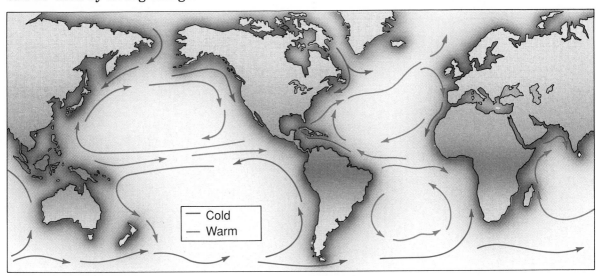

Cold
Warm

# COMPUTER APPLICATION

# Ocean Size

## 1. DESCRIPTION

This program represents the oceans of the world by rectangles. The area of each rectangle gives the relative size of the ocean. The area of a rectangle is the width multiplied by the height. The upper left hand corner is common to all the rectangles. To select an ocean, enter the rank of ocean in size. For example, selecting 1 gives a rectangle representing the largest ocean, the Pacific Ocean. Selections 5 and 6 give the option to rerun the program or to end it.

## 2. PROGRAM

Input the following program. After it is completely input, key the computer to run the program. If the program does not run, check to make sure you have input correctly. If the program runs correctly, go on to steps 3 and 4.

## 3. HELPFUL HINTS

When keying in the program, be careful to avoid errors. When using the program, press the ⟨RETURN⟩ key after each selection.

## 4. GOING FURTHER

Change the program so that the border used for each ocean is different. Use * for the Pacific, + for the Atlantic, . for the Indian, and # for the Arctic.

```
100    HOME : PRINT "R E L A T I V E   O C E A N   S I Z E S"
110    LET U$ = "M SQ KM"
120    FOR K = 1 TO 4: READ N$(K),S$(K),RM(K),LM(K): NEXT
130    DATA "PACIFIC","166.2",38,22,"ATLANTIC","86.6",27,16

140    DATA "INDIAN","73.4",20,12,"ARCTIC","12.2",10,6
150    VTAB 2: HTAB 4
160    INPUT "ENTER: 1-4=OCEAN, 5=RERUN, 6=END ";N
170    IF N = 5 THEN  RUN

180    IF N = 6 THEN  VTAB 20: END
190    VTAB 3: HTAB 1: FOR W = 1 TO RM(N): PRINT "*";: NEXT
200    FOR V = 3 TO LM(N): HTAB 1: PRINT "*";
210    HTAB RM(N): PRINT "*": NEXT V

220    FOR W = 1 TO RM(N): PRINT "*": NEXT W
230    VTAB LM(N) - 2: HTAB 2: PRINT N$(N)
240    VTAB LM(N) - 1: HTAB 3: PRINT S$(N)
250    VTAB LM(N): HTAB 2: PRINT U$

260    GOTO 150
```

# 22.6 Waves

A **sea wave** is a periodic motion of the sea surface. In wave motion, the only thing that travels is the wave. As the wave moves through the water, the water moves up and down. Waves occur when friction between the wind and the water surface causes ripples. These ripples are made larger by the impact of the wind on one side and air suction on the other side. This process is illustrated in Figure 22–9. However, the size of waves is limited by gravity, which tends to flatten them.

A **swell** consists of waves several hundred meters in wavelength that travel out of storm areas. These waves may cross an entire ocean at speeds of tens of kilometers per hour without losing much energy. Waves produced by storms around Antarctica, for instance, often cross the entire Pacific Ocean and reach Alaska.

## ACTIVITY

**Drawing Wave Activity**

Fill a pan with water and drop a cork into the water. Create wave disturbances and sketch the path the cork takes in the wave.

The faster ocean currents travel at 9.25 km/hr, while the slower currents travel at about 1.85 km/hr.

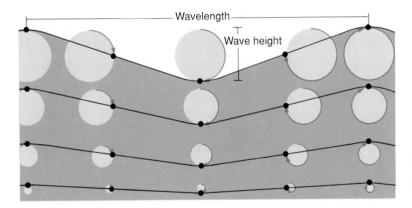

**Figure 22-9.** Particles of water in a wave move in a circle. Wave motion decreases with depth.

Waves develop best in the open ocean where there is no interference with the ocean floor. However, when a wave enters shallow water, the ocean floor disrupts the movement of the wave. Then the wave breaks and the water crashes onto the beach.

Water crashing onto a beach must return to the sea. Usually the returning water moves back to sea along the bottom underneath the next wave coming into shore. This water movement is called *undertow* and can be quite strong in some areas. Sometimes, the returning water forms a current flowing out along a channel perpendicular to the beach. This type of current is called a **rip current**. The speed of a rip current may be as high as 1 m per second. It is powerful enough to drag even a strong swimmer out to sea. Swimmers should not try to swim against a rip current. Swim with the current until you are out past the breakers. To escape a rip current, swim parallel to the beach until you are away from the current. Only then should you try to swim back to shore.

**Figure 22–10.** This photograph shows a tsunami hitting the town of Hilo, Hawaii. The wave overwhelmed the pier and rushed inland. The arrow points to a man caught in the torrent of the water.

Water builds up as it approaches the shore.

Sea waves caused by earthquakes are called *tsunamis* (tsoo NAH meez). You may have heard them referred to as "tidal waves," although they have nothing to do with tides. Tsunamis travel across the Pacific at speeds close to 800 km per hour. Tsunamis generated by earthquakes along the Alaskan coast reach Hawaii in about five hours.

During the Alaskan earthquake of 1964, the sudden uplift of the sea floor offshore caused the ocean surface to rise. The level of the sea rose less than 2 m and appeared as a long, gentle swell. However, as the sea water rolled onshore, it built into a wave more than 10 m tall. Several more waves followed at half-hour intervals before the sea quieted down. What causes a 2-m swell to build into a 10-m-high tsunami?

A cubic meter of water, which is about the size of a classroom desk, has the same mass as an elephant. Therefore, a tsunami hits with the force of a giant freight train. When the tsunami struck Alaska, the waterfront of all coastal towns and villages in the area of the tsunami was destroyed. The Alaskan pipeline terminal at Valdez caught fire and exploded.

In 1883, the volcano on the island of Krakatoa in the South Pacific erupted. One side of the island collapsed, and sea water rushed into a cavity containing hot lava. The whole island blew up with a tremendous explosion. The explosion created a tsunami 35 m high. This wave was equal in height to a ten-story building.

Today, seismic stations around the Pacific warn Hawaii, Japan, and the west coast of North America of any earthquake that might produce a tsunami. This system allows people enough time to leave low-lying coastal areas and seek refuge on higher ground.

## 22.7 Tides

The alternate rise and fall of the oceans and seas and the bodies of water connected to them are called **tides.** The gravity of the moon pulls the water away from the earth. This pull results in tides.

The moon orbits the earth over the tropics. As the earth rotates, the moon pulls up a crest of sea water. A second crest is also created on the side of the earth opposite the moon. The two tidal crests circle the earth in 24 hours and 50 minutes. The extra 50 minutes results from the fact that the moon travels around the earth in the same direction that the earth rotates. This means that the earth has to turn an additional 50 minutes per day in order for the same point on Earth to be under the moon. About how many hours separate low and high tides? 12 hours

An earth without continents would have two high tides and two low tides every 24 hours and 50 minutes. The continents, however, greatly distort the progress of the tides. Special charts have been produced showing the time of day when high tide or low tide occurs at different locations on Earth. These charts are important to navigation, especially in shallow water and in the entrance of harbors.

The tide is only 0.55 m high in the open ocean. However, its height may reach 2 to 3 m as the tide runs into a coastline. If the structure of the coastline creates a funnel for the water, the tide can rise much higher.

When an incoming tide flows into a narrowing channel, the funneling process causes the water to flow much more quickly than it would if it were allowed to spread out. The water at the front of the tide slows down due to the narrowing, but the water behind rushes up at normal speed, so that the water increases in height and velocity, resulting in a wall of water that surges up the channel. This phenomenon is called a *tidal bore*.

The time of high tide changes from day to day, repeating approximately every 10 days when the moon has completed half of its orbit.

**Figure 22–11.** The Bay of Fundy in Nova Scotia, Canada, has one of the most extreme variations in water height between high tide (left) and low tide (right).

The sun also produces tides. However, although the sun is much bigger than the moon, it is also much farther away. The sun's effect on tides is not as strong because the attraction the sun exerts on the earth does not change as much from place to place. As a result, solar tides are about half as high as those of the moon.

When the moon and sun are aligned, the lunar and solar tides add up, producing higher tides. These tides are called **spring tides**. The name does not refer to the spring season, but to the fact that the tides "spring up." Spring tides occur twice during a lunar month, at the full moon and at the new moon.

When the moon and sun are at 90° angles from each other as seen from the earth, only small tides develop. These small tides are called **neap tides**. These tides also occur twice a month, between spring tides. The production of spring tides and neap tides is illustrated in Figure 22–12.

The time of high and low tide at any point on Earth can be predicted. Scientists are able to make these predictions because the tides depend on the rotation of the earth, and the position of the moon in its orbit around the earth. Variations in tidal height and frequency depend on

**Figure 22–12.** Spring tides (left) occur when the gravitational forces of the sun and moon are combined. Neap tides (right) occur when the moon and sun are at right angles to the earth, pulling the water in opposite directions.

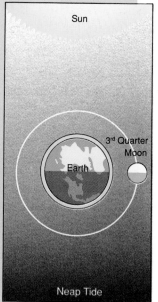

the shape of the coastline, and the latitudes and angles of the moon and sun relative to the equator. Many industries, such as fishing and shipping industries, make use of the tides to plan their routes.

Strong, dangerous tidal currents develop in narrow passages connecting sea basins. The most famous is Charybdis (kuh RIHB dihs), a tidal whirlpool that develops in the Strait of Messina between Sicily and mainland Italy.

## Section Review

1. What causes ocean water to form currents?
2. What is the difference between currents and waves?
3. Why are spring tides particularly high and neap tides particularly low?
4. THINKING CRITICALLY  Do continents have the greatest effect on currents, waves, or tides? Explain your answer.

1. Surface currents are pushed by the wind. Deep water currents are caused by differences in water density.
2. Currents are horizontal movements of water from one place to another. Waves are the periodic vertical movements of surface water.
3. Spring high tides are higher than normal because the sun and moon are pulling in the same direction. Neap tides are lower than normal because the sun and moon are pulling at a 90° angle.
4. on currents, because they block, divert, and direct the currents' movement

# CAREER

## Commercial Diver

**DESCRIPTION**  A commercial diver performs a variety of underwater jobs. Commercial divers use diving equipment ranging from shallow-water scuba gear to deep-sea diving suits. Divers may use sensitive measuring instruments, such as ultrasonic probes, or may perform arc-welding jobs under water. Divers may also use simple hand tools and power equipment to construct, install, clean, inspect, and repair various objects and structures.

**REQUIREMENTS**  A student who plans to be a commercial diver should take physics, chemistry, and mathematics courses in high school. After graduation, the student should complete a two-year course of study at a college or technical school, earning a certificate as a deep-water diver and life-support technician.

**INFORMATION**  Association of Diving Contractors, Building 7, Suite 4, 1799 Stump Boulevard, Gretna, LA 70053

# INVESTIGATION 22: Wave Action

## How can you determine the effects of waves on the shores?

### PURPOSE

To demonstrate the effects of wave action on a beach.

### MATERIALS

glass or metal flat
  cake pan
sand and gravel mixture

water
wooden block
2 blocks of wax

### PROCEDURE

1. At one end of the shallow pan, construct a beach out of the sand and gravel mixture, as shown in Figure 1. Firmly pack the mixture into place with your hands.

2. Slowly add water to the pan to a depth of 2 to 3 cm. Be careful not to disturb the beach while adding water to the pan.

3. Float the wooden block in the pan at the opposite end from the beach. Push the block forward and backward until large waves are formed. Continue making waves until about half of the beach has shown movement. Record your observations.

4. Rebuild the beach at one end of the pan. You may have to empty the water from the pan to do so. If so, refill the pan with water to a depth of 2 to 3 cm. Place the two wax blocks in the pan as shown in Figure 2. Use the wooden block to make waves in the pan. Record your observations.

### RESULTS    Answers: see page T109.

1. Describe any movement of the beach when water was first added to the pan.

2. Describe the surface of the beach before and after the wave action began.

3. Describe the composition of the beach before and after the wave action began.

4. What happened to the sand after the wave action began?

5. Describe the wave action and its effects on the beach after the wax blocks were added to the pan.

### CONCLUSIONS    Answers: see page T109.

1. What would happen to the beach in the first part of the investigation if there were no source of additional sand for the beach?

2. What would happen to the beach in the second part of the investigation if there were no source of additional sand for the beach?

### APPLICATION    Answers: see page T109.

1. Beaches along the entire east coast of the United States are being eroded at an alarming rate. Based on what you have learned from this investigation, how could this erosion be slowed down or stopped?

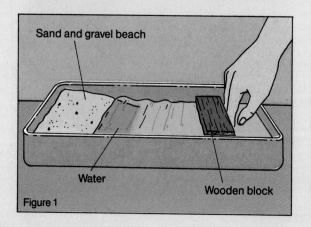

Sand and gravel beach

Water

Wooden block

Figure 1

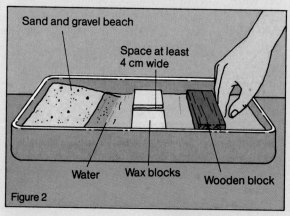

Sand and gravel beach

Space at least 4 cm wide

Water    Wax blocks    Wooden block

Figure 2

## Summary

1. Active continental margins have high, rocky coasts, while passive continental margins have low coastlines with broad beaches. **(22.1)**

2. The continental shelf is the land under water that forms a shelf along the edge of a continent. **(22.2)**

3. Deep-sea trenches trap sediment. The depth of oceans depends in part on the deep-sea trenches they contain. **(22.3)**

4. Salinity is the total amount of salts dissolved in a kilogram of sea water. **(22.4)**

5. The thermocline is a layer below the surface of the ocean through which temperature changes rapidly. **(22.4)**

6. Ocean currents are produced by wind or tides. **(22.5)**

7. A swell is a system of long waves traveling out of a storm center. **(22.6)**

8. Tides are produced by the gravitational attraction exerted on the earth by the moon and the sun. **(22.7)**

## Science Terms

On a separate sheet of paper, define each term in a sentence.

active continental margin **(457)**
continental shelf **(459)**
continental slope **(459)**
delta **(458)**
estuary **(458)**
neap tide **(470)**

ocean current **(465)**
oceanography **(459)**
passive continental margin **(457)**
rip current **(467)**
salinity **(460)**
sea wave **(467)**

spring tide **(470)**
swell **(467)**
thermocline **(463)**
tides **(469)**

## Modified True-False

On a separate sheet of paper, mark each true statement *TRUE* and each false statement *FALSE*. If false, change the underlined term to make the statement true.

1. Tsunamis are sea waves caused by earthquake motion on the sea floor. T

2. Calcium chloride is the most abundant compound in sea water. F, sodium chloride

3. Active continental margins have high, rocky coastlines with intense wave action. T

4. Surface sea ice is generally no thicker than 3 m. T

5. Deep-sea sediment composed of clay and the shells of sea creatures is called red clay. F, ooze

6. The thermocline is the layer between warm and cold water. T

7. The transport of ocean water is called a tide. F, current

8. In wave motion, the only thing that travels is the water. F, wave

9. The thickness of deep-sea sediment increases with distance from the crest of the mid-ocean ridge. T

10. Winds transport 20 percent of the heat on Earth. F, 80 percent *(continues)*

## Multiple Choice

On a separate sheet of paper, write the letter of the term that best answers the question or completes the statement.

1. Two tidal crests circle the earth in
   a. 25 hours.
   b. 23 hours, 50 minutes.
   (c.) 24 hours, 50 minutes.
   d. 24 hours.

2. Elements in sea water not found in fresh water are _____ and sodium.
   a. nitrogen
   b. oxygen
   c. hydrogen
   (d.) chlorine

3. Ocean areas where evaporation is low and the supply of fresh water is abundant have
   (a.) low salinity.
   b. average salinity.
   c. high salinity.
   d. no salinity.

4. The ocean functions as a temperature _____ for the entire globe.
   (a.) equalizer
   b. absorber
   c. releaser
   d. neutralizer

5. The freezing point of sea water is lower than that of
   a. brine.
   (b.) pure water.
   c. chlorine.
   d. mercury.

6. The layer between the warm water of the ocean surface and the colder water below is known as
   a. a delta.
   b. ooze.
   c. a tsunami.
   (d.) the thermocline.

7. The periodic motion of the sea surface is a
   a. current.
   b. tsunami.
   c. thermocline.
   (d.) wave.

8. One cause of _____ is the gravitational attraction the moon exerts on the earth.
   (a.) tides
   b. tsunamis
   c. waves
   d. currents

9. The spring tides are due to the alignment of the moon and
   a. the earth.
   (b.) the sun.
   c. Mars.
   d. Venus.

10. Neap tides occur when the moon and the sun are at _____ to each other as seen from Earth.
    a. 180°
    b. 60°
    c. 45°
    (d.) 90°

## Completion

On a separate sheet of paper, complete each statement by supplying the correct term.

1. Shorelines are also known as continental margins _____ .

2. The study of the oceans is called oceanography _____ .

3. The continental slope _____ marks where the continental shelf drops off to the ocean floor.

4. Because the Pacific Ocean has many trenches , the floor of the Pacific is deeper than those of other oceans.

5. The total amount of salts dissolved in 1 kg of sea water is known as salinity .

6. When sea water freezes, the ice contains little or no salt .

7. The movement of ocean water is called a wave .

8. The pressure of the atmosphere at sea level is one atmosphere .

9. A swell consists of waves several hundred meters in wavelength.

10. A rip tide is a current of water flowing out along a channel perpendicular to the beach.

## Writing Critically Answers: see page T109.

1. How do different continental margins affect the appearance of the shorelines?

2. Describe how the amount of sediment and the depth of the oceans are affected by deep-sea trenches.

3. CHALLENGE Compare and contrast tsunamis, swells, and rip currents.

4. CHALLENGE Describe the special characteristics of sea water and explain how these characteristics determine the effects of sea water.

## Skill Reinforcement

The Skill Activity on page 464 describes how to interpret tables. Using the table in the activity, do the following problem.

If a diver is wearing an air tank holding 85 cubic feet of air and is breathing air at a rate of 2.4 cubic feet per minute at a depth of 99 feet, how long will the air last? Justify your answer.

## Research Ideas

1. Research the effect of plate tectonics on the appearance of a coastline.

2. Many communities along the Atlantic coast have constructed sea wall barriers to protect their beaches. In some cases the sea walls themselves have been washed away. Research the effect of sea walls on the shape of a coastline. Find out how effective sea walls are.

3. CHALLENGE Reseach and graph the height of daily tides on the shores of the Pacific coast and the Atlantic coast in the United States.

4. CHALLENGE Tsunamis have demonstrated their destructive power. Fortunately, today tsunamis can be detected and coastline communities can be warned. Find out what the evacuation procedures are in your area for high water levels such as flooding, hurricanes, or even tsunamis.

## For Further Reading

Ballard, R. D. "A Long Last Look at Titanic." *National Geographic* (December 1986) 170, 697. This article describes the exploration of the *Titanic,* using deep-sea submersibles such as *Alvin.*

Gilbreath, Alice. *The Continental Shelf: An Underwater Frontier.* Minneapolis: Dillon, 1986. This book provides an overview of the geology and ecology of the continental shelf. All the species living on the shelf are discussed.

Glaser, Michael. *The Nature of the Seashore.* Fiskdale, Mass.: Knickerbocker, 1986. The field-guide covers sand, wind, waves, and animal and plant life of the seashore.

Nelson, C. H., and K. R. Johnson. "Whales and Walruses as Tillers of the Sea Floor." *Scientific American* (February, 1987) 256:112. This article describes side-scan sonar studies of the Bering Sea that resulted in some surprising discoveries.

Sibbald, Jean H. *Homes in the Sea: From the Shore to the Deep.* Minneapolis: Dillon, 1985. This text describes the different ocean habitats and how organisms adapt to these environments.

# THE DISCOVERY OF THE TITANIC

On April 15, 1912, the *S.S. Titanic* sank in the North Atlantic. More than 1500 people were killed. In 1985, testing new underwater exploration technologies, searchers set out to find the sunken ship. These new technologies, if successful, would provide scientists with new tools with which to explore the ocean's depths.

## A Sonar Search

According to records of the sinking, the *Titanic* went down about 650 kilometers off the coast of Newfoundland. The sunken luxury liner lay in darkness, under the crushing pressure of more than 4 kilometers of water. Finding the vessel under these conditions was even more difficult because the precise location was not known.

Searchers narrowed their target area to a region of about 240 square kilometers. To search the area, SAR (*Systems Acoustic Remote*) was used. SAR is a bullet-shaped vehicle that transmits sonar pulses and receives their echoes as they bounce off the ocean floor.

Towed behind the search vessel *Le Suroit*, SAR provided a sonar map of a kilometer-wide strip of ocean bottom. SAR was used to cover about 80 percent of the search zone. Searchers found nothing.

## Discovery!

The search ship *Knorr* resumed the hunt, using *Argo,* a deep-sea, remote-controlled vehicle. *Argo's* sensitive video cameras and bright strobe lights provided a continuous picture of the ocean floor. The cable that connected *Argo* with the *Knorr* transmitted images of the ocean floor from the vehicle to television monitors aboard ship.

At 1:05 A.M. on September 1, 1985, members of the *Knorr* search team were watching the television screens. It was monotonous work. Research-

A model of how *Argo* sweeps the ocean floor

ers spent hours watching the featureless ocean floor roll by as *Argo* was towed along 25 meters from the bottom of the ocean. Suddenly, the picture changed.

Watchers saw the round front panel and circular furnace doors of one of *Titanic's* huge boilers. A cheer went up. The ship had been found!

## A Closer Look

For more detailed photographic records, *ANGUS* (*A*coustically *N*avigated *G*eological *U*nderwater *S*urveyor) was attached to *Argo*. AN-GUS is an underwater sled that carries lights and a camera loaded with 400 feet of film. It can take 3200 photographs before needing reloading.

*ANGUS* provided an extraordinary record of the sunken vessel through over 20,000 photographs. These pictures showed that the ship was well preserved, although it had broken in two on its trip to the bottom.

*Alvin* ready to go to work

### Exploring the *Titanic*

In August of 1986, the searchers returned, this time to explore the liner. They brought *Alvin,* a three-passenger mini-submarine, and *Jason, Jr.,* a robot explorer about the size of a lawn mower. *Alvin* maneuvered over each section of the ship, revealing a good view of the wreck, which was covered with marine organisms and layers of rust.

*Jason Jr.,* attached by cable to *Alvin,* glided down the liner's grand staircase, taking

photographs of the interior—including a huge chandelier, still remarkably intact. The photographs would eventually be assembled into a composite showing the entire ship just as she rests on the bottom.

### A Surprise

Historians had assumed that the *Titanic* went down when the iceberg with which she collided ripped a huge gash in her hull. The search team found no such damage. The photographs taken from *Alvin* and *ANGUS* show that the ship's metal plates were only buckled. Rivets popped, and water leaked steadily into the liner, filling compartment after compartment and finally sinking the "unsinkable" luxury liner.

Decades after the event, technology undreamed of in the time of the *Titanic* has revealed the true nature of this maritime disaster.

*Alvin* approaching the *Titanic*

# UNIT 6

# The Living World

Photograph right: macaws, Bermuda

What do you, these birds, and these plants all have in common? All are living things. *Biology* is the science that deals with living things. This unit discusses the similarities and differences between all living things and the processes that occur in all living things.

478

# 23

# Living Things

The world is full of living things. People, other animals, and plants obviously fall into this category. However, there are thousands of other living things that are not so easily seen. Microscopic organisms, such as those in the photograph below, are also part of the living world. All living things are made up of cells—the building blocks of life.

For additional information, see pages T112–T113.

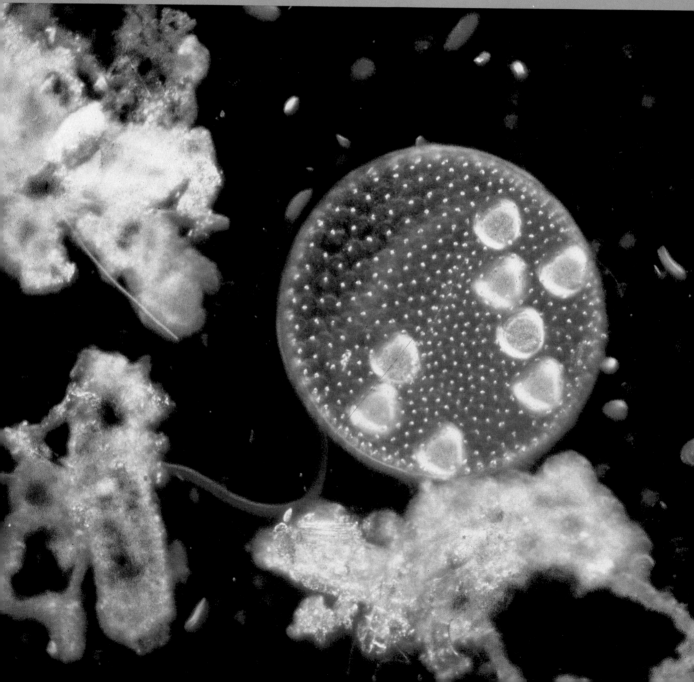

# The Building Blocks of Life

### SECTION OBJECTIVES

- **Restate** the cell theory.
- **List** the major parts of the cell and their functions.
- **Analyze** the relationship of cells, tissues, organs, and systems to one another.

Photograph left: *Volvox*, a colonial organism

NEW TERMS IN THIS SECTION

| | |
|---|---|
| cell | cell wall |
| cell theory | chlorophyll |
| organelles | epithelial tissue |
| cell membrane | connective tissue |
| nucleus | muscle tissue |
| cytoplasm | nervous tissue |

## 23.1 The Structure of Cells

In 1665, Robert Hooke, a British chemist and physicist, used a microscope to look at pieces of cork similar to those in Figure 23–1. He noticed the cork was made up of tiny chambers or boxes. He called these chambers *cells*. Today we know that the basic unit of structure and function in all living things is the **cell**. The **cell theory** states that cells are the basic units of structure and function in all living things. The theory also states that all cells come from other cells.

Living things perform many functions, such as growth and reproduction. Individual cells must also perform these functions. Therefore, it is not hard to realize how complex the cell must be. Look at Figure 23–2 to see the many parts an animal cell may have.

Scientists use different kinds of microscopes to examine the parts of a cell. A *light microscope*, such as the one you might use in school, can magnify an image several hundred times. A light microscope directs a beam of light through a specimen. However, only the larger parts of a cell can be seen with this type of microscope. An *electron microscope* uses a beam of electrons to magnify the cell 300,000 times or more. Under an electron micro-

Anton van Leeuwenhoek built the first microscope that enabled scientists to first see cells.

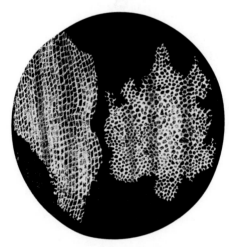

**Figure 23–1.** Robert Hooke used his microscope to look at vegetable cells, such as these cork cells, in 1665. Almost 200 years passed before scientists realized that cells were the basic units of structure in all living things.

During the 1830s, Matthias Schleiden and Theodor Schwann published separate statements explaining that all living things are made up of cells.

scope, the cell appears crowded with structures. These structures inside the cell are called **organelles**. They perform special functions in the cell.

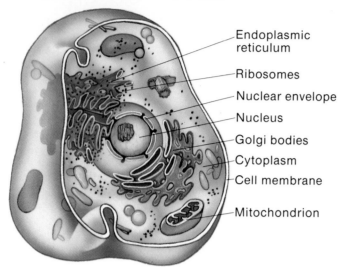

**Figure 23–2.** A typical animal cell contains many microscopic structures within its cytoplasm and nucleus. The details of most of these structures can be seen only with the aid of an electron microscope.

Endoplasmic reticulum
Ribosomes
Nuclear envelope
Nucleus
Golgi bodies
Cytoplasm
Cell membrane
Mitochondrion

### Animal Cells

Look again at the cell shown in Figure 23–2. This illustration shows a typical animal cell. Locate the cell membrane. The **cell membrane** is the flexible boundary around the cell. Somewhat like the surface of a balloon, the cell membrane can be pressed or squeezed. It controls the movement of materials into and out of the cell.

The **nucleus** (NOO klee uhs) regulates the activities in a cell. The *nuclear envelope* surrounds the nucleus. This structure is a double membrane that controls the movement of materials into and out of the nucleus.

Between the nuclear envelope and cell membrane is a region of the cell called **cytoplasm** (SYT uh plaz uhm). Under a light microscope, cytoplasm appears as a grainy fluid. Many organelles are found in the cytoplasm. The kind and number of organelles found in a cell depend on the specific function of that cell.

## *READING CRITICALLY*

If a cell were a factory, which part would be the supervisor? Explain your answer.

the nucleus, because it regulates activities in the cell

### Plant Cells

Plant cells contain all of the same basic parts as animal cells have. However, plant cells differ from animal cells in several ways. Figure 23–3 on page 484 shows that a plant cell has not only a flexible cell membrane but also a rigid cell wall outside the membrane. The **cell wall** is not a living part of the cell. The cell wall helps support the plant. It also has tiny holes that allow materials to pass into and out of the cell. The cell membrane, however, still controls the movement of materials into and out of the plant cell.

| TABLE 23–1 | PLANT AND ANIMAL ORGANELLES |
|---|---|
| Cell membrane (boundary of cell) | Allows certain substances to pass into and out of the cell |
| Nucleus (located in center of cell) | Controls the activities of the cell |
| Nuclear envelope (surrounds nucleus) | Selects which substances will pass into and out of the nucleus |
| Chromosomes (located in nucleus) | Contain the information that determines the characteristics of the individual organism |
| Cytoplasm (flows throughout cell) | Contains organelles |
| Endoplasmic reticulum (found in cytoplasm) | Forms pathways through which material moves throughout the cell |
| Mitochondria (found in cytoplasm) | Release energy from the nutrients taken in by the cell |
| Golgi bodies (found in cytoplasm) | Store and release many substances made in the cell |
| Ribosomes (found in cytoplasm) | Make proteins |
| Lysosomes (formed in Golgi bodies) | Digest proteins with powerful enzymes |
| Cell wall (surrounds cell membrane in plants) | Provides rigid support in plant cells; allows certain substances to pass from cell to cell |
| Plastids (found in cytoplasm) | Contain either pigment or stored food; found only in plant cells and cells of some algae |
| Chloroplasts (found in cytoplasm) | Store chlorophyll in plant cells |
| Vacuoles (found in cytoplasm) | Store water, food, or wastes in plant and animal cells; provide structural support in plant cells |

## ACTIVITY

**Identifying Cells**

Look again at the photograph on page 480. Determine if the organisms shown are single-celled or multicelled organisms. Compare them with Figures 23–2 and 23–3.

Explain to the students that the organism pictured on page 480 is neither single-celled or multi-celled. It is a colonial organism—a group of single-celled organisms living together for mutual benefit.

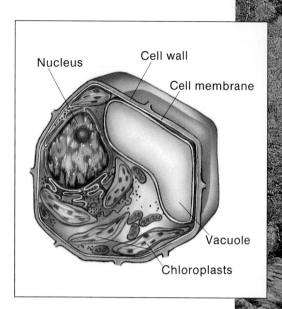

Nucleus

Cell wall

Cell membrane

Vacuole

Chloroplasts

**Figure 23–3.** The cell wall of a plant cell (left) contains cellulose, a substance that makes the cell wall rigid. The change of leaves in autumn from green to yellow, orange, or red (right) is caused by the breakdown of chlorophyll, which allows the colors of other pigments to be seen.

Other pigments found in plastids are responsible for the colors seen in flower petals or in ripened fruit.

Cell organelles known as *lysosomes*, have been nicknamed "suicide bags." Lysosomes contain a powerful digestive substance that can actually digest the rest of the cell. Although this does not generally happen, occasionally the lysosome membrane is ruptured by foreign matter. For example, asbestos inhaled by a person can rupture the lysosome and cause the entire cell to be destroyed.

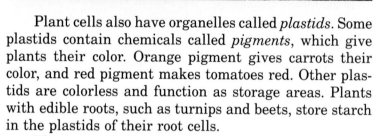

Plant cells also have organelles called *plastids*. Some plastids contain chemicals called *pigments*, which give plants their color. Orange pigment gives carrots their color, and red pigment makes tomatoes red. Other plastids are colorless and function as storage areas. Plants with edible roots, such as turnips and beets, store starch in the plastids of their root cells.

Plants may contain green, yellow, orange, or red pigments, or combinations of these. **Chlorophyll** (KLAWR uh fihl), a green pigment, is the most common pigment found in plants. Chlorophyll is contained in special plastids called *chloroplasts* (KLAWR uh plasts). Chlorophyll allows plant cells to trap energy from the sun. Plant cells use this energy to make sugar during *photosynthesis* (foh toh SIHN thuh sihs).

One or more *vacuoles* (VAK yoo wohlz) may be found in the cell. A vacuole is a fluid-filled structure surrounded by a membrane. In plant cells, the pressure of the water in the vacuole helps maintain the shape of the cell. Vacuoles are also used to store water, waste materials, or nutrients in the cell.

Remind the students of chlorophyll-containing products such as chewing gum, breath mints, and certain types of air fresheners.

## 23.2 Tissues, Organs, and Systems

The cells that make up an organism can be very different from one another, depending on the job they must do. The cells work together according to their specialties. Groups of similar cells that work together to perform a specific job are called *tissues*. Tissues rarely act alone;

they group together to form *organs*. Organs, in turn, act together to form *systems*. When grouped together, these systems make up a complete organism.

Animal tissues can be classified into four categories: epithelial, connective, muscle, and nervous. **Epithelial** (ehp uh THEE lee uhl) **tissue** covers the body or provides a lining for its parts. Examples of epithelial tissue include the outer layer of skin, the lining inside the nose and mouth, and the linings of the stomach, intestines, and breathing passages. The tissues lining the breathing passages are made up of cells with tiny hairlike projections called *cilia* (SIHL ee uh). These cilia wave back and forth to move dust and other particles out of the breathing passages.

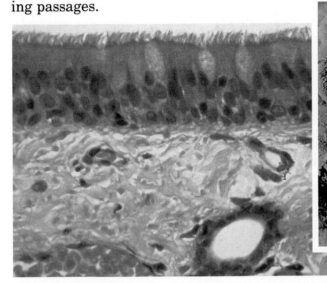

**Figure 23–4.** Epithelial cells (left) work together to form the epithelial tissue that lines many organs of the body. The cilia lining the inside of the trachea (right) can be seen magnified 8000 times in this photomicrograph.

**Connective tissue** joins, supports, or protects other types of tissues. Some examples of connective tissue are blood, bone, cartilage, ligaments, and tendons. Blood is a liquid tissue that contains red cells, white cells, platelets, and a liquid called *plasma* (PLAZ muh). Although blood is a vital tissue in an animal's body, it does not fit the pattern of other cells and tissues.

Bone, cartilage, ligaments, and tendons make up the skeleton and provide support for the body. Bones are hard because they contain the minerals calcium and phosphorus. Bones, however, are not as solid as they appear to be. Their centers contain a soft, spongelike material called *marrow*.

At birth, most of the skeleton is cartilage. As a person grows, cartilage is replaced by bone. Some cartilage remains and can be felt in places such as the outer part of the ears and at the tip of the nose. In some animals, such as sharks, the skeleton is never replaced by bone but is completely made up of cartilage.

Ligaments and tendons are special connective tissues. *Ligaments* are strong bands of tissue that hold bones together. If you have ever sprained your ankle, the pain you experienced was from the stretching and tearing of ligaments. *Tendons* are bands of tissue that connect muscle to bone at joints such as the elbow and the knee. Without tendons, movement would be impossible. The soreness felt from an injury such as "tennis elbow" is the result of straining the tendons and muscles around a joint.

**Muscle tissue** is made up of long cells that are usually grouped in bundles. Muscle cells have the ability to shorten, or contract, and then to relax. The contraction of muscle cells allows parts of the body to move. Some muscles are controlled by the individual. For example, you can decide whether or not to move your foot as you sit at your desk. If you want to ask a question, you can decide to raise your hand. Muscles you can control in this way are called *voluntary muscles*.

Muscles you cannot control are called *involuntary muscles*. These include the muscles of your digestive system. You also cannot decide when to let your heart beat. The muscles of the heart are a special kind of muscle called *cardiac muscle*. Cardiac muscle also contracts in a regular pattern, or a beat. The heart beats regularly throughout your life. <u>What might cause an interruption of the heartbeat?</u> electrical shock, chemical influence, injury, or illness

Have the students consider just how important it is that some muscles are involuntary. Have each student find the pulse in his or her wrist. Each pulse indicates a heartbeat. For a period of two minutes have the students think "beat" each time they feel the pulse in their wrists. Discuss what life would be like if they had to voluntarily control their hearts.

**Figure 23–5.** Shaped roughly like a pear, the heart (right) lies slightly to the left in the chest cavity. The human heart is an involuntary muscle that continuously pumps blood through the body. A neuron (below) consists of a cell body with a nucleus and several strands linking it to other neurons. While most cells are usually too small to be seen without a microscope, some neurons can be up to one meter long.

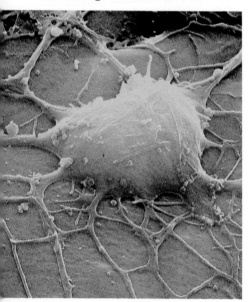

**Nervous tissue** is made up of cells that can transmit impulses. The cells that make up nervous tissue are called *neurons*. As Figure 23–5 shows, neurons are made up of a cell body and long, thin fibers. Many neurons

grouped together make up a nerve. Nervous tissue, muscle tissue, and connective tissue such as ligaments work together to allow movement in animals.

Remember, tissues work together to form organs, and organs make up systems. An example of an organ formed by tissues is *skin*. Epithelial, muscle, nervous, and connective tissues are all found in human skin. Figure 23–6 shows the various tissues in a section of skin.

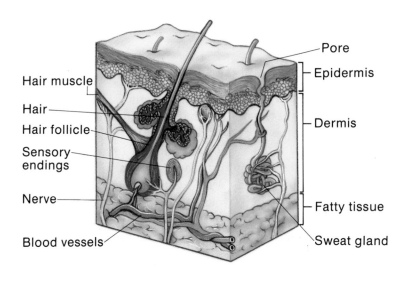

**Figure 23–6.** The skin has two main layers—the epidermis and the dermis. The skin is the body's largest organ, with an average surface area of about 1.75 square meters.

As a memory aid, remind students that since one type of plant tissue is called permanent there must be something temporary about the other type. This may help them remember that meristematic tissue is only in the forming stage.

Plants also contain tissues, organs, and systems. There are two main types of tissues in plants. *Meristematic* (mehr uh stuh MAT ihk) *tissue* is made up of cells that are just forming and have not yet been determined as parts of a root, a stem, or a leaf. *Permanent tissues* are all of the other tissues or parts of a plant. Plant tissues, like animal tissues, form organs. Roots, stems, and leaves are all plant organs. How plants function and use their tissues and organs are discussed in Chapter 26.

## Section Review

1. State the cell theory.
2. Name three cell organelles and explain their functions.
3. Describe how cells, tissues, organs, and systems are related to one another.
4. THINKING CRITICALLY Hooke was looking at cork when he saw and named cells. Cork comes from the bark of trees, but the cells are no longer living. Explain how Hooke could still see the cells, even though they were dead.

1. Cells are the basic units of structure and function of all living things. All cells come from other cells.
2. Answers may vary. Cell organelles and their functions are listed in Table 23–1 on page 483.
3. Cells are the most basic structure and are found in all others. Tissues are in all organs, organs are in all systems.
4. What Hooke actually saw was the cell wall. Since the cell wall is not living matter, it remains after the internal, living parts of the cell die and disintegrate.

# The Nature of Life

NEW TERMS IN THIS SECTION
digestion
absorption

## SECTION OBJECTIVES

- **State** three differences between living and nonliving things.
- **Relate** the functions of cells to the functions of entire organisms.
- **Explain** the cell theory as it relates to cell division.

Any movement of a plant or an animal in response to a stimulus is called a *tropism*.

Explain to the students that movement does not just mean changing position from point A to point B. Movement also refers to internal movement and metabolism.

**Figure 23–7.** Plants require light to grow. To obtain the necessary light, plants respond to the stimulus of light by moving toward the light source.

## 23.3 Functions of Cells

Living organisms perform functions that nonliving things cannot perform. The most obvious of these functions are movement, growth, and reproduction. If you set a key on a table, it will not move itself to another place. You may momentarily forget where you put it, but you know it has not moved. While you are searching for the key, you do not have to worry that it is growing and that it is going to be too big for the lock once it is found. You also know it will not reproduce and provide you with extra keys.

## SCIENCE FACT

The day and night opening and closing of flowers is due to water pressure within the plant. During the day the leaf bases are filled with water, which presses the leaves apart. At night, they collapse and the outer leaves close.

While it is easy to observe life functions, such as movement, growth, and reproduction in organisms, it is difficult to see—or even to realize—that these same functions take place in a single cell. As you think about cells performing life functions, remember that not all cells can perform all functions. That is why complex organisms, such as humans, need many different types of cells.

## 23.4 Digestion and Absorption

The process by which large, complex food particles are broken down into simple ones that an organism can use is called **digestion**. In complex animals, such as humans, digestion begins when food is *ingested*, or taken in, through the mouth. The food goes through many mechanical and chemical changes in order to make it usable. Mechanical digestion is the tearing and grinding of food into smaller pieces. Chemical changes occur when enzymes further break down these pieces into nutrient molecules used by the entire body.

One of the most important processes related to digestion is absorption. **Absorption** is the movement of nutrient molecules through a membrane. Absorption of food in humans first takes place in the blood vessels of the small intestine. The blood carries the nutrients to the cells. These nutrients are used for energy, growth, and repair. Absorption also occurs at all surfaces of the cell as material is filtered through the membrane. In a one-celled organism, the processes of ingestion, digestion, and absorption take place within that one cell.

When food reaches the point of entering individual cells, it must be in a form that allows it to pass through the cell membrane. Once in the cell, the food continues to be digested by the different organelles you read about earlier. The nutrients from the food are then used for various processes in the cell.

## 23.5 Respiration

To most people, respiration means breathing. Breathing is the act of taking in oxygen and releasing carbon dioxide. This is the *external* part of respiration. Respiration also occurs at the cellular level, as individual cells use oxygen in a process called *cellular respiration*. Cellular respiration is the process by which energy from food is made available to cells. Are breathing and respiration the same thing? Explain your answer.

*Mitochondria* (myt uh KAHN dree uh) are the organelles in which energy is released from digested food. Food particles, which have been changed to a sugar called *glucose*, are combined with oxygen in the mitochondria. This combination produces carbon dioxide, water, and energy. Some energy is released in the form of heat. Energy is also used for the other functions of the cell. Nerve cells, for example, use this energy to transmit messages. The carbon dioxide and excess water are removed as waste products.

No. Breathing is the exchange of oxygen and carbon dioxide. Respiration is the use of oxygen by a cell to produce energy.

**READING CRITICALLY**
What would happen to a plant that could no longer absorb nutrients and water?

First individual cells would die; then the whole plant would die.

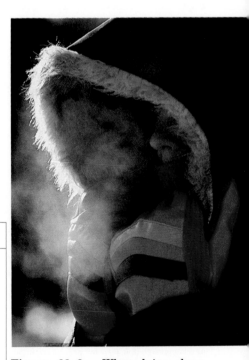

**Figure 23–8.** When lying down, your body must breath about 7.6 liters of air per minute. By sitting up, you double your air requirements to 15.2 liters per minute.

**Stimulating Growth**

Stand a large shoe box on one end. Place a small plant, such as a coleus, in the box. Do not place the lid on the box. Next, put a desk lamp or other small lamp with an uncovered bulb in front of the box, facing the plant. Turn on the light. Observe the plant several hours later. What changes do you notice? Based on your observations, why should you rotate plants toward sunlight?

plant bent toward light; rotation promotes even growth

**Figure 23–9.** The cell theory states that all cells come from other cells. Shown here are two animal cells undergoing cell division.

1. Answers may include movement, growth, reproduction, absorption, digestion, or respiration.
2. Answers may vary. Acceptable answers may include the movement of cilia, the movement of substances through membranes, cell division for reproduction or for growth, digestion of food, respiration, and gas exchange.
3. Since all cells come from other cells, cell division is the process by which this occurs.
4. the mitochondria, because they are the organelles that release energy from nutrients
5. Answers will vary but should reflect an understanding of the difficulties with support, movement, and transport of nutrients resulting from increased size.

# 23.6 Reproduction and Growth

Cells reproduce by dividing to make more cells. When a one-celled organism divides, that division results in two separate and complete organisms. Thus, reproduction has occurred. However, when cells in a multicellular organism divide, that organism simply grows in size. Reproduction in multicellular organisms is a complex process that is discussed in more detail in Chapter 24.

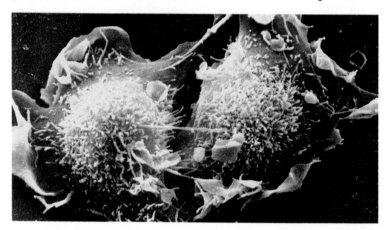

Growth, like reproduction, can occur only in living things. In most animals, cell division results in growth within certain limits. A Siamese kitten will grow to Siamese-cat size, not to the size of a tiger. An elephant will grow until it is elephant size. Many plants, however, do not appear to have such clear limits. If asked "How large is an oak tree?" you might have trouble answering. Many trees continue to increase in size throughout their lives. When an organism stops growing in size, cell division takes place mostly to repair or replace damaged or lost cells. In what parts of your body might cells be reproducing now? Many tissues if growth is still occurring; skin, nails, hair, blood

## Section Review

1. List three differences between living and nonliving things.
2. Give an example of an individual cell performing a function that is also performed by a human being.
3. How is cell division related to the cell theory?
4. Which organelle has the greatest role in cellular respiration? Explain your answer.
5. THINKING CRITICALLY  How would animals be affected if they continued to grow throughout their lives, as do many plants?

For teacher information about this Investigation, see page T113.

# SKILL ACTIVITY     Using a Branched Key

**INTRODUCTION** _____ Branched, or dichotomous, keys are helpful when you want to identify and classify organisms. A branched key is a set of general descriptions used to determine the identity of an organism.

**PROCEDURE** _____

1. Begin with step 1 of the key. Decide whether choice (a) or (b) better describes the organism you are trying to identify.

2. When you decide on the better description, go to the step of the key noted in the right-hand column following the description.

3. Continue to follow the numbered steps until the step you choose is the name of the organism you are identifying.

**APPLICATION** _____ Use the branched key below to identify these animal tracks. On a separate sheet of paper, write the name of the animal next to the corresponding letter for its tracks.

### Branched Key to Animal Tracks

| | | |
|---|---|---|
| **1a.** | Toe print separate from sole print | Go to 2 |
| **b.** | Toe print attached to sole print | Go to 4 |
| **2a.** | Toes with long claws | Skunk |
| **b.** | Toes with short claws | Go to 3 |
| **3a.** | Broad toe print | Fox |
| **b.** | Medium-sized toe print | Weasel |
| **4a.** | Edge of toes smooth | Go to 5 |
| **b.** | Edge of toes indented | Opossum |
| **5a.** | Hind toes webbed | Beaver |
| **b.** | Hind toes not webbed | Raccoon |

A. Raccoon
B. Weasel
C. Beaver
D. Opossum
E. Fox
F. Skunk

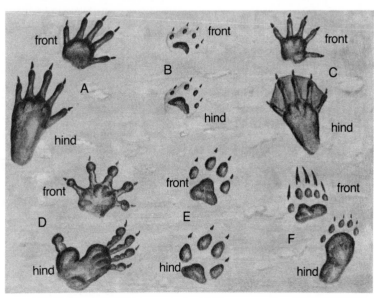

# The Diversity of Living Things

**SECTION OBJECTIVES**

● **List** the categories used in classification of living organisms.
● **Compare** the classification of several different organisms.
● **Identify** a member of each of the five kingdoms of living things.

## 23.7 A System of Classification

Imagine how long it would take to look up a word in the dictionary if the words were not in alphabetical order. That order provides a system for organizing information. Almost any time humans are confronted with large amounts of information, they rely on some system to sort the information into categories.

Classification systems are used to separate things into groups based on their similarities and differences.

**Figure 23–10.** Suppose you are handed six items and told to divide them into two groups. Should you group them by color, material, or use? Scientists who classify living things have an even more complex job.

In the earliest systems of classification, organisms were grouped simply as plants or animals. In the 1700s, a Swedish botanist named Carolus Linnaeus (lih NEE uhs) developed a system of grouping living things based on similarities in their appearance and structure. Linnaeus's work is the basis for the modern classification system scientists use today.

In the classification system used today, all living things are divided into five major categories called *kingdoms*. **Kingdoms** are the largest, most general groups in the classification system. There is a plant kingdom, an animal kingdom, and three other kingdoms, which are described later in this chapter.

Having all the animals or all the plants of the world in one group does not do much to clear up confusion. For that reason each kingdom is divided into smaller groups called **phyla** (singular, *phylum*). Phyla are still very large groups. For example, phylum Chordata includes

## ACTIVITY

**Using Classification Skills**

Make categories to classify all the clothes you own. Make up scientific names for the different articles of clothing.

animals as different as a goldfish, a sea gull, a bear, and a human. The next smaller classification group is a **class**. At this level the system begins to do a good job of sorting. For example, class Aves, which includes all birds, is part of phylum Chordata, but there are no fish, no bears, and no humans in class Aves.

The grouping after class is called an **order**. If you were examining the birds in class Aves, the various orders would sort them out still further. Owls, for example, would be in one order and turkeys in another. Other categories used in the classification system are **family**, **genus**, and **species**. To help you remember the names of the categories, think of them as a pyramid like the one in Figure 23–11. Each group has fewer members than the previous one because of fewer and fewer similarities among the organisms in the groups.

Since Latin was used by scientists throughout the world during Linnaeus's time, organisms were given Latin names. An organism's Latin name is also known as its *scientific name*. The scientific name is a combination of the genus name (with a capital letter) and the specific name (with a small letter). Because the scientific name is in Latin, it is always in italic type or underlined.

The system of using two names to name an organism is called a *binomial system*. For example, when called by its species name, the white oak tree is *Quercus alba*. The white oak is *Quercus alba* whether it is growing in Japan, France, the United States, or any other country.

## READING CRITICALLY
Which classification group contains the most members? Explain your answer.

the kingdom because it is based on very broad, general similarities

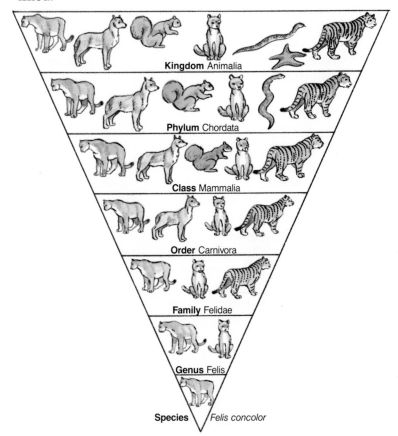

**Figure 23–11.** This upside-down pyramid shows how a category gets more specific as the number of living things in the category decreases.

A cougar, a puma, and a mountain lion are all common names for the same animal. All the different common names makes it difficult to positively identify an organism. The scientific name leaves no doubt as to the identity of a particular organism.

**Kingdom** Animalia

**Phylum** Chordata

**Class** Mammalia

**Order** Carnivora

**Family** Felidae

**Genus** Felis

**Species** *Felis concolor*

## SCIENCE FACT
Scientists estimate that there are from 5 million to 30 million species in the world. Only about 1.6 million species have been described by scientists so far.

## 23.8 The Five Kingdoms

The five kingdoms in the classification system are *Monera*, *Protista*, *Fungi*, *Plantae*, and *Animalia*. Organisms are grouped into kingdoms based on characteristics such as the types of cells they have and how they get food.

### Kingdom Monera

Kingdom Monera contains simple one-celled organisms such as bacteria and blue-green bacteria. The blue-green bacteria are sometimes called the blue-green algae. The cells of monerans can be easily classified because they lack most organelles. They do not have a true nucleus, so the nuclear material is not surrounded by a nuclear envelope.

Bacteria are usually thought of as dangerous or harmful. Some bacteria are responsible for diseases such as diphtheria, typhoid, tuberculosis, and pneumonia. Most bacteria, however, are useful. Bacteria are used extensively in the food industry, especially in the making of cheeses. Other industries that rely on helpful bacteria are farming, leather treatment, rope making, and the production of medicines.

Blue-green bacteria get their name from the chlorophyll and other pigments they contain. Most blue-green bacteria are one-celled organisms. However, some blue-green bacteria cells have specialized functions. Scientists consider these blue-green bacteria to be a simple type of multicellular organism. They are often found growing on damp flowerpots, on rocks, and on the surface of ponds. One specialized function carried out by some blue-green bacteria is *nitrogen fixation*. Nitrogen fixation is a process in which bacteria take nitrogen from the air and make it into nitrogen compounds. In Southeast Asia, nitrogen fixation by blue-green bacteria in rice paddies enables farmers to grow rice on the same land year after year without adding fertilizer.

The students may be interested and amused to know that blue-green bacteria can also be red, purple, or several other colors. The colors are determined by the kind and amount of pigment present.

**Figure 23–12.** Bacteria (below) are monerans. *Anabaena* (bottom left) and *Oscillatoria* (bottom right) are moneras known as blue-green bacteria. Blue-green bacteria carry out nitrogen fixation, a process by which nitrogen from the air is made into nitrogen compounds.

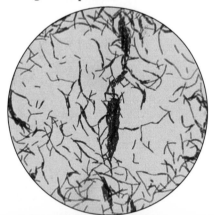

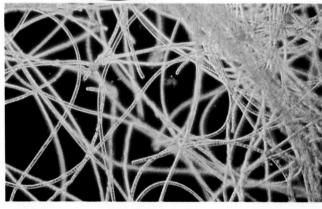

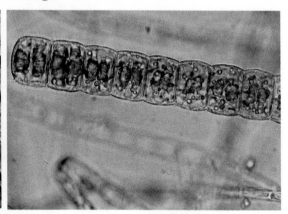

## Kingdom Protista

Like Monera, kingdom Protista consists mostly of single-celled organisms. However, all protists, as well as all other living things in the higher kingdoms, have cells that have a true nucleus and organelles. Protists are divided into two main types—*protozoa* (proht uh ZOH uh) and *algae*.

## READING CRITICALLY

Why are blue-green bacteria not classified as protists?

because their cells lack a true nucleus and most organelles

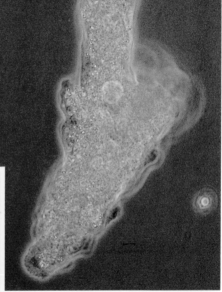

**Figure 23–13.** The *Euplotes* and *Dileptus* (top left) and *Paramecium* (bottom left) and the amoeba (top) are all protists. The paramecium has just ingested stained yeast, which can be seen inside the organism.

The **protozoa** (singular, *protozoan*) are the largest group of protists. The word *protozoa* means "first animal." Protozoa are like animals because they cannot make their own food. Most move from place to place to find food. Some protozoa, such as the paramecium (par uh MEE cee uhm), use cilia to move and to capture prey. The amoeba (uh MEE buh) uses extensions of the cell membrane to surround and engulf its food. Most protozoa are found in pond water and are easy to observe under a microscope.

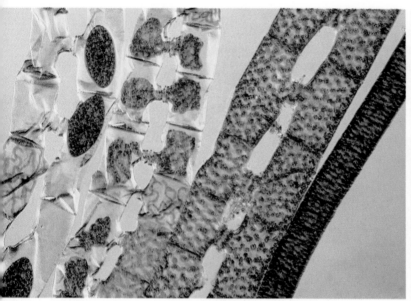

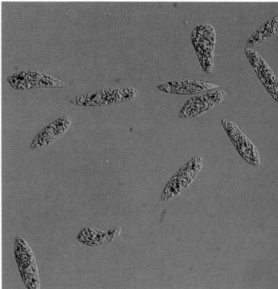

**Figure 23–14.** The *Spirogyra* (left) and *Euglena* (right) are examples of protists.

The algae extract, known as agar, is a thickener and stabilizer.

Remind students that wild mushrooms may be extremely poisonous and deadly. Caution should be exercised when considering eating any plant product found growing in the wild.

**Figure 23–15.** Mushrooms are an example of fungi that are found in damp, wooded areas.

**Algae** are protists that contain chlorophyll and therefore can make their own food. Algae (singular, *alga*) are found in both fresh water and salt water. "Pond scum" is green algae. "Seaweed" is red or brown algae. Although most seaweeds grow in salt water, a few grow in fresh water. Red algae have some unusual uses in the food industry. Extracts of red algae are used in ice creams, icings, and marshmallows.

The *Euglena* (yoo GLEE nuh) is an example of a protist that has chlorophyll but can also take in food from its environment. The *Euglena* lives in water. If it is in sunlight, the *Euglena* uses its ability to make food. When it moves to darker waters, it takes in food from the environment.

## Kingdom Fungi

Kingdom Fungi includes many organisms you may recognize. Mushrooms, molds, and even the yeast that helps bread dough rise are all fungi. Fungi have no chlorophyll, so they must take in food from other sources. The black, fuzzy mold on bread is an example of a fungus that has found a nourishing place to grow and develop. Bread mold gets its food directly from the bread, digesting it with enzymes found in its hairy, rootlike structures. Why do fungi not need light to grow?

Although some fungi are responsible for skin diseases such as ringworm and athlete's foot, others help fight disease. The antibiotic *penicillin* is made from a fungus. Alexander Fleming, a British scientist, discovered penicillin in 1928 when he observed that a fungus called *Penicillium* was able to destroy certain bacteria.

Fungi do not need light because they contain no chlorophyll; they absorb nutrients from whatever they grow on

## Kingdom Plantae

Kingdom Plantae may be more familiar to you than the first three kingdoms. Trees, grasses, shrubs, mosses, and ferns are members of the plant kingdom, as shown in Figure 23–16.

**Figure 23–16.** Since the first appearance of plant life on Earth, millions of plant species have populated the planet. Most of these are now extinct. Today, about 350,000 species of plants are known including moss (top left), ferns (bottom left), and giant sequoias (right).

Mosses are simple plants that grow in damp places. They do not have roots, stems, or leaves like more advanced plants. Mosses make up the thick ground covering of a forest or a marsh and can also be seen growing on rocks and trees.

Ferns are more advanced plants. Although they do not make seeds, they do have true roots, stems, and leaves. Seed plants are the most advanced in the plant kingdom. Seed plants include pine trees, oak trees, fruit and vegetable plants, wildflowers, grasses, and many others. The types and functions of plants are discussed more fully in Chapter 26.

Starting at top left and moving clockwise: red breast sunfish, octopus, humans, flamingos, coral snake, giant coral and sea fans, earthworm, St. Andrew's spider (male and female), African red starfish, tapeworm

**Figure 23–17.** The animal kingdom contains an enormous variety of living things. Humans are only one of hundreds of thousands of species belonging to the animal kingdom.

## Kingdom Animalia

There are over one million different species of animals in the Kingdom Animalia. They range from sponges—which at first glance hardly seem like animals at all—to humans. Figure 23–17 shows the wide diversity of this kingdom.

Animals can be roughly grouped into those that have a backbone and those that do not. Animals with a backbone are called *vertebrates*. Animals without a backbone are called *invertebrates*. Animals are discussed in much more detail in Chapter 26.

## Section Review

1. What are the seven categories scientists use in classifying organisms?
2. Which of the seven categories of classification has the fewest members? Why?
3. What are the five kingdoms in the classification system?
4. THINKING CRITICALLY  Which of the five kingdoms is the most primitive? Explain your answer.

### ACTIVITY

**Making a Classification Table**

Using the information on each of the kingdoms in this section, make a table showing the characteristics of each kingdom. Include in your table examples of members of each kingdom.

1. kingdom, phylum, class, order, family, genus, and species
2. The fewest members are found in species. The species is the most specific category of classification. Different species within the same genus have different characteristics.
3. Monera, Protista, Fungi, Plantae, Animalia
4. Monerans are the most primitive; they have no organelles and lack a true nucleus.

## CAREER

# Treatment Plant Operator

**DESCRIPTION**  Water treatment plants prepare water pumped from rivers and streams for use in homes and businesses. Sewage treatment plants purify waste materials. Operators monitor gauges and adjust controls to make sure that various processes are carried out correctly. Most treatment plant operators work for local governments.

**REQUIREMENTS**  If you plan to become a treatment plant operator, you should take shop courses to learn to work with many kinds of tools and machinery. Biology and mathematics courses would also be helpful. After graduation from high school, an operator trainee may learn on the job or may be required to take special training courses. Most states require operators to pass a certifying examination.

**INFORMATION**  National Environmental Training Association, 158 South Napoleon Street, P.O. Box 346, Valparaiso, IN 46383

# INVESTIGATION 23: Plant and Animal Cells

*How can you tell the difference between a plant cell and an animal cell?*

## PURPOSE

To identify plant cells and animal cells viewed under a microscope

## MATERIALS

compound microscope
prepared slides (1 labeled "Plant," 1 labeled "Animal")
4 prepared slides (unlabeled) numbered 3, 4, 5, 6
1 set colored pencils
1 compass (or any other object that will make a circle)

## PROCEDURE

1. Copy Table 1 onto a sheet of paper.

2. Draw six circles on the same sheet of paper. Label circle 1 "Plant." Label circle 2 "Animal." Circles 3 through 6 should be numbered only.

3. Place the prepared plant slide under the microscope. Study the slide carefully. Draw exactly what you see in circle 1.

4. Place the prepared animal slide under the microscope. Study the slide carefully. Draw exactly what you see in circle 2.

5. Obtain four numbered slides (3, 4, 5, 6) from your teacher.

6. Place each numbered slide under the microscope. Study each slide carefully. Draw exactly what you see in the appropriate circle.

## RESULTS

Compare your drawings in circles 3, 4, 5, and 6 with the plant and animal drawings in circles 1 and 2 and with Figures 1 and 2 on this page. Determine which drawings represent plant cells and which represent animal cells. Place a check mark in the appropriate box in Table 1.

## CONCLUSIONS

1. Name two characteristics of plant cells that helped you determine which slides belong in the plant category. cell wall, vacuoles

2. Name two characteristics of animal cells that helped you determine which slides belong in the animal category. no cell wall, no plastids

3. Name three characteristics shared by both plant cells and animal cells. nucleus, cytoplasm, organelles, cell membrane

| TABLE 1 | PLANT AND ANIMAL CELLS | |
| --- | --- | --- |
| **Slide** | **Plant** | **Animal** |
| 3 | Answers will vary with | teacher's selection. |
| 4 | | |
| 5 | | |
| 6 | | |

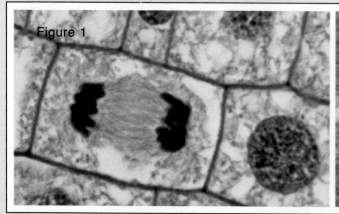

Figure 1

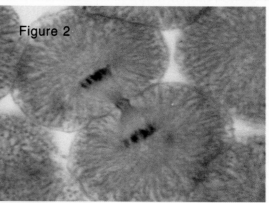

Figure 2

# CHAPTER 23 REVIEW

## Summary

1. Cells are the basic units of structure and function in all living things. **(23.1, 23.6)**

2. Cells contain organelles that perform many functions. **(23.1)**

3. Plant cells differ from animal cells because plant cells have a cell wall and contain chlorophyll. **(23.1)**

4. An organism may have one or many cells. Multicelled organisms are organized into tissues, organs, and systems. **(23.2)**

5. Movement, growth, and reproduction are functions of living things. **(23.3)**

6. Digestion is the breaking down of complex food particles into usable form. **(23.4)**

7. Cellular respiration occurs in the mitochondria and releases energy for the cell. **(23.5)**

8. Single-celled organisms reproduce in order to form new organisms. Cells in a multicellular organism reproduce to repair or replace damaged or lost cells. **(23.6)**

9. Living things are classified into seven groups: kingdom, phylum, class, order, family, genus, and species. **(23.7)**

10. Members of kingdom Monera lack most organelles and a true nucleus. Bacteria and blue-green algae are examples of monerans. **(23.8)**

11. Protists have true nuclei and organelles. Most are single-celled and are often found in pond water. Protozoa and algae are protists. **(23.8)**

12. Fungi have no chlorophyll and must take in food from other sources. **(23.8)**

13. Animals with backbones are called vertebrates. Animals without backbones are called invertebrates. **(23.8)**

## Science Terms

On a separate sheet of paper, define each term in a sentence.

absorption **(489)**
algae **(496)**
cell **(481)**
cell membrane **(482)**
cell theory **(481)**
cell wall **(482)**

chlorophyll **(484)**
class **(493)**
connective tissue **(485)**
cytoplasm **(482)**
digestion **(489)**
epithelial tissue **(485)**

family **(493)**
genus **(493)**
kingdom **(492)**
muscle tissue **(486)**
nervous tissue **(486)**
nucleus **(482)**

order **(493)**
organelles **(482)**
phyla **(492)**
protozoa **(495)**
species **(493)**

## Modified True-False

On a separate sheet of paper, mark each true statement *TRUE* and each false statement *FALSE*. If false, change the underlined term to make the statement true.

1. Robert Hooke was the first scientist to use the term <u>cells</u>. T

2. <u>Organelles</u> are small structures inside cells. T

3. The <u>nuclear envelope</u> is the center of activity in the cell. F, nucleus

4. Plants use <u>chlorophyll</u> to make their food. T

5. The outer layer of human skin is made up of <u>epithelial</u> cells. T

6. Neurons are part of <u>connective</u> tissue. F, nervous

7. All living cells come from other living cells. T

8. Paramecia are members of the <u>protist</u> kingdom. T

9. Members of Kingdom <u>Fungi</u> have no nuclear envelope. F, Monera

10. <u>Phylum</u> is the largest of the classification categories. F, Kingdom

*(continues)*

# CHAPTER REVIEW

## Multiple Choice

On a separate sheet of paper, write the letter of the term that best answers the question or completes the statement.

1. Blood is an example of
   a. connective tissue.
   b. muscle tissue.
   c. nervous tissue.
   d. epithelial tissue.

2. Which organelles are found in animal cells?
   a. mitochondria
   b. ribosomes
   c. lysosomes
   d. all of the above

3. Chlorophyll is used in
   a. digestion.
   b. respiration.
   c. absorbtion.
   d. photosynthesis.

4. Human skin is an example of
   a. a tissue.
   b. an organelle.
   c. an organ.
   d. an organism.

5. A process by which complex food particles are broken down into simpler substances is
   a. absorption.
   b. respiration.
   c. digestion.
   d. movement.

6. Bread mold is a member of which kingdom?
   a. Monera
   b. Protista
   c. Fungi
   d. Plantae

7. *Euglena* is an example of
   a. a moneran.
   b. a protist.
   c. a protozoan.
   d. a plant.

8. Plant tissue that has just formed and has not been determined is called
   a. epithelial.
   b. permanent.
   c. meristematic.
   d. connective.

9. The movement of nutrient molecules through a membrane is called
   a. digestion.
   b. absorption.
   c. respiration.
   d. movement

10. Blue-green bacteria are members of the Kingdom
    a. Animalia.
    b. Fungi.
    c. Fungi.
    d. Monera.

11. Bands of tissue that connect muscle to bone are called
    a. skin.
    b. neurons.
    c. ligaments.
    d. tendons.

12. Nitrogen-fixation is a function carried out by
    a. *Euglena*.
    b. blue-green algae.
    c. *Spirogyra*.
    d. fungi.

## Completion

On a separate sheet of paper, complete each statement by supplying the correct term.

1. The <u>cell membrane</u> provides a flexible boundary around the cell.

2. The organelles in which energy is released from digested food are the <u>mitochondria</u>.

3. Plastids known as <u>chloroplasts</u> contain chlorophyll.

4. Tissues are groups of <u>cells</u> acting together.

5. Tiny hairlike projections found on some cells are called <u>cilia</u> .

6. The muscles of the digestive system are <u>involuntary</u> muscles.

7. A fluid-filled structure within a cell surrounded by a membrane is a <u>vacuole</u> .

8. Cell division results in either the reproduction or the <u>growth</u> of an organism.

9. The two gases exchanged during respiration are <u>oxygen</u> and carbon dioxide.

10. Bacteria are members of the Kingdom <u>Monera</u> .

## Writing Critically

1. Explain why a classification system of living things is necessary. Include as much evidence as you can to support your reasons.

2. You and a friend have found a strange organism you cannot identify. Explain how a microscope would help you determine if the organism is a plant or an animal.

1. provides for easy identification; some organisms have many different common names— cougar, bobcat, panther for example; some organisms have similar appearances—fish and sea mammals such as porpoises

3. **CHALLENGE** Not every cell in your body continues to grow throughout your life. However, your body continues to produce cells throughout your life. Why doesn't your body continue growing?

2. If it is a plant, cell walls will be visible.
3. New cells are used to replace old or injured cells. Each organism, especially an animal, seems to have a built-in growth limit.

## Skill Reinforcement

The Skill Activity on page 491 describes how to use a branched key to classify organisms. Collect 10 different leaves. Make a branched key to record the general characteristics you observe in each leaf. In the right-hand column, indicate which step should follow each description. Add the names of the leaves where appropriate. Use a reference book to help you identify those leaves you do not already know. Then give the leaves and your key to a classmate to use. What other things could you classify using a branched key?

## Research Ideas

1. Find out who won the Nobel Prize in Biology, Biochemistry, and Zoology for the last three years. Explain each winner's area of work and how each scientist's research contributed to that particular area.

2. Investigate the process by which bacteria and molds are used in the production of medicines. Write a report on some of these medicines. Include in your report the name of the diseases or illnesses for which the medicines are used.

3. **CHALLENGE** Leading biologists predict that a large percentage of living species will disappear before they are even discovered. The tropical rain forests, where a great variety of organisms live, are being destroyed. Look into this problem and discuss what scientists are doing to try to solve it. Why is the discovery and classification of new species important?

## For Further Reading

Conniff, R. "The Name Game." *Science 82* (June 1982):66–67. This entertaining article offers interesting explanations of why some newly discovered organisms were given their particular genus and species names.

Hoagland, Mahlon B. *The Roots of Life.* New York: Discus Books, 1979. This book describes the structure and behavior of cells such as why some cells "decide" to become brain cells while others become skin cells or nerve cells.

O'Tode, Christopher, ed. *The Encyclopedia of Insects.* New York: Facts on File, 1986. Just look up "bugs," and you will soon find yourself reading about book lice, scorpion flies, wolf spiders, and other fascinating insects.

Patent, Dorothy Hinshaw. *Bacteria: How They Affect Other Living Things.* New York: Holiday House, 1980. Life would be impossible without bacteria. The function of bacteria in the life cycles of plants and animals, as well as bacteria as a food source, is explained.

# 24 Continuity of Life

All living organisms depend on the previous generation to receive life. Parents pass characteristics on to their children. With today's technology, scientists are able to alter and create certain organisms. The photograph below shows a computer-generated model of an enzyme that was created by scientists in a laboratory.

For additional information, see pages T114–T115.

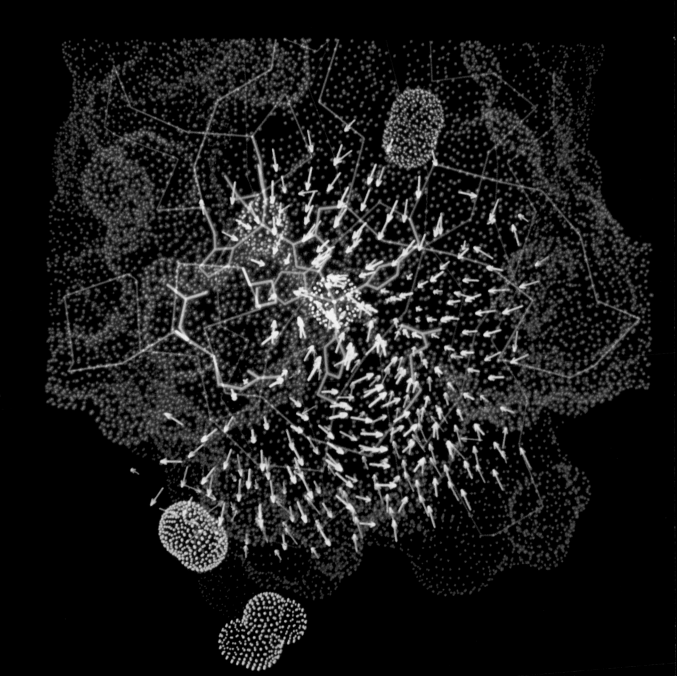

# Cell Reproduction

## SECTION OBJECTIVES

- **Explain** the need for continuous cell production.
- **Describe** the stages of mitosis.
- **Distinguish** between body cells and gametes.
- **Differentiate** between mitosis and meiosis.

Photograph left: genetically engineered enzyme; may be used to heal damage from heart attacks

## 24.1 Simple Cell Division

At birth, the human body contains several billion cells. By the time a person becomes an adult, the human body is made up of over 10 trillion cells. Where do all these cells come from? Do you still have the same cells you had when you were born?

All living cells come from other living cells. The body of an adult human produces about 2 trillion additional cells every day. That is about 25 million new cells per second. These new cells replace old, worn-out, or damaged cells.

All organisms produce new cells continuously. The method by which organisms produce new cells depends on how complex the organism is. Bacteria and blue-green bacteria, for example, are simple organisms. They, and other members of Kingdom Monera, produce new cells by a simple process called *binary fission*. **Binary fission** is a method of cell division in which the original cell splits into two cells. The two new cells that are formed are called *daughter cells*. Binary fission is therefore a form of reproduction for single-celled organisms.

The genetic material that guides the monerans' development and contains the blueprint of their simple

NEW TERMS IN THIS SECTION

binary fission
chromosome
replication
mitosis
gamete
meiosis
sexual reproduction

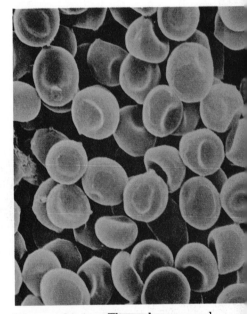

**Figure 24–1.** These human red blood cells have been magnified 3000 times using scanning electron microscopy. Red blood cells live only about four months before they are destroyed by the body and replaced. New red blood cells are produced at a rate of over 100 million per hour.

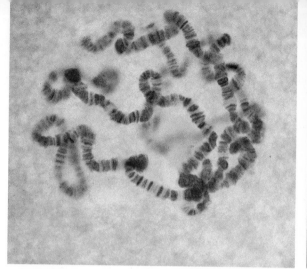

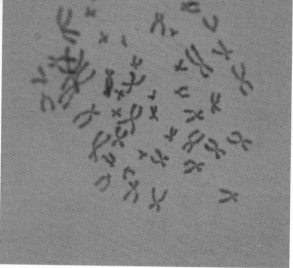

**Figure 24–2.** The chromosomes of each organism are different. The chromosomes on the left are from the salivary glands of a fruitfly. The chromosomes on the right are from a human female.

Eucaryotes, or cells with a true nucleus, have rod-shaped chromosomes. Procaryotes, cells without a true nucleus, have a single chromosome that forms a loop.

Replication ensures that each daughter cell receives a copy of the genetic material because replication is the process by which the genetic material is duplicated.

traits is located on a single chromosome (KROH muh sohm). **Chromosomes** carry the hereditary information from one generation of cells to the next. In organisms other than monerans, chromosomes are usually rod shaped.

Before binary fission takes place, the single chromosome must be duplicated. The duplication of genetic material before cell division is called **replication** (rehp luh KAY shuhn). How does replication ensure that each daughter cell receives a copy of the genetic material?

After the original chromosome replicates, the two chromosomes move to opposite ends of the cell. The cell then begins to pinch together in the middle, forming two new cells. Each daughter cell is a complete, independent organism. Figure 24–3 illustrates the process of binary fission in bacteria. Bacteria can reproduce in this manner about once every 20 minutes. Over 16 million bacteria can be produced from one cell in just eight hours.

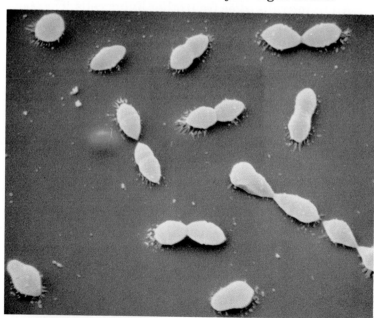

**Figure 24–3.** This photomicrograph shows the bacteria *Streptococcus pneumoniae* undergoing binary fission. These cells have been magnified 8800 times.

# 24.2 Mitosis

Cell division in multicellular organisms is more complex because plant and animal cells have more parts and more chromosomes than monerans. Where monerans have only a single chromosome and no true nucleus, cells of plants and animals may have several pairs of chromosomes, as well as other material, in the nucleus. Before plant and animal cells divide, all the chromosomes within the nucleus must be replicated. The nucleus then divides through a process called *mitosis* (my TOH sihs). **Mitosis** is a process that results in the formation of two daughter cells that are exact copies of the original cell.

Living organisms, including humans, have only two main types of cells. The first type of cells are body cells, which make up the body of the organism. Body cells include blood cells, nerve cells, and leaf cells. The second type of cells are involved only in reproduction. A cell involved only in reproduction is called a **gamete** (GAM eet). In a female, the gamete is an *egg cell*. In a male, the gamete is a *sperm cell*. The process of mitosis takes place only in the body cells, not in the gametes. Mitosis results in the growth and repair of a plant or an animal, but not in the reproduction of a new individual.

Before mitosis begins, a cell is in interphase. During this time, the cell prepares itself for mitosis. The chromosomes are replicated. Special structures are necessary for mitosis to occur. These structures are produced during interphase. The four phases of mitosis are (1) *prophase*, (2) *metaphase*, (3) *anaphase*, and (4) *telophase*. Figure 24–4 shows these four phases.

**Figure 24–4.** This series of photographs shows the process of mitosis in a whitefish. Mitosis creates two cells that have the same number of chromosomes as the original cell. Shown here left to right are (top) interphase, prophase, metaphase and (bottom) anaphase, telophase, and the resulting daughter cells. Although interphase and the creation of daughter cells are not true phases of mitosis, they are necessary for cell division.

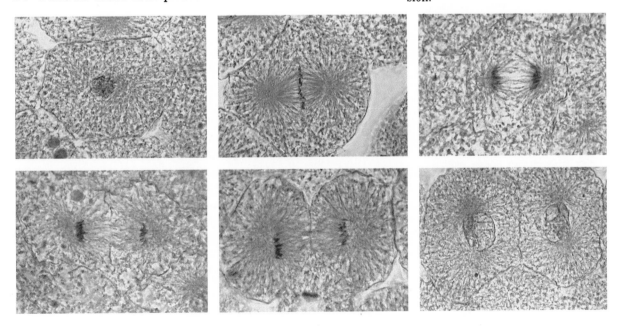

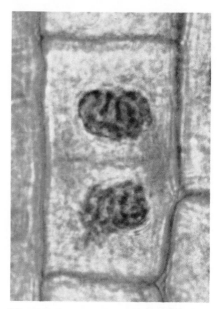

**Figure 24–5.** In plants, the cell walls do not break during mitosis. This photograph shows telophase in an onion root tip. The cell plate is forming between the two new daughter cells. The cell plate will form the new cell wall.

In meiosis the cell actually goes through two divisions—meiosis I and meiosis II. Chromatid formation, spindle formation, and separation of chromosomes are similar to that in mitosis. The phases of meiosis are similarly named—that is, prophase I, prophase II, and so on.

At the beginning of prophase, the chromosomes resemble long, twisted threads. As prophase continues, the chromosomes become shorter and thicker. The nuclear envelope disappears completely. During metaphase the doubled chromosomes cluster at the center of the cell.

During anaphase, the doubled chromosomes split into two separate chromosomes and move to opposite ends of the cell. Half of the chromosomes travel to one end, and the other half move to the other end. The cytoplasm of the cell also starts to divide. The final phase, or telophase, begins when a new nuclear envelope forms around each of the two sets of chromosomes. The chromosomes return to their original threadlike appearance. The cytoplasm continues to divide until the two new daughter cells are completely formed.

It is important to notice that the chromosomes first replicate and then separate. As a result, each daughter cell receives an exact copy of each chromosome that was present in the original cell. In animal cells, the cell membrane pinches together completely, forming two separate cells. Each daughter cell is an exact copy of the original cell. In plant cells, the cell wall is too stiff to be pinched in half. Instead, plant cells form a *cell plate* in the middle of the cytoplasm. The cell plate will form a new cell wall between the daughter cells.

Anticipate some confusion with the words *mitosis* and *meiosis*. It will be helpful to put both words on the chalkboard and draw attention to the two-letter difference in the words. Have the class pronounce the two words several times.

## 24.3 Meiosis

Another type of cell division is called *meiosis* (my OH sihs). **Meiosis** is a type of cell division that takes place only in reproductive cells. The purpose of meiosis is to produce gametes.

Human reproduction, as well as reproduction in most other animals and in plants, begins with meiosis. Reproduction in these organisms is sexual reproduction. **Sexual reproduction** is the process by which two gametes fuse, or join together, to produce one cell that develops into a new individual. If gametes had the same number of chromosomes as body cells have, the united egg and sperm and the new individual that results would have twice the number of chromosomes. Clearly, something has to happen to control the chromosome number if sexual reproduction is to occur.

This problem is solved by meiosis. Before meiosis begins, the chromosomes within the cell replicate, just as they do before mitosis. Meiosis involves two divisions. Meiosis results in four daughter cells instead of two, as in mitosis. In the male, the resulting cells become sperm

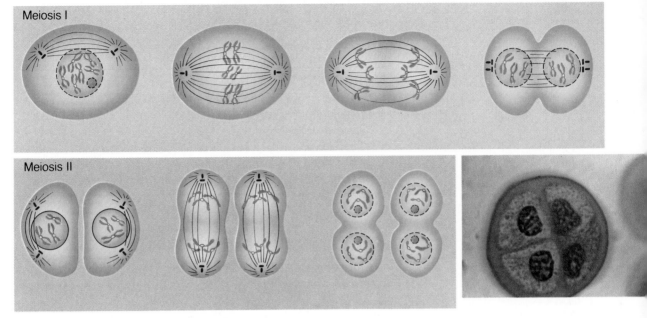

Meiosis I

Meiosis II

cells. In the female, one daughter cell becomes an egg cell while the other three die. Each egg cell or sperm cell contains only half the number of chromosomes as the original cell. All chromosome pairs are separated in meiosis. Gametes, then, contain only one half of the paired chromosomes needed to successfully produce a new individual. In a human, this means that each gamete has only 23 chromosomes, or only half the normal number of a human cell.

Egg and sperm cells must fuse, or unite, to reestablish the chromosome pairs and the normal chromosome numbers. The union of sperm and egg cell is called *fertilization*. Since both the egg cell and the sperm cell have 23 chromosomes, the new cell formed when the gametes fuse will have a total of 46 chromosomes—exactly the right number for a human. It is from this single fertilized egg that each human develops.

**Figure 24–6.** The process of meiosis (left) involves two divisions. The photograph on the right shows the four cells that result from the second division. Each of these cells has half the number of chromosomes present in the original cell.

because they do not reproduce sexually

## READING CRITICALLY
Why do single-celled organisms not undergo meiosis?

1. Cells must be continuously reproduced to replace old and worn-out cells that die and to maintain the organism.
2. binary fission; the hereditary material replicates, and the cell pinches in the middle and splits into two new cells
3. prophase: chromosomes shorten and thicken and the nuclear envelope disappears; metaphase: chromosomes cluster at the center of the cell; anaphase: doubled chromosomes separate and move to opposite ends of cell, cell begins to divide; telophase: the new nuclear envelope forms around chromosomes and daughter cells divide
4. Meiosis produces four new cells, each with half the normal number of chromosomes. Mitosis produces two new cells, each with the same number of chromosomes as the parent cell.
5. to reduce the number of chromosomes in the gametes to one half the normal number so that after fertilization the normal number of chromosomes will be restored

## Section Review

1. Why is it important for organisms to continuously produce cells?
2. Name and describe the process by which bacteria divide.
3. Name and describe the four stages of mitosis.
4. What are the major differences between the processes of mitosis and meiosis?
5. THINKING CRITICALLY Why must there be two cell divisions in meiosis?

# Genetics

NEW TERMS IN THIS SECTION

gene phenotype
dominant pure
recessive hybrid
genotype DNA

**SECTION OBJECTIVES**

- **Describe** genes and how they affect traits.
- **Distinguish** between the genotype and phenotype of individuals.
- **Construct** and **interpret** Punnett squares to demonstrate genetic principles.
- **Describe** the structure of DNA and **list** its components.

## 24.4 Genetic Principles

A monastery garden of the 1800s probably does not sound like an exciting frontier of science. Fortunately, however, Gregor Mendel realized that the best subjects for an experiment were those with which he was already familiar. Mendel, an Austrian monk who lived from 1822 to 1884, enjoyed gardening. He was especially interested in pea plants.

Mendel observed the pea plants over several generations, long enough to recognize that they had definite characteristics. The plants were always short or tall—never of medium height. Their seeds were either yellow or green and were either wrinkled or smooth. In all, Mendel selected seven distinct and contrasting characteristics in the pea plants to study. These characteristics are summarized in Figure 24–7.

Mendel identified other characteristics, but only these seven are discussed in most writings.

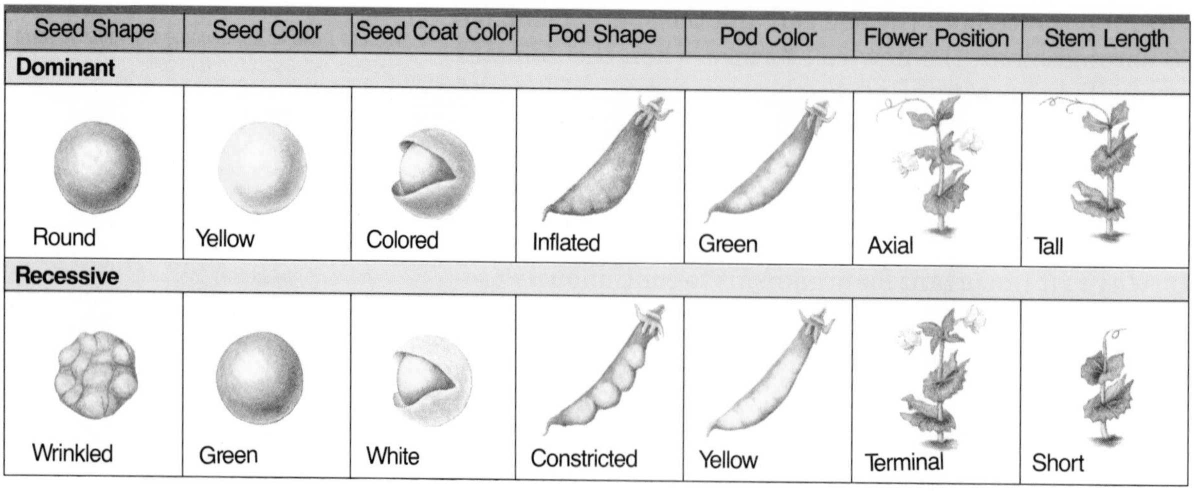
Seed Shape
Seed Color
Seed Coat Color
Pod Shape
Pod Color
Flower Position
Stem Length
Dominant
Round
Yellow
Colored
Inflated
Green
Axial
Tall
Recessive
Wrinkled
Green
White
Constricted
Yellow
Terminal
Short

**Figure 24–7.** When studying the pea plant, Mendel chose to study these seven contrasting pairs of traits.

Mendel was curious about what would happen to those characteristics if he transferred pollen from a tall plant to the flower of a short plant. To find out, Mendel did just that. Mendel, a mathematician by training, kept careful records of his procedures as he cross-pollinated a short plant and a tall plant. He gathered the seeds that were produced and planted them. Mendel repeated his experiments many times. He eventually raised seven generations of pea plants. Mendel's experiment is summarized in Figure 24–8.

For more information about plant reproduction, refer to chapter 26. The specific parts of the stamen and pistil are illustrated in that chapter.

| P | tall | short | F₁ | all tall | F₂ | 3/4 tall | 1/4 short |

Mendel believed that each of the characteristics, or *traits*, that he had observed in the pea plants was caused by two factors. For example, the trait of height was caused by a factor for tallness and a factor for shortness. Seed color was caused by a factor for green and a factor for yellow. You may realize by now that what Mendel called factors are what scientists now call *genes*. **Genes** carry traits that are passed on from one generation to the next. Genes are located on the chromosomes that replicate and separate during mitosis and meiosis.

Genes are always paired except in gametes. Each trait, then, is determined by the two genes in the gene pair. These genes may be dominant or recessive. A gene that shows its trait in the organism and hides, or masks, the trait of the other gene of the pair called **dominant**. A **recessive** gene has its trait hidden by the dominant gene. The recessive trait only shows itself if both genes of the gene pair are recessive.

Mendel realized that in pea plants, tallness is the dominant gene and shortness is the recessive gene. Since each trait is determined by two genes, he reasoned that any short plant had to have two recessive genes. If the short plant had even one dominant gene, it would be tall and the trait of shortness would be hidden.

**Figure 24–8.** When Mendel crossed the pea plants to observe contrasting traits, one trait in each pair disappeared in the first generation but reappeared in the second. *P* stands for *parent* while *F* stands for *filial*, which means the "generation following the parents."

The idea of dominant and recessive genes is called the *Principle of Dominance*.

# 24.5 Chromosomes and Genes

Today, scientists who study the effects of inherited traits use capital letters to refer to dominant genes and lowercase letters to refer to recessive ones. The letter used is usually the first letter in the name of the dominant trait. For example, tallness in a pea plant is dominant and is shown with a *T*. Shortness in a pea plant is recessive and is shown with a *t*. Since tallness is dominant,

## READING CRITICALLY
When would a person's phenotype and genotype be identical?

---

when the genotype is pure, or double recessive

**Figure 24–9.** Punnett squares can be used to determine the probable results of a genetic cross. All the possible combinations appear in the boxes of the square. This square shows all the possible results of crossing a pure with a pure.

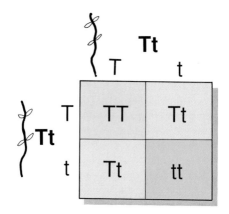

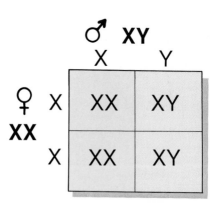

**Figure 24–10.** The Punnett square on top shows the possible results of crossing a hybrid with another hybrid, while the square on the bottom shows the possible results of crossing traits for sex.

a plant will be tall even if it has only one gene for tallness. The genes on an individual's chromosomes are its **genotype** (JEE nuh typ). What an individual looks like as the result of those genes is its **phenotype** (FEE nuh typ). A plant with a genotype of TT will be tall. A plant whose genotype is Tt also will be tall. Suppose you have a plant whose phenotype is short. <u>Since shortness is recessive, what is the plant's genotype?</u> tt

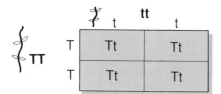

When both genes are dominant or both are recessive, the individual is said to be **pure** for that trait. A TT plant is an example of a plant that is pure for tallness. If the individual has one dominant and one recessive gene, it is a **hybrid** for that trait. The tall pea plant that has the genotype Tt is a hybrid tall plant.

R. C. Punnett, a British scientist, developed a simple chart to demonstrate how dominant and recessive genes might combine in an offspring. Look at the *Punnett square* in Figure 24–9. To use a Punnett square, you must first select two possible parents. For this demonstration, pick a short plant (tt) and a pure tall plant (TT). Place the genes for one parent across the top of the square and the genes for the other parent down the left side. Keep in mind that the genes represented in the Punnett square actually represent the genes in gametes that separate with chromosomes during meiosis. Take turns moving the genes down and across and combining them in the boxes of the square. Each combination, or *cross*, represents the fusing of two gametes. Each of the smaller squares represents the resulting genotype of a possible offspring.

The Punnett square can also be used to show how an individual's sex is determined. In humans, the sex of an individual is determined by a special pair of chromosomes called the sex chromosomes. A male has an X chromosome and a Y chromosome. A female has two X chromosomes. Females can contribute only an X chromosome to the offspring. A male, on the other hand, can contribute either the X or the Y chromosome. The offspring has a 50/50 chance of receiving an X or Y chromosome from the male parent. In humans, therefore, the sex of the offspring is determined by the male parent and is strictly a matter of chance.

In some animals such as birds, butterflies, and moths sex is determined by the female. The male has two X chromosomes and the female has an X and a Y.

# 24.6 DNA

Each chromosome of a cell is made of a special chemical called *DNA*. **DNA** is a nucleic (noo KLAY ihk) acid, a special type of acid formed in the nucleus of the cell. DNA stands for *deoxyribonucleic* (dee AHK sih ry boh noo KLAY ihk) *acid*. DNA contains a sugar called *deoxyribose* (dee ahk sih RY bohs), a group of substances called a *phosphate group*, and four chemical bases—*adenine* (AD uh neen), *guanine* (GWAH neen), *thymine* (THY meen), and *cytosine* (SYT uh seen). These four bases are abbreviated A, G, T, and C, respectively.

James D. Watson, an American biologist, and Francis H. C. Crick, a British biophysicist, discovered the structure of DNA in 1953. Building upon the contributions of many scientists, Watson and Crick knew that chromosomes were made of protein and DNA. Watson and Crick were the first scientists to determine how the substances in a molecule of DNA fit together. Through their efforts, scientists now know that DNA resembles a ladder that has been twisted into a spiral shape called a *helix*. The DNA molecule is similar to a ladder—it has two sides. Therefore, the shape of the DNA molecule is a *double helix*. The sides of the ladder—the part you hold on to as you climb—are made of the sugar molecules and phosphate groups. The rungs of the ladder are the four bases, A, T, G, and C. Figure 24–11 shows the structure of a DNA molecule.

Watson and Crick found that the ladder rungs have certain patterns. The A and T always join together to make a rung. Likewise, C and G always join together to make a rung. The bases may combine as G-C or C-G, as T-A or as A-T, but they never change partners. T will not pair with G, nor will A pair with C. The order in which the rungs are arranged provides the code, or "blueprint," of heredity. The DNA code can be thought of as a four-letter alphabet. Scientists now know that the genes that determine each individual's hereditary characteristics are specific sections of a DNA molecule.

**Figure 24–11.** A DNA molecule is made up of three kinds of substances: a sugar, a phosphate group, and four chemical bases. These three components combine to form a molecule that resembles a twisted ladder.

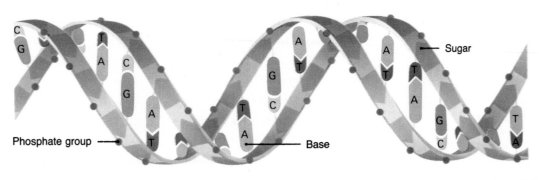

Each chromosome contains one molecule of DNA. Chromosomes replicate before mitosis and meiosis take place. Therefore, DNA must also replicate before mitosis or meiosis. When replication occurs, the double helix separates where the bases of the rungs are joined. Each side of the DNA molecule then becomes a pattern for the formation of a new side.

The new side of the molecule is made up of chemicals from within the cell. Each base of the original molecule combines with its partner base. That is, adenine always combines with thymine and cytosine always combines with quanine.

because only certain bases will bond with each other, thereby producing an exact duplicate

Figure 24–12 shows how a molecule of DNA replicates. After it replicates, there are two complete molecules of DNA. Why is the new molecule of DNA exactly like the original molecule?

**Figure 24–12.** When a DNA molecule replicates, it separates itself. Two complementary strands form, each using one of the single DNA strands as a template.

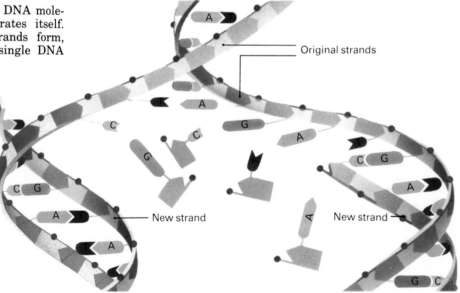

Original strands

New strand

New strand

1. A dominant gene masks the trait of a recessive gene. In peas, the gene for tallness is dominant over the gene for shortness. In order for a pea plant to be short, it must have two recessive genes.
2. a, tall; b, short; c, tall
3. Genes are important because they determine all the characteristics of an individual.
4. The discovery of DNA led to an understanding of how hereditary characteristics are determined. Replication of DNA also answers the question of how characteristics are passed from generation to generation.

## Section Review

1. Describe what is meant by dominance and recessiveness in terms of Mendel's work with pea plants.
2. What are the phenotypes of pea plants with the following genotypes? (a) Tt (b) tt (c) TT
3. How are genes important to life?
4. THINKING CRITICALLY Why was the discovery of the structure of DNA so important? Explain your answer in terms of how DNA replicates.

# COMPUTER APPLICATION

## Replication of DNA

### 1. DESCRIPTION

The ability of a DNA molecule to replicate itself is the fundamental process by which living organisms reproduce themselves. This program represents the process of DNA replication. Note the splitting of the initial molecule into two strands with active positions represented by dots, and the replication of both strands to a copy of the original molecule.

### 2. PROGRAM

Input the following program. After it is completely input, key the computer to run the program. If the program does not run, check to make sure you have input correctly. If the program runs correctly, go on to steps 3 and 4.

### 3. HELPFUL HINTS

The letters of the alphabet are produced by using CHR$(n). When n is 65, the letter is A, 66 is B, and so on.

### 4. GOING FURTHER

- Modify the program so that each of the molecules replicates again to form four copies of original molecule.
- Individual links in the DNA molecule are not letters of the alphabet. What are they? How could you modify the program to use the correct names of these links?

```
100    HOME
110    VTAB 23
120    INPUT "PRESS RETURN TO SEE DNA MOLECULE ";K9$
130    HOME
140    FOR C = 65 TO 85

150    PRINT  TAB( 20); CHR$ (C); CHR$ (C)
160    NEXT
170    VTAB 23
180    INPUT "RETURN TO SEE MOLECULE DIVIDE ";K9$
190    VTAB 1

200    FOR C = 65 TO 85
210    PRINT  TAB( 17); CHR$ (C);".    ." CHR$ (C)
220    FOR P = 1 TO 100
230    NEXT P
240    NEXT C

250    VTAB 23
260    INPUT "RETURN TO SEE MOLECULE REPLICATE ";K9$
270    VTAB 1
280    FOR C = 65 TO 85
290    HTAB 18

300    PRINT  TAB( 18); CHR$ (C);"    "; CHR$ (C)
310    FOR P = 1 TO 100
320    NEXT P
330    NEXT C
340    VTAB 23

350    PRINT "              <<< THE  END >>>           ";
999    END
```

# SKILL ACTIVITY    Reading for Comprehension

**INTRODUCTION**

Taking good notes as you read through material is an important skill. Note-taking helps reinforce the main idea and supporting details of what you read. Good notes are also helpful tools for studying and for writing papers.

**PROCEDURE**

1. Read the whole selection to get an overview of what you have to study. This will help you see the organization of the material.
2. Choose one part of the selection to read at a time.
3. Note the topic of the paragraph or group of paragraphs you choose. Write the topic or topics in your notebook.
4. After you finish reading each paragraph, state its main idea. Write down only important supporting details under the main idea. Indent your list so that the relation of supporting material to main ideas is clear.
5. Summarize what you have read, stating only facts.
6. Do not take notes on matters of common knowledge.
7. Do not take notes on the same information twice unless you are using information to prove or disprove a point.

**APPLICATION**

Take notes on the following selection. From your notes, write a paragraph about hemophilia.

---

**Hemophilia: Curse of the Crowned Heads of Europe**

Hemophilia (hee muh FIHL ee uh) is a hereditary disease in which the blood clots more slowly than normal. People with hemophilia are called *hemophiliacs*. Because of the practice of intermarriage in many royal families, hemophilia has been a problem in royal families of Europe.

Almost all hemophiliacs are males. Hemophilia is caused by a defective gene on the X chromosome. The Y chromosome has no genes for clotting factors. A male who inherits the hemophilia defect on his X chromosome will be a hemophiliac. A female who inherits the defective gene on one of her X chromosomes will be a carrier. A female may transmit the defective gene to her children, but it is very rare for a female to inherit the defective gene on both X chromosomes so that she becomes a hemophiliac.

There is no cure for hemophilia, but it can be treated. Hemophiliacs can be injected with the clotting factor they lack to temporarily cause normal clotting. These injections must be given as soon as possible after an injury so that blood does not accumulate and cause damage to body tissues.

Queen Victoria of Great Britain was a carrier of the gene for hemophilia. She passed the gene onto some of her children. These children went on to marry into many of the royal houses of Europe, bringing the gene for hemophilia with them. As a result, some male children in the Prussian, Russian, and Spanish royal houses were hemophiliacs.

# Patterns of Heredity

## SECTION OBJECTIVES

- **Define** *sex-linked characteristic* and give examples.
- **Identify** the causes and effects of some mutations.
- **Explain** a benefit of recombinant DNA.

NEW TERMS IN THIS SECTION
mutation
polyploidy
recombinant DNA

## 24.7 Human Traits

Each human cell has 23 pairs of chromosomes. Packed onto those 46 individual chromosomes are thousands of genes. These genes control everything from hair color to the length of one's fingers and toes. Genes also control every chemical reaction that occurs in every cell of an organism. It is these chemical reactions that keep organisms alive. Some inherited traits, such as dimples and cleft chins, are determined by a single pair of genes. Others, such as hair color, eye color, height, and blood type, are determined by groups of genes. In fact, most human traits require more than a single gene pair.

In all discussions about human traits avoid absolutes such as "always" and "never." Fear and embarrassment may occur when students see no way they could have certain characteristics and still be the offspring of their parents. Emphasize that research is still being conducted to determine exactly how genes produce complicated traits such as hair color and eye color.

attached ear lobes, no cleft in chin, no dimples, no freckles, straight hair, normal skin

**Figure 24–13.** <u>List the recessive traits that are shown in these photographs.</u>

| TABLE 24–1 | SAMPLE HUMAN TRAITS |
|---|---|
| **Dominant** | **Recessive** |
| Curly hair | Straight hair |
| Much body hair | Little body hair |
| Ichthyosis (scaly skin) | Normal skin |
| Long eyelashes | Short eyelashes |
| Short fingers | Long fingers |
| Chin cleft | No cleft |
| Dimples | No dimples |
| Tongue rolling | Inability to roll tongue |
| Free ear lobes | Attached ear lobes |
| Sweat glands present | Sweat glands absent |
| Freckles | No freckles |

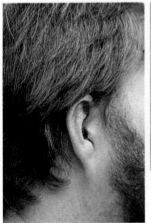

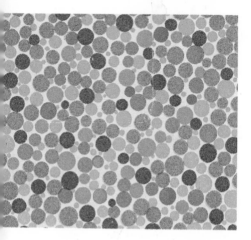

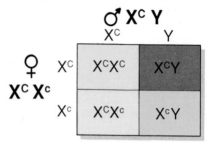

**Figure 24–14.** Tests, such as the one shown above, are used to determine colorblindness. <u>What number do you see?</u> The Punnett square shows how parents with normal vision could have a colorblind child.

Students should be able to see the number 42.

An individual's sex is determined by sex chromosomes. Each person normally has two sex chromosomes. The other 22 pairs of chromosomes are called *autosomes*. The genes for most traits are carried on autosomes. However, genes for some traits are carried on the sex chromosomes. These traits are called *sex-linked* characteristics.

Sex-linked genes are nearly always recessive genes and are usually found on the X chromosome. Since males have only one X chromosome, the recessive sex-linked trait is more likely to show up in a male than in a female. Remember that a recessive gene can be hidden or covered by a dominant gene. Since females have two X chromosomes, they have a better chance to carry a dominant gene on one X chromosome. This dominant gene will cover a recessive gene that appears on the other X chromosome. A person who has a recessive gene but does not show the trait is called a *carrier*.

Colorblindness is an example of a sex-linked trait. Colorblindness is the inability to distinguish certain colors. The Punnett square in Figure 24–14 diagrams a cross between two parents with normal vision. Notice it is necessary to use two sets of symbols in this example. The X and Y represent the sex, C represents normal vision, which is dominant, and c represents the recessive trait of colorblindness.

## 24.8 Mutations and Disorders

Chromosomes may not always replicate or divide properly. Genetic problems may occur when a chromosome breaks, is lost, or moves out of its proper order. These chromosomes result in genes that are out of place or lost and are therefore not passed on to the gametes in the process of meiosis. A change in chromosome structure or in a gene is called a **mutation.**

Mutations are often harmful or fatal. Mutations are especially harmful when they occur in gametes. Mutations in gametes are repeated in each cell of the new individual if that gamete takes part in fertilization and reproduction. Mutations in body cells affect only the individual with the mutation, not its offspring.

Some mutations are actually beneficial. Mutations have helped provide the great variety of living things. Some mutations make an organism better able to survive in its environment. These mutations are responsible for evolution, or the changes in species over long periods. Evolution is discussed further in Chapter 25.

---

***READING CRITICALLY***

Why are mutations especially harmful when they occur in gametes?

---

because gametes pass the mutation on to the next generation

**518**     Chapter 24

Down syndrome, as well as other conditions named for an individual, are now spelled without the 's, as recommended by the American Society for Human Genetics.

Occasionally a single pair of chromosomes does not separate during meiosis as the other 22 pairs do. When this occurs, the egg or sperm cell has an extra chromosome to pass on to the offspring. One result of such an error is *trisomy 21*, or *Down syndrome*. An individual with this condition has three chromosomes of the twenty-first pair. An individual with Down syndrome has 47 chromosomes instead of the normal 46. Persons with Down syndrome have distinctive physical features and some degree of mental retardation. With special training, these individuals can learn many skills and increase their independence. They can become contributing members of society.

Mutations can also occur in individual genes. One example of a gene mutation is *albinism* (AL buh nihz uhm). Albinism is a condition that prevents pigment from forming. In animals the result can be a striking appearance of white hair, very pale skin, and pink eyes. The skin and eyes have a pink tone because the color of the blood cells is not masked by normal skin tones or by green, blue, or brown eye color.

## SCIENCE FACT

Sickle-cell disease is a genetic disorder resulting from a mutation that causes abnormal hemoglobin production. The blood cells become shaped like sickles instead of the normal disk shape. The sickle-shaped cells cannot carry oxygen and therefore tissues are deprived of oxygen, causing severe pain.

Down syndrome is named for John Down, the British physician who wrote about the disorder in 1866.

**Figure 24–15.** Albinism, the result of a mutation in an individual gene, can occur in both plants and animals, as shown in the albino opossum and the albino corn.

# 24.9 Genetic Technology

As skills increase and tools improve, scientists are better able to understand the secrets of the DNA molecule. Biologists who use the DNA molecule to cause changes in organisms are called *genetic engineers*.

Mutations that occur naturally in some plants can now be imitated in laboratories. Scientists are experimenting with plant mutations that increase the size of crops and that produce better-tasting or larger fruits and vegetables. Genetic engineers work closely with farmers to develop better crops through a type of change called *polyploidy* (PAHL ih ploy dee). In **polyploidy**, a plant has more than two complete sets of chromosomes. A polyploid plant may have three, four, or even more sets of chromosomes. Polyploidy results when a plant is exposed to a chemical that interferes with the normal chromosome activity during meiosis. The gametes that result have more chromosomes than they would normally have.

**Figure 24–16.** Geneticists have been using polyploidy to increase the size and yield of plants. The plant on the left is a normal orchid, while the plant in the center has undergone polyploidy. The size, number, and texture of flowers may change as a result of chromosome manipulation.

Genetic engineers also have found ways to combine the DNA of two different species to produce recombinant DNA. **Recombinant DNA** is a DNA molecule that is made up of DNA from more than one cell or organism. The process of making recombinant DNA involves cutting a molecule of DNA and fastening a piece of another DNA molecule to the cut ends. The cut ends of the DNA molecules stick together, forming a new molecule of DNA. Why is this new DNA called recombinant?

because it is a combination of DNA from more than one cell or organism and is recombined into a new DNA molecule

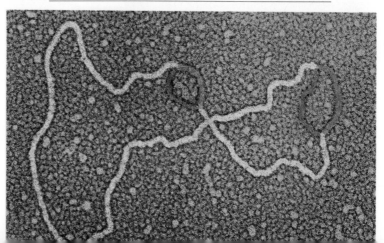

**Figure 24–17.** This electron micrograph shows a circular loop of bacterial DNA. The area where another strand of foreign material has been inserted is colored red. The ordinary double-stranded DNA is yellow. The blue portions are individual genes that have been isolated.

Experiments with recombinant DNA are usually done with bacteria. The advantage of recombinant DNA is that it enables the bacteria to make large amounts of valuable substances. Two substances currently being produced are insulin and interferon. Insulin is used to control diabetes. Interferon is useful in treating some types of cancer. Experimentation is currently under way to produce the human growth hormone in large enough quantities to treat children who suffer from dwarfism.

## Section Review

1. What are sex-linked characteristics? Are they usually dominant or recessive?

2. Give two examples of conditions resulting from chromosome mutations.

3. How is recombinant DNA made? What are some advantages of recombinant DNA?

4. THINKING CRITICALLY Construct a Punnett square showing the genotypes of a hybrid male with free ear lobes (dominant) and a female with attached ear lobes (recessive). Complete the square. Describe the possible genotypes and phenotypes of the offspring.

**SCIENCE FACT**

Scientists have produced a new variety of onion that will not make you cry. The gene that produces the chemical that causes tears was removed.

1. Sex-linked characteristic are traits whose genes are always on the sex chromosome. They are usually recessive.
2. Down syndrome and albinism
3. Recombinant DNA is made from the DNA of more than one cell or organism by cutting one molecule of DNA and attaching another molecule to the cut ends. Recombinant DNA enables certain organisms, such as bacteria, to make large quantities of organic substances.
4. Ee: hybrid, free; ee: pure, attached

# CAREER

## Genetic Counselor

**DESCRIPTION** A genetic counselor provides and explains information about human genetics. Genetic counselors help people who are at risk, or who may have children at risk, for genetic diseases. Genetic counselors take family health histories, order tests, and analyze test results. Some genetic counselors work for hospitals or physicians. Others are self-employed.

**REQUIREMENTS** To prepare for a career as a genetic counselor, you should take courses in science, especially biology and mathematics, in high school. Genetic counselors must be board certified. This certification requires that counselors earn a master's degree in human genetics and pass a certification examination.

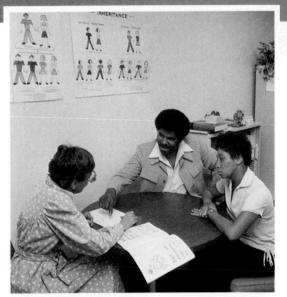

**INFORMATION** National Society of Genetic Counselors, Genetic Counseling Education Program, Dept. OB-GYN/Hutzel Hospital, 4707 Saint Antoine Boulevard, Detroit, MI 48201

For teacher information about this Investigation, see page T115.

# INVESTIGATION 24: Predicting Genetic Traits

*Could two parents who are unable to roll their tongues have any offspring that could?*

## PURPOSE

To practice making genetic crosses using a Punnett square

## MATERIALS

paper and pencil

## PROCEDURE

1. On a separate sheet of paper, make two Punnett squares like the ones shown.

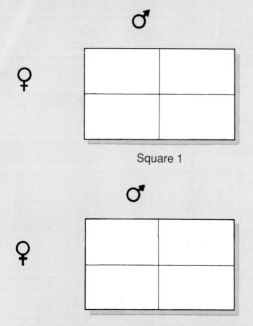

Square 1

Square 2

2. Complete the first square by performing the following cross. In humans, tongue rolling (T) is dominant over the inability to roll the tongue (t). Show the genotype of two parents who are both unable to roll their tongue. Also show the possible gametes from each parent.

3. In the second square, show the genotype of a father who is hybrid for tongue rolling and a mother who is unable to roll her tongue. Also show the possible gametes from each parent.

## RESULTS

1. Describe the phenotypes of the offspring from the parents in square 1. All are nonrollers (tt).

2. Describe the phenotypes of the offspring from the parents in square 2.
Half are hybrid tongue rollers (Tt) and half are pure nonrollers (tt).

## CONCLUSIONS

1. How many offspring in square 1 can roll their tongues? None

2. How many offspring in square 2 can roll their tongues? Half

3. Did your prediction at the beginning of this investigation prove to be correct after you completed your Punnett squares? If not, how would you change your squares to get the predicted outcome? Answers will vary.

## APPLICATIONS

1. Two parents are tongue rollers. They have a son who is unable to roll his tongue. What is the genotype of each parent? Tt

2. How would Punnett squares help physicians determine if an individual or that person's offspring is at risk for a genetic disorder? They would show the probability of having or inheriting the defective gene or genes.

## Summary

1. Monerans and other simple organisms reproduce by binary fission. **(24.1)**

2. Mitosis is a process of cell division that produces two cells exactly the same as the original cell. **(24.2)**

3. Meiosis is a type of cell division that produces gametes. Meiosis reduces by one half the number of chromosomes in each gamete. **(24.3)**

4. Mendel's experiments with pea plants led to the discovery of genes and how hereditary traits are passed on from one generation to the next. Genes for each trait can be dominant or recessive. **(24.4)**

5. The genes on an individual's chromosomes are its genotype. What an individual looks like as a result of the expression of those genes is its phenotype. Punnett squares are used to determine how dominant and recessive genes might combine in an offspring. **(24.5)**

6. Chromosomes are made up of DNA. DNA provides the blueprint for the traits each individual inherits. **(24.6)**

7. Human traits may be determined by a single pair of genes or several pairs of genes. Sex-linked characteristics are determined by genes carried on the X chromosomes. **(24.7)**

8. Changes in the structure of chromosomes or genes result in mutations. **(24.8)**

9. Genetic engineers can combine the DNA of two different species to produce recombinant DNA. **(24.9)**

## Science Terms

On a separate sheet of paper, define each term in a sentence.

| | | | |
|---|---|---|---|
| binary fission **(505)** | gene **(511)** | mutation **(518)** | recombinant DNA **(520)** |
| chromosome **(506)** | genotype **(512)** | phenotype **(512)** | replication **(506)** |
| DNA **(513)** | hybrid **(512)** | polyploidy **(520)** | sexual reproduction **(508)** |
| dominant **(511)** | meiosis **(508)** | pure **(512)** | |
| gamete **(507)** | mitosis **(507)** | recessive **(511)** | |

## Modified True-False

On a separate sheet of paper, mark each true statement *TRUE* and each false statement *FALSE*. If false, change the underlined term to make the statement true.

1. Bacteria reproduce by simple cell division called <u>binary fission</u>. T

2. <u>Mitosis</u> can increase the size of an organism but not the number of organisms. T

3. The duplication of genetic material before cell division is called <u>reproduction</u>. F, replication

4. If an individual has one dominant gene and one recessive gene, it is <u>hybrid</u> for that trait. T

5. A cell involved only in reproduction is called a <u>chromosome</u>. F, gamete

6. Sexual reproduction is the process by which two gametes <u>separate</u> to produce a new individual. F, combine

7. <u>DNA</u> determines an individual's hereditary characteristics. T

8. Colorblindness is determined by <u>one pair</u> of genes. T

9. <u>Albinism</u> is a condition in which pigment is not formed. T

10. Experiments with recombinant DNA are usually done with <u>bacteria</u>. T *(continues)*

## Multiple Choice

On a separate sheet of paper, write the letter of the term that best answers the question or completes the statement.

1. Binary fission results in
   a. two gametes.
   **b.** two daughter cells.
   c. one exact duplicate of the original cell.
   d. four daughter cells.

2. The term hybrid
   a. refers to an individual carrying a recessive gene.
   b. refers to the genotype of the individual.
   c. indicates the individual is not pure for a certain trait.
   **d.** means all of the above.

3. In the first phase of mitosis
   a. DNA replicates.
   **c.** chromosomes are pulled apart.
   b. cell membranes form.
   d. cytoplasm divides.

4. The fusing of gametes is called
   **a.** fertilization.
   c. meiosis.
   b. mitosis.
   d. fission.

5. An example of a sex-linked characteristic is
   a. blond hair.
   c. long eyelashes.
   **b.** colorblindness.
   d. all of the above.

6. Which of the following is not found in DNA?
   a. guanine
   **c.** insulin
   b. adenine
   d. cytosine

7. Trisomy 21 is the more exact name for
   **a.** Down syndrome.
   b. hemophilia.
   c. albinism.
   d. polyploidy.

8. A substance whose production has been increased through a recombinant DNA process is
   a. guanine.
   c. pigment.
   **b.** insulin.
   d. cytosine.

9. Genetic engineers use _____ to produce changes in organisms.
   **a.** polyploidy
   c. DNA
   b. meiosis
   d. thymine

10. The condition of polyploidy
    a. increases the number of chromosomes.
    b. is the result of mutations.
    c. results in better fruits and vegetables.
    **d.** results in all of the above.

## Completion

On a separate sheet of paper, complete each statement by supplying the correct term.

1. The phase of mitosis in which the chromosome pairs cluster toward the center of the cell is called <u>metaphase</u>.

2. Meiosis occurs only in <u>reproductive</u> cells.

3. The normal number of chromosomes in human egg and sperm cells is <u>23</u>.

4. The heredity factors described by Mendel are now called <u>genes</u>.

5. Human <u>females</u> have two X chromosomes.

6. A change in chromosome structure is called a <u>mutation</u>.

7. A <u>Punnett square</u> is a chart that shows the possible results of a genetic cross.

8. Persons who have a recessive gene but do not show the trait are called <u>hybrid</u>.

9. The combination of DNA from two different species produces <u>recombinant DNA</u>.

10. When mutations occur in <u>body cells</u>, only the individual is affected.

# Writing Critically

1. Compare and contrast mitosis and meiosis. Give examples of cells in which each process takes place.
2. Discuss the advantages of recombinant DNA. Suggest substances other than those mentioned in the chapter that might be produced by recombinant DNA.
3. Explain how you would go about testing what flower color in roses is dominant. Describe the type and number of experiments you would conduct.
4. **CHALLENGE** Discuss the social implications of genetic technology.

# Skill Reinforcement

The Skill Activity on page 516 describes how to take notes. Choose any section of this chapter and follow the procedure for note-taking found in the Skill Activity.

# Research Ideas

1. Investigate the role of interferon in cancer treatment. Report on its success and the impact of interferon produced from recombinant DNA.
2. *E. coli* is a bacterium commonly found in the small intestine of humans. Research how *E. coli* is used in the manufacture of recombinant DNA and, in turn, how this process results in the increased production of substances such as insulin and interferon.
3. **CHALLENGE** In 1902, Walter S. Sutton proposed the Chromosome Theory. Find out who Sutton was, and explain how his theory is used today in the study of genetics.

# For Further Reading

Antebi, Elizabeth, and David Fishlock. *Biotechnology: Strategies for Life.* Cambridge, Mass.: MIT Press, 1986. This beautifully illustrated book explains the techniques used in biotechnology such as genetic engineering, cell fusion, microbiological engineering, and more. Applications for biotechnology in medicine, food, energy, pollution, and other areas are discussed.

"Does X Mark the Spot?" *Health* (May 1982) 14, 23. This article discusses the role of so-called fragile X, an abnormal form of the sex chromosome, in producing mental retardation in males.

Sutton, Caroline. "How Do They Splice Genes?" from *How Do They Do That?* New York: Quill, 1982. A two-page article dealing with cutting and splicing a strand of DNA. The DNA of a bacterium that lives in the stomach and intestine of humans *(E. coli)* is used for this discussion.

Watson, J. D. *The Double Helix.* New York: Atheneum, 1968. Watson provides a stimulating day-to-day account of how he, Crick, and their coworkers developed the double helix model of DNA.

Answers to Writing Critically

1. Both are types of cell reproduction. Mitosis results in the formation of two new daughter cells that are exact copies of the original cell. Mitosis occurs in all body cells. Meiosis results in four cells, each containing half the number of chromosomes as the original cell. Meiosis takes place only in reproductive cells.
2. Recombinant DNA allows scientists to manufacture large amounts of substances that are normally made in only small amounts. Suggestions will vary but may include antibodies and hormones.
3. Students should present a logical method of testing dominance by crossing flowers of the same color until pures are established and then crossing different-colored flowers.
4. Answers will vary but may include mention of preventing hereditary diseases or choosing the phenotypes of humans before they are born.

# 25 Evolution and Natural Selection

The fossils shown in these photographs are millions of years old. They are fossil trilobites—the ancestors of modern crabs and lobsters. The changes that produced the modern species took millions of years to occur. Studying fossils gives scientists clues about how living things have changed over time.

For additional information, see pages T116–T117.

that the flamingo has a complicated feeding arrangement that involves sucking, sifting, and sorting. The flamingo does all of this with its head in an upside-down feeding position. What interests Gould and his fellow observers is that the movement of the bird's jaw matches the bird's feeding position.

Place your hand on your lower jaw and open your mouth. What moved? Was it your upper jaw or your lower jaw? In most higher animals, the lower jaw moves. The upper jaw stays firmly in place. In the flamingo, the opposite is true. With its head upside down, the bird moves its upper jaw while its lower jaw stays in place. Did the flamingo begin to feed upside down because of a change in its jaw? Did the changing jaw represent some necessary change in feeding style?

## Natural Selection

Darwin's theory of evolution is based on the process of natural selection. **Natural selection** is the process by which those individuals best adapted to their environment will be the most successful. Success means having a better chance of surviving and of reproducing. The offspring of these individuals will, in turn, have a better chance of survival than the offspring of individuals not as well adapted. Even without a knowledge of genes, Darwin had reasoned how characteristics are passed to offspring.

Darwin's ideas of natural selection form the basis for modern evolutionary theory. His ideas, however, do not fully explain all the evidence of evolution. There are other scientific theories about how evolution may occur. These theories generally do not conflict with each other in important details. Probably no single theory can adequately explain how life changes, but taken together they do a fairly good job of explaining the evidence.

**Figure 25–4.** The flamingo has an unusual feeding arrangement. The structure of its jaws is adapted for this purpose.

## SCIENCE FACT

Natural selection is sometimes called "survival of the fittest" because the environment acts to preserve, or select, fit individuals.

## Section Review

1. Why is the fossil record incomplete?
2. Why was the discovery of fossilized blue-green bacteria important?
3. How are fossils usually formed?
4. What is the process by which evolution occurs? Explain your answer.
5. THINKING CRITICALLY Why are changes that occur between one generation and the next not considered evolutionary changes? Explain your answer.

1. Not all organisms form fossils, and many fossils that do form may be hidden or destroyed by the movement of land and water.
2. These fossils could be dated, confirming the belief that these simple organisms were among the first life forms to evolve.
3. There are three ways: imprint, mold, and preserved. In any case, the body of the organism leaves some image of itself through the pressure of earth or the hardening of the preserving material.
4. Evolution occurs through the adaptation and resulting change in organisms; these mutations are passed from parent to offspring.
5. One generation is not long enough to establish a shift in the genes of a population, making the change stable or constant.

# SKILL ACTIVITY Interpreting Illustrations

## INTRODUCTION

Scientists find out how organisms are related by studying their structures. The forelimb, or arm, is used for a different purpose by each of the animals shown in Figure 1. However, the bones in the forelimbs of each of these animals are *homologous*—that is, they have similar origins. Before birth, these parts all develop in the same way. In addition, these bones can be traced to similar bones in a common ancestor.

By comparison, the wings of a bird and of an insect are analogous—that is, they are used for the same function. However, the wings of a bird and the wings of an insect do not have similar origins. In addition, the wings of a bird and of an insect cannot be traced to a common ancestor.

## PROCEDURE

1. Study the illustrations of the three animals shown. The key will help you identify the radius, the ulna, and the phalanges, or "fingers."

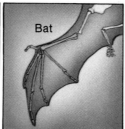
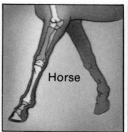
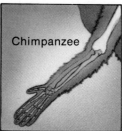

2. Compare the wing of the bird and the wing of the insect shown below.

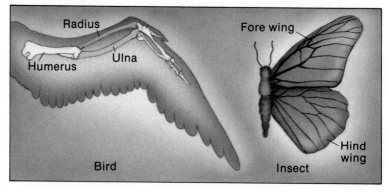

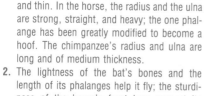

1. The bat's radius, ulna, and phalanges are long and thin. In the horse, the radius and the ulna are strong, straight, and heavy; the one phalange has been greatly modified to become a hoof. The chimpanzee's radius and ulna are long and of medium thickness.

2. The lightness of the bat's bones and the length of its phalanges help it fly; the sturdiness of the horse's front legs support its weight and help it run; the flexibility of the chimpanzee's hand helps to climb trees, pick fruits, and handle objects.

3. Answers will vary but should include that the common ancestor's forelimb would have bones, such as the radius, ulna, and digits, but that these bones might have been shorter and thicker.

## APPLICATION

4. The wing of an insect is made of a light-weight, transparent material and has no bones. The wing of a bird has bones and is covered by skin and feathers. They serve a similar purpose but have a different structure and origin.

1. How do the radius, the ulna, and the phalanges compare in the bat, the horse, and the chimp?

2. How is the forelimb of each of these animals adapted for a particular function?

3. If these animals had a common ancestor, what might its forelimb have been like?

4. How does the wing of an insect differ from the wing of a bird?

# Planned and Unplanned Changes

NEW TERMS IN THIS SECTION
selective breeding
inbreeding
pesticides

## 25.3 Improved Breeding

In his work with pea plants, Mendel carefully selected the traits he wanted to study and reproduce. Scientists after Mendel and Darwin realized that natural selection made some organisms more successful than others. They began to search for ways to increase the number of organisms with those successful traits. For example, ranchers told scientists they wanted cattle that could survive in poor climates, resist disease, and still produce quality beef. To produce animals with these desired traits, scientists and breeders began to crossbreed different types of cattle. The goal was to produce new breeds with combinations of the best qualities from two or more parent breeds. This process is called **selective breeding**.

**Figure 25–5.** These two cattle are the results of selective breeding. The Brahman (left) was bred to live in a harsh climate; the Hereford (right) was bred for superior beef and milk.

**Predicting New Species**

Suggest some beneficial cross-breedings in plants or animals. Sketch what your new organisms would look like.

The Brangus is another breed that combines characteristics of Brahman with those of other cattle. In this case the Black Angus was chosen for the exceptional quality of its beef and the Brahman for its hardiness.

## SCIENCE FACT

Because the American elm has been inbred for generations, there is now a lack of other elm strains that might provide resistance to Dutch elm disease.

**Figure 25–6.** Plant breeders use genetics to improve flowers, fruits, and vegetables. In the example of the crape myrtle, three different varieties have been bred: the traditional myrtle (left), the dwarf myrtle (middle), and the miniature myrtle (right).

Cattle breeders first identified parent animals that had the desired traits. They selected Brahman cattle because these cattle are very hardy. Brahmans can graze in scrubby brush country and are not affected by heat. Their loose skin makes them more resistant to insects than are other breeds. Cattle breeders also selected shorthorn and Herefords as parent types. Both of these types of cattle produce large amounts of beef and enough good milk to nourish their offspring.

The result of selectively breeding Brahman, Shorthorn, and Hereford cattle was a new breed called *Beefmaster*. Beefmaster cattle were first bred in Texas. These cattle were exactly what the ranchers asked for. They survived in hot climates, resisted disease, and produced large amounts of beef. The beefalo is another result of selective breeding. What animals do you think were bred to produce this new breed? cattle and buffalo

A decorative plant that has been improved through selective breeding is the crape myrtle. Breeders have increased the color choices and size ranges available. The traditional crape myrtle is 4 to 5 m high. This height limits the uses of the plant and, therefore, limits the opportunities for those who grow and sell it. However, crape myrtles can now be found in dwarf (2 m) and miniature (1 m) sizes. These smaller plants are used in hanging baskets and as decorative plants. To develop these smaller plants, breeders used a process called *inbreeding*. **Inbreeding** involves breeding two closely related individuals. This process allows breeders to be more sure that a desirable trait will be passed to the offspring.

## 25.4 Increased Resistance

Increasing the disease and insect resistance of a plant or an animal is usually a helpful change. Beefmaster cattle are resistant to heat and insects. The new crape myrtles are resistant to *mildew*, a fungus that damages plants. Sometimes, however, an unplanned resistance develops that has a damaging effect.

Most insects are useful to humans. Those that are not are called *pests*. These insects are controlled with chemicals called **pesticides**. Sometimes, however, insect pests develop a resistance to the pesticides. For example, aphids are tiny sucking insects found on plants. Pesticides can prevent or control their occurrence. However, if the aphids develop a resistance to the pesticides, the number of insects will increase rapidly. The rapid increase will cause even more damage to the plants.

Resistance in insects develops in a way similar to selective breeding. Suppose only a few insects carry genes that allow them to be unaffected by certain pesticides. Those few insects survive to mate with other survivors. As the matings of surviving insects continue, more and more insects hatch that are resistant. Eventually, large numbers of insects that are resistant to the pesticides are produced.

**Figure 25–7.** This boll weevil has developed a resistance to the pesticides farmers spray on their cotton crops.

Farmers have asked scientists to help them with the problem of pesticide-resistant insects. One successful method for dealing with resistant insects is to alternate the type of pesticide used. Farmers spray or dust with one pesticide to destroy most of the pests. They then follow up with a different pesticide to destroy the insects that were resistant to the first one. Other scientists are working to develop plants that will be resistant to pests.

**Figure 25–8.** The continuous spraying of crops with pesticides has caused some pests to become resistant to the chemicals.

Some bacteria that cause disease in humans have also developed resistance. In this case, the bacteria become resistant to the antibiotic that the patient takes to kill the bacteria. New antibiotics are being researched and developed to solve this medical problem.

## Section Review

1. What is selective breeding?
2. What were the benefits of the three different types of cattle bred to produce the Beefmaster?
3. Explain how increased resistance can be both helpful and harmful.
4. What new strains of animals and plants have been developed through selective breeding, and what are the advantages of these breeds?
5. THINKING CRITICALLY Imagine that you are a plant breeder living in northern Florida. You want to develop a new variety of tomato plant that is resistant to occasional cold temperatures and produces large numbers of evenly sized tomatoes. How would you produce such a variety of tomato plant?

1. combining the desired traits of two parent breeds to obtain an offspring that has both desired traits
2. They survive in hot climates, they resist disease, and they produce large amounts of beef.
3. It is helpful when it results in increased resistance to disease or adverse conditions. It is harmful when it allows strains that are harmful to crops and animals to become unaffected by the pesticides intended to destroy them.
4. Beefmaster cattle produce more beef, some fruits and vegetables produce better flowers or larger fruits, and crape myrtle plants are smaller and may be used as houseplants.
5. Cross-breed tomato plants that have cold resistance, high yield, and equally sized fruit.

# A Human Time Line

## SECTION OBJECTIVES
● **Identify** the characteristics of some early hominids.
● **Summarize** the significant discoveries of hominid fossils.
● **Describe** the Neanderthal and Cro-Magnon people.

NEW TERMS IN THIS SECTION
hominids
Neanderthal
Cro-Magnon

## 25.5 Early Humans

Adaptation and change have been involved in the evolution of humans. However, scientists disagree on just how this evolution occurred. Scientists do agree that humans are classified as primates and have evolved from early hominids. **Hominids** are the early ancestors of modern humans.

Disagreement has occurred because the record of early hominid evolution is incomplete. Very few entire skeletons have been found. In fact, most hominid fossils that have been found are just jaws, skulls, and teeth.

The oldest hominid fossil found so far was discovered in Africa in 1974. The discovery was made by Donald Johanson, an American scientist. The fossil is a partial skeleton of a female believed to have been about 22 years old at death. The workers who discovered the skeleton named her Lucy. Lucy has provided scientists with a great deal of information about early hominids.

Lucy lived about 3.6 million years ago. She was about 1 m tall and weighed about 22.5 kg. She walked on two legs and had a brain larger for her size than that found in apes. Lucy's scientific name is *Australopithecus afarensis* (aws truh loh PIHTH uh kuhs a fahr EHN suhs).

Another fossil of *Australopithecus* was found in 1924 in Africa by Dr. Raymond Dart, a South African scientist. The fossil is a skull of a young hominid who died at about the age of five. The skull is about 2.5 to 3 million years old—many thousands of years younger than Lucy.

A British family of scientists—Mary, Louis, and Richard Leakey—have also found valuable fossil remains. The Leakeys named one of their discoveries *Homo habilis*, which means "handy human." They chose that name because several tools were found near the bones. *Homo habilis* lived between 2.2 and 1.5 million years ago. The Leakeys have stated that *Homo habilis*, not *Australopithecus*, evolved into modern humans.

Other items found near fossils aid in dating fossils and in describing their way of life.

## READING CRITICALLY
How do other items found with fossils help scientists learn about early humans?

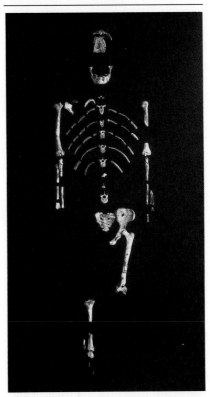

**Figure 25–9.** The *A. afarensis* skeleton known as "Lucy" represents the oldest known hominid.

Ask students to hypothesize what might have caused Lucy's death at 22 years of age. (disease, natural disaster, natural enemies)

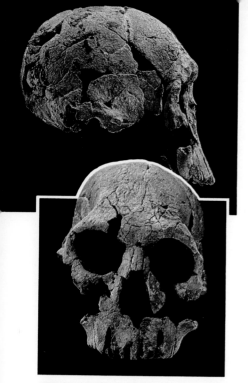

**Figure 25–10.** The *Homo habilis* lived between 2.2 million and 1.5 million years ago. There is some dispute as to whether the *H. habilis* is related to the *Australopithecus*.

Because they were able to study artifacts the Neanderthal had buried with their dead. Earlier peoples did not do this and so left little evidence of themselves.

**Figure 25–11.** This collection of human skulls shows the evolution of humans. The top row are the oldest fossils while the bottom row are more recent fossils.

Probably the closest ancestor of humans is *Homo erectus*, whose name means "erect human." *Homo erectus* lived about 1.5 to 2 million years ago. Fossil remains of *Homo erectus* have been found in Africa and Asia. The skulls show a greatly increased brain size when compared with earlier fossils. The pelvic bones show that this hominid walked in a fully upright position. In 1984, Richard Leakey discovered a nearly complete skeleton of a 12-year-old male *Homo erectus* in Kenya, Africa.

## 25.6 Modern Humans

*Homo sapiens*, which means "wise human," is the scientific name of modern humans. Modern, in this case, dates back to 130,000 years ago. At that time, the **Neanderthal** (nee AN duhr thawl) people first appeared. Their name comes from the name of the Neander valley in Germany where their skeletons were discovered in 1856. Many Neanderthal remains have been found because these humans were the first to formally bury their dead. Some of the burial sites have contained tools and other objects buried with their dead.

The Neanderthal people were strong and had large bones. Their brain size appears to have been even larger than that of today's humans. These people lived during the very harsh, cold conditions of an ice age. Neanderthals lived in communities and sheltered themselves in caves. They made weapons and tools with which they killed and skinned animals. Some of the bones from the animals provided new weapons and tools. Why do scientists know so much more about Neanderthal people than the other early humans?

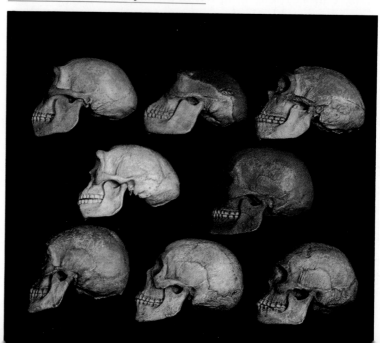

The Neanderthals disappeared about 35,000 years ago. However, no one knows what caused their disappearance. At the time the Neanderthals disappeared, the Cro-Magnons (kroh MAG nuhnz) appeared. **Cro-Magnons** were the most direct ancestors of today's humans. They were intelligent people whose physical appearance was similar to ours. Cro-Magnons lived in large communities. They were accomplished in hunting and fishing. They also produced artwork such as cave paintings, stone carvings, and sculptures of bone and ivory.

## Section Review

1. List two important hominid fossils and the scientists who discovered them.
2. Give three characteristics of Cro-Magnons.
3. Which early humans were the first to formally bury their dead and why is this fact important?
4. THINKING CRITICALLY Imagine that you are a paleontologist studying an ancient rock formation. You discover fossil bones that appear to be human. Among the bones you find charred remains of animals. What might you conclude about these early humans from their remains?

1. Lucy—discovered by Donald Johanson; *Homo habilis*—discovered by the Leakeys
2. Intelligent, artistic, good hunters, physical appearance like today's human beings
3. Neanderthals; it tells much about their way of life, the tools they made, the clothing they wore, and so on.
4. They were probably hunters and used fire to cook their food.

# CAREER

## Animal Breeder

**DESCRIPTION**  An animal breeder breeds animals to help or change the animal's characteristics. For example, breeders have developed heavier beef cattle, cows that give more milk, and miniature pigs that can be used in laboratory experiments. Most animal breeders work for the federal and state governments and for colleges and universities.

**REQUIREMENTS**  A student planning to be an animal breeder should take science and mathematics courses in high school. After graduation, the student needs to earn a bachelor's degree in agricultural science. Many positions in animal breeding are open only to applicants who have an advanced degree such as a master's or Ph.D.

**INFORMATION**  Science and Education Higher Education Programs, U.S. Department of Agriculture, Administration Building, 14th Street and Independence Avenue S.W., Washington, DC 20250

# INVESTIGATION 25: Amino Acids and Evolution

*What evidence might indicate that animals are closely related genetically?*

## PURPOSE

To count the number and kinds of amino acids in three different animals

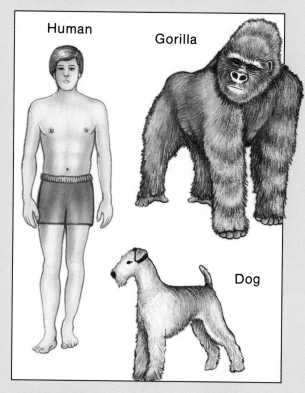

Human

Gorilla

Dog

## PROCEDURE

Amino acids are the building blocks of proteins, and all animal tissue is made of proteins. The more amino acids that animals have in common, the more proteins the animals have in common, and the more closely related they are to one another.

1. Table 1 below shows the names and number of some of the amino acids, the building blocks of proteins, that are found in the tissue of the three animals listed.

2. Copy Table 1 onto a sheet of paper. Enter all data from this investigation onto your table.

3. Add up the amino acids for each of the three animals and record them in the space provided at the end of the table.

| TABLE 1 | NAME AND NUMBER OF EACH AMINO ACID | | |
|---|---|---|---|
| **Amino Acid Name** | **Human** | **Gorilla** | **Dog** |
| Alanine | 15 | 15 | 8 |
| Arginine | 3 | 2 | 10 |
| Glutamic acid | 11 | 11 | 10 |
| Glycine | 13 | 13 | 12 |
| Proline | 7 | 7 | 5 |
| Serine | 5 | 5 | 5 |
| Theonine | 7 | 7 | 6 |
| Tryptophan | 2 | 2 | 2 |
| Tyrosine | 3 | 3 | 2 |
| Valine | 16 | 16 | 10 |
| TOTAL | 82 | 81 | 70 |

## RESULTS
1. humans, dogs

1. Which of the animals has the greatest number of amino acids? Which of the animals has the least number of amino acids?

2. What is the difference between the number and kinds of amino acids in humans and dogs? 2. 12, vary most in alanine, arginine, and valine

3. What is the difference in the number and kinds of amino acids in gorillas and dogs?

4. What is the difference between the number and kinds of amino acids in humans and gorillas? 3. 11, vary most in alanine, arginine, and valine
4. 1, humans have one more arginine amino acid

## CONCLUSION

1. Considering the evidence on amino acids shown in Table 1, which two of the three animals seem to be closely related? Explain your answer.
Humans and gorillas are more closely related; the number and kinds of amino acids are almost identical.

## APPLICATION

1. Make a list of any other similarities that humans and gorillas share that neither shares with dogs. larger brains; walk on two legs; use their hands to grasp things

2. What hypothesis could you state about the number of amino acids some animals have in common and how this makes them more closely related?
The closer the number and kinds of amino acids, the more similar the species are.

# CHAPTER 25 REVIEW

## Summary

1. The oldest fossils that have been found are about 3.5 billion years old. **(25.1)**
2. Evolution is the change in species over long periods. **(25.2)**
3. Charles Darwin's theory of evolution is based upon the process of natural selection. **(25.2)**
4. Natural selection is the process by which those individuals best adapted to their environment will be most successful. **(25.2)**
5. Selective breeding is a means by which traits of animals or crops can be strengthened or improved. **(25.3)**
6. A disadvantage of selective breeding is the resistance of certain species to pesticides or antibiotics. **(25.4)**
7. The ancestors of modern humans are known as hominids. **(25.5)**
8. Lucy, an example of *Australopithecus afarensis*, is the oldest hominid fossil found so far. **(25.5)**
9. Neanderthals and Cro-Magnons are both *Homo sapiens*. **(25.6)**
10. Cro-Magnons are the most direct ancestors of today's humans. Cro-Magnons were intelligent, strong, and artistic. **(25.6)**

## Science Terms

On a separate sheet of paper, define each term in a sentence.

adaptations **(529)**
Cro-Magnon **(539)**
evolution **(529)**
fossil **(527)**

hominid **(537)**
inbreeding **(534)**
natural selection **(531)**
Neanderthal **(538)**

paleontologist **(528)**
pesticides **(535)**
selective breeding **(533)**

## Modified True-False

On a separate sheet of paper, mark each true statement *TRUE* and each false statement *FALSE*. If false, change the underlined term to make the statement true.

1. An imprint is any preserved organism or part of an organism that once lived. F, A fossil
2. A paleontologist is a scientist who studies fossil records. T
3. The process by which individuals best adapted to their environment will be most successful is natural selection. T
4. Evolution is the adaptations and changes in living things over time. T
5. Darwin studied giraffes on the Galapagos Islands. F, tortoises
6. Breeding two closely related individuals is called crossbreeding. F, inbreeding
7. Mildew is a fungus that damages plants. T
8. Primates are the early ancestors of humans. F, hominids
9. *Homo sapiens* means "old humans." F, wise
10. Pesticides are chemicals used to kill harmful insects. T

*(continues)*

# CHAPTER REVIEW

## Multiple Choice

On a separate sheet of paper, write the letter of the term that best answers the question or completes the statement.

1. A fossil may be
   a. a bone.
   b. a leg.
   c. a footprint.
   d. any of the above.

2. Tortoises with long necks were successful when
   a. water was scarce.
   b. the climate became colder.
   c. vegetation was plentiful.
   d. vegetation was limited to tree leaves.

3. Fossil insects are sometimes found in
   a. amber.
   b. wood.
   c. shells.
   d. water.

4. Many Neanderthal skeletons have been found because Neanderthals
   a. buried their dead.
   b. were very large.
   c. all lived in one place.
   d. lived during an ice age.

5. "Handy human" is the meaning of the name
   a. Homo erectus.
   b. Homo sapiens.
   c. Homo habilis.
   d. hominid.

6. The oldest hominid fossil found to date was discovered by
   a. Darwin.
   b. Johanson.
   c. Mendel.
   d. Leakey.

7. Which is probably the closest ancestor of modern humans?
   a. Australopithecus afarensis
   b. Homo habilis
   c. Neanderthal
   d. Homo erectus

8. Cro-Magnons
   a. lived in large communities.
   b. produced artwork.
   c. were good hunters and fishers.
   d. All of the above are correct.

9. A fossil that is formed when an organism decays in mud or clay that hardens is
   a. an imprint.
   b. a mold.
   c. a skeleton.
   d. a hominid.

10. Which of the following was not crossbred to develop the beefmaster?
    a. Hereford
    b. Brahman
    c. shorthorn
    d. beefalo

## Completion

On a separate sheet of paper, complete each statement by supplying the correct term.

1. Darwin was studying the _Galapagos_ Islands when he observed the tortoises.

2. Hominids and humans are both classified as _primates_.

3. The Cro-Magnons first appeared nearly _35,000_ years ago.

4. The process of breeding animals and plants for special traits is called _selective breeding_.

5. An _imprint_ fossil results when a thin object such as a leaf or feather is trapped and preserved between layers of mud or clay.

6. Homo sapiens, which means _wise human_, is the scientific name of modern humans.

7. _Evolution_ occurs over great lengths of time and many generations of living organisms and results in the change in species.

8. Scientists bred Brahman cattle with Shorthorns and Herefords to produce _Beefmaster_ cattle.

9. The effect that occurs when an insect is no longer killed by a pesticide is called _resistance_.

10. The scientific name the fossil Lucy is _Australopithecus afarensis_.

# Writing Critically

1. Explain how the principles of genetics support Darwin's theory.
2. Compare how the different types of fossils form, and explain why soft tissue such as muscle and skin usually does not form fossils.
3. CHALLENGE Describe some ways in which selective breeding and inbreeding might have negative effects on the offspring.
4. CHALLENGE Prior to Neanderthals, hominids apparently did not bury their dead. Discuss why this fact has probably contributed to the incomplete record of early hominids.

# Skill Reinforcement

The Skill Activity on page 532 describes a method of interpreting illustrations. Choose any illustration in this book and write two or three questions that require interpretation of the illustration. Give the illustration and your questions to several classmates and ask them to interpret the illustration. Be sure you know the correct answer yourself.

# Research Ideas

1. Inbreeding can have both good and bad results. For example, a gene causing deafness has become common in Dalmatians—an inbred pure-line variety of dog. Investigate some of the effects of inbreeding on small, isolated populations, such as Dalmatians.
2. Find out what index fossils are and prepare a short presentation on their use in determining the age of layers of rocks.
3. CHALLENGE Illustrations of early hominids are often developed from just a few bones or bone fragments. Research how these illustrations are prepared from so few biological clues.

# For Further Reading

Attenborough, David. *Discovering Life on Earth.* Boston: Little, Brown and Co., 1982. This book presents a survey of the evolution of life on Earth. The book is based on the 13-part television series.

Leakey, Richard E. *Human Origins.* New York: Lodestar Books, 1982. This book is heavily illustrated and provides a detailed description of origins of hominids and *Homo sapiens.*

Resenberger, Boyce. "Bones of Our Ancestors." *Science 84* (April 1984), 29. This article shows a large collection of photographs of human fossils.

Smith, Howard E. *Living Fossils.* New York: Dodd, Mead and Co., 1982. This book introduces the reader to 11 different living fossils.

Time-Life, Editors. *Life Before Man.* New York: Time Life Books, 1972. This book summarizes early life, fossils, dinosaurs, and hominids.

Answers to Writing Critically

1. A genetic trait that enables an organism to survive and reproduce is passed on to the offspring. The offspring also have the trait and they also survive and reproduce.
2. Imprints are fossils of leaves or other thin objects trapped between layers of mud. Molds are fossils in which the organism is buried and then decays, leaving its shape. When a whole organism is preserved, it is caught in a substance that hardens, leaving the organism completely intact.
3. Breeding for a certain trait may also result in inbreeding undesirable or weak traits. For example, inbreeding dogs for a desirable appearance may also produce dogs that are less healthy.
4. No other evidence remains to fill out the picture of the lives of these early humans.

# CHAPTER 26
# Plants and Animals

The earth's beauty is increased by the wide variety of plants and animals on it. Many people enjoy observing the natural beauty of plants and animals. Plants and animals also add to the quality of life in many other ways. They are the source of many food, clothing, and industrial products.

For additional information, see pages T118–T119.

# Plants

## SECTION OBJECTIVES

- **List** the characteristics of mosses and ferns.
- **Compare** and **contrast** gymnosperms and angiosperms.
- **Relate** the roles of flowers and fruits in plant reproduction.
- **Evaluate** the possible advantages of seed production.

Photograph left: red-banded leafhopper

NEW TERMS IN THIS SECTION

| | |
|---|---|
| nonvascular | pistil |
| vascular | anther |
| gymnosperms | stigma |
| angiosperms | ovary |
| stamens | |

## 26.1 Mosses and Ferns

The earth gains much of its color from the wide variety of plants that live on its surface. More importantly, plants provide most of the oxygen used by both plants and animals for cellular respiration. All of the plants on the earth can be divided into two major groups—nonvascular (nahn VAS kyuh luhr) plants and vascular (VAS kyuh luhr) plants. **Nonvascular** plants do not have any internal system to move water and nutrients throughout the plant. Therefore, they are usually small in size. **Vascular** plants do have a system of interconnecting tissues that transport water and nutrients. This system enables some vascular plants to grow very large. Vascular plants are further divided into plants that produce seeds and plants that do not.

Of all the plants in the world, mosses are among the simplest. They grow on rocks and tree trunks, and make soft spongy carpets on the damp ground of many forests. Mosses are nonvascular plants. They do not have true roots, stems, or leaves, and they do not produce seeds. Since they do not have vascular tissue, water and nutrients are absorbed directly into the plant cells. Therefore, mosses need an almost constant supply of water.

Some students may have heard of Spanish Moss. Explain to the students that Spanish Moss is really not a moss at all. It is actually a rootless member of the pineapple family.

**Figure 26–1.** The mosses are the most primitive of land plants. There are about 14,000 species of mosses. Why are mosses found in damp, dark places? to avoid drying out, because, since they have no vascular tissue they need a constant supply of water

Plants and Animals **545**

**Figure 26-2.** The first ferns appeared 400 million years ago and have flourised ever since. Ferns vary widely in their appearance, ranging from the tree ferns (left) that can reach a height of 12 m to the woodland ferns (right) that cover the ground in a forest.

## READING CRITICALLY

What characteristics of ferns allow some to grow so tall?

vascular tissue, which enables ferns to transport materials throughout the plant

## SCIENCE FACT

The word *gymnosperm* comes from the Greek word *gymnos*, which means naked. Gymnosperms were so named because their seeds are not found in an ovary, but are out in the open, or naked.

Ferns are more advanced plants than mosses. However, ferns have a relatively simple structure as compared to seed plants. Unlike mosses, ferns have true roots, stems, and leaves. The presence of vascular tissue enables ferns to transport materials throughout the plant. Ferns are, therefore, able to grow to greater heights than mosses are. During the Carboniferous Period, ferns provided most of the vegetable matter that later formed the great coal deposits around the world.

## 26.2 Gymnosperms

Plants that produce seeds are the most advanced in the plant kingdom. Gymnosperms (JIHM nuh spuhrmz) are one type of seed plant. **Gymnosperms** produce seeds in special structures called *cones*. Gymnosperms are also called *conifers*. The best-known gymnosperms are evergreen trees such as pine, spruce, fir, and cedar. In addition to cones, conifers also have specialized leaves. Instead of broad, flat leaves, most conifers have needle-shaped leaves that they keep throughout the year. What are some benefits of needle-shaped leaves as compared to broad leaves? reduced moisture loss

The cones of the conifers are either male or female. Male cones are called *pollen cones* because they produce

Female cones are usually larger than male cones, and their scales are further apart.

**Figure 26-3.** The sugar pine on the left, the Jeffrey pine on the right, and the yellow pine in the foreground are all gymnosperms. The gymnosperms are the largest group of nonflowering plants, bridging the gap between the ferns and the angiosperms.

pollen. The pollen produces sperm cells. The female cones are called *seed cones*. These cones contain egg cells that are fertilized by sperm when both types of cells mature. Seeds lie uncovered on the scales of the female cone. When the seeds have fully developed, the wind carries them away from the cone. Many seeds land in the soil and grow into new plants.

## 26.3 Angiosperms

There are more than 200,000 kinds of angiosperms.

**Figure 26–4.** The branch from a white spruce tree (left) shows the female cones. The winged seeds can be seen emerging from the mature cone of this Scotch pine (right).

Another group of seed plants is the angiosperms (AN jee uh spuhrms). **Angiosperms** produce seeds in specialized structures called *flowers*. Flowers are more than just decorations. They are the reproductive system of the plants.

The seeds of angiosperms are produced differently from those of gymnosperms. Gymnosperm seeds are exposed in the cone. Angiosperm seeds are enclosed within a fruit. The fruit may be sweet and fleshy like an apple or a strawberry, or it may be dry like an acorn or a burr.

Angiosperms include plants, such as roses, lilies, and carnations, which are best known for their flowers. However, they also include oak trees, corn plants, berry bushes, grasses, and more than 200,000 other plants.

While the petals may be pretty and serve a useful purpose, other flower parts are more important in reproduction. The reproductive parts of the flower are usually surrounded by the decorative petals.

Most flowers contain both male and female parts. The male parts are called **stamens**. The female part is called the **pistil**. Figure 26–5 shows a common arrangement of the male and female flower parts. Notice that the stamens and pistil have been labeled to show their own special parts. The **anther** is the part of the stamen that produces pollen. The pistil has a sticky top part called the **stigma**. The stigma is sticky in order to hold the pollen grains that fall on it. The base of the pistil contains the **ovary** in which the eggs are produced.

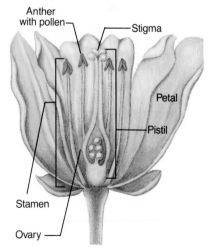

**Figure 26–5.** A perfect, complete flower is composed of both essential and nonessential parts. The pistil and the stamens are essential parts. When the petals, stamens, and pistil of the flower wilt, it is the time of greatest activity within.

Flowers with male parts only are called *staminate flowers*. Those with female parts only are called *pistillate flowers*.

**Figure 26–6.** This series of photos illustrates the reproductive stages of an angiosperm. On the far left, the flower blossoms, making the stigma available for pollination. As the flower withers, the ovary begins to develop into the fruit. The fruit holds the seeds that may become another apple tree.

In some cases, pollen that lands on the stigma will be from an anther of the same flower—this is *self-pollination*. When the pollen is from another flower the process is called *cross-pollination*.

## ACTIVITY

**Identifying Angiosperms**

Examine several different types of flowering plants. (Do not overlook trees and bushes.) Locate the fruit of the plant where the seeds are found. What differences do you notice in the fruits of various plants?

1. Mosses do not have roots, stems, leaves, or vascular tissue; ferns do.
2. Gymnosperms produce seeds in cones; angiosperms produce seeds in flowers.
3. See Figure 26–5.
4. Flowers are reproductive systems, the fruit is produced by the flower and, in turn, produces the seed.
5. protects the seeds; provides nutrients when the seed begins to grow

The first stage of reproduction in angiosperms begins when pollen lands on the sticky stigma of the pistil. The pollen may have been blown toward the pistil by the wind, or it may have been brushed on by an insect. The transfer of pollen from the stamen to the pistil is called *pollination*. The pollen begins to grow a tube down through the pistil toward the ovary. During this time, sperm cells are developing within the pollen grains. When the pollen tube reaches the ovary, a sperm cell joins with an egg cell and fertilization occurs.

The fertilized egg cell develops into an embryo, or a tiny young plant. The embryo and its protective coating become a seed. The ovary that held the egg cells now begins to develop into a fruit, such as an apple or a plum. The seeds are still safely hidden inside the fruit. The seeds will eventually be released and scattered when the fruit decomposes or is eaten. Other examples of fruits are acorns, walnuts, pea pods, tomatoes, cucumbers, and maple "helicopters." These are all fruits because a fruit is a structure containing seeds that originate as a flower part. Seeds that fall on the ground may grow into new plants. Some fruits are soft and pulpy; some have hard shells; some are large; others are very small.

## Section Review

1. How are mosses and ferns different from each other?
2. How do gymnosperms and angiosperms differ?
3. Diagram a flower and label the male and female parts.
4. Compare the purpose of flowers with that of fruits.
5. THINKING CRITICALLY Describe some advantages of seeds being enclosed in a fruit.

For teacher information about this activity, see page T119.

# SKILL ACTIVITY Constructing an Outline

**INTRODUCTION**

Outlines are useful for organizing information. Outlining a chapter you are reading can help you improve your studying skills. Outlines can also help you better remember the information in the chapter.

**PROCEDURE**

1. In order to construct an outline, first list the main ideas. Label the main ideas with roman numerals (I, II).
2. Beneath each main idea, list topics related to the idea. Label these topics with capital letters (A, B).
3. Beneath each topic, list two concepts. Label each concept with an arabic numeral (1, 2).
4. Review the chapter outline shown below for an example of how to start an outline.
5. Fill in the concepts under each topic. Use either phrases or complete sentences. However, do not mix phrases and complete sentences.

**PLANTS AND ANIMALS**

**I. Plants**
- **A.** Mosses and Ferns
- **B.** Gymnosperms
- **C.** Angiosperms

**II. Animals**
- **A.** Animals Without a Backbone
- **B.** Animals With a Backbone

**APPLICATION**

1. Choose a chapter from any of your other textbooks and construct an outline of that chapter. Check to see that the topics are related to the main ideas under which they are listed. Fill in two concepts under each topic.
2. Use your outline to write a paragraph about each main idea. Make sure all the topics and concepts under each main idea are covered in the paragraphs.
3. Use the outline and your paragraphs to study the chapter. Ask a friend to quiz you on the contents.

# Animals

## SECTION OBJECTIVES

- **Describe** some differences and similarities between vertebrates and invertebrates.
- **Explain** how different invertebrates move from place to place.
- **Differentiate** among the five classes of vertebrates.

## SCIENCE FACT

The monarch butterfly, an invertebrate, travels 3300-4400 km (one way) during its yearly migration.

## 26.4 Animals Without a Backbone

For many people the word *animal* means cat, dog, elephant, fish, bird, or other creature seen in zoos or kept as a house pet. All of these animals have a backbone and are, therefore, called **vertebrates** (VUR tuh brihts). Although vertebrates are familiar to most people, they represent only about 10 percent of the total number of animals on the earth. The other 90 percent of the animals are invertebrates.

**Invertebrates** (ihn VUR tuh brihts) are animals that have no backbone for support. Many of these animals

live in water. Some move from place to place by swimming or floating. Others crawl along the bottom of the ocean or sea. Some water-dwelling invertebrates have shells to protect their soft bodies. Others have developed stingers or sharp spines for protection.

Land-dwelling invertebrates have developed many different ways of moving from place to place. Worms crawl without legs, while spiders move about on eight legs. Most insects have wings for flying. The flea, although an insect, has no wings and relies on hopping to move from place to place. One good hop can carry it forward 33 cm at a time. By comparison, if a 1.8-m-tall human were to equal this feat, he or she would have to jump five city blocks at once.

Invertebrates are valuable in many ways. Many of these animals are used as food. Lobsters, clams, oysters, and other shellfish are common foods. Bees provide honey, a natural sweetener. Jewelry is made from the skeletons of coral. An entire industry has been built around the hobby of collecting the shells of sea-dwelling invertebrates. The common earthworm burrows through the soil, breaking it up and providing spaces where oxygen can more easily reach plant roots. In what other ways are invertebrates valuable? Answers will vary but may include the following: bees and other insects help pollinate flowers; spiders and praying mantises help control the populations of other insects

Students with an interest in art or in collecting may enjoy a project of drawing or collecting sea shells. If locale or interest makes sea shells a poor choice, try butterflies or other invertebrates. Interest in photography can also be applied in this chapter.

**Figure 26–7.** All the animals shown here are invertebrates. Clockwise from top left they are a centipede, a Monarch butterfly, a jellyfish, a Brown Cowrie, coral and sponge, a black and yellow garden spider, a giant hairy scorpion, a scarlet reef lobster, and a blue starfish.

# 26.5 Animals With a Backbone

All vertebrates have some common features, including a backbone. The backbone is part of an internal skeleton. The vertebrates are divided into five major classes—fishes, amphibians, reptiles, birds, and mammals. Some characteristics of the different classes of vertebrates are summarized in Table 26–1.

### Fishes

Fishes are one group of vertebrates. Nearly all the world's fishes belong to a class called *bony fishes*. This class includes trout, perch, flounder, red snapper, catfish, and nearly any other fish you might name. Most bony fish are covered with scales. Their bodies are long and rather flat. They use their fins to move through the water. Their gills absorb oxygen directly from the water. Some bony fishes live in fresh water. Others live in salt water.

One well-known type of fish that is not a bony fish is the shark. The shark has a skeleton made of a flexible tissue called *cartilage*. Sharks always live in salt water. Sting rays and manta rays also have skeletons made of cartilage.

The heart of fishes is not as complicated as that of other vertebrates such as birds and mammals. The fish heart has only two chambers. Fishes are said to be cold-blooded animals. This means they do not have a constant body temperature. The body temperature of a fish changes as the temperature of its environment changes.

Fishes reproduce sexually through the fertilization of eggs by sperm. In most fishes, fertilization is external, or outside the body. The female fish lays a large number

The smallest fish in the world is the pygmy goby of the Philipines—13 mm long and a few grams in weight. The largest fish is the whale shark—up to 18 m long and weighing 14 metric tons. The world's most dangerous fish, the stonefish, weighs only a few kilograms and secretes a poison from its spines that can kill an adult human in a matter of minutes.

**Figure 26–8.** The butterfly fish (left) and the stingray (right) are both fish. However, the butterfly fish is a bony fish, while the stingray has a skeleton made of cartilage.

TABLE 26–1     VERTEBRATE CHARACTERISTICS

| Class | Body Covering | Respiration | No. of Heart Chambers | Warm- or Cold-Blooded | Main Habitats | Fertilization/ Development | Reproductive Structures |
|---|---|---|---|---|---|---|---|
| Fishes | Scales | Gills | 2 | Cold | Water | External/ External | Eggs with no shells, laid in water, some live bearers |
| Amphibians | Skin | Gills and Lungs | 3 | Cold | Water and land | External/ External | Eggs with no shells, laid in water |
| Reptiles | Scales, plates | Lungs | 3 | Cold | Water and land | Internal/ External | Leathery to hard-shelled eggs, laid on land |
| Birds | Feathers | Lungs | 4 | Warm | Land, most fly | Internal/ External | Hard-shelled eggs, laid on land |
| Mammals | Hair or fur | Lungs | 4 | Warm | Water, land, some fly | Internal/ Internal | Mostly placental, live birth |

of eggs in a selected place. The male fish swims over the eggs and sprays them with a fluid containing sperm. Depending on the species of fish, the fertilized eggs will develop and hatch anywhere from days to months after fertilization occurs. In some types of fishes, the eggs are fertilized inside the body of the female. After a period of development, the young fish are born.

**Amphibians**

The process by which a young animal changes in form or structure as it becomes an adult is called *metamorphosis*.

*Amphibians* (am FIHB ee uhnz) are vertebrates that spend part of their life in water and part on land. In order to live this way, amphibians have two different stages of life. Frogs, for example, develop into tadpoles after the eggs hatch. As tadpoles they live in water and use gills to obtain oxygen from the water. As the tadpole grows, it matures into the second stage—an adult frog. Adult frogs live on land and do not have gills. Lungs replace gills so that the frog can take oxygen directly from the air.

The adult frog does not look like the tadpole. In fact, the tadpole looks more like a fish and it has some fishlike characteristics. Although adult amphibians can live on land, they are never really free of water. They must always keep their skin moist in order for oxygen to be absorbed. Amphibians are closely tied to water because most need to return to water to reproduce.

Amphibians must return to water to reproduce. In addition an amphibian must keep its skin moist.

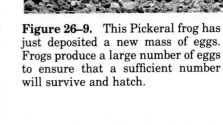

**Figure 26–9.** This Pickeral frog has just deposited a new mass of eggs. Frogs produce a large number of eggs to ensure that a sufficient number will survive and hatch.

## READING CRITICALLY
Why are amphibians never completely free of water?

**Figure 26–10.** The tough skin of some reptiles has a leatherlike texture, prized by the fashion industry. To date, however, no one is too interested in making a handbag out of the skin of a Texas horned lizard.

There are about 6,000 different species of reptiles, and they vary greatly in size. An anaconda (a South American snake) can grow to more than 9 m in length, and leatherback turtles may weigh almost a metric ton. By comparison some species of lizards measure less than 5 cm in length and weigh only a few grams.

## Reptiles

Reptiles are vertebrates that have a body covering made of scales or tough plates. Lizards, snakes, turtles, alligators, and crocodiles are all reptiles. Like fishes and amphibians, reptiles are cold-blooded animals. Unlike fish and amphibians, they do not need to spend part of their lives in water. They are completely air-breathing animals. Even though turtles, alligators, and crocodiles are often seen in water, reptiles do not have gills. They simply hold air in their lungs while under the water. Like amphibians, reptiles have a three-chambered heart.

Reptiles are very successful at living on land. Their freedom from the water allows them a wide range of movement. Fertilization of reptile eggs takes place inside the female's body. Therefore, reptiles do not have to lay their eggs in water. Since the eggs are laid in dry places, the eggs have shells to protect them. Reptile-egg shells are leathery and not as breakable as bird eggs. After the eggs are fertilized, they are laid in a protected area. Most reptiles abandon their eggs to hatch on their own. When the eggs hatch, the young have very little protection against other animals. However, some reptiles, such as alligators, do protect their nests and their young.

Reptiles eat both animals and plants. The jaws of most snakes can detach from one another to allow the snake to swallow animals larger than itself. Crocodile teeth are strong and well suited for meat eating. Tortoises, on the other hand, have no teeth as adults.

Some reptiles are venomous. Venomous animals are able to inject a venom, or poison, into another animal. The rattlesnake is probably the best known venomous snake. Other venomous snakes found in the United States include the copperhead, water moccasin, and coral snake. The Gila Monster and the Mexican beaded lizard are the only venomous lizards known.

**Figure 26–11.** The structure of a snake's jaw is designed perfectly for its job. Since the snake cannot chew its food, the snake must swallow its prey whole. In order to accomplish this, the snake's jaws detach allowing the food to be moved into its throat. As the food is swallowed, the snake's ribs spread to allow the food to pass.

## Birds

Birds are probably the most easily recognized of all vertebrate classes. Sometimes amphibians, such as salamanders, are confused with reptiles, such as lizards. Even some of the water mammals such as whales and dolphins are confused with fishes. Birds, however, are very clearly birds. They have wings, a bill or beak, two legs, and a covering of feathers over their bodies.

Birds are warm-blooded. That is, they maintain a constant body temperature. The body temperature of a bird is usually much higher than the normal human body temperature of 37°C. A sparrow's average temperature is 42°C, while a thrush has a body temperature of 45°C.

The fastest animals on earth are birds. Peregrine falcons have been clocked at 290 km/hr as they sweep down on their prey.

**Figure 26–12.** The lightweight skeleton of most birds (right) is an adaptation for efficient flight. The loon (left) is an exception. A loon needs heavier bones in order to dive through the water.

Birds have bodies designed for flying. Even their skeleton is designed by shape and weight to assist them in flight. Most birds have hollow bones in order to reduce body weight. Some birds, such as the loon, have solid bones because they feed on plants and small animals underwater. The weight of the solid bones helps the loon dive through the water.

A bird's heart has four chambers and therefore is more advanced than that of fishes, amphibians, and reptiles. The heart is very powerful and large in relation to the rest of the bird's body. Observe a bird for a few minutes. Its activity is almost constant. This steady activity places great demands on a bird's heart. <u>What effect, does a bird's constant activity and high body temperature have upon its eating habits?</u>

Birds must eat large quantities of food to maintain their activity and body temperature. "Eating like a bird" is based more on appearance than on reality.

## SCIENCE FACT

Birds that nest on cliffs and ledges lay eggs that are pointed at one end so that, if disturbed, the eggs will roll in circles instead of rolling off the edge.

## ACTIVITY

### Classifying Vertebrates

Using the characteristics listed in Table 26–1, make another table listing examples of animals in each class of vertebrate.

**Figure 26–13.** Because mammals include so many varied types of animals, it is impossible to state that all mammals have wings, fins, or legs. Scientists must rely on the presence of mammary glands and hair or fur to correctly classify an animal as a mammal.

## Mammals

Mammals are a class of warm-blooded vertebrates whose most obvious characteristics are a covering of hair and the presence of mammary glands. **Mammary glands** produce milk with which the young mammals are fed. Over 4000 different types of mammals live on Earth. These include animals as different as bats, whales, kangaroos, elephants, dogs, and humans.

The heart of a mammal is similar to that of a bird. It has four complete chambers. A four-chambered heart allows blood to flow through the lungs for a fresh supply of oxygen before the heart sends it back out to circulate through the body again.

All mammals fertilize their eggs inside the female body. Although this process also occurs in reptiles and birds, a very special difference exists in most mammals.

Young mammals develop inside the body of the female parent. Most mammals are called *placental mammals* because of an organ called the placenta. The **placenta** is an organ through which the developing young receive nourishment. One group of mammals, the *marsupials* (mahr soo pee uhlz), give birth to premature young. The young are then carried in a pouch until they are mature. Placental mammals give birth to fully developed young and do not have pouches. A third order of mammals—the monotremes—are very primitive and do not give birth to live young. They lay eggs. The only two species of monotremes on earth are found in Australia and New Zealand. They are the platypus and the echidna.

## Section Review

1. How do vertebrates and invertebrates differ? How are they alike?
2. Describe some different methods used by invertebrates to move from place to place.
3. List the five classes of vertebrates.
4. What is the origin of the name mammal?
5. THINKING CRITICALLY Why do you think there are more placental mammals than marsupials?

1. Invertebrates do not have backbones; vertebrates do. They are all animals.
2. fly, crawl, float, walk, swim
3. fish, amphibians, reptiles, birds, mammals
4. the presence of mammary glands that produce milk with which the young are fed
5. Placentals have a better chance of surviving because they are born more fully developed and are protected longer.

# CAREER

## Veterinary Science Technician

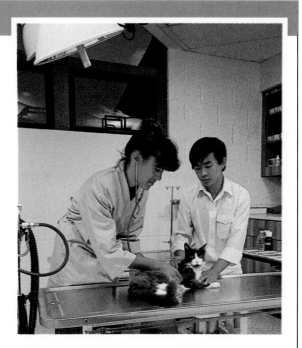

**DESCRIPTION**   A veterinary science technician, or veterinarian's assistant, helps a veterinarian care for animals. Technicians tend to routine needs such as shots and examinations. They also assist the veterinarian during surgery and other procedures. Technicians usually work in veterinary clinics, but some technicians assist in laboratory research work or are employed by large agricultural operations.

**REQUIREMENTS**   A student who plans to be a veterinarian's assistant should take math, science, and English courses in high school. Following graduation, the student completes a two-year program at a community college or technical school.

**INFORMATION**   American Veterinary Medical Association, 930 N. Meacham Road, Schaumburg, IL 60196

# INVESTIGATION 26: Movement of Water in Celery

## How do water and nutrients move from a plant's roots to its leaves?

## PURPOSE

To observe and measure the movement of water in plants with roots, stems, and leaves

## MATERIALS

600-mL beaker
red food coloring
centimeter ruler
graph paper

stalk of celery
watch or clock
scalpel
graduate

## PROCEDURE

1. Copy Table 1 onto a separate sheet of paper. As you do the investigation, record your results in the table.

2. Fill the 600-mL beaker with 300 mL of water.

3. Add 5 mL of red food coloring to the water in the beaker.

4. Obtain a freshly cut stalk of celery from your teacher.

5. Place the freshly cut celery, cut end down, into the colored water in the beaker.

6. At the end of two minutes cut the celery vertically as shown. Make sure you keep the rest of the celery in the water, cut end down, and remove only the section that you cut.

7. Measure the height that the colored water has reached in the piece of celery that you have just cut.

8. Repeat this procedure every two minutes until you have four measurements. Record the measurement each time.

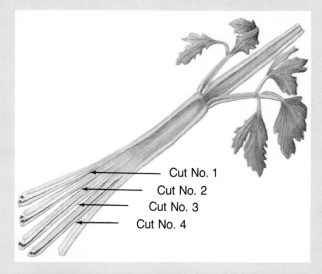

Cut No. 1
Cut No. 2
Cut No. 3
Cut No. 4

## RESULTS

1. Plot the four measurements on a graph. Plot time in minutes on the horizontal axis, and height in centimeters on the vertical axis.

2. Make a cross-section cut near the top of the celery stalk and observe the tubes, or *vascular bundles*. You will be able to recognize them because they will be colored red. Make a drawing of what you observe.

1. The red dye can be seen throughout the stem and possibly in the leaves.

## CONCLUSIONS

2. The red dye appears as circles in the cross section.
3. No, wilting indicates that it was not getting any water

1. What evidence can you show that helps explain that water moves up through the celery stalk?

2. What evidence do you have that proves the existence of vascular bundles?

3. If the stalk of celery wilted, would you expect water to be moving through the vascular bundles? Explain your answer.

1. to prevent wilting as a result of water loss
2. by placing the cut ends of the stems in colored liquid
the colored liquid will move up the stem to the flowers

## APPLICATIONS

1. Explain why produce in the grocery store is sprayed with water several times throughout the day.

2. Describe how florists can change white carnations to red or to blue.

| TABLE 1 | HEIGHT OF RED COLORING IN CELERY STALK |
|---------|----------------------------------------|
| Cut 1 | |
| Cut 2 | |
| Cut 3 | |
| Cut 4 | |

## Summary

1. Nonvascular plants have no true roots, stems, leaves, or seeds. Vascular plants have true roots, stems, and leaves, and some also have seeds. **(26.1)**

2. Gymnosperms are vascular plants that produce seeds in special structures called *cones*. **(26.2)**

3. Angiosperms are flowering vascular plants. They produce seeds protected in fruits. **(26.3)**

4. Vertebrates are animals with a backbone. Invertebrates are animals without a backbone. **(26.4)**

5. Invertebrates make up over 90 percent of the animal kingdom. **(26.4)**

6. Fishes, amphibians, and reptiles are cold-blooded vertebrates. **(26.5)**

7. Adult amphibians can live on land, but they must return to water to lay eggs. **(26.5)**

8. Birds are warm-blooded and have bodies designed especially for flight. **(26.5)**

9. Mammals are warm-blooded vertebrates characterized by the presence of hair or fur and mammary glands. **(26.5)**

## Science Terms

On a separate sheet of paper, define each term in a sentence.

angiosperm **(547)**       nonvascular **(545)**       stigma **(547)**
anther **(547)**           ovary **(547)**             vascular **(545)**
gymnosperm **(546)**       pistil **(547)**            vertebrate **(550)**
invertebrate **(550)**     placenta **(557)**
mammary glands **(556)**   stamen **(547)**

## Modified True-False

On a separate sheet of paper, mark each true statement *TRUE* and each false statement *FALSE*. If false, change the underlined term to make the statement true.

1. Nonvascular plants are usually <u>large</u> in size. F, small

2. Ferns are <u>vascular</u> plants. T

3. Conifers have <u>needle-shaped</u> leaves that they keep throughout the year. T

4. <u>Female</u> cones produce pollen. F, male

5. Conifers are a type of <u>angiosperm</u>. F, gymnosperm

6. The <u>pistil</u> is the female part of a flower. T

7. There are <u>more</u> vertebrates than invertebrates in the animal kingdom. F, fewer

8. <u>Gymnosperms</u> are flowering plants. F, angiosperms

9. <u>Reptiles</u> live part of their lives in the water and part on land. F, amphibians

10. A bat is a member of the class of <u>birds</u>. F, mammals

11. The transfer of pollen from the stamen to the pistil is called <u>pollination</u>. T

12. <u>Amphibians</u> are vertebrates that have a body covering made of scales or tough plates. F, reptiles

*(continues)*

## Multiple Choice

On a separate sheet of paper, write the letter of the term that best answers the question or completes the statement.

1. When plant egg and sperm cells join, the new cell forms a
   a. cone.
   **c.** seed.
   b. stamen.
   d. pistil.

2. Which of these structures is not found in fern plants?
   **a.** seeds
   c. roots
   b. stems
   d. leaves

3. Invertebrates never
   a. carry disease.
   c. live in water.
   **b.** have a backbone.
   d. develop shells.

4. Sharks and rays have _____ made of cartilage.
   a. bones
   c. scales
   **b.** skeletons
   d. wings

5. The base of the pistil of a flower contains the
   **a.** ovary.
   c. anther.
   b. stamen.
   d. stigma.

6. Which class of vertebrates lives both in water and on land?
   a. fish
   **c.** amphibians
   b. reptiles
   d. birds

7. Eggs with leathery shells are produced by
   a. bony fish.
   c. mammals.
   b. birds.
   **d.** reptiles.

8. Which of the following is not a reptile?
   a. snake
   c. alligator
   b. lizard
   **d.** frog

9. Which of these vertebrates is not a mammal?
   a. whale
   c. human
   **b.** catfish
   d. bat

10. Which characteristic is not found in mammals?
    **a.** three-chambered heart
    b. milk-producing glands
    c. placenta
    d. hair

11. A _____ heart is very powerful and strong in relation to its body.
    **a.** bird's
    c. mammal's
    b. reptile's
    d. amphibian's

12. Which of the following is not a vascular plant?
    a. fern
    c. gymnosperm
    **b.** moss
    d. angiosperm

## Completion

On a separate sheet of paper, complete each statement by supplying the correct term.

1. A fruit is a ripened __ovary__ .

2. The __anther__ is the part of the stamen that produces pollen.

3. The stigma is the sticky part of the __pistil__ .

4. Jewelry is made from mineral deposits of invertebrates called __coral__ .

5. Warm-blooded animals include __birds__ and mammals.

6. A shark has a skeleton made of __cartilage__ .

7. Nearly all the world's fishes belong to a class called __bony fish__ .

8. Developing mammals receive nourishment through an organ called the __placenta__ .

9. A young frog is called a __tadpole__ .

10. Animals that are __warm-blooded__ maintain a constant body temperature.

## Writing Critically

1. Explain why a whale is classified as a mammal instead of as a fish.
2. Describe the differences between vertebrates and invertebrates.
3. CHALLENGE How an organism fertilizes its

1. A whale is warmblooded, has mammary glands, breathes air, and is placental.

eggs is tied to its environment. Describe the difference between internal and external fertilization, and explain how an animal's environment is related to the fertilization method used.

2. Vertebrates have backbones—invertebrates do not.
3. External fertilization requires some way for the sperm to travel to the egg—water. Only animals that reproduce in water can use external fertilization.

## Skill Reinforcement

The Skill Activity on page 549 describes how to construct an outline. As a way of previewing the next chapter, construct an outline of the chapter. Be sure to outline all the headings and

subheadings. Review your outline after you have read the chapter carefully. Make any necessary changes.

## Research Ideas

1. Collect and identify as many different types of cones (pine, spruce, fir) as possible in your area. Find out how many species there are of each. Learn to recognize them by their distinguishable features.
2. Research the state flower and state bird of your state. Why were these specifically chosen to represent your state?
3. CHALLENGE Investigate the reproductive

process of marsupials. Describe the differences between marsupial, monotreme, and placental mammals.

4. CHALLENGE There are two animals that are classified as monotremes. Find out what these two mammals are and give a full description of them. Include the reasons why they are classified as mammals in your report.

## For Further Reading

Attenborough, David. *The Living Planet*. Boston: Little, Brown and Co., 1984. Attenborough takes the reader through mountain areas, swamps, the Great Barrier Reef, and many other places while exploring the animals of each area.

Freedman, Russell. *Animal Superstars*. Englewood Cliffs, New Jersey: Prentice Hall, 1981. This book discusses and ranks the biggest,

strongest, and fastest animals. Other categories include the animals that live the longest and those considered the smartest.

Stewart, Darryl. *The North American Animal Almanac*. New York: Stewart, Tabori and Chang, 1984. This book is a well-illustrated collection of facts and statistics about animals.

# CHAPTER 27

# Human Biology

The human body can be compared to an efficient machine. Bones and muscles act as levers. This MRI scan of a child's head shows the energy needed to run the machine. Being one's own mechanic requires developing a wellness program that focuses on prevention, rather than repair.

For additional information, see pages T120–T121.

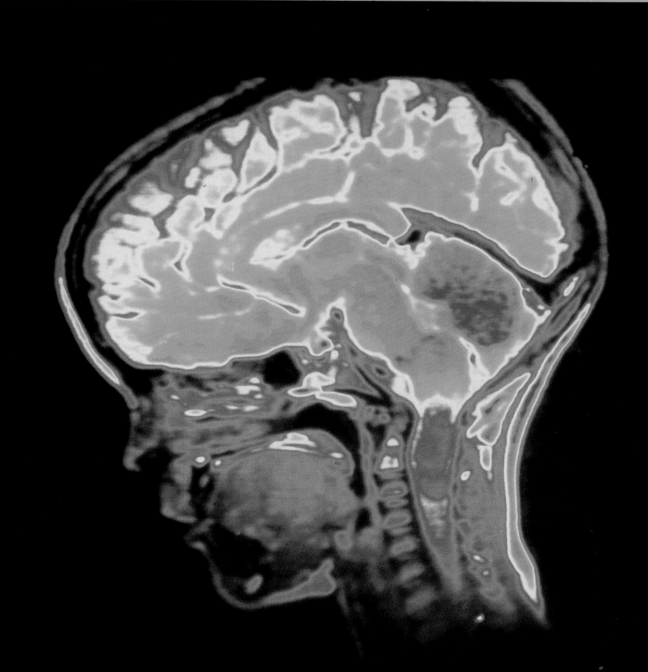

# Systems of the Body

## SECTION OBJECTIVES

- **Discuss** the various jobs of bone and muscle tissues.
- **Explain** the functions of the different parts of the nervous system.
- **Explain** the transport function of the circulatory system.
- **Trace** the path of food through the digestive system.
- **Describe** the functions of the reproductive and endocrine systems.

NEW TERMS IN THIS SECTION

| | |
|---|---|
| immune deficiency | ovaries |
| enzymes | pregnancy |
| gonads | hormones |
| testes | |

Photograph left: Magnetic Resonance Imaging (MRI) scan showing a tumor (shaded red) on the spinal cord

## 27.1 Skeletal and Muscular Systems

The human body is truly amazing. It is made up of several major body systems that work together. Without the *skeletal system* the body could not maintain its normal shape and would collapse into a lumpy mass.

The skeleton of an adult contains 206 bones. These bones perform different jobs. Long bones such as those in arms and legs provide support during standing, walking, lifting, or pushing. Flat bones protect the chest cavity and the brain. Short bones such as those in the wrists and ankles allow twisting and turning movements.

Bone is a tissue composed of living cells and nonliving minerals such as calcium and phosphorus. Minerals are the substances that make bones hard. Some bones contain a soft tissue called *marrow*. The body contains two kinds of marrow—yellow and red. Yellow marrow, found in the long bones, stores fat that the body may use in an emergency. Red marrow, found in flat bones and the ends of long bones, manufactures red blood cells and white blood cells.

There is one small bone in the body that is not connected to any other bone—the hyoid bone located at the base of the tongue. This small bone serves as the anchor for various muscles in the mouth. Scientists who work in crime laboratories look at the hyoid bone when they suspect a victim has been strangled. A broken hyoid provides possible evidence of strangulation.

## SCIENCE FACT

The bones of an adult human contain enough phosphorus to make 2000 match heads.

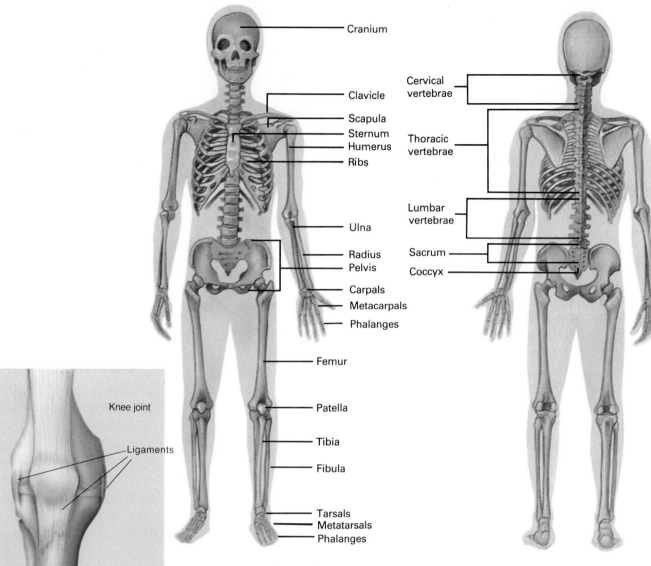

**Figure 27–1.** The bones of the skeletal system (right) provide form and support, motion, protection, mineral storage, and blood cell production. This close-up of the knee joint (left) shows how bones and ligaments interact.

*Labels on figure:*
Cranium
Clavicle
Scapula
Sternum
Humerus
Ribs
Ulna
Radius
Pelvis
Carpals
Metacarpals
Phalanges
Femur
Patella
Tibia
Fibula
Tarsals
Metatarsals
Phalanges

Cervical vertebrae
Thoracic vertebrae
Lumbar vertebrae
Sacrum
Coccyx

Knee joint
Ligaments

## SCIENCE FACT

There are no muscles in the fingers. Tendons extend into the fingers, but there are no muscles. The lack of muscles is the reason you cannot move just the tip of your fingers.

Infants and young children have only red marrow. As a child grows older and the body has a good supply of blood cells, some of the red marrow changes to yellow marrow. If disease causes the body to have a shortage of red blood cells, the yellow marrow can once again become red marrow and start producing the needed blood cells.

Most bones in the body are connected to one another. The place where two bones meet is called a *joint*. At the joint, specialized tissues called *ligaments* hold many bones together. What are some of the joints in your body? The skeletal system works with the *muscular system* to move bones. Muscle is attached to bone by a type of connective tissue called *tendon*. Some muscles, called *skeletal muscles*, attach to and help move bones. Skeletal muscles move bones by contracting, or tightening. The muscles pull, not push, on the bone to cause movement.

Answers may include the following: knees, knuckles, elbows, wrists, shoulders, hips, ankles, head and neck, and jaw.

Skeletal muscles are called *voluntary muscles* because they can be moved at will by a person. The biceps muscle in the upper arm is a skeletal muscle that can be easily seen when the arm is bent. Muscles, however, can only contract. The triceps, an opposing muscle located underneath the upper arm, straightens the arm. All muscles in the body work in opposing pairs in this way.

Moving bones is only one of several functions muscles perform in the body. *Smooth muscles* are those that line the outer walls of many organs. Their movements help to circulate material throughout the body. They move blood through the blood vessels, and they help to churn and to move food during digestion. Smooth muscles are also called *involuntary muscles* because a person cannot control their movement.

A unique type of muscle is called *cardiac muscle*. This type of muscle makes up the heart. The heart is one of the most powerful muscles in the body. The heart muscle beats about 3 billion times over an average lifetime—about 74 years. It pumps such a huge volume of blood that scientists estimate that it could fill the fuel tanks of a Saturn V moon rocket in 74 years of pumping.

## 27.2 Nervous System

The nervous system controls and regulates all of the body's activities. Without the nervous system the entire body would be like an expensive, complicated machine that was not plugged in. The nervous system consists of the brain, the spinal cord, and a network of nerves that reaches to every part of the body. The nervous system operates by a series of electrical impulses that travel back and forth between the brain and other parts of the body. These impulses travel through approximately 99 km of nerves, sometimes reaching speeds of 100 km/s.

The brain has three main parts—the *cerebrum* (SEHR uh bruhm), the *cerebellum* (sehr uh BEHL uhm), and the *brain stem*. The cerebrum is the part of the brain in which a person interprets messages or sensations. Memory, intelligence, and emotions are rooted in the cerebrum. The cerebrum is divided into right and left halves, or hemispheres. The right hemisphere controls the left side of the body. The left hemisphere controls the right side of the body. The cerebellum is much smaller than the cerebrum. The cerebellum helps the body coordinate voluntary movements. The brain stem connects the spinal cord to the brain. Parts of the brain stem help

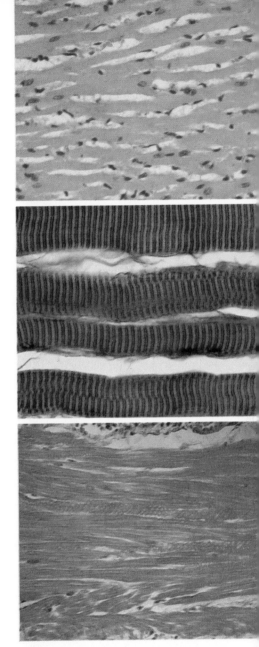

**Figure 27–2.** The appearances of different muscles are distinctive: smooth muscle (top), skeletal muscle (middle), and cardiac muscle (bottom). The cells in cardiac muscle are smaller and more closely packed than the others. The close connection allows them to function as a whole; the entire heart, therefore, beats with a steady rhythm.

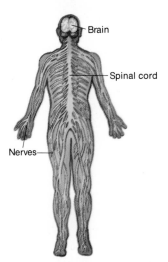

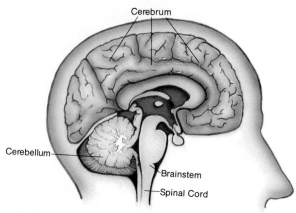

**Figure 27–3.** The spinal cord (left) can be thought of as a super extension cord. All parts of the body are plugged into that cord. The brain (right) receives all its information from the nervous sytstem.

control the involuntary activities of the body such as breathing and digesting food.

The *spinal cord* runs through the bones of the spinal column. The cord is about the diameter of your index finger and is approximately 51 cm long. The spinal cord is the link between the brain and all the other parts of the body.

## 27.3 Circulatory and Immune Systems

The body's energy and defense resources must have a way to move from one part of the body to the next. The circulatory system and the immune system work together to meet all these needs

### The Circulatory System

The *circulatory system* is the transport system of the body. It carries food, water, and gases to the body cells and carries away cell wastes. The circulatory system consists of the heart, blood vessels, and blood.

Human blood is made up of solid and liquid parts. The liquid part of the blood is called *plasma* (PLAZ muh). Plasma, which is nonliving, carries many nutrients throughout the body. It also carries cell waste products to be removed from the body. The solid parts of blood include red blood cells, white blood cells, and platelets. *Red blood cells* carry oxygen to body cells and carry away carbon dioxide. *White blood cells* fight infection and disease. *Platelets* help the blood to clot. In addition to transporting materials to and from the cells, blood also helps to regulate body temperature.

Blood is an electrolyte. You may recall from Chapter 6 that electrolytes contain ions that allow current to flow. Blood and other body fluids provide the ions for electrical impulses for the nervous system.

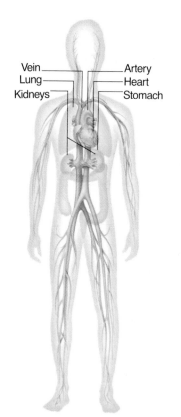

**Figure 27–4.** Blood vessels extend to all areas of the body. The heart and the blood circulation are the major elements of the body's internal transportation system.

If the electrolyte level in a person's body becomes substantially reduced, the nervous system will no longer function properly. If this happens, the heart will beat irregularly and may stop.

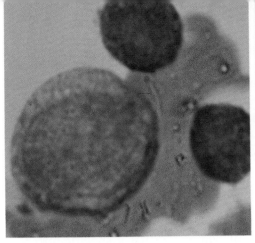
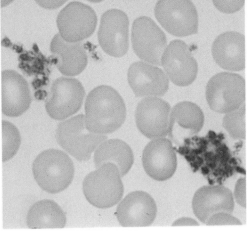

As blood flows through the body, it travels through vessels called *arteries, veins*, and *capillaries*. Arteries are blood vessels that carry blood away from the heart. Veins carry blood back to the heart. Capillaries are the smallest blood vessels. They connect arteries to veins. Blood is pumped through all these vessels by the heart. The exchange of substances between the blood and body cells takes place through the capillary walls, which are only one cell thick.

The human heart has four sections called chambers. They are the *right atrium* and *left atrium*, and the *right ventricle* and *left ventricle*. Blood leaves the right ventricle and enters the lungs. In the lungs, the blood receives a supply of oxygen to distribute throughout the body. Carrying its vital oxygen, the blood travels through veins and enters the left atrium of the heart. From the left atrium, blood is pumped to the left ventricle. As the left ventricle squeezes, it forces the oxygen-filled blood into the *aorta* (ay AWR tuh). The aorta, which is the largest of the arteries, directs the blood into other arteries that carry it throughout the entire body. The oxygen supply is used by the body, and the blood is returned to the right atrium of the heart. From there it is pumped to the right ventricle, and the entire process is repeated.

**Figure 27–5.** The solid parts of blood include white blood cells (left), platelets and red blood cells (right). White blood cells fight infection and disease. Platelets help the blood to clot. Red blood cells carry oxygen to body cells and carry carbon dioxide away.

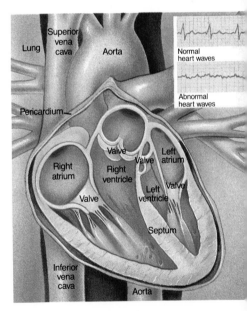

**Figure 27–6.** Open-heart surgery (left) has been made possible with the use of machines that do the work of the heart while it is being operated on. The heart is a fist-sized organ composed of tough, cardiac muscle. It contracts rhythmically to keep blood coursing through the arteries and veins.

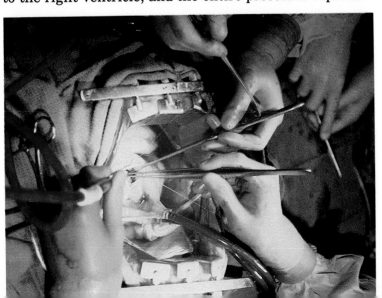

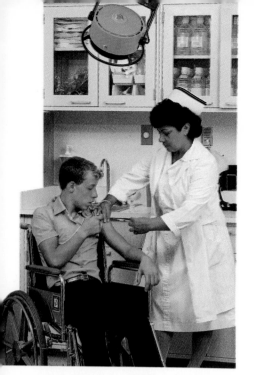

**Figure 27–7.** Vaccination provides immunity to specific diseases. Children must be vaccinated against poliomyelitis, tetanus, whooping cough, and diphtheria before beginning school.

Ask students to explain why people with heart disease often have difficulty breathing. (If the heart is not functioning properly, blood is not pumped through the body efficiently. As a result, oxygen is not being transported to the cells, nor is carbon dioxide being transported away from the cells. The person will gasp for breath in order to supply the cells with oxygen.)

The weakened virus causes the body to produce antibodies.

## The Immune System

Besides carrying nutrients, oxygen, and cell waste products to and from parts of the body, blood also carries part of the body's defense against disease. When the body is invaded by foreign substances, such as bacteria or viruses, the defense moves into action and produces additional white cells. Some of these cells produce specialized chemicals called *antibodies*. The antibodies surround and help destroy the invading substance, which is called an *antigen*. The production of enough antibodies to control the antigen may take up to several days. But once the body has produced antibodies against a specific antigen, it remembers how to do so. If the same antigen again invades the body, the body's defense is faster than the first time. This process of fighting off invading antigens by the production of antibodies is called *immunity*. Identifying, remembering, and destroying the enemy are jobs of the *immune system*. How does vaccination with a weakened virus provide immunity against a disease?

If the immune system loses its ability to perform these jobs, a condition called an **immune deficiency** results. Extreme immune deficiency almost always causes death. Acquired immune deficiency syndrome (AIDS) is a disorder caused by a virus that is transmitted through sexual contact, blood products, and infected needles. AIDS somehow shuts down the body's immune system, leaving the individual unable to fight off antigens. At this time, no cure for AIDS has been discovered.

AIDS patients do not die of AIDS directly. they die of other diseases their bodies are no longer able to fight. A common cold, for example, may become pneumonia, which may often be fatal.

## 27.4 Respiratory and Excretory Systems

The function of the *respiratory system* can be divided into two main parts. The first is breathing—taking oxygen into the lungs and removing carbon dioxide from the lungs. The second part is *respiration*. Respiration involves the transport of oxygen to body cells, the use of oxygen by the cells, and the removal of waste gases from the cells.

Breathing involves the drawing of air containing oxygen into the body through the mouth and nose. Once inside the body, the oxygen travels through the organs of the respiratory system, shown in Figure 27–8.

Once oxygen enters the air sacs in the lungs, respiration begins. Oxygen in the air sacs enters the blood in the capillaries by a process called *diffusion* (dih FYOOZ zhuhn). Once the oxygen is in the capillaries, the blood carries it to all cells of the body. In the cells, oxygen is

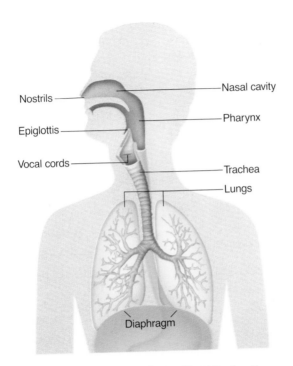

Nostrils

Epiglottis

Vocal cords

Nasal cavity

Pharynx

Trachea

Lungs

Diaphragm

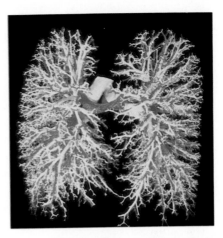

**Figure 27–8.** In the respiratory system the air moves from the mouth and nostrils into the throat and through the trachea. The trachea carries the air to the lungs, the major breathing organ. Before it enters the lungs, the trachea branches into two main tubes called the bronchi shown above with lung tissue removed.

exchanged with waste carbon dioxide in the respiration process. The carbon dioxide is then removed from the body when a person breathes out.

One function of the respiratory system is to remove gaseous wastes such as carbon dioxide. Another body system, the *excretory* (EKS kruh tawr ee) *system*, removes liquid waste products from the body. Liquid wastes are removed by the kidneys.

The kidneys filter the waste material and return the usable parts to the body. The waste that remains, called *urine*, travels to the ureter where it enters the urinary bladder. The bladder has a capacity of slightly less than a pint of liquid waste. Urine is eliminated from the body through the urethra.

Rib cage

Stomach

Right kidney

Left kidney

Ureters

Urinary bladder

Urethra

**Figure 27–9.** In the urinary system, the kidneys filter blood. Waste products are collected and drained into the bladder through the ureters. The stomach and rib cage are not part of the excretory system, but are shown in the diagram for reference.

## 27.5 Digestive System

The *digestive system* includes organs that physically and chemically change food into a form useful to the body. This physical and chemical changing of food is called *digestion*. Refer to Figure 27–10 as you follow the pathway of food through the digestive system.

Digestion begins in the mouth, where the teeth tear and chew the food into small pieces. In the mouth, the food mixes with saliva, a liquid that contains enzymes (EHN zymz). **Enzymes** are chemicals that help in the digestion of food. The enzyme in saliva changes starches to sugars.

Students can prove that saliva changes starches to sugar with a simple demonstration. Have the students chew unsalted crackers for 30-60 seconds without swallowing. Ask them to raise their hands when the cracker begins to taste sweet.

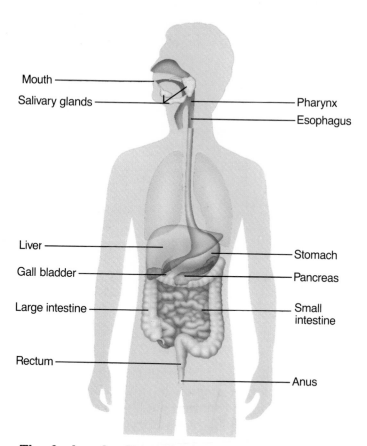

Mouth

Salivary glands

Pharynx

Esophagus

Liver

Stomach

Gall bladder

Pancreas

Large intestine

Small intestine

Rectum

Anus

**Figure 27–10.** The digestive system, shown here, consists of a long and convoluted tube, in which food is broken down physically and chemically so that the nutrients it contains can be absorbed.

Food stays in the stomach for 3-5 hours.

## READING CRITICALLY
What is one illness that might indicate that the large intestine is not functioning properly?

Answers may include diarrhea, colitis, and dysentery.

The food and saliva mixture is then swallowed. As food leaves the mouth, it enters a muscular tube called the *esophagus* (ih SAHF uh guhs). The esophagus carries the food to the stomach. In the stomach, enzymes and acids break down the food until it is a creamy liquid. The small intestine completes the process of digestion. Here the nutrients in the fully digested food are then absorbed into the blood and carried to the cells where they are used for cell processes.

Not everything that is eaten and swallowed is useful to the body. After most of the nutrients have been absorbed in the small intestine, the waste is passed to the *large intestine.* The large intestine removes any nutrients and excess water that may still be present. The remaining solid waste matter, called *feces,* is eliminated through the anus.

## 27.6 Reproductive and Endocrine Systems

The function of the reproductive system is to produce sex cells, which, when joined, will produce a new individual. The organs that produce sex cells are called **gonads.** The male gonads are called the **testes;** the female gonads are the **ovaries.** The testes produce sperm cells. After sexual maturity, or puberty, the testes continually produce sperm cells, usually throughout the life of the individual. Sperm cells are produced at the rate of about 400 million at one time. In comparison, a female produces a relatively small number of egg cells during her lifetime. After puberty, the ovaries usually produce only one egg cell per month. Egg-cell production usually ceases at about 45 to 50 years of age.

Sperm cells travel from the testes through the sperm duct and out of the body through the urethra. Sperm are deposited in the vagina during intercourse. Sperm may travel through the uterus and into the Fallopian tubes. In the female, an egg is released from the ovary in a process called *ovulation.* The egg enters the Fallopian tube. If sperm cells are present, the egg may be fertilized.

The monthly release of an egg from an ovary is part of an adult female's menstrual cycle.

Sperm cells are only about 0.005 mm long—too small to be seen with the naked eye. The ovum, however, is the largest single cell in the body— about the size of a pin head—and can be seen with the naked eye.

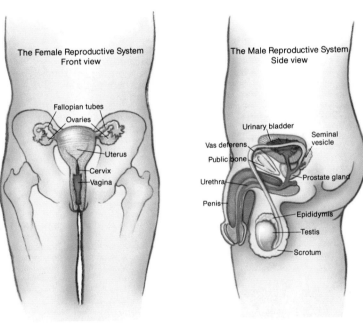

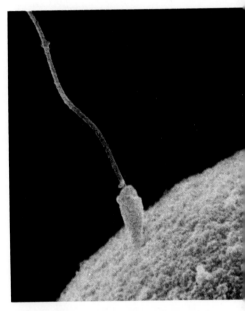

**Figure 27–11.** The male and female reproductive systems (left) are perfectly designed for the job they have to do. The end result is fertilization (right). Fertilization, which takes place in the Fallopian tube, is the point at which a single sperm penetrates the egg.

The fertilized egg travels to the uterus where it attaches to the inside lining of the uterus. Development of the fertilized egg, now called an *embryo,* will begin. After about eight weeks, the embryo is called a *fetus.* The period of development of an embryo and a fetus is called **pregnancy.** This development continues for about 266 days, or nine months. At the end of this time, the muscles of the uterus contract, pushing the fetus out through the vagina, or birth canal.

If there are no sperm in the Fallopian tube after ovulation, the unfertilized egg will disintegrate. The lining

**Making a Flow Chart**

Make a flow chart explaining the functions of the systems of the body.

of the uterus, not needed for the developing embryo and fetus, is shed from the body in a process called *menstruation* (mehn stroo WAY shuhn).

The events of the reproductive cycle are controlled by hormones. **Hormones** are chemicals that are produced in one part of the body but that have their effect on another part. Hormones are produced by *endocrine glands*. Hormones affect many functions of the body including growth, heartbeat rate, regulation of various functions, and use of nutrients by the cells.

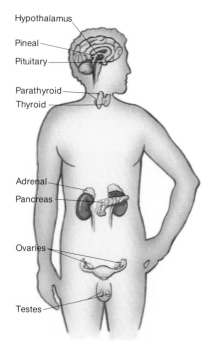

**Figure 27–12.** This illustration shows the human endocrine system. The ovaries in females and testes in males are also endocrine glands.

| TABLE 27–1 | THE ENDOCRINE SYSTEM | |
|---|---|---|
| **Gland** | **Hormone** | **Function** |
| Adrenals | Adrenaline (epinephrine) | Increases heartbeat rate, blood flow, and sugar level; activates nervous system; maintains water and mineral balance |
| Ovaries | Estrogen (females) | Regulates development of reproductive organs and female sex characteristics |
| Pituitary | Growth hormone and others | Controls growth of skeleton, kidney function, and blood pressure; regulates release of hormones from other endocrine glands |
| Pancreas | Insulin | Regulates use of sugar in body and causes liver to store sugar |
| Parathyroid | Parathyroid hormone | Regulates body's use of calcium |
| Testes | Testosterone (males) | Regulates development of reproductive organs and male sex characteristics |
| Thyroid | Thyroxine | Controls the release of energy in body |

1. Bones provide the framework for muscles to act on. Together they provide movement.
2. the spinal cord links brain and all other parts of the body; the brain coordinates and controls all body activities; nerves transmit messages throughout the body
3. blood, nutrients, water, gases, antibodies, hormones
4. food is broken down in mouth with the help of enzymes, is made into a liquid in the stomach, and the small intestine finishes the job of digestion; absorption of nutrients occurs in the small intestine, water is reabsorbed in the large intestine and wastes are accumulated
5. The endocrine system regulates the growth and development of all the reproductive organs. Hormones from endocrine glands control events in reproduction.
6. nerves send electrical impulses to the muscles causing them to contract; muscles contract and move the bones of the skeletal system.

# Section Review

1. How do muscles and bones work together to make the body move?
2. What is the function of the various parts of the nervous system?
3. What substances are transported by the circulatory system?
4. What happens to food once it enters your mouth?
5. Explain the relationship between the reproductive and endocrine systems.
6. THINKING CRITICALLY How do the nervous, muscular, and skeletal systems work together?

# SKILL ACTIVITY — Interpreting Labels

**INTRODUCTION** — Healthful eating not only includes eating carbohydrates, fats, and proteins but also watching how much of each of these nutrients you eat. Avoiding too much animal protein will reduce the fat you eat. Only 20 to 30 percent of the calories you consume should be fat. The amount of sodium in food also should be carefully controlled. Excess sodium can cause high blood pressure.

**PROCEDURE** —
1. Read the labels below.
2. Compare the foods in the table for the amount of calories, fats, carbohydrates, and sodium they contain.

Nutrition Information for Potato Chips: $0.59/56-gram package

Serving size 28 grams—15 potato chips
Number of servings per Package...... 2
Calories................ 150
Protein ................ 2 grams
Carbohydrate ........... 14 grams
Fat.................... 12 grams (90 fat calories)

Sodium ................ 200 milligrams

Nutrition Information for Crackers: $1.89/340-gram package

Serving size 28 grams—8 crackers
Servings per box............ 12
Calories.................... 140
Protein .................... 2 grams
Carbohydrate ............... 18 grams
Fat......................... 8 grams (72 fat calories)
Sodium ..................... 120 milligrams

| | Weight | Calories | Fat Calories | Sodium |
|---|---|---|---|---|
| potato chips | 99 g | 525 | 315 | 700 mg |
| potatoes | 99 g | 70 | 0 | 7 mg |

**APPLICATION** —
1. Which of the snacks—potato chips or crackers—has better nutritional value? Explain. crackers—fewer calories, less fat, and less sodium
2. Notice the cost of the potato chips and crackers. Which of the snacks would be a better buy?

Crackers—12 servings for $1.89 as opposed to 2 servings for $.59

3. Compare potato chips and cooked fresh potatoes for nutritional value. fresh potatoes have fewer calories, less fat, and less sodium

# Maintaining Wellness

## SECTION OBJECTIVES
- **Define** *wellness*.
- **Plan** an individual wellness program.
- **Summarize** the effects of alcohol and tobacco on the body.
- **Explain** how drugs are abused.

## 27.7 A Question of Choices

Most people can explain what sickness is and can give examples to illustrate their explanations. Defining wellness, however, may be a little more difficult. Wellness is more than just the opposite of sickness. **Wellness** has been described as the highest level of health a person can achieve. It involves not just feeling well but also feeling good about yourself. Achieving wellness involves making choices.

The choices made toward achieving wellness are usually not big, dramatic choices. Taken one at a time, they may even appear unimportant. Deciding to eat a balanced meal instead of a snack, deciding to wear a jacket in cold weather, or simply deciding to wash your hands before eating are small decisions that contribute to wellness.

Other decisions that must be made as you work to achieve wellness include those concerning exercise and sufficient rest. Decisions concerning the use of harmful substances are also important.

The effect of alcohol is felt very rapidly because alcohol immediately passes through the lining of the stomach and is absorbed by the circulatory system. Once in the circulatory system, the alcohol reaches the brain within just a few seconds.

## 27.8 Alcohol, Tobacco, and Other Drugs

A **drug** is a chemical that changes the way a person feels, thinks, or behaves. The effects of drugs on a person can be severe to mild. Abusing drugs is risking health and wellness.

### Alcohol
Ethyl alcohol is a chemical compound that is present in beer and wine, as well as in whiskey and other liquors. When a person consumes a drink containing alcohol, the alcohol is absorbed by the stomach and the small intestine. The alcohol passes through the membranes of these

**SCIENCE FACT**

Alcohol use is especially dangerous during pregnancy. Alcohol-related birth defects occur frequently. Most physicians advise against drinking during pregnancy.

two organs and enters the blood within about two minutes. Once in the blood, alcohol is carried to all parts of the body. In the liver, the alcohol is broken down into water, carbon dioxide, and energy. The liver, however, can break down only about 15 mL of alcohol each hour. One drink usually contains a minimum of 22 mL of 80- to 100-proof alcohol.

Alcohol presents risks to all parts of the body. The liver may be damaged to the extent that it can no longer function. In fact, liver disease is the main cause of death in people who abuse alcohol. The heart and the digestive system may also be damaged by excessive alcohol consumption. Figure 27–13 summarizes the effects of alcohol on the body.

### READING CRITICALLY
What factors might affect how fast a person feels the effects of alcohol?

height, weight, whether or not the person is eating while drinking, and level of health

| Effects of Alcohol Consumption | | |
|---|---|---|
| Milliliters of 80-100 proof alcohol | Blood alcohol level (g/100 cc) | Effects |
| ▽▽ | 0.05 | Sense of well being |
| ▽▽▽ | 0.10 | Confusion |
| ▽▽▽▽▽ | 0.15 | Intoxication |
| ▽▽▽▽▽▽ | 0.20 | Depression |
| ▽▽▽▽▽▽▽▽ | 0.25 | Slurred speech |
| ▽▽ ▽▽▽▽▽▽▽▽ | 0.30 | Stupor |
| ▽▽▽ ▽▽▽▽▽▽▽▽ | 0.40 | Coma |
| ▽▽▽▽▽▽▽▽▽▽ ▽▽▽▽▽▽▽▽▽▽ | over 0.45 | Death |

Figure 27–13. Alcohol produces a sense of euphoria and a loss of mental and physical control. Alcohol can damage every system in the body.

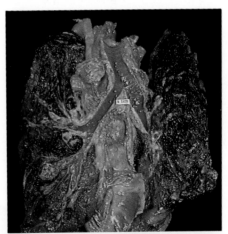

Figure 27–14. Tobacco smoke is a major cause of personal ill health. The damage to the lung on top is due to smoking. The lung below is a healthy lung.

## Tobacco

Decisions made regarding tobacco use will also have a serious influence on wellness. Tobacco smoke contains a drug called **nicotine** (NIHK uh teen). Nicotine increases blood pressure and causes the heart to beat faster.

Tobacco smoke also contains tar and carbon monoxide. Tar is a sticky substance that coats the lungs and other parts of a smoker's respiratory system. Carbon monoxide is a gas that interferes with the oxygen supply carried by the red blood cells. This decrease in oxygen causes the shortness of breath often experienced by heavy smokers. Smoking contributes to heart disease, lung cancer, and *emphysema* (ehm fuh SEE muh), a disease that prevents the lungs from exchanging carbon dioxide and oxygen.

Even though no smoke is inhaled, smokeless tobacco products are considered causes of mouth cancer.

## Legal Drugs

Medicines, even aspirin, are drugs. However, they are drugs that can be sold legally. Some medicines require prescriptions from a physician; others can simply be sold over-the-counter. When taken under the supervision of a physician, medicines are generally safe.

Medicines become a problem when they are abused. Borrowing a prescription drug from a friend because you believe the drug might help you is a form of drug abuse. What is safe and helpful for one person may be harmful, or even fatal, to another. Increasing the amount of medicine without instructions from the physician is also a form of drug abuse.

Some legally sold drugs do not seem like drugs at all. Caffeine (KAF een) is an example. **Caffeine** is a stimulant found in many soft drinks, coffee, tea, and chocolate. Even though it is easily purchased, caffeine can raise blood pressure, cause the heart to beat faster, and produce nervousness and sleeplessness.

## Illegal Drugs

Many drugs are illegal. These are often referred to as "street drugs." Many of these drugs cannot be purchased legally even with a prescription. **Cocaine**, for example, is an illegal stimulant usually used in powder form. Cocaine is popular because it temporarily fills the person with energy and with a sense of being able to conquer the world. Unfortunately, the feeling does not last and is replaced by tiredness, extreme depression, and the need for more cocaine. What is this need for more of a drug called? addiction

**Figure 27-15.** Cocaine is extracted from the leaves (right) of the coca plant, which grows in South America (left). The plant was first cultivated by the Incas, a people that built an empire in ancient Peru.

Both LSD and PCP are **hallucinogens** (huh LOO suh nuh jehnz). They cause things to appear different from reality. The hallucinations are like dreams that occur while the user is awake. However, many hallucinations are terrifying. Because the user is awake during the hallucination, he or she sometimes acts out what is being hallucinated. Users of hallucinogens often do serious physical damage to themselves while hallucinating.

**Marijuana** is an illegal drug that is widely used and sold. Research continues in an effort to identify the effects of this drug. It is already known that marijuana temporarily interferes with memory and reasoning. The drug sometimes causes its user to experience severe depression after the first rush of excitement has ended. Since the drug also interferes with brain function, researchers are trying to find out what lasting effect that interference might have on the brain.

## Section Review

1. Define wellness. 1. the highest level of health a person can achieve
2. List three decisions that could be made to improve wellness. 2. Answers will vary, but may include decisions concerning eating properly, exercise, sleep, cleanliness, and avoiding drug abuse.
3. What are some effects alcohol and tobacco may have on the body? 3. liver damage, lung damage, heart damage, death of brain cells, and respiratory distress
4. Explain how legal drugs may be abused.
5. **THINKING CRITICALLY** What might be the combined effects of alcohol and tobacco use?

**Figure 27–16.** The leaves and flowering tops of these hemp plants can be dried to make a tobacco-like substance called marijuana.

4. using someone else's prescription, taking a prescription improperly
5. double the effects of either individually; harming more systems

# CAREER

## Licensed Practical Nurse

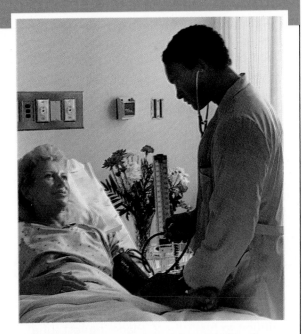

**DESCRIPTION** A licensed practical nurse (LPN) works in a physician's office or clinic, assisting the physician in routine examinations, laboratory work, and patient care. In hospitals, they administer medicines and record patients' vital signs; they help patients bathe and dress; and they aid in health maintenance and rehabilitation after injury or serious illness. LPNs also may work in private homes, providing daily nursing care for patients confined to their homes.

**REQUIREMENTS** After graduation from high school, the student who plans to be an LPN must complete a one-year program in practical nursing. All states require LPNs to be licensed. To earn a license, a person must complete an approved program in nursing and pass a written examination.

**INFORMATION** National Association for Practical Nurse Education and Service, Inc., 10801 Pear Tree Lane, Suite 151, St. Louis, MO 63074

# INVESTIGATION 27:  Enzyme Action on Starch

## What effect do digestive enzymes have on starches?

## PURPOSE

To observe the action of the enzyme ptyalin, or salivary amylase, on potato

## MATERIALS

test-tube rack
4 small test tubes
250-mL beaker
hot plate
cubes of raw white potato
dropping bottle of Benedict's solution
dropping bottle of iodine solution
mortar and pestle
graduate
glass-marking pencil
test-tube holder

## PROCEDURE

1. Copy Table 1 onto a separate sheet of paper. Record your results onto this table. Label the test-tubes 1–4 with a glass marking pencil.

2. Place several cubes of potato into the mortar and grind thoroughly with 4 mL of water until well mixed.

3. Divide this mixture between test tubes 1 and 2, putting 2 mL in each test tube.

4. Add 10 drops of iodine to test tube 1. If starch is present in the potato, a blue-black color will appear. Record any color change in Table 1.

5. **CAUTION: Put on safety goggles and a lab apron. Benedict's solution is caustic. If you get it on your skin, wash immediately. When handling hot test tubes, use a test tube holder.** Add 1 mL of Benedict's solution to test tube 2. Place the test tube in a hot water bath and boil it for 10 minutes. If sugar is present, a red color will appear. Record any color change in Table A.

6. Place several cubes of potato into your mouth and chew vigorously until the potato is well mixed with saliva.

7. Place about 1 mL of the potato and saliva mixture into test tube 3. Add 10 drops of iodine to this mixture. Record any color change in Table 1.

8. Place several fresh cubes of potato into your mouth and chew vigorously until the potato is well mixed with saliva.

9. Place about 1 mL of the potato and saliva mixture into test tube 4. Add 1 mL of Benedict's solution to this mixture and heat for 10 minutes in a hot-water bath. Record any color change in Table 1.

## RESULTS

| Test tube # | Test | Results |
|---|---|---|
| **TABLE 1** | | |
| 1 | Color after adding iodine | blue-black |
| 2 | Color after adding Benedict's solution and heating | no change |
| 3 | Color after adding iodine | no change |
| 4 | Color after adding Benedict's solution and heating | red |

1. starch—1; sugar—4
2. Starch was digested in some of the samples.
3. salivary amylase

## CONCLUSIONS

1. Which solutions contained starch? Sugar?

2. How do you account for the presence of sugar in some of the potato samples but not in the others?

3. What caused sugar to be present?

# CHAPTER 27 REVIEW

## Summary

1. The skeletal system provides the body with support and protection. **(27.1)**

2. The nervous system sends electrical impulses to all parts of the body, giving instructions for body functions. It consists of the brain, spinal cord, and nerves. **(27.2)**

3. The heart pumps blood into and out of its four chambers. The chambers are the right atrium, left atrium, right ventricle, and left ventricle. **(27.3)**

4. The immune system helps the body make antibodies to destroy antigens that invade it. **(27.3)**

5. Respiration involves not only breathing, but also using oxygen at the cellular level. **(27.4)**

6. Kidneys, ureters, and the bladder are parts of the excretory system. **(27.4)**

7. The digestive system includes organs that physically and chemically change food into a form useful to the body. **(27.5)**

8. The male reproductive organs are testes. The female reproductive organs are ovaries. **(27.6)**

9. Endocrine glands affect growth and development. **(27.6)**

10. Wellness is the highest level of health a person can achieve. **(27.7)**

11. Alcohol, tobacco, and other drugs can cause serious mental and physical problems for abusers. **(27.8)**

## Science Terms

On a separate sheet of paper, define each term in a sentence.

caffeine **(576)**
cocaine **(576)**
drug **(574)**
enzyme **(569)**
gonads **(570)**
hallucinogen **(576)**
hormones **(572)**
immune deficiency **(568)**
marijuana **(577)**
nicotine **(575)**
ovaries **(571)**
pregnancy **(571)**
testes **(570)**
wellness **(574)**

## Modified True-False

On a separate sheet of paper, mark each true statement *TRUE* and each false statement *FALSE*. If false, change the underlined term to make the statement true.

1. Flat bones provide support during lifting and pushing. F, long

2. LSD and PCP are hallucinogens. T

3. Specialized tissue called muscles hold many bones together. F, ligaments

4. The brain stem controls memory and intelligence. F, cerebrum

5. The spinal cord is the link between the brain and the rest of the body. T

6. Arteries are blood vessels that return blood to the heart. F, veins

7. Antibodies surround and destroy antigens. T

8. The kidneys are part of the reproductive system. F, excretory

9. Hormones are secreted by endocrine glands. T

10. One function of the respiratory system is to remove gaseous wastes such as carbon dioxide. T *(continues)*

# CHAPTER REVIEW

## Multiple Choice

On a separate sheet of paper, write the letter of the term that best answers the question or completes the statement.

1. Which of the following is a legal drug?
   a. PCP
   **c.** caffeine
   b. LSD
   d. cocaine

2. The place where two bones meet is a
   **a.** joint.
   c. ligament.
   b. muscle.
   d. tendon.

3. The largest artery in the body is the
   a. left atrium.
   c. ventricle.
   **b.** aorta.
   d. right atrium.

4. The _____ helps the body coordinate voluntary movement.
   a. brain stem
   b. cerebrum
   **c.** cerebellum
   d. spinal cord

5. The final stage of digestion occurs in the
   a. stomach.
   b. large intestine.
   c. esophagus.
   **d.** small intestine.

6. Females produce eggs in the
   a. Fallopian tubes.
   **b.** ovaries.
   c. uterus.
   d. none of the above.

7. The liquid part of blood is called
   a. white blood cells.
   c. marrow.
   b. red blood cells.
   **d.** plasma.

8. Oxygen in the lungs' air sacs enters the blood in the capillaries by a process called
   a. respiration.
   c. inhalation.
   **b.** diffusion.
   d. breathing.

9. Food is carried from the mouth to the stomach by the
   **a.** esophagus.
   c. small intestine.
   b. aorta.
   d. large intestine.

10. When a fertilized egg attaches to the lining of the uterus, the result is
    a. menstruation.
    **c.** pregnancy.
    b. ovulation.
    d. puberty.

11. The gland that regulates the use of sugar in the body is the
    a. thyroid.
    **b.** pancreas.
    c. adrenals.
    d. pituitary.

12. Infants and young children have only ____ marrow.
    **a.** red
    b. white
    c. yellow
    d. clear

## Completion

On a separate sheet of paper, complete each statement by supplying the correct term.

1. Fat is stored in _yellow_ marrow.
2. Heart muscle is called _cardiac_ muscle.
3. The brain stem connects the brain to the _spinal cord_.
4. Hormones are secreted by the _endocrine_ .
5. If the body loses the ability to destroy invading organisms, it has an _immune_ deficiency.
6. The trachea and bronchi are part of the _respiratory_ system.
7. Nutrients are changed into energy in the _digestive_ system
8. The _excretory system_ removes any nutrients or excess water that may be present in digested food.
9. _Nicotine_ is a drug in tobacco that increases blood pressure and causes the heart to beat faster.
10. A human fetus needs approximately _226_ days to completely develop.

## Writing Critically

1. Explain why the muscular and skeletal systems are so closely linked with one another.
2. Make a list of the disadvantages of smoking. Use all the ideas you can think of, even if they were not mentioned in the chapter.
3. **CHALLENGE** Explain how the respiratory and circulatory systems are closely linked to one another.

1. Muscles are needed to move bones.

4. **CHALLENGE** Describe the effects of drugs on the body. Include systems that are affected by the use of drugs and the damage that can result. Include addiction possibilities in your discussion.

2. Answers may include cancer, high blood pressure, emphysema, loss of appetite, and loss of senses of smell and taste.
3. Circulatory system carries oxygen from lungs to cells and $CO_2$ from cells to lungs.
4. alter nervous system, speed up or slow down respiratory and circulatory systems, can cause heart and brain damage; addiction can be physical and/or emotional to all drugs

## Skill Reinforcement

The Skill Activity on page 573 describes how to interpret labels on food containers. Go to the grocery store and examine several brands of the same product. Make a table comparing the contents of each brand of the product. Discuss your findings with the class.

## Research Ideas

1. Investigate the health and wellness precautions a pregnant woman should observe. Include the effects of poor prenatal care on the baby.
2. Research alcoholism as a disease. Share your findings with the class.
3. **CHALLENGE** Research smokeless tobacco. When did it come into use? Why is it popular? How is it harmful to the body?

4. **CHALLENGE** This chapter has discussed the major systems of the human body and how they operate. Pick one system and find out what happens to the body when that system breaks down. Include diseases and disorders associated with the system and how they affect the function of the system.

## For Further Reading

Curtis, Neil. *Longman Illustrated Dictionary of Biology*. New York: York Press, 1985. This illustrated book clusters words together as not only to define them, but to relate them to their specific areas.

Miller, Jonathan. *The Human Body*. New York: Viking Press, 1983. This book contains illustrations, referred to as operating scale models, that unfold out from the pages for a three-dimensional effect.

Oldendorf, W. H., and W. Zabielski. "The World Divided: Your Brain's Split Universe." *Science Digest* (January 1982), 90, 56. This article explains how the brain hemispheres are linked and how brain damage affects perceptions.

Yudkin, John. *This Nutrition Business*. New York: Norton, 1981. The personal nutritionist discusses the fundamentals of nutrition and the most commonly asked questions about the subject.

# NEW TRACKING TECHNOLOGIES

The eagle left Maryland and took a leisurely trip down the coast, reaching Florida in December. For nearly a year the eagle's movements were followed using a new technology called *biotelemetry*.

## Biotelemetry

Strapped to the eagle's back was a tiny radio transmitter. Its signals were monitored by two satellites, which were used to fix the eagle's daily position.

Two devices are used in biotelemetry. The first device, a battery-powered transmitter, which transmits a radio signal, is attached to the animal. Second, a receiver is used to pinpoint the signal's location. The transmitter can be fitted with sensors to give scientists information about body temperature, heartbeat rate, and respiration. It can transmit sounds made by the animal. The transmitter can be made small enough to fit a rat and durable enough to survive a seal's dive into icy ocean waters. The receiver can be hand carried or installed on a truck, a boat, an airplane, or even a satellite.

## Animal Secrets

The giant panda of mountainous eastern China is one of the rarer animals on Earth. Wildlife biologists have recently begun an intensive effort to learn about the panda's daily activities. One of the tools of this study is biotelemetry.

A captured panda is fitted with a radio collar, then freed. Signals are used to locate the animal periodically, and researchers can then study its behavior from concealed locations nearby. Researchers also use these radio transmitters to study panda activity.

The giant Panda feeds on bamboo leaves.

When the panda rests, the transmitter puts out a slow-pulsing signal. When the panda is eating or traveling, the signal is fast.

Many other species have been the subjects of biotelemetry studies. In Nepal, scientists are examining the habits of the rare snow leopard. In Wyoming, they are using biotelemetry to follow grizzly bears. In Florida, the technique has been used to study the Florida panther in the Everglades.

More common species are the usual subjects of biotelemetry studies. Where does a blue crab in Maryland's Rhode River spend its time and how often does it feed? What kind of habitats are preferred by sandhill cranes along the

Solar panels on this monitor give the transmitter the power to monitor the bird's habits.

Platte River in Nebraska? What is the heartbeat rate of a grazing mule deer? How does the pileated woodpecker of western Oregon forests use its habitat? All these questions, and many more, have been answered using biotelemetry.

## Advances in Biotelemetry

Wildlife biologists are constantly improving the devices used in biotelemetry. Externally mounted radio packs used on waterfowl can interfere with diving and feeding. Researchers are experimenting with implanting transmitters surgically into ducks' abdominal cavity. For use on large birds, researchers are developing leg-band transmitters that will be powered by solar energy. Tiny solar panels on the leg bands provide energy for the transmitter during daylight hours.

Recently, a group of researchers studied the behavior of rats in Los Angeles by fitting the rats with tiny radio collars. The researchers discovered that the city's lush landscaping provides a perfect habitat for the rat.

Biologists are finding more and more uses for biotelemetry. This new technology makes it possible to follow and study virtually any animal, from a whale to a rat, and to solve many mysteries of animal behavior.

Biotelemetry is used to monitor animals ranging from the ground squirrel (left) to the snow leopard (right).

# UNIT 7

# Science and Society

Photograph right: solar collectors at Solar One in Barstow, California

Why do living things depend so much on their surroundings, or environment? The relationship between living organisms and their environment is called *ecology*. Many scientific and technological advances have irreversibly changed our environment. As a result, the supplies of many of our natural resources are rapidly decreasing. This unit describes the delicate balance that exists between living and nonliving things and some ways to maintain that balance.

**584**

CHAPTER

# 28

# Ecology

For hundreds of thousands of years, alligators have been digging "gator holes" in marshes and swamps. When rainfall is low, other animals such as insects, frogs, turtles, snakes, and birds also use these holes as sources of food and shelter. The use of gator holes shows some ways in which animals adapt to the environment.

For additional information, see pages T124-T125.

# Organization of Ecosystems

### SECTION OBJECTIVES

- **Describe** ways in which living and nonliving parts of an ecosystem interact.
- **Distinguish** between ecosystem, population, and community.
- **List** two examples of ecological change.
- **Explain** how biotic potential and environmental resistance interact.

NEW TERMS IN THIS SECTION

| | |
|---|---|
| ecology | niche |
| ecosystem | biotic potential |
| abiotic | limiting factor |
| biotic | environment resistance |
| population | succession |
| community | climax community |
| habitat | |

Photograph left: dwarf cypress forest, Everglades National Park, Florida

## 28.1 Nonliving Components of Ecosystems

The study of how living and nonliving things interact is called **ecology** (ee KAHL uh jee). Ecologists, those who study ecology, can study these interactions in a drop of water, a plot of soil, or a large forest. Such areas are called *ecosystems* (EE koh sihs tuhmz). An **ecosystem** is a group of living and nonliving things that interact with each other over time.

The kind and number of organisms that live in an ecosystem are affected by other living things and by nonliving factors. The nonliving factors that affect an ecosystem are called **abiotic** factors. Climate and soil are two important abiotic factors in ecosystems. Climate, in turn, depends on amount of moisture and average yearly temperature.

Moisture includes precipitation such as rain and snow, and humidity. *Humidity* is the amount of water vapor in the air. The amount of precipitation is influenced by wind patterns and features of the land. For example, mountain ecosystems vary according to the

**Figure 28–1.** An ecosystem can be as small as that of the mourning cloak larva in a small pool of water formed by the cup of a leaf.

Ecology **587**

Draw three interconnecting circles on the chalkboard. Label the one on top air; the one on the bottom left water; and the one on the bottom right, land. Draw a fourth circle that takes in the area where the other three circles intersect. This represents the ecosphere, that part of Earth that supports life.

amount of moisture they receive. An ecologist might find a tropical forest on one side of a mountain and a desert on the other.

Another abiotic factor that affects an ecosystem is the amount of sunlight, or solar energy, received. The amount of sunlight that reaches a system depends on the latitude. The nearer the equator an ecosystem is, the more sunlight it will receive. Therefore, tropical ecosystems receive more solar energy than do polar ecosystems. The movement of the earth around the sun causes the amount of sunlight received in any ecosystem to change by season.

The sunlight received by an ecosystem also helps determine the temperature of the ecosystem. The temperature of an ecosystem also changes according to its distance from the equator. The farther an ecosystem is from the equator, the cooler the temperature. Areas that receive the same amount of moisture but have different temperatures support very different ecosystems. Figure 28–2 illustrates the effects of temperature on ecosystems.

**Figure 28-2.** These bison have adapted to the extremes in temperature found within their ecosystem. By growing and shedding heavy fur coats, they are comfortable year round.

A third abiotic factor that affects an ecosystem is soil. Soil supports plant life. Plants support most other life in the ecosystem. Soil is a mixture of minerals, organic material from plants and animals, water, and gases. In addition to supporting plant life, soil is the home of organisms such as bacteria, fungi, insects, and invertebrates such as worms.

**Figure 28-3.** This farmland is fertile due to a combination of abiotic factors.

The kind of soil that is found in an ecosystem depends on the climate and the geological history of the area. Soils in cool, moist climates have more organic material than soils in hot, dry climates. The soil in Nebraska, for instance, is very fertile and can produce large quantities of crops. The soil in the tropical rain forest of Brazil, however, is very low in organic materials and cannot produce crops at all unless it is heavily fertilized. Soils formed in mountain valleys have more kinds of minerals than soils formed on beds of old oceans. The fertile soils of some mountain valleys support some of the richest farming areas in the world.

## 28.2 Living Components of Ecosystems

The living, or **biotic** (by AHT ihk), components of ecosystems include all living things. The biotic members of an ecosystem interact with each other and with the abiotic factors of the ecosystem.

Everything in an ecosystem affects everything else. For example, oak trees require sunlight, soil, and moisture to grow. When leaves fall from the trees, the organic material decomposes and enters the soil, thereby improving the soil's ability to hold water and nutrients.

*READING CRITICALLY*

Why is the interaction of all three abiotic factors important to an ecosystem?

Each abiotic factor is infuenced by the others. If one factor changes, it may change the other factors, which can then affect the ecosystem. For example, if the amount of precipitation changes, then the soil can change, causing some crop failure.

Extend the idea of connectedness by having students develop lists of people who help them and whom they help after school. Emphasize the notion that all interactions are two way, whether they acknowledge it or not.

Squirrels depend on oak trees for food and as places to build nests. In turn, the squirrels help the oak tree to reproduce by burying acorns. The oak tree, the squirrel, and the soil all depend on one another.

A group of organisms of a single species, living in a certain area, is a **population.** For example, a population of panthers might include all the panthers in Florida's Big Cypress Swamp. Abiotic factors such as climate and nutrient supplies can affect the size of a population. When soil is too dry and is low in nutrients, the ability of populations to grow within that ecosystem is limited. When soil contains enough moisture and nutrients, the potential for larger populations is much greater.

Biotic factors also affect populations. The bobcat population, which feeds on rabbits, tends to keep the rabbit population at low levels. Sometimes a population may affect itself. If the population becomes too large, members compete with one another for food, space, and mates. What factors might keep the bobcat population in check?

All the populations in an ecosystem are members of the same biotic community. A **community** consists of all the living organisms in an ecosystem. Abiotic factors are not considered part of a community. For example, a freshwater community could include algae, insects, and fish. Even humans that visit the lake to fish or swim would be part of the community. Likewise, a forest community includes all the populations that live in or visit the forest.

## ACTIVITY

**Describing Communities**

Over a period of a week, make a list of all the organisms and abiotic factors in your community. Include plant and animal life, as well as climate conditions.

The size of the rabbit population and the number of other bobcats in the area would keep bobcat populations in check.

**Figure 28–4.** This community found in Africa is large and varied. These zebra and wildebeest depend on the abiotic factors, especially the pond, for life.

**Figure 28–5.** The habitat of this blue crab is a salt marsh.

Each population of organisms lives in a certain area within the ecosystem. The place where an organism lives is its **habitat.** A habitat could be compared to an address. A healthy ecosystem has many habitats providing food and shelter to a variety of populations.

The biotic parts of an ecosystem each perform certain functions. For example, green plants make food for animals. The function or role of an organism in the ecosystem is called its **niche** (NIHCH). Although many different organisms may share the same habitat, they cannot occupy the same niche. Organisms that appear to have similar niches usually have different ways of using the same habitat. For example, there are many species of sharks in the ocean. All sharks have the same habitat, but they do not have the same niche. Each shark population is located in a different part of the ocean or at a different level in the water. Further, different types of sharks usually feed on different organisms. What is the niche of the algae in a pond? Algae are primary producers; they function like grass does in a land ecosystem.

Students often confuse niche and habitat. A corny (but effective) mnemonic is that habitat is where an organism "makes a habit of being at." Its niche is its job or the role it plays in the habitat.

## SCIENCE FACT

Five different species of North American warblers can feed from the same tree because each species stays in a separate section of the tree.

# 28.3 Changes in Ecosystems

Under natural conditions, changes in an ecosystem occur very slowly. Changes in populations and communities can occur much faster.

### Changes in Population

Populations increase through the birth of new individuals and through *immigration.* Immigration is the movement of new individuals into an area occupied by an existing population. The movement of organisms away from the area where a population is located is known as *emigration.* Emigration and the death of organisms are two ways a population decreases. When births plus

Ask, "Why aren't elephants found in North America?" Students will give a variety of answers. Point out that at one time elephants *were* common in many parts of North America, but because of major changes in the climate, the elephants disappeared. We know them only from fossil records. Changes in climate can have large effects on plant and animal life.

**Figure 28–6.** The snake in these photographs is a limiting factor on the bird population.

Deaths plus emigration is greater than births plus immigration.

Call your city or county government and get population figures for your area for the last two decades. Using the figures, construct a graph on population changes in your area. How can you determine how much change is from immigration or from emigration? Challenge students to find out. (The number of births and deaths each year are recorded in city and county records.)

**Figure 28–7.** Limiting factors vary from population to population. However, the environmental resistance is fairly constant from population to population.

Add some liquid plant food to a 1-L glass jar. Set up another jar as a control. Add 750 mL of tap water and 100 mL of pond or puddle water to each jar. Have students make daily observations of the changes in each jar.

immigration are larger than deaths plus emigration, population size increases. What relationship among these factors would cause population size to decrease?

All organisms have the potential to produce offspring. A population's **biotic potential** is its ability to grow in an environment and to reproduce itself without any limits. For example, if bacteria were allowed to reproduce to their full biotic potential, they would cover the earth in a few weeks. A single pair of houseflies could produce almost 30 million offspring in just two months. A single pair of elephants would have over 19 million descendants after 750 years.

Fortunately, the earth is not covered with bacteria, houseflies, or elephants. Certain factors limit the biotic potential of organisms. Common **limiting factors** are space, weather, food, predation, and disease. For populations that live in water, the water temperature and the amount of dissolved oxygen are also important limiting factors.

In most cases, more than one limiting factor keeps a population from growing too large. The sum of all the limiting factors is the **environmental resistance.** Figure 28–7 shows the relationship between biotic potential and environmental resistance. The illustration shows the population growing slowly but then starting to increase very rapidly. When the population reaches a certain level, environmental resistance begins to prevent the population from increasing any more.

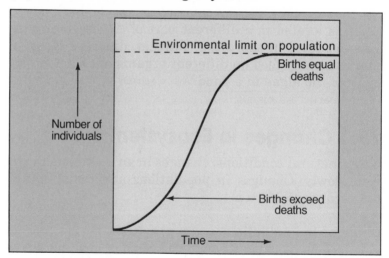

## Changes in Communities

As populations grow and change, so do the communities of which they are a part. The change in ecological communities over time is called **succession.** There are two kinds of succession, primary and secondary.

In *primary succession,* communities are established on newly formed areas of the earth. These new areas include recent lava flows, rocky outcrops on mountains, and areas such as sand dunes where wind or water has recently deposited sand or clay. *Secondary succession* takes place on land that once supported a community that was later disturbed or destroyed. Vacant lots, roadsides, and old farmland are examples of places where secondary succession occurs.

**Figure 28–8.** The barn and trees shown on the left are an example of secondary succession. The clear lake above is an example of primary succession.

A stable community that is no longer undergoing succession is called a **climax community.** Climax communities cycle the energy and nutrients in a particular environment. Once established, climax communities may not change for hundreds of years. However, natural disasters such as wildfires or hurricanes may disturb the community. Over long periods of time, the climax community will be restored.

## Section Review

1. List three abiotic components of ecosystems.
2. Give an example of a biotic component and an abiotic component interacting with each other in an ecosystem.
3. Define the terms ecosystem, population, and community. Explain how each is organized.
4. Define and give an example of primary succession.
5. THINKING CRITICALLY Describe how primary succession can eventually result in a climax community.

1. moisture, sunlight, and soil
2. Answers will vary. One example would be plants decaying and thereby fertilizing the soil, and the soil providing plants nutrients for growth.
3. ecosystem: a group of living and nonliving things interacting over time; population: group of organisms of a single species living in a certain area; community: all living organisms in an ecosystem
4. Primary succession is communities becoming established on a new area of the earth. Answers will vary but one example is plants beginning to grow on a recent lava flow.
5. Over time the primary growth may be supplanted by a secondary growth until no new changes take place.

# SKILL ACTIVITY   Calculating Percentages

### INTRODUCTION

Percentages help you to see what part of the whole is repeated by a certain quantity. Percentages can be helpful in studying the energy levels in a food chain. For example, percentages can help you find out how much of the sun's energy is converted to food at the plant level. Each level of the food chain has available for its needs only a certain percentage of the Calories in the food eaten.

### PROCEDURE

1. To obtain a percentage, first determine what number represents the amount of which you want to know the percentage.
2. Then determine the total number of items involved.
3. Divide the first number by the total number.
4. Multiply the number arrived at in step 3 by 100.
5. As an example, suppose that 10 rabbits out of the 50 rabbits in a population are brown. Ten divided by 50 equals 0.2, which when multiplied by 100 gives an answer of 20 percent. Twenty percent of the rabbits in the population are brown.

### APPLICATION

Study the food chain in the picture. Notice in the key which symbol stands for the Calories produced by the organism and which symbol represents the Calories consumed by the next organism in the chain.

1. What percentage of the Calories available in the plants does the rabbit consume? 20 percent
2. What percentage of the Calories consumed by the rabbit is converted into its body tissue? 10 percent
3. What percentage of the Calories produced by the rabbit is consumed by the coyote? 30 percent
4. What percentage of the Calories consumed by the coyote is converted into its body tissue? 10 percent
5. In each of the organisms, what happens to the Calories that are consumed but that are not converted to body tissue? The rest is given off as heat.

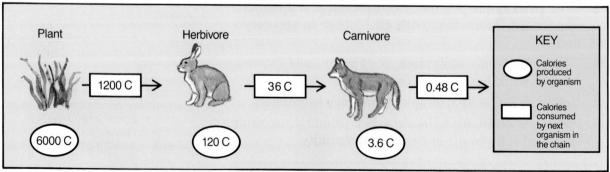

| Plant | Herbivore | Carnivore | KEY |
|---|---|---|---|

1200 C    36 C    0.48 C

6000 C    120 C    3.6 C

KEY
Calories produced by organism
Calories consumed by next organism in the chain

# Functions of Ecosystems

## SECTION OBJECTIVES

- **Describe** how water and nitrogen are cycled through an ecosystem.
- **Identify** the energy source for chemical cycles.
- **Contrast** energy flow and chemical cycles.

NEW TERMS IN THIS SECTION
producer
consumer
decomposer
food chain
food web
ecological pyramid

## 28.4 Chemical Cycles

Two important functions of an ecosystem are the capture and use of energy and the recycling of various chemicals necessary for life. Energy flows into natural ecosystems from the sun. This energy is used as light and heat. Light energy can be changed into chemical energy by plants during photosynthesis. The relationship between energy and chemical cycles makes it possible for life on Earth to continue. Three of the most important chemical cycles are the *water cycle,* the *nitrogen cycle,* and the *oxygen-carbon cycle.*

### The Water Cycle

The water cycle begins when the sun's energy changes water from oceans, lakes, and plant leaves into water vapor. The water vapor rises and forms clouds. Clouds hold the water as vapor, liquid, and ice. When the clouds are large enough and the temperature is cool enough, moisture is released as rain or snow. The water is returned to the earth to be cycled again. The water cycle

Ask the students to take a deep breath. Tell them they just breathed in molecules of oxygen—the same oxygen that could have been inhaled by your grandfather 50 years ago or George Washington 200 years ago. Point out that the water they brushed their teeth with this morning could have been used by an English Queen or an African hunter centuries ago. Explain that water and oxygen are just two of many important chemicals that cycle through our environment.

Two laws regulate energy flow through ecosystems. The law of energy conservation says that energy flowing into an ecosystem must equal the energy flowing out *plus* any energy that is stored in animal and plant tissue. The law of energy dispersal says that each time energy is changed from one form to another, some energy is lost or moves out of the ecosystem.

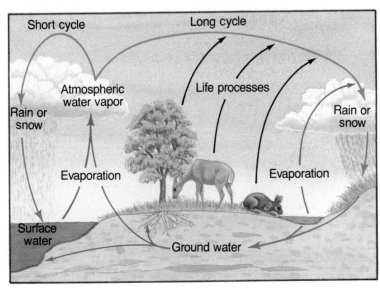

**Figure 28–9.** The water cycle provides water for washing, industry, and irrigation.

provides all the drinking water humans use. <u>What would happen to water supplies if there were no sunlight for a year?</u> All life would cease and all the water would turn to ice.

### The Nitrogen Cycle

Another important cycle is the nitrogen cycle. Nitrogen is a plentiful element found in every living thing. About 78 percent of air is nitrogen gas, but it cannot be used by most organisms. Instead, the nitrogen must be changed into usable forms during the nitrogen cycle.

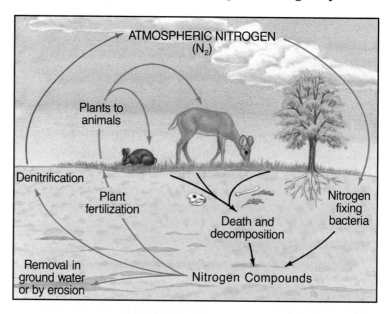

**Figure 28–10.** The nitrogen cycle is important in maintaining the fertility of soil.

Other bacteria convert ammonia, nitrite, and nitrate back into nitrogen gas. This process is called *denitrification*.

Figure 28–10 shows how the nitrogen cycle works. Bacteria take nitrogen from the air and combine it with other elements to form compounds called *nitrates* (NY trayts). Nitrates are compounds that plants can use. Animals get needed nitrogen by eating plants or plant products. The process by which nitrogen gas is formed into nitrates is called *nitrogen fixation.*

Not all nitrogen comes directly from the air. When dead organisms begin to break down, or decompose, the nitrogen in their bodies is recycled by bacteria. Some of this nitrogen is first used by plants, and then by animals. Some of the nitrogen goes back into the air to complete the cycle. Without nitrogen-fixing bacteria, the ecosystem would run out of nitrates but would be surrounded by nitrogen gas. Plant and animal growth would stop.

### The Oxygen-Carbon Cycle

The oxygen-carbon cycle, illustrated in Figure 28–11, is the result of photosynthesis and respiration. During photosynthesis, plants take in carbon dioxide ($CO_2$) from the air. As carbon dioxide combines with water in plant tis-

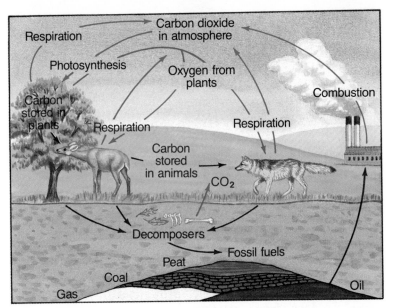

**Figure 28-11.** In this oxygen-carbon cycle, some of the carbon remains in the ground as fossil fuel.

sue, oxygen gas ($O_2$) is released into the air. The carbon from carbon dioxide is used by plants to make sugars and starches. These sugars and starches are sources of chemical energy produced during respiration. When plants use their stored food or when plants are eaten by animals, the sugars and starches are broken down and carbon dioxide is released. The carbon dioxide is returned to the air.

Carbon dioxide is released into the atmosphere in two other ways. When plants and animals die, bacteria and fungi break down the tissue and release carbon dioxide. When fossil fuels are burned, carbon dioxide is also given off. The importance of fossil fuels is discussed in Chapter 29.

Photosynthesis produces 50 to 60 billion metric tons of sugar annually.

## 28.5 Energy Flow

The earth receives energy from the sun. Some of this energy is used to run the chemical cycles, and some energy warms the earth. Green plants collect less than one percent of the sun's energy. However, this small amount supports life.

Green plants and other organisms that make their own food are called **producers.** Since animals cannot make their own food, they must eat other animals, plants, or both. Organisms that do not make their own food are called **consumers.**

Consumers are divided into three groups based on what the animals eat. *Herbivores*, such as elk, sheep, and cows, eat only plants. Herbivores also include organisms that eat algae, such as fish and baleen whales. Elephants and many insects are also herbivores.

**Figure 28–12.** The cougar chasing the bighorn (left) is a predator. The white-backed vultures at this zebra kill are scavengers.

A scavenger may be a herbivore, a carnivore, or an omnivore. For example, the crayfish is a scavenger.

Animals that eat other animals are called *carnivores*. Spiders, frogs, snakes, and bobcats are examples of carnivores. Carnivores that hunt and kill other animals are *predators* (PREHD uh tuhrz). Carnivores like vultures and jackals, that eat dead animals, are called *scavengers* (SKAV ihn juhrz).

The third category of consumers, *omnivores*, are organisms that eat both plants and animals. The diets of omnivores vary with seasonal food supplies. Foxes, raccoons, and humans are examples of omnivores.

Organisms that obtain energy and release nutrients from dead organic material are called **decomposers**. Decomposers are important because they help recycle nutrients. The nutrients are then made available to other plants and animals. Examples of decomposers include bacteria and fungi.

### Food Chains and Food Webs

Energy flows through the ecosystem in **food chains**. Food chains begin with the sun and green plants. Plants collect and store energy from the sun. Herbivores that eat plants get energy from them. As energy is moved from one organism to another, some of it is lost to the environment as heat. Plant and animal respiration and growth account for some of this lost energy.

Food chains show part of the complex way in which energy is transferred in ecosystems. Organisms seldom eat just one kind of plant or animal. The many interactions of plants and animals in food chains are usually connected by **food webs.** Figure 28–13 is an example of a food web. By following the path of energy from the sun, you can see how the plants and animals are all interconnected. You should be able to identify several different food chains within this food web.

## ACTIVITY

### Creating Food Webs

Draw a food web of the living organisms in your community. Include and label producers, consumers, and decomposers.

## Ecological Pyramids

The relationships among producers and consumers can be shown as energy flow in **ecological pyramids**. These pyramids are based on the various feeding levels, or *trophic* (TRAHF ihk) *levels*, in an ecosystem. Plants are at the lowest trophic level. The next level contains the herbivores, or *first-order consumers*. Animals that eat first-order consumers are *second-order consumers*. At the top of the pyramid are animals that eat second-order consumers. These animals are *third-order consumers*.

The energy relationship among trophic levels can be shown in an *energy pyramid*. Energy comes into the pyramid from the sun. The base of the pyramid is made up of producers, such as grasses and trees. The size of each level represents the total amount of energy stored on that level.

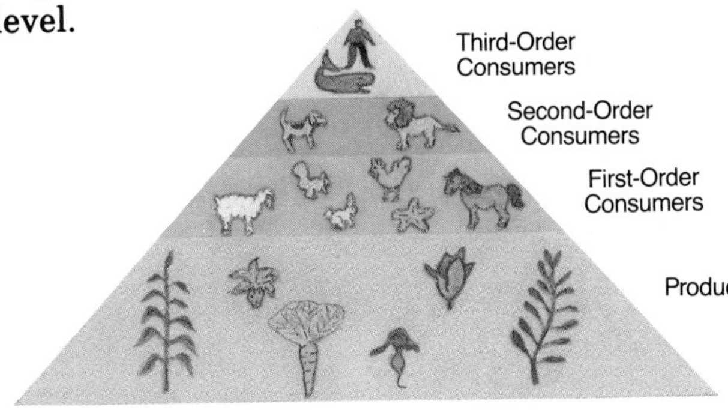

Third-Order Consumers

Second-Order Consumers

First-Order Consumers

Producers

**Figure 28–13.** Food webs illustrate how interdependent all organisms are on Earth.

Only about 10 percent of the energy at one trophic level is passed on to the next trophic level. Land-based food webs are less efficient than aquatic food webs.

## READING CRITICALLY

What would happen to the carnivore population in a habitat if all the producers disappeared?

The carnivore population would either move its habitat or die.

**Figure 28–14.** The ecological pyramid shows that less energy is found at the top level than at the bottom level. The energy missing between the levels is scattered into the environment.

## Section Review

1. Diagram and describe the nitrogen cycle.
2. How is a food web different from a food chain?
3. How are predators different from scavengers?
4. THINKING CRITICALLY Describe how a three-month drought in a swamp ecosystem might affect the food web.

1. See Figure 28-10.
2. A food chain is linear; it only flows down. Organisms in a food web interact and depend on each other for continued existence.
3. Predators hunt and kill for food; scavengers eat only dead organisms, they pick up the leftovers of other animals.
4. Too little water may kill off plants that animals depend on, resulting in their deaths and the destruction of balance in the ecosystem.

Ecology **599**

# Types of Ecosystems

## SECTION OBJECTIVES
- **Compare** various water and land biomes.
- **Relate** human ecosystems to natural ecosystems.
- **Describe** abiotic factors that influence biomes.

## 28.6 The World's Biomes

Have a "Biomes Day." Select a day when students who have lived or visited other biomes show slides or describe them. Be sure to have a globe handy.

The earth is often divided into regions that contain particular types of plants and animals. These regions are called *biomes* (BY ohmz). A **biome** is a large area of similar climate and vegetation. A biome may contain several different ecosystems. For example, most forest biomes contain freshwater ecosystems. Figure 28–15 shows the major biomes on Earth.

### Water Biomes

Over 70 percent of Earth's surface is covered by water. Most bodies of water support a great variety of living things. Water biomes are divided into two types, depending on the amount of salt in the water. The *marine biome* includes the world's oceans and other salt waters. The *freshwater biome* contains bodies of water with very little salt, such as lakes, rivers, streams, and ponds.

**Figure 28–15.** Ecologists compare biomes by measuring and comparing their productivity, which is a measure of the rate at which green plants convert sunlight to chemical energy.

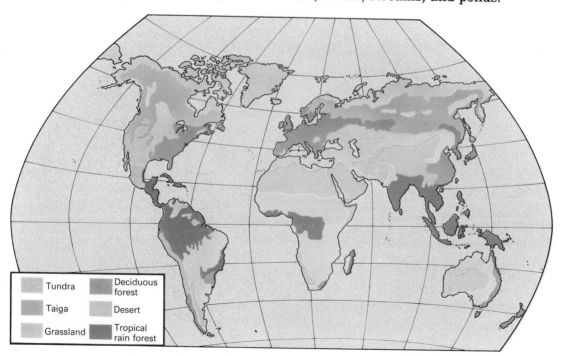

Tundra | Deciduous forest
Taiga | Desert
Grassland | Tropical rain forest

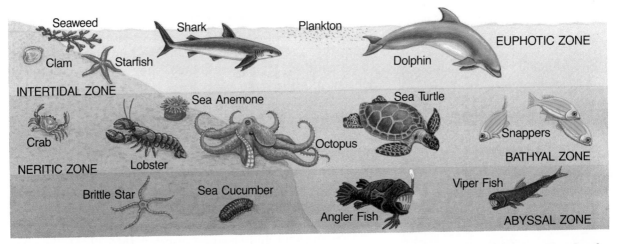

Figure 28–16. The three levels of the ocean support many varied organisms.

Marine biomes can be further divided into *zones*. Figure 28–16 illustrates the major zones found in marine biomes. The open sea is divided into zones based on the amount of light that comes through the water. The top, or *euphotic* (yoo FAHT ihk) *zone*, receives the most light and supports the most life. This zone extends to a depth of about 200 m and is the most productive part of the open sea.

The *bathyal* (BATH ee uhl) *zone* of the open sea is the zone between 200 m and 1000 m deep. Because little light reaches it, the bathyal zone is sometimes called the underwater twilight zone.

In the deepest parts of the ocean, between 2000 m and the ocean floor, lies the *abyssal* (uh BIHS uhl) *zone*. Almost no light penetrates to the abyssal zone. Not surprisingly, few producers live there. Organisms that do manage to survive in the abyssal zone are adapted to withstand high pressures.

Marine biomes found closer to land are able to support more and varied life. When approaching land, the ocean becomes shallower, allowing light to get to the bottom, or the continental shelf. The shallow ocean area, over the continental shelf, is the *neritic zone*. This zone provides a habitat for many fishes and other animals such as crabs, lobsters, and shellfish.

The ocean zone found closest to the land is the *intertidal zone*. In this zone, the ecosystem is alternately covered with water or exposed to air, depending on the level of the tides. Organisms in the intertidal zone have adapted to survive under constantly changing conditions. For example, because of the force of waves and tides, organisms such as barnacles have special structures to hold on to rocks. Other organisms, such as sand fleas, tunnel into the sand or mud and let the flowing ocean water bring food to them.

**Figure 28–17.** Wetlands also store water. They act as reservoirs during dry periods and as water storage areas during times of high water. This function greatly reduces damage from droughts and floods.

Although estuaries are very productive, they make up a very small portion of the marine biome. This makes their protection even more important.

There is more moisture during the night, and the animals can function better in the cool temperatures of night.

The shallow areas where freshwater and saltwater mix are called **estuaries**. Estuaries are narrow zones along the coast. Although estuaries represent less than 10 percent of the marine biome, they contain almost 90 percent of all marine life.

Nutrients that wash off the land partly account for the large productivity of estuaries. Marsh and sea grasses thrive in the rich, moist conditions that estuaries provide. Even the mud is filled with organisms that play important roles in the food web. Many shellfish, including some types of oysters and clams, live in estuaries. The estuaries are an important transition between ocean biomes and freshwater biomes.

Freshwater biomes are divided into habitats with moving water, such as rivers and streams, and habitats with standing water, such as ponds and lakes.

Freshwater biomes are used for many purposes. Fishing, swimming, boating, and other recreational activities are enjoyed by millions of people in these biomes. Freshwater habitats are also important because they are a major source of drinking water.

The places where water and land biomes meet are known as *wetlands*. Marshes and swamps are examples of wetlands. Wetlands represent the stages of succession between water and land biomes. Wetlands usually have some characteristics of both systems, and they perform vital functions for both. For example, wetlands store nutrients that run off the land, gradually releasing them into aquatic systems. This filtering action reduces pollutants and controls the cloudiness of the water.

## Land Biomes

Climate is the major factor determining the location and development of land biomes. Temperature and rainfall are especially important. Refer to Figure 28–15 to find the location of the different types of land biomes.

The **desert** biome receives less than 20 cm of precipitation per year, and temperatures range from 24°C to 32°C. Desert plants have adaptations that help them survive these climate conditions. Why are most desert animals active at night, when it is cool?

The **tundra** biome receives only 10 to 40 cm of precipitation per year. The temperature in the tundra ranges from −25°C to 25°C. For most of the year, the tundra is covered with ice and snow.

**Grasslands**, or prairies, are the largest biome in North America. They receive 10 to 60 cm of precipitation each year. Grasslands support large populations of grazing animals.

The three major kinds of forest biomes are *coniferous* (kuh NIHF uhr uhs) *forests*, *deciduous* (dih SIHJ oo wuhs) *forests*, and *tropical rain forests*.

The coniferous forest biome, or **taiga** (TY guh), is found south of the tundra. Yearly precipitation ranges from 20 to 60 cm. The coniferous forest is an important source of wood for both lumber and paper products. Many of these forests have been harvested and replanted to increase supplies of wood and other forest products.

The temperate **deciduous forest** biome develops in areas that have short winters and long summer growing seasons. Precipitation ranges from 60 to 100 cm per year and is evenly distributed throughout the year. Deciduous forests supply wood for paper products and lumber and are important recreational sites for camping and hunting. These forests are found throughout the eastern and central United States.

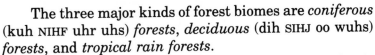

**Figure 28–18.** Three different biomes are shown here from top left: grasslands, desert, and deciduous forest.

**Figure 28–19.** The rain forest is the most productive land biome.

**Figure 28–20.** Modern technology, including machines and chemicals, have enabled humans to change systems to meet human needs. Often the natural ecosystem is destroyed in the process.

**Tropical rain forest** biomes develop where the temperature is warm and 200 cm or more of rain falls each year. Warm temperatures, an abundance of moisture, and long growing seasons provide excellent conditions for plants and animals. About 40 percent of all species of plants and animals live in tropical rain forests. The Amazon rain forest in South America, shown in Figure 28–19, is the largest rain forest in the world.

Tropical rain forests are being destroyed at an alarming rate. Arrange for an outside speaker to discuss the global implications of the destruction of this vast forest biome.

## 28.7 Human Ecosystems

When natural biomes or ecosystems are managed by humans, they are called human ecosystems. Human ecosystems are found in every biome. Where human populations are small, their overall impact on the natural ecosystem may also be small. The way in which humans choose to use a particular ecosystem is critical to the functioning and survival of that system.

Agricultural areas are examples of ecosystems that humans control. Agricultural systems are influenced by abiotic factors such as soil, temperature, and water. Humans enrich soils with fertilizer and add water through irrigation. They provide machines for planting, weeding, and harvesting. They provide a way of getting products to market. Agricultural systems are the world's major source of food. The creation of these agricultural areas, however, has destroyed natural ecosystems and caused damage to many plant and animal populations.

Cities are also examples of human ecosystems. Cities show the same patterns of energy flow as forests and oceans. They have producers, consumers, and decomposers that cycle nutrients and convert energy to different forms. Cities are the world's largest consumers of raw materials and stored energy.

Unlike natural ecosystems that operate on solar energy alone, human ecosystems require additional energy from fossil fuels. Fossil fuels, such as oil and coal, represent energy from the sun that has been stored in the earth's crust for millions of years. The role of fossil fuels in supporting human ecosystems is discussed in more detail in Chapter 29.

## Section Review

1. What is a biome?
2. Name and describe two water biomes.
3. Compare and contrast the desert biome and the tundra biome.
4. Name and describe two types of forest biomes.
5. THINKING CRITICALLY Describe how a city is like a natural ecosystem.

## CAREER

# Ecologist

**DESCRIPTION** An ecologist studies the relationship between living things and the environment. Ecologists examine the effects of abiotic factors on plants and animals. They also study the effects of pollution and human activities, such as fishing and land clearing. Some ecologists work in laboratories, studying living things in controlled environments; other ecologists work in natural surroundings.

**REQUIREMENTS** A high-school student planning to become an ecologist should take biology, chemistry, and mathematics courses. Following graduation, a college major in biological science must be completed. Many ecologists go on to earn a master's or a Ph.D. degree.

**INFORMATION** Ecological Society of America, Department of Biology, Notre Dame University, Notre Dame, IN 46556

# INVESTIGATION 28: Measuring Dissolved Oxygen

*How can the amount of dissolved oxygen in water be determined?*

## PURPOSE

To investigate the amounts of dissolved oxygen in different water samples

## MATERIALS

water samples, 4
(see table)
test tubes, 4
wax pencil
test-tube rack
graduate, 25-mL
methylene blue
stopwatch, or watch
with second hand

## PROCEDURE

1. Copy Table 1 onto a sheet of paper. Enter all data from this investigation on your table.
2. Label four test tubes 1, 2, 3, and 4, respectively.
3. Pour 10 mL of water sample 1 into test tube 1.
4. Add 2 mL of methylene blue to the sample. Methylene blue is an indicator of dissolved oxygen.
5. On Table 1, record the time in seconds that it takes for a color change, if any, to occur. In oxygen-rich water, the indicator will stay dark blue. In oxygen-poor water,

the indicator will fade to light yellow or clear.
6. Clean the test tube and repeat steps 3–5 using sample 1 again. Find the average of the two times and record it in the table. Also record the final color of the sample.
7. Repeat steps 3–6 using the other test tubes and water samples.

## CONCLUSION

Based on your observations, list the water samples in order of greatest to least amount of dissolved oxygen. Write a sentence that summarizes your findings.

## APPLICATIONS

1. What other kinds of gases would be present in water containing aquatic organisms?
2. Which sample had the most dissolved oxygen? What was the source of the oxygen?
3. Which sample had the least dissolved oxygen? What are some reasons why this source had the least oxygen?
4. Would you find more dissolved oxygen in fast-moving streams or in lakes? Explain your answer.

1. nitrogen and carbon dioxide
2. lake water because it contains organisms in the water that can respire
3. tap water because it has been purified of all organisms that could create oxygen in the water
4. lakes because no opportunity for carbon-oxygen cycles is available in fast moving circumstances such as streams and rivers

## RESULTS

| TABLE 1 | DISSOLVED OXYGEN IN WATER SAMPLES | | | | | |
|---|---|---|---|---|---|---|
| | Trial 1 | | Trial 2 | | Avg. Time | |
| Sample | Color Change | Time (Sec.) | Color Change | Time (Sec.) | (Sec.) | |
| Tap water | | | | | | |
| Lake water | | | | | | |
| Stream water | | | | | | |
| Pond water | | | | | | |

## Summary

1. The abiotic components of ecosystems include moisture, solar energy, and soil. **(28.1)**

2. The biotic components of ecosystems are organized into organisms, populations, and communities, all of which interact with the abiotic components of the environment. **(28.2)**

3. Ecosystems are always changing. Populations increase and decrease, and communities change through succession. **(28.3)**

4. Water, nitrogen, carbon dioxide, oxygen, and other chemicals are cycled through ecosystems. **(28.4)**

5. Energy from the sun flows through ecosystems via food chains and food webs. **(28.5)**

6. Biomes are large regions that have similar organisms and climates. **(28.6)**

7. Human-dominated ecosystems are regulated by the same laws as natural ecosystems. **(28.7)**

## Science Terms

On a separate sheet of paper, define each term in a sentence.

abiotic **(587)**
biome **(600)**
biotic **(589)**
biotic potential **(592)**
climax community **(593)**
community **(590)**
consumer **(597)**
deciduous forest **(603)**
decomposer **(598)**

desert **(602)**
ecological pyramid **(599)**
ecology **(587)**
ecosystem **(587)**
environmental resistance **(592)**
estuary **(602)**
food chain **(598)**
food web **(598)**
grasslands **(602)**

habitat **(591)**
limiting factor **(592)**
niche **(591)**
population **(590)**
producer **(597)**
succession **(592)**
taiga **(603)**
tropical rain forest **(604)**
tundra **(602)**

## Modified True-False

On a separate sheet of paper, mark each true statement *TRUE* and each false statement *FALSE*. If false, change the underlined term to make the statement true.

1. <u>Ecosystems</u> have living and nonliving parts. T

2. Most energy for human ecosystems comes from <u>oil and gas</u>. T

3. <u>Consumers</u> are organisms that make their own food. F, producers

4. <u>Communities</u> are groups of similar organisms. F, populations

5. The <u>nitrogen</u> cycle provides the earth with fresh water. F, water

6. There is more energy at the <u>top</u> of an energy pyramid. F, bottom

7. The sum of all limiting factors is the <u>environmental resistance</u>. T

8. <u>Estuaries</u> are places where marine and freshwater biomes meet. T

9. A vacant lot is an example of a place where <u>primary</u> succession occurs. F, secondary

10. Forest biomes receive <u>less</u> moisture than grasslands. F, more *(continues)*

# CHAPTER REVIEW

## Multiple Choice

On a separate sheet of paper, write the letter of the term that best completes the statement.

1. A square meter of grass, a lake, or a whole forest is
   - **a.** a biome.
   - **b.** a consumer.
   - **(c.)** an ecosystem.
   - **d.** a species.

2. Bacteria and fungi are examples of
   - **a.** producers.
   - **(b.)** decomposers.
   - **c.** consumers.
   - **d.** omnivores.

3. Animals that eat plants are
   - **a.** carnivores.
   - **b.** predators.
   - **c.** scavengers.
   - **(d.)** herbivores.

4. The place in an ecosystem where an organism is usually found is its
   - **(a.)** habitat.
   - **b.** community.
   - **c.** niche.
   - **d.** population.

5. When organisms die, the minerals from their bodies are
   - **a.** lost forever.
   - **(b.)** recycled.
   - **c.** turned into water.
   - **d.** turned into rocks.

6. As energy moves through food chains, some of it may be
   - **(a.)** lost.
   - **b.** scattered.
   - **c.** recycled.
   - **d.** concentrated.

7. Animals that eat both plants and animals are
   - **a.** predators.
   - **b.** scavengers.
   - **(c.)** omnivores.
   - **d.** herbivores.

8. Which of the following is not a freshwater biome?
   - **(a.)** ocean
   - **b.** river
   - **c.** stream
   - **d.** lake

9. Another name for the taiga is the
   - **a.** tundra.
   - **b.** rain forest.
   - **c.** deciduous forest.
   - **(d.)** coniferous forest.

10. Deserts and tundra are alike in that they have the same
   - **a.** temperature.
   - **(b.)** moisture.
   - **c.** organisms.
   - **d.** soils.

## Completion

On a separate sheet of paper, complete each statement by supplying the correct term.

1. Temperature and moisture are part of an ecosystem's <u>abiotic factors</u>.

2. Organisms that make their own food are <u>producers</u>.

3. Animals that hunt and eat other animals are called <u>predators</u>.

4. An organism's role in the ecosystem is its <u>niche</u>.

5. The process by which nitrogen gas is formed into nitrates is nitrogen <u>fixation</u>.

6. The process of community change over time is <u>succession</u>.

7. Nitrogen and water are chemicals that <u>cycle</u> through the ecosystem.

8. The relationship between the different feeding levels in an ecosystem can be shown in an <u>energy pyramid</u>.

9. A <u>deciduous</u> forest biome is found in areas with short winters and long summers.

10. Although organisms can share <u>habitats</u>, they cannot share niches.

## Writing Critically Answers: see page T125.

1. Describe some ways in which the biotic and abiotic components of ecosystems interact. Use examples.

2. As has been discussed in previous chapters, bacteria play an important role in the continuity of life. Relate the importance of bacteria in chemical cycles.

3. CHALLENGE The city was mentioned briefly in this chapter as an ecosystem. Compare and contrast natural and human ecosystems.

4. CHALLENGE Many large farms lie along river banks. Explain how this ecosystem under human control can affect the water biomes it adjoins.

## Skill Reinforcement

The Skill Activity on page 594 describes how to obtain a percentage. Using the method described in the Skill Activity, work the following problem. A rabbit eats 200 carrots at 30 calories per carrot in its lifetime. A coyote eats the rabbit and gains 150 Calories. Excluding the Calories lost during respiration and other processes, what percentage of the total Calories eaten by the rabbit was transferred to the coyote?   2.5 percent

## Research Ideas

1. Set up and observe an ecosystem in a 3- or 4-L glass jar.

2. Many minerals are washed off the land and enter the ocean. How do they get back onto the land?

3. CHALLENGE Create a flow chart that shows energy flowing into and out of your community.

4. CHALLENGE The giant redwood trees found along the coast of California and Oregon are the largest trees in the world. However, the area they grow in does not have extremely high rainfall. Research the biology of redwood trees and describe how they obtain their moisture.

## For Further Reading

Caras, Roger. *The Forest*. New York: Holt, Rinehart & Winston, 1979. Caras uses a golden eagle to observe the ecological events in a coniferous forest.

Clapham, W. B. *Natural Ecosystems*. New York: Macmillan, 1983. This well-written and interesting book examines the relationships among the major natural ecosystems.

Hess, Lilo. *Secrets in the Meadow*. New York: Scribner's, 1986. A complete discussion of life in a meadow community, including animal diversity, behavior, life cycle, and adaptation.

Keller, J. "From Yellowthroats to Woodpeckers." *Conservationist* (July/August 1982) 37, 300. This article shows how bird life in a given area changes during ecological succession.

Maltby, Edwards. *Waterlogged Wealth: Why Waste the Earth's Wet Places?* Washington, D.C.: International Institute for Environment and Development, 1986. An excellent review of wetlands of the world.

# 29 Managing Natural Resources

Natural resources such as water, air, and soil are essential for life on Earth. The quality of these and other vital resources, must be preserved so that all organisms on the planet can survive.

For additional information, see pages T126–T127.

# Abiotic Resources

NEW TERMS IN THIS SECTION

resource    humus    ground water
renewable resource    erosion    mineral
nonrenewable resource    surface water

## SECTION OBJECTIVES

- **Distinguish** between renewable and nonrenewable resources.
- **Explain** how sources of drinking water are established.
- **Give** examples of some minerals and how they are used.
- **List** several ways in which minerals may be conserved.

Photograph left: Rocky Mountain watershed, Glacier Park, Montana

## 29.1 Natural Resources

A **resource** is any material used by people for their advantage. Natural resources include air, water, and land. Animals, plants, and minerals are also resources. Resources may be biotic or abiotic.

Natural resources are in danger of being used up. Pollution and the overuse of materials such as fossil fuels are greatly reducing the supplies of many resources. Resources may be conserved by careful use and by reuse whenever possible.

Resources can be classified as renewable or nonrenewable. A **renewable resource** is one that may be reused or replaced. Air, water, plants, and animals are renewable resources. A **nonrenewable resource** cannot be reused or replaced. Once a nonrenewable resource is used, it is gone, sometimes forever. Minerals and petroleum are examples of nonrenewable resources.

Point out that some renewable resources may become nonrenewable if they are overused. Ask students for examples of overused renewable resources (wildlife, tropical rain forests).

## 29.2 Soil

Soil is an abiotic resource. Like all abiotic resources, soil plays an important part in supporting many living things. Soil is a source of food and shelter for both plants

Turn off the lights in your classroom for 2 minutes and ask the students to think about all the natural resources that are being saved. Turn the lights back on and start a class list of the saved resources. The primary energy (coal, oil, nuclear) used to make the electricity was one resource saved. Get students to extend the idea to land not mined; reduction of solid wastes, air pollution, acid rain, energy needed to transport fuel and wastes, and so forth. Emphasize that individual actions have a dramatic effect on saving natural resources and preserving the environment.

**Figure 29–1.** Refineries such as the one shown here contribute to the pollutant called smog, which hangs over many large cities, while decreasing the amount of nonrenewable resources available.

**Figure 29–2.** Contour plowing (left) protects the soil from erosion by creating a pattern of furrows that holds the rainwater. Terracing (right) holds water in steps.

Soils are dynamic mixtures of materials teeming with life. A few grams of soil may contain billions of organisms ranging from simple bacteria and fungi to insects, spiders, and even vertebrates. While the soil is not living, it provides an important habitat for a myriad of organisms.

## ACTIVITY

### Observing Soil Components

Fill a 1-L jar about one-third full of soil, and then add water until the jar is full. Cover the jar and shake it well. Describe the appearance of the water and the soil. Note any differences in the sizes of the soil particles. Observe the contents of the jar until the soil has settled. Record your observations. <u>Which soil particles settled faster, the larger ones or the smaller ones? How long did it take for the water to clear?</u>

The larger particles should settle faster. Clearing time will depend on the type of soil.

Show the difference in porosity of clay soils and sandy soils by adding water to samples of each. The water will "sit" on the clay soils but drains rapidly through the sandy soils.

and animals. Plants that grow in the soil provide food for other organisms. They also provide many useful products. For example, trees are the source of paper and lumber. The cotton plant is used to make cotton fibers, which are used in clothing.

Soil is formed over hundreds, even thousands, of years. Soil develops in layers. The bottom layer is solid rock called *bedrock*. The bedrock is worn down and breaks up into smaller pieces of rock through the process of weathering. This weathered rock forms the next layer of soil.

Over time, small plants and animals start to live in the layer of weathered rock. Weathering is also discussed in Chapter 21. As these organisms die, their decayed remains mix with the weathered rock and form the uppermost layer of soil. This layer is called *topsoil*. Topsoil is rich in nutrients because of the organic material, or **humus** (HYOO muhs), present. The amount of humus in the soil determines what types of crops or other plant life can grow.

After the topsoil has formed, another layer forms under it. This layer is called *subsoil*. Subsoil is usually lighter in color than topsoil. It is formed from mineral particles, such as sand, silt, and clay, that are carried down through the topsoil by water.

When forests are cleared for farming or when the land is stripped for mining, the soil can be destroyed by erosion. **Erosion** is the loosening and movement of soil from one place to another by wind and water. The effects of erosion can be seen in Figure 29–3.

The most damaging effect of erosion is the removal of topsoil, which is needed for crops to grow. Topsoil is being lost ten times faster than it is being formed. To

You may wish to take a "field trip" around your school to find evidence of water and wind erosion.

Figure 29–3. Where land is drained or forests are cleared, the natural forces protecting the soil are destroyed and erosion can result.

help prevent this, good soil management techniques must be used.

In one sense, soil is a nonrenewable resource. Soil takes thousands of years to form. If soil is lost through erosion, it cannot be replaced. In another sense, soil is renewable. Through careful management, soil can be kept fertile and erosion can be prevented. Fertilizers can be added to soil so that it can be used over and over for many different crops.

## 29.3 Water

Water is essential for all life on Earth. Without water for plant growth, there would be no food. Chapter 28 described how water is cycled through the environment. Most water comes from precipitation in the form of rain, snow, or hail. Water is stored on Earth as *surface water* or as *groundwater.*

**Surface water** is all the water collected in oceans, rivers, lakes, streams, and ponds. People who live in climates that receive large amounts of precipitation usually depend on surface water for their water supply. **Ground water** is water found beneath the earth's surface. It is a major source of drinking water for people in drier climates.

Water is a renewable resource. Since the earth receives precipitation almost constantly, surface-water and ground water supplies are continually renewed. Water is, however, a limited resource. When an area goes for long periods without precipitation, supplies of surface water decrease through evaporation. Such a condition is called a *drought.* In areas where drought is common, dams and reservoirs are built to provide storage places for water. Why is water a renewable resource?

because it can be recycled through the environment

Figure 29–4. Drip irrigation systems, such as the one shown here, are replacing wasteful spray irrigation systems used in agriculture.

About 71% of the earth's surface is water, but only about 0.003% is available for human use.

**SCIENCE FACT**

Until 1971, no rain had fallen on the town of Calama, Chile, for 400 years. Then it rained and the town was washed out by floods and landslides.

For additional information about this activity, see pages T32–T34.

 **APPLICATION**

# Geometric and Arithmetic Growth

## 1. DESCRIPTION

This program demonstrates two types of growth—arithmetic growth and geometric growth. In arithmetic growth, increases are made by adding to what was originally present. In geometric growth, the increases are made by multiplication.

## 2. PROGRAM

Input the following program. After it is completely input, key the computer to run the program. If the program does not run, check to make sure you have input correctly. If the program runs correctly, go on to steps 3 and 4.

## 3. HELPFUL HINTS

Note that the program uses a loop inside another loop. This is called "nested loops." The inner loop for geometric growth is in lines 230 to 250, and the outer loop is in lines 220 to 280. What are the numbers of the lines for the other nested loops in this program?

## 4. GOING FURTHER

- Plot a graph of the number of A's and G's present after each press of the RETURN key.
- How does arithmetic growth differ from geometric growth?
- Modify the program so that it can work with different rates of arithmetic growth, geometric growth, or both types of growth.

```
100    PRINT "PROGRAM DEMONSTRATES GROWTH OF SYSTEM"
110    PRINT "SELECT ARITHMETIC GROWTH(A)"
120    INPUT "OR GEOMETIC GROWTH(G) ";A$
130    IF A$ = "A" GOTO 500
200    PRINT  TAB( 12);"GEOMETRIC GROWTH"

210    LET N = 1
220    FOR J = 1 TO 11
230    FOR Z = 1 TO N
240    PRINT "G";
250    NEXT Z

260    LET N = N * 2
270    INPUT K9$
280    NEXT J
290    PRINT "GEOMETRIC GROWTH!!"
300    GOTO 999

500    PRINT  TAB( 12);"ADDITIVE GROWTH"
510    FOR J = 1 TO 39
520    FOR Z = 1 TO J
530    PRINT "A";
540    NEXT Z

550    INPUT K9$
560    NEXT J
570    PRINT "ARITHMETIC GROWTH."
999    END
```

## 29.4 Minerals

Inorganic substances found naturally in the earth are called **minerals**. Most minerals are nonrenewable resources. Once they are used, no new supplies are available. Mineral reserves are the estimated supplies of minerals that may be obtained economically. This estimate changes when new mineral discoveries are made or new technologies for obtaining or processing mineral ores are developed. The United States has large mineral reserves. If these minerals are used wisely, they will last for generations. However, some important minerals are in short supply.

Many industries have already substituted materials to make their products. Plumbers and builders now use plastic pipe in place of the copper pipe that was widely used 20 years ago. Many automobile parts that were once made of aluminum are made of fiberglass and plastic today.

**Figure 29–5.** Every person in the United States uses over 2200 kg of iron, 110 kg of aluminum, and 100 kg each of copper, lead, and zinc every year. Recycling programs, such as the ones shown here, are one way to maintain levels of minerals that cannot be replaced.

Emphasize that recycling saves not only minerals but also land and energy. A kilogram of virgin bauxite requires 95% more energy to be made into aluminum cans than a kilogram of recycled aluminum. A typical weekday edition of a city newspaper can be recycled to obtain the energy equivalent to a half glass of gasoline.

| TABLE 29–1 | SOME MINERALS AND THEIR USES |
|---|---|
| **Mineral** | **Uses** |
| Aluminum | Car parts, wire, construction |
| Boron | Glass, ceramics |
| Chromium | Alloys, stainless steel |
| Cobalt | Alloys, magnets |
| Corrundum | Abrasives |
| Iron | Steel, cast iron |
| Lead | Batteries, construction |
| Magnesium | Building materials |
| Nickel | Alloys, stainless steel |
| Phosphates | Fertilizers, chemicals |
| Potassium | Chemicals, fertilizer |
| Sulfur | Fertilizers, acids, paper making |
| Tin | Tin plating, solder |
| Titanium | Paint, acid-resistant materials |
| Zinc | Plating, chemicals |

## Section Review

1. Define and give an example of a renewable resource and a nonrenewable resource.
2. Explain how soil is affected by erosion.
3. What is the difference between ground water and surface water?
4. Describe a method of conserving mineral resources.
5. THINKING CRITICALLY Why does the United States, with only 6 percent of the world's population, use 30 percent of all the minerals on Earth?

1. renewable: can be replaced or reused (air, water, plants); nonrenewable: cannot be replaced or reused (minerals, fossil fuels)
2. Erosion by water or wind removes the topsoil that supports vegetation and holds the soil together.
3. Surface water is on the surface of the earth such as oceans and lakes. Ground water is below the earth's surface.
4. substituting more plentiful materials for those minerals that are in short supply; or recycling
5. because our high technology (computers, cars, appliances, and so on) requires more minerals

# Biotic Resources

NEW TERMS IN THIS SECTION
extinct
endangered
refuge
watershed
sustained yield management
multiple use management

**SECTION OBJECTIVES**
- **Discuss** the importance of biotic resources to humans.
- **Identify** how national forests are managed.
- **Explain** how national forests are managed.
- **Describe** how technology affects marine fishing.

## 29.5 Wildlife

Wildlife and humans belong to a common food chain and must share natural resources. As human populations grow, the demand for housing, roads, shopping malls, and other types of construction increases. Some species of wildlife, such as squirrels and raccoons, have learned to adapt and live in the same habitat as people. However, many animals cannot adapt to such changes in their environment.

If the natural habitat of a species is changed or destroyed, the species may begin to die out. A species that is no longer in existence is said to be **extinct**. When the number of individuals in a population is very low and the species is in danger of becoming extinct, the species is considered to be **endangered**. In 1973, Congress enacted the Endangered Species Act. This act established a list of endangered species. The act also encouraged efforts to save these species from extinction.

## ACTIVITY

**Managing Deer Populations**

Deer are a species of wildlife that is carefully managed in the United States. Call the local office of your state's wildlife management agency and get information on how deer are managed and how many are harvested each year. Your teacher may assign students to investigate the management of other animals.

All nondomesticated species of animals and plants may be considered wildlife. Sometimes the term wildlife refers only to birds and mammals, excluding invertebrates and coldblooded vertebrates. Wildlife resources refers to those species of wildlife that humans use in some way.

**Figure 29–6.** Bears such as these in Yellowstone National Park have become used to the presence of humans in their habitat.

Table 29–2 lists some endangered animals. The Endangered Species Act came too late for some species, such as the passenger pigeon, which have disappeared entirely.

To help endangered species survive, special refuges, such as the one shown in Figure 29–7 have been established. A **refuge** is a protected area set aside for wildlife. About 30 years ago the population of key deer in southern Florida consisted of only 30 individuals. Now that number has increased to 600. The key deer were protected by creating a refuge and saving their habitat from development.

Wildlife resources are also protected in other ways. Alligators have made a strong comeback in the southern United States since hunting them was outlawed. The banning of pesticides, such as DDT, that concentrate in food chains has stabilized the populations of both the bald eagle and the brown pelican. The peregrine falcon also is making a comeback in its traditional home in the western United States now that DDT has been banned.

## 29.6 Forests

Forests and other land areas provide a variety of resources, including timber, fuel wood, turpentine, petroleums, nuts, and fruits. They are also habitats for many species of plants and animals. Rain forests are home to over 40 percent of all species found on Earth.

Forests provide people with recreational areas for hiking, camping, fishing, and hunting. Forest lands are also important parts of **watersheds**—areas that receive, retain, and slowly release water from precipitation.

| TABLE 29–2 | SOME ENDANGERED SPECIES |
|---|---|
| **Name** | **Range** |
| Blue whale | Oceans |
| Caribou | Canada, western U.S. |
| Giant armadillo | Venezuela, Guyana |
| Gorilla | Central and west Africa |
| Grizzly bear | Canada, western U.S. |
| Jaguar | U.S., Central and South America |
| Leopard | India, southeast Asia, Africa |
| Manatee | Southeast U.S., South America |
| Mountain zebra | South Africa |

You may wish to have some students research and list some species of wildlife that have become extinct in recent times. List the name of each species on the chalkboard. Have the students report on the reasons for the extinction, if known.

**Figure 29–7.** Today there are 425 national wildlife refuges in the United States. People may not build, hunt, fish, or remove any wildlife from these refuges.

Although endangered animals receive the most attention in the popular press, many more plants are endangered. Some scientist estimate that 10% of the world's plant species are near extinction and another 15% could disappear by the year 2000.

### READING CRITICALLY
How do forests help provide water for rivers?

as watersheds

Lumber is usually classified as softwoods, such as pine and spruce, or hardwoods, such as maple and oak. Assign students to report to the class about the difference between hardwoods and softwoods and the uses of each.

## SCIENCE FACT

Bamboo, which is a grass and not a tree, can grow as much as 1 meter in a day.

Forest resources are an important part of the North American economy. Properly managed forests are renewable and can replenish themselves every 10 to 100 years, depending on the species and the climate. Wilderness areas are managed by being left alone. Forests may be managed for wildlife, recreation, grazing, pulpwood, or lumber.

because the forest is maintained; it is not chopped down all at once

**Figure 29–8.** Some forests are owned by large companies that harvest timber. National forests make up less than 20 percent of America's forests, but they contain more than 30 percent of the country's timber supplies.

Most of the larger forests in the United States are located in the West. Most forests are managed according to either the principle of sustained yield or of multiple use. **Sustained yield management** is based on harvesting timber at a rate equal to the rate at which timber is being replaced. By practicing sustained yield management, foresters can ensure regular supplies of forest products each year. Under **multiple use management,** forests are used for a variety of purposes besides growing timber. Wildlife protection, watershed management, recreation, and cattle grazing are examples of the many uses of forest lands.

New forestry practices may produce trees that grow at faster rates. For example, through genetic engineering, the Douglas fir can now be grown to harvest size in 40 years instead of 120.

Shorter growing cycles do have drawbacks. Trees that reach maturity faster generally have lower quality wood when compared to trees that mature at the normal rate. Trees that normally produce large amounts of leaf litter are cut down sooner when they have shorter growing cycles. This loss of litter decreases the amount of organic material in the soil, making it less fertile. Wildlife species that depend on dying or dead trees for habitat may disappear with such management practices.

Only about 20 percent of the earth now supports forests. If forests continue to decrease at the present rate, experts predict that 25 percent of the world's remaining forests will be lost over the next two decades. Increased management efforts and programs to plant new trees are needed to prevent the forests from disappearing forever. How can sustained yield management help prevent the loss of valuable forests?

active. Only about 4 percent of the energy produced in the United States today comes from nuclear fission.

Instead of splitting large atoms, **nuclear fusion** combines isotopes of hydrogen to form helium. Like fission, fusion produces large amounts of heat. Fusion is the source of the energy produced by the sun and other stars. The advantage of using fusion for energy is that very little waste is produced. However, much more research needs to be completed before fusion technology can produce useful energy. Fusion may be an option for producing electricity in the future.

Nuclear power was originally thought to be safe and relatively inexpensive to produce. As the first nuclear plants were completed, however, important questions about public safety, waste disposal, and processing nuclear wastes into nuclear weapons emerged. Today, these scientific questions remain unanswered.

# 29.10 Renewable Energy Resources

The amount and distribution of solar energy captured in the United States varies according to geographic location. Most states receive a large amount of solar energy each day. **Solar energy** is energy received directly from the sun. Solar energy is renewable because the sun is an unlimited source of energy. Solar energy must be converted into a concentrated form to be useful to humans. The best solar energy conversion device is a plant. For millions of years, photosynthesis has provided the food energy to support life on Earth.

**Figure 29–12.** These solar cells cover the roof of this house, but provide more electricity than the house uses. What happens to the extra energy? It is sold to the utility or power companies.

**Figure 29–13.** This wind farm in Altamont, California is able to generate large amounts of electricity.

Modern technology has produced many solar conversion devices. Solar energy in the form of heat can be concentrated using *solar collectors.* Collectors are usually made of glass and copper, although special plastics can be used. Solar heat energy is either stored as hot water or used to heat rocks. This energy can then be used for heating buildings or operating specially designed mechanical equipment.

Solar energy can also be converted into electricity. Solar cells, or *photoelectric cells,* have been developed that convert solar energy to electricity. When light energy hits a solar cell, electrons are released. These electrons flow through a grid. The flow of electrons is electricity, which is then carried through wires to power electrical devices. You may have a calculator that runs on the energy provided by a solar cell.

**Wind energy** is an indirect form of solar energy. Wind energy has been used for centuries to generate electricity. Not every location is suitable for wind-generated electricity. However, California and Hawaii now have large wind-powered electric systems. Figure 29–13 shows a "wind farm" where many wind generators operate to produce electricity.

**Geothermal energy** comes from steam that occurs naturally in the earth's hot interior. Geothermal energy plants have been built in many parts of the world. Geothermal energy is inexpensive, but it can cause some environmental problems. The hot steam and water

brought to the surface usually contain salts. These salts corrode equipment and result in air and water pollution. Careful research is needed to develop this resource.

**Biomass** is the term for all living matter and its products, such as wood and manure. Biomass energy can be used to replace some natural gas and petroleum. On a worldwide basis, wood biomass provides more energy for heating and cooking than any other source. If properly managed, wood will continue to be an important fuel. The biological process of producing methane gas ($CH_4$) from plant and animal wastes supplies energy in many countries.

## Section Review

1. What are three common fossil fuels?
2. Why is coal considered a "dirty" energy resource?
3. What are some negative aspects of geothermal energy?
4. What are some positive aspects of nuclear energy?

   THINKING CRITICALLY Why may solar energy be described as more economical than any other form of energy?

1. coal, petroleum, and natural gas
2. Burning it causes air pollution, and mining it destroys the land
3. Salts in the steam and water damage machinery and may result in water pollution.
4. It is clean and inexpensive to produce.
5. It costs nothing to obtain and is in limitless supply.

## CAREER

### Forester

**DESCRIPTION** A forester plans and supervises the growing and harvesting of trees. Foresters map forest areas, estimate the size of future harvests, and manage timber sales. They supervise and carry out measures to protect trees from diseases, harmful insects and other animals, and fire. Some foresters also supervise camps and parks found in large forested areas.

**REQUIREMENTS** A high-school student planning to become a forester should take biology, chemistry, and mathematics courses. Following high-school graduation, the student should attend college and earn a bachelor's degree in forestry.

**INFORMATION** Society of American Foresters, 5400 Grosvenor Lane, Bethesda, MD 20814

# INVESTIGATION 29: Comparing Drinking Water

*What is in your drinking water?*

## PURPOSE

To compare water taken from a well and water taken from an inside water tap

## MATERIALS

| | |
|---|---|
| test tubes (2) | distilled water |
| wax pencil | chlorine test kit |
| test-tube rack | medicine droppers (2) |
| 25-mL graduates (2) | microscope slides (2) |
| well water | coverslips (2) |
| thermometer | microscope |
| pH paper (wide range) | |

## PROCEDURE

1. Copy Table 1 onto a sheet of notebook paper. Enter all data from this investigation on your table.

| TABLE 1 | WATER TEST RESULTS | |
|---|---|---|
| **Test** | **Well Water** | **Tap Water** |
| Chlorine | | |
| pH | | |
| Number of living organisms | | |

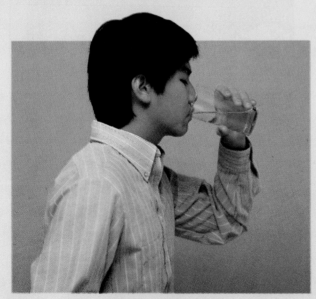

2. Label the first test tube "well water" and the second test tube "tap water."

3. Place 25 mL of well water into a graduate. Label the graduate 1.

4. Place 25 mL of tap water into a graduate. Label the graduate 2.

5. Pour 10 mL of water from graduate 1 into test tube 1 and test for pH. Record your results.

6. Rinse test tube 1 with distilled water.

7. Pour 10 mL of water from graduate 1 into test tube 1 and test for chlorine.

8. Repeat steps 5–7 using graduate 2 and test tube 2.

9. Make a wet mount of each sample. Examine each slide under the microscope and make a drawing of any living things that you see.

## RESULTS

1. Was the chlorine level the same in both samples of water? Answers will vary depending on the well.

2. Was the pH of the two samples of water the same? Answers will vary.

3. Why is it necessary to rinse the test tube after each test? some of the previous materials might change the test being done at this time

4. Did you find the same number and kinds of living things in each sample of water?
Answers will vary. There should be few types of living things in either water source.

## CONCLUSIONS
The tap water because there are no living organisms in it and the pH is neutral.

1. Which sample of water would you feel safer drinking?

2. Why do you think water companies put chlorine in drinking water? to kill any living organisms.

3. If there were a natural disaster such as a hurricane or an earthquake that damaged the public water system in your area, how could you treat your water to help make it safe for you to drink?
Boil it or put small amounts of chlorine bleach in it. (If bleach is added, the water should be allowed to "age" for at least 24 hours to allow the chlorine to dissipate.)

## Summary

1. Nonrenewable resources are those that cannot be replaced naturally once they have been used. **(29.1)**

2. Renewable resources are resources that can be replaced and reused in a relatively short period of time. **(29.1)**

3. Soil is formed over thousands of years from the weathering of rock and from the action of living things. **(29.2)**

4. Water is a renewable resource that is supplied through the water cycle. **(29.3)**

5. Recycling is a way to reuse resources. Minerals are examples of resources that can be recycled. **(29.4)**

6. Wildlife refuges are protected areas set aside to prevent the destruction of natural habitats. Many endangered species live in refuges. **(29.5)**

7. The principles of sustained yield and multiple use are used in managing many forest resources. **(29.6)**

8. Marine resources need to be protected from development, pollution, and overharvesting. **(29.7)**

9. Fossil fuels are the largest source of energy. Petroleum, natural gas, and coal are examples of fossil fuels. **(29.8)**

10. Nuclear energy is a controversial energy resource. Many questions still remain about its safety and its effects on humans and the environment. **(29.9)**

11. Technology is used to convert solar energy into many forms so that it is useful to humans. **(29.10)**

## Science Terms

On a separate sheet of paper, define each term in a sentence.

biomass **(625)**
endangered **(616)**
erosion **(612)**
extinct **(616)**
fossil fuel **(621)**
geothermal energy **(624)**
ground water **(613)**

humus **(612)**
mineral **(615)**
multiple use management **(618)**
nonrenewable resource **(611)**
nuclear fission **(622)**
nuclear fusion **(623)**
refuge **(617)**

renewable resource **(611)**
resource **(611)**
solar energy **(623)**
surface water **(613)**
sustained yield management **(618)**
watershed **(617)**
wind energy **(624)**

## Modified True-False

On a separate sheet of paper, mark each true statement *TRUE* and each false statement *FALSE*. If false, change the underlined term to make the statement true.

1. <u>Geothermal</u> energy is an indirect form of solar energy. F, Wind

2. <u>Erosion</u> is the loosening and movement of soil from one place to another by wind and water. T

3. When an area goes without precipitation for a long period of time, a <u>drought</u> may occur. T

4. The estimated supplies of minerals that may be obtained economically are <u>reserves</u>. T

5. Coal is a <u>metal</u> found in the earth's crust. F, fossil fuel

6. Global estimates of petroleum reserves <u>have not</u> changed much. T

7. Forests are managed by the principles of sustained yield and <u>recycling</u>. F, multiple use

8. A protected area set aside for wildlife is a <u>watershed</u>. F, refuge

9. Most marine wildlife live on the <u>coastal</u> areas. T

10. Many countries are replacing petroleum with <u>coal</u>. T

*(continues)*

## Multiple Choice

On a separate sheet of paper, write the letter of the term that best answers the question or completes the statement.

1. A mixture of minerals, rocks, water, air, and humus makes up
   a. sulfur.
   (b.) soil.
   c. fertilizer.
   d. particles.

2. Which of the following is not a fossil fuel?
   a. coal
   b. gas
   c. petroleum
   (d.) geothermal energy

3. A species whose numbers are low is said to be
   a. extinct.
   (b.) endangered.
   c. protected.
   d. limited.

4. Areas of land that store water and slowly release it are.
   (a.) watersheds.
   b. ground water.
   c. aquifers.
   d. reservoirs.

5. Cells that convert solar energy to electricity are called
   a. transformers.
   b. fusion.
   c. collectors.
   (d.) photoelectric.

6. The bottom layer of soil is called
   a. subsoil.
   b. topsoil.
   (c.) bedrock.
   d. humus.

7. Petroleum, natural gas, and coal are examples of
   a. biomass.
   b. energy.
   (c.) fossil fuels.
   d. technology.

8. A fossil fuel that is often found with petroleum is
   a. coal.
   b. phosphorous.
   (c.) natural gas.
   d. helium.

9. Steam that occurs naturally in the earth's hot interior is a source of
   a. solar energy.
   (b.) geothermal energy.
   c. wind energy.
   d. fossil fuel

10. A relatively unlimited, renewable energy resource that must be converted into a concentrated form to be useful to humans is
    (a.) solar energy.
    b. fossil fuel.
    c. nuclear energy.
    d. biomass.

11. Organic material found in topsoil is called
    (a.) humus.
    b. bedrock.
    c. subsoil.
    d. watersheds.

## Completion

On a separate sheet of paper, complete each statement by supplying the correct term.

1. A species that is no longer in existence is <u>extinct</u>.

2. <u>Rain forests</u> are home to over 40 percent of all species on Earth.

3. Forests that are used for a variety of purposes are said to be under <u>multiple use</u> management.

4. One wildlife management technique is <u>environmental</u> protection.

5. When forests are harvested at the same rate that they are replaced, _____ has been achieved. <u>sustained yield</u>

6. Solar energy in the form of heat can be concentrated using <u>solar collectors</u>.

7. Inorganic substances that occur naturally in the earth are called <u>minerals</u>.

8. Heat and steam brought up from beneath the surface of the earth produce <u>geothermal</u> energy.

9. Resources that are naturally replaced are called <u>renewable</u> resources.

10. Two nuclear processes used to generate energy are <u>fission</u> and <u>fusion</u>.

## Writing Critically

1. What impact would the total loss of nonrenewable resources such as petroleum and natural gas have on your quality of life?

2. What energy conservation techniques have become commonplace since the energy crisis of the mid-1970s? What other ways can you think of to conserve energy in your own home and community?

3. Do you think nuclear energy should be used to generate electricity? Why or why not?

4. **CHALLENGE** Erosion has become a serious problem in some parts of the country due to overuse of the land. Explain how erosion can completely ruin once prosperous farm land.

## Skill Reinforcement

The Skill Activity on page 620 describes how to interpret bar graphs. Using the steps outlined in the activity, make a bar graph for the following problem. Which country would be most quickly affected by a worldwide drought? Rank the countries from most affected to least affected.

## Research Ideas

1. On a global basis, deserts are growing at an alarming rate. Investigate the causes for this problem and identify some possible solutions.

2. Investigate how many and what kinds of endangered species live in your state.

3. **CHALLENGE** What is your state's energy budget? Find out how much energy your state uses and where the energy comes from.

4. **CHALLENGE** Cogeneration is a method of heating buildings using heat that results as a byproduct of the generation of electricity. Use your library to research cogeneration as an alternative energy source.

## For Further Reading

Caulfield, Catherine. *In the Rainforest.* Chicago: University of Chicago Press, 1986. This book describes the rainforests of Africa, South and Central America, and Asia. The reasons for the destruction of these fragile ecosystems are discussed.

League of Women Voters Education Fund. *The Nuclear Waste Primer.* New York: Nick Lyons Books, 1985. This book offers the nonexpert a brief introduction to nuclear wastes.

McKay, Alwyn. *The Making of the Atomic Age.* London: University of Oxford Press, 1984. This comprehensive text follows the development of the nuclear age from the discovery of the electron to the industrial development of nuclear power.

# OBSERVING PLANET EARTH

The photograph shows coastline and ocean, and something more—an oil slick many kilometers long. An oil-tanker captain is accused of washing out his tanks offshore. The evidence? A satellite image. Satellites can provide many kinds of information about the earth.

## Images from Space

Satellites can record images, not only of light visible to the human eye, but of the whole spectrum of electromagnetic radiation. An oil slick, for example, can be imaged from infrared or ultraviolet radiation. Satellite imaging makes it possible to identify features on the earth's surface through the energy they reflect from the sun or from the energy they release. Ice, rock, soil, and water all give off different radiation. Radiation from diseased vegetation and healthy vegetation, forest and grassland, warm ocean water and cooler ocean water is different also.

Satellite sensors pick up and record this radiation, transmitting their data to Earth stations. Images can be studied on computer monitor screens or in the form of photographs. Different wavelengths of radiation can be assigned colors, providing *false-color images*. That is, areas with different characteristics produce different wavelengths of radiation and therefore appear in different colors.

## Monitoring the Atmosphere

In recent years, some scientists have voiced special concern about the loss of ozone from the earth's upper atmosphere.

They believe this loss is caused by the escape into the atmosphere of fluorocarbons, gases used in products such as aerosol sprays and refrigerants. These gases destroy ozone.

In the mid-1980s, the Total Ozone Mapping Spectrometer aboard the Nimbus 7 satellite revealed that a "hole" in the ozone layer now appears over Antarctica every October.

False-color imaging shows algae blooms in the Atlantic (left) and mineral deposits in Nevada (right).

Scientists warn that this may be the beginning of more serious losses of ozone. Monitoring continues.

In the lower atmosphere, weather satellites transmit a constant stream of data. Satellites track vast storm systems that could spawn killer winds and floods. Experts estimate that thousands of lives have been saved by the early warnings these satellites provide.

## Imaging the Oceans

Weather satellites also measure infrared or microwave radiation from the water. They are used to map ocean surface temperatures. This data is used by fishers to locate schools of various kinds of fish, which are found in waters of characteristic temperature. The shipping industry also finds this data useful. Temperature boundaries can be used to locate currents that will speed ships on their way—or slow them down.

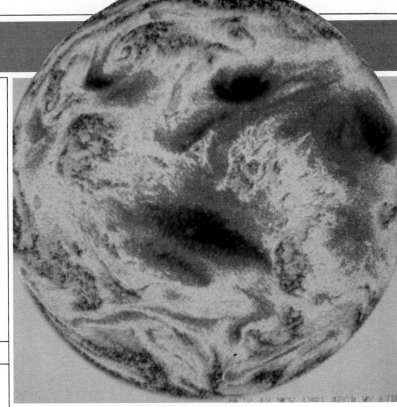

Landsat photographs help spot holes in the ozone layer.

Satellite *Tiros* in orbit

## Mapping the Land

The launching of the first Landsat satellite in 1972 made it possible to view remote regions of the earth. Improvements in later Landsats, and in the processing of their data, have provided increasingly detailed images. Agricultural experts in developing countries use Landsat data to assess land use and to find new ways to produce more crops. Over the past few years, Landsat satellites have been used to find resources—uranium deposits in Australia, tin in Bolivia, oil in the Sudan, and water in the Sinai-Negev peninsula. To find this underground wealth, geologists search for surface features, such as faults, that are often associated with particular kinds of resources.

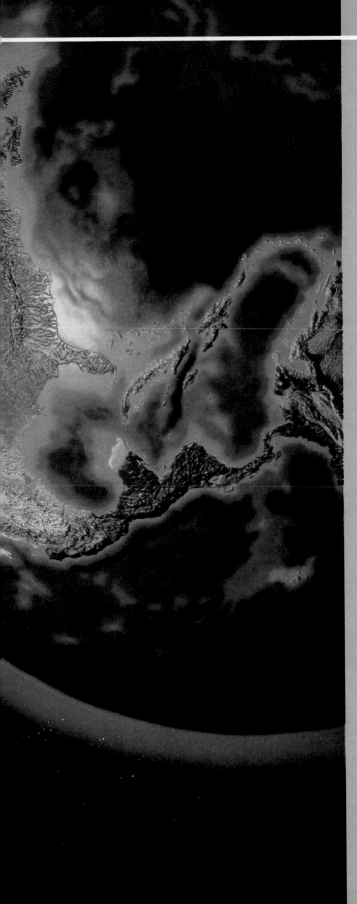

# Reference Section

## CONTENTS

# Safety Guidelines

Participating in laboratory investigations should be an enjoyable experience as well as a learning experience. You can ensure both learning and enjoyment of the experience by making the laboratory a safe place in which to work. Carelessness, lack of attention, and showing off are the major sources of laboratory accidents. It is, therefore, important that you follow safety guidelines at all times. If an accident should occur, you should know exactly where to locate emergency equipment. Good safety practice means being responsible for your fellow students' safety as well as your own.

You will be expected to practice the following safety guidelines whenever you are in the laboratory:

1. **Preparation** Study your laboratory assignment in advance. Before beginning your investigation, ask your teacher to explain any procedures you do not understand.

2. **Eye Safety** Wear goggles when handling acids or bases, using an open flame, or performing any activity that could harm the eyes. If a solution is splashed into the eyes, wash the eyes with plenty of water and notify your teacher at once. Never use reflected sunlight to illuminate a microscope. This practice is dangerous to the eyes.

3. **Safety Equipment** Know the location of all safety equipment. This includes fire extinguishers, fire blankets, first-aid kits, eyewash fountains, and emergency showers. Note the location of the nearest telephone. Take responsibility for your fellow students and report all accidents and emergencies to your teacher immediately.

4. **Neatness** Keep work areas free of all unnecessary books and papers. Tie back long, loose hair and button or roll up loose sleeves when working with chemicals or near an open flame.

5. **Chemicals and Other Dangerous Substances** Chemicals can be dangerous if they are handled carelessly.

   **Never taste chemicals or place them near your eyes.** Do not use mouth suction when using a pipette to transfer chemicals. Use a suction bulb instead.

   **Never pour water into a strong acid or base.** The mixture produces heat. Sometimes the heat causes splattering. To keep the mixture cool, pour the acid or base slowly into the water.

   If any solution is spilled on a work surface, wash it off at once with plenty of water. When noting the odor of chemical substances, wave the fumes toward your nose with your hand rather than putting your nose close to the source of the odor.

   **Never eat in the laboratory.** Counters and glassware may contain substances that can contaminate food. Do not use flammable substances near flame. Handle toxic substances in a well-ventilated area or under a ventilation hood. Do not place flammable chemicals in a refrigerator. Sparks from the refrigeration unit can ignite these substances or their fumes.

6. **Heat** Whenever possible use an electric hot plate instead of an open flame. If you must use an open flame, shield it with a wire screen with a ceramic

center. When heating chemicals in a test tube, do not point the test tube toward anyone. Keep combustible materials away from heat sources.

7. **Electricity** Be cautious around electrical wiring. When using a microscope with a lamp, do not place its cord where it can cause someone to trip and fall. Do not let cords hang loose over a table edge in a way that permits equipment to fall if the cord is tugged. Do not use equipment with frayed cords.

8. **Knives** Use knives, razor blades, and other sharp instruments with extreme care. Do not use double-edged razor blades in the laboratory.

9. **Glassware** Examine all glassware before heating. Glass containers for heating should be made of boro-silicate glass or some other heat-resistant material. Never use cracked or chipped glassware. Never force glass tubing into rubber stoppers. Broken glassware should be swept up immediately, never picked up with the fingers. Broken glassware should be discarded in a special container, never into a sink.

10. **First Aid** In case of severe bleeding, apply pressure or a compress directly to the wounded area and see that the injured student reports immediately to the school nurse or a physician.

    Minor burns caused by heat should be treated by applying ice. Immerse the burn in cold water if ice is not available. Treat acid burns by applying sodium bicarbonate (baking soda). Use boric acid to treat burns caused by bases. Any burn, regardless of cause, should be reported to your teacher and referred to the school nurse or a physician.

    In case of fainting, place the person's head lower than the rest of the body and see that the person has fresh air. Report to your teacher immediately.

    In case of poisoning, report to your teacher at once. Try to determine the poisoning agent if possible.

11. **Unauthorized Experiments** Do not perform any experiment that has not been assigned by your teacher. Never work alone in the laboratory.

12. **Cleanup** Wash your hands immediately after handling hazardous materials. Before leaving the laboratory, clean up all work areas. Put away all equipment and supplies. Make sure water, gas, burners, and electric hot plates are turned off.

Remember at all times that a laboratory is a safe place only if you regard laboratory work as serious work.

The instructions for your laboratory investigations will include cautionary statements where necessary. In addition you will find that the following safety symbols appear whenever a procedure requires extra caution:

 Wear goggles

 Flame/heat

 Wear laboratory apron

 Dangerous chemical/poison

 Sharp/pointed object

 Electrical hazard

# Laboratory Procedures

## Using a Compound Light Microscope

### Parts of the Compound Light Microscope

- The *eyepiece* magnifies the image 10×.
- The *low-power objective* magnifies the image 10×.
- The *high-power objective* magnifies the image either 40× or 43×.
- The *revolving nosepiece* holds the objectives and can be turned to change from one magnification to the other.
- The *body tube* maintains the correct distance between eyepiece and objectives.
- The *coarse adjustment* moves the body tube up and down to allow focusing of the image.
- The *fine adjustment* moves the body tube slightly to bring the image into sharper focus.
- The *stage* supports a slide.
- *Stage clips* secure the slide in position for viewing.
- The *diaphragm* controls the amount of light coming through the stage.
- The *light source* provides light for viewing the slide.
- The *arm* supports the body tube.
- The *base* supports the microscope.

### Proper Use of the Compound Light Microscope

1. Carry the microscope to your lab table using both hands, one hand beneath the base and the other holding the arm of the microscope. Hold the microscope close to your body.
2. Place the microscope on the lab table, at least 5 cm in from the edge of the table.

**Compound light microscope**

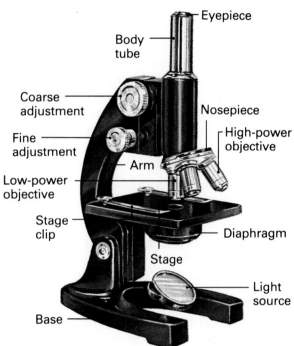

3. Check to see what type of light source the microscope has. If the microscope has a lamp, plug it in, making sure that the cord is out of the way. If the microscope has a mirror, adjust it to reflect light through the hole in the stage. **CAUTION: If your microscope has a mirror, do not use direct sunlight as a light source. Direct sunlight can damage your eyes.**
4. Adjust the revolving nosepiece so that the low-power objective is in line with the body tube.
5. Place a prepared slide over the hole in the stage and secure the slide with stage clips.
6. Look through the eyepiece and move the diaphragm to adjust the amount of light coming through the stage.

7. Now, look at the stage from eye level, and slowly turn the coarse adjustment to lower the objective until it almost touches the slide. Do not allow the objective to touch the slide.

8. While looking through the eyepiece, turn the coarse adjustment to raise the objective until the image is in focus. **Never focus objectives downward.** Use the fine adjustment to sharpen the focus. Keep both eyes open while viewing a slide.

9. Make sure that the image is exactly in the center of your field of vision. Then, switch to the higher-power objective. Focus the image with the fine adjustment. **Never use the coarse adjustment at high power.**

10. When you are finished using the microscope, remove the slide. Clean the eyepiece and objectives with lens paper and return the microscope to its storage area.

## Making a Wet Mount

1. Use lens paper to clean a glass slide and coverslip.
2. Place the specimen you wish to observe in the center of the slide.

**Wet mount**

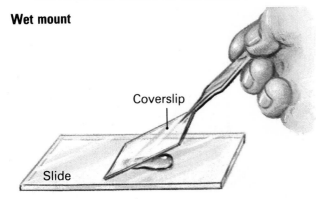

Coverslip

Slide

3. Using a medicine dropper, place one drop of water on the specimen.
4. Position the coverslip so that it is at the edge of the drop of water and at a 45° angle to the slide. Make sure that the water runs along the edge of the coverslip.
5. Lower the coverslip slowly to avoid trapping air bubbles.
6. As the water evaporates from the slide, add another drop of water by placing the tip of the medicine dropper next to the edge of the coverslip. (Use this technique also when adding stains or solutions to a wet mount.) If you have added too much water, remove the excess by using the corner of a paper towel as a blotter. Do not lift the coverslip to add or remove water.

## Lighting a Bunsen Burner

1. Before lighting the burner, observe the locations of fire extinguishers, fire blankets, and sand buckets. Wear safety goggles, gloves, and an apron. Tie back long hair and roll up long sleeves.
2. Turn the gas full on by using the valve at the laboratory gas outlet.
3. Make a spark with a striker. If you are using a match, hold it slightly to the side of the opening in the barrel.
4. Adjust the air ports until you can clearly see an inner cone within the flame.
5. Adjust the gas flow for the desired flame height by using the gas adjustment valve either on the burner or at

the gas outlet. **CAUTION: If the burner is not operating properly, the flame may burn inside the base of the barrel. Carbon monoxide, an odorless gas, is released from this type of flame. Should this situation occur, turn off the gas at the laboratory gas valve immediately. Do not touch the barrel of the burner.** After the barrel has cooled, partially close the air ports before relighting the burner.

## Using a Triple-Beam Balance

1. Make sure the balance is on a level surface. Use the leveling screws at the bottom of the balance to make any necessary adjustments.
2. Place all the counterweights at zero. The pointer should be at zero. If it is not, adjust the balancing knob until the pointer rests at zero.
3. Place the object you wish to measure on the pan. **CAUTION: Do not place hot objects or chemicals directly on the balance pan as they can damage its surface.**
4. Move the largest counterweight along the beam to the right until it is at the last notch that does not tip the balance. Follow the same procedure with the next largest counterweight. Then, move the smallest counterweight until the pointer rests at zero.
5. Total the readings on all beams to determine the mass of the object.
6. When weighing crystals or powders, use a filter paper. First weigh the paper, then add the crystals and powders

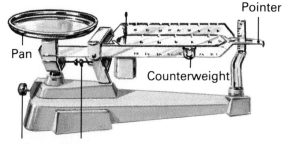

**Triple-beam balance**

Pointer

Pan

Counterweight

Leveling screw    Balancing knob

and reweigh. The actual weight is the total less the weight of the paper. When weighing liquids, first weigh the empty container, then the liquid and container.

## Measuring Volume in a Graduate

1. Set the graduate (graduated cylinder) on a level surface.
2. Carefully pour the liquid you wish to measure into the cylinder. Notice that the surface of the liquid has a lens-shaped curve, the *meniscus*.
3. With the surface of the liquid at eye level, read the measurement at the bottom of the meniscus.

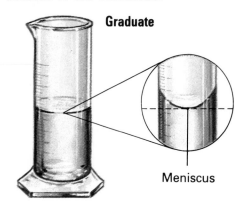

**Graduate**

Meniscus

# Using Mathematics in Science

## Scientific Notation

Scientists must often work with very small or very large measurements. Scientists use a decimal system called **scientific notation** to work with these numbers. In scientific notation, all numbers are written with just one nonzero numeral before, or to the left of, the decimal point. The magnitude of numbers is indicated by a power of ten.

For example, the number 123.4 in scientific notation would be written $1.234 \times 10^2$. The first part of the number (1.234) is never smaller than 1.0 and never as large as 10.0. The number of digits indicates the number of significant figures that were recorded when the measurement was made. The second part of the number ($10^2$) is a power of ten. The ten never changes, and the small numeral written above and to the right of the 10 tells you how many spaces to the right or left you should move

the decimal point. This small numeral is called the *superscript,* or the *exponent.*

**Example:** Write the number six hundred forty-five and two-tenths in scientific notation.

**Solution:**
- *Write* the number in decimal form.
  645.2
- *Write* the decimal number so that there is only one nonzero digit to the left of the decimal point.
  $645.2 \rightarrow 6.452$
- *Multiply* this number by the factor of ten needed to restore the decimal to the original number.
  $6.452 \times 100 = 645.2$
- *Express* the factor of ten as a power of ten.
  $6.452 \times 100 = 6.452 \times 10^2$

## SI Unit Prefixes

| Multiplication Factor | Prefix | Symbol | Pronunciation Term | |
|---|---|---|---|---|
| 1 000 000 000 000 000 000 = $10^{18}$ | exa | E | x uh | one quintillion |
| 1 000 000 000 000 000 = $10^{15}$ | peta | P | PEHT uh | one quadrillion |
| 1 000 000 000 000 = $10^{12}$ | tera | T | TAIR uh | one trillion |
| 1 000 000 000 = $10^9$ | giga | G | JIHG uh | one billion |
| 1 000 000 = $10^6$ | mega | M | MEGH uh | one million |
| 1 000 = $10^3$ | kilo | k | KIHL uh | one thousand |
| 100 = $10^2$ | hecto | h | HEHK toh | one hundred |
| 10 = 10 | deka | da | DEHK uh | ten |
| 0.1 = $10^{-1}$ | deci | d | DEHS uh | one tenth |
| 0.01 = $10^{-2}$ | centi | c | SEHN tuh | one hundredth |
| 0.001 = $10^{-3}$ | milli | m | MIHL uh | one thousandth |
| 0.000 001 = $10^{-6}$ | micro | u | MY kruh | one millionth |
| 0.000 000 001 = $10^{-9}$ | nano | μ | NAN oh | one billionth |
| 0.000 000 000 001 = $10^{-12}$ | pico | p | PEEK oh | one trillionth |
| 0.000 000 000 000 001 = $10^{-15}$ | femto | f | FEHM toh | one quadrillionth |
| 0.000 000 000 000 000 001 = $10^{-18}$ | atto | a | AT oh | one quintillionth |

# Metric Conversion Table

| Metric Units | | Converting Metric to English | | Converting English to Metric | |
|---|---|---|---|---|---|
| **Length** | | | | | |
| kilometer (km) | = 1000 m | 1 km | = 0.62 mile | 1 mile | = 1.609 km |
| meter (m) | = 100 cm | 1 m | = 1.09 yards | 1 yard | = 0.914 m |
| | | | = 3.28 feet | 1 foot | = 0.305 m |
| centimeter (cm) | = 0.01 m | 1 cm | = 0.394 inch | | = 30.5 cm |
| millimeter (mm) | = 0.001 m | 1 mm | = 0.039 inch | 1 inch | = 2.54 cm |
| micrometer (μm) | = 0.000001 m | | | | |
| nanometer (nm) | = 0.000000001 m | | | | |
| **Area** | | | | | |
| square kilometer (km$^2$) | = 100 hectares | 1 km$^2$ | = 0.3861 square mile | 1 square mile | = 2.590 km$^2$ |
| hectare (ha) | = 10,000 m$^2$ | 1 ha | = 2.471 acres | 1 acre | = 0.4047 ha |
| square meter (m$^2$) | = 10,000 cm$^2$ | 1 m$^2$ | = 1.1960 square yards | 1 square yard | = 0.8361 m$^2$ |
| | | | | 1 square foot | = 0.0929 m$^2$ |
| square centimeter (cm$^2$) | = 100 mm$^2$ | 1 cm$^2$ | = 0.155 square inch | 1 square inch | = 6.4516 cm$^2$ |
| **Mass** | | | | | |
| kilogram (kg) | = 1000 g | 1 kg | = 2.205 pounds | 1 pound | = 0.4536 kg |
| gram (g) | = 1000 mg | 1 g | = 0.0353 ounce | 1 ounce | = 28.35 g |
| milligram (mg) | = 0.001 g | | | | |
| microgram (μg) | = 0.000001 g | | | | |
| **Volume of Solids** | | | | | |
| 1 cubic meter (m$^3$) | = 1,000,000 cm$^3$ | 1 m$^3$ | = 1.3080 cubic yards | 1 cubic yard | = 0.7646 m$^3$ |
| | | | = 35.315 cubic feet | 1 cubic foot | = 0.0283 m$^3$ |
| 1 cubic centimeter (cm$^3$) | = 1000 mm$^3$ | 1 cm$^3$ | = 0.0610 cubic inch | 1 cubic inch | = 16.387 cm$^3$ |
| **Volume of Liquids** | | | | | |
| kiloliter (kL) | = 1000 L | 1 kL | = 264.17 gallons | 1 gallon | = 3.785 L |
| liter (L) | = 1000 mL | 1 L | = 1.06 quarts | 1 quart | = 0.94 L |
| milliliter (mL) | = 0.001 L | 1 mL | = 0.034 fluid ounce | 1 pint | = 0.47 L |
| microliter (μL) | = 0.000001 L | | | 1 fluid ounce | = 29.57 mL |

# Temperature Conversion

The top of the thermometer is marked off in degrees Fahrenheit (°F). To read the corresponding temperature in degrees Celsius (°C), look at the bottom side of the thermometer. For example, 50°F is the same temperature as 10°C. You may also use the formulas below to make conversions.

Conversion of Fahrenheit to Celsius:

$$°C = \tfrac{5}{9} \, (°F - 32)$$

Conversion of Celsius to Fahrenheit:

$$°F = \tfrac{9}{5} \, °C + 32$$

Freezing point of water      Boiling point of water

# Common Equations in Science

| | Equation | SI Unit |
|---|---|---|
| **Acceleration** (Chapter 9) | acceleration = change in velocity/time<br>$A = v/t$<br>$A = \dfrac{v_{final} - v_{initial}}{t}$ | m/s$^2$ |
| **Area** (Chapter 1) | area = length × width<br>$A = l \times w$ | Varies |
| **Average speed** (Chapter 9) | average speed = distance/time<br>$S = d/t$ | Varies |
| **Current** (Chapter 12) | current = voltage/resistance<br>$I = V/R$ | Amperes |
| **Density** (Chapter 3) | density = mass/volume<br>$D = m/v$ | kg/m$^3$ |
| **Efficiency** (Chapter 10) | efficiency = $\dfrac{\text{useful energy output} \times 100\%}{\text{energy input}}$ | Percentage |
| **Electrical power** (Chapter 12) | electrical power = voltage × current<br>$P = V \times I$ | Watts |
| **Energy** (Chapter 12) | energy = power × time<br>$E = P \times t$ | Varies |
| **Force** (Chapter 9) | force = mass × acceleration<br>$F = m \times a$ | Newton |
| **Kinetic energy** (Chapter 10) | kinetic energy = 1/2 mass × speed$^2$<br>$KE = 1/2\ mv^2$ | Joule |
| **Mechanical advantage** (Chapter 10) | mechanical advantage = $\dfrac{\text{resistance force}}{\text{effort}}$ | Varies |
| **Momentum** (Chapter 9) | momentum = mass × velocity<br>$P = m \times v$ | kg • m/s |
| **Pressure** (Chapter 11) | pressure = force/area<br>$P = F/A$ | kilopascal |
| **Potential energy** (Chapter 10) | potential energy = weight × height<br>$PE = w \times h$ | Joule |
| **Power** (Chapter 10) | power = work/time<br>$P = w/t$ | Watts |
| **Volume of a rectangular solid** (Chapter 1) | volume = length × width × height<br>$V = l \times w \times h$ | Varies |
| **Work** (Chapter 10) | work = force × distance<br>$W = F \times d$ | Joule |

# Five-Kingdom Classification of Organisms

## Kingdom Monera

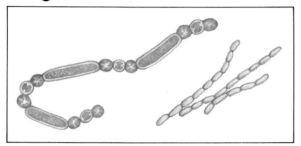

Organisms in this kingdom have cells that lack a true nucleus and membrane-bound organelles; mostly unicellular.

**Phylum Schizophyta:** Bacteria; about 2500 species including eubacteria (true bacteria), rickettsias, mycoplasmas, and spirochetes

**Phylum Cyanophyta:** Blue-green algae, or cyanobacteria; about 200 species

## Kingdom Protista

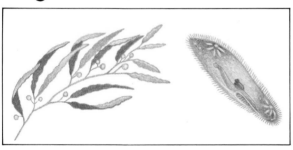

Organisms in this kingdom include a diverse group of unicellular and simple multicellular organisms whose cells have a true nucleus and membrane-bound organelles.

**Phylum Euglenophyta:** Euglenoids; about 800 species

**Phylum Mastigophora:** Flagellates; about 2500 species

**Phylum Sarcodina:** Sarcodines; about 11,500 species; includes amoebas

**Phylum Ciliophora:** Ciliates; about 7200 species; includes paramecia

**Phylum Sporozoa:** Sporozoans; about 6000 species; includes *Plasmodia*, the cause of malaria

**Phylum Chrysophyta:** Golden algae; about 12,000 species

**Phylum Pyrrophyta:** Fire algae; about 1100 species; major component of marine phytoplankton

## Kingdom Fungi

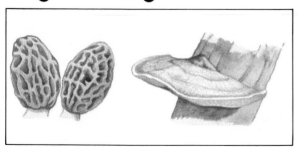

Organisms in this kingdom obtain food by absorption; most are multicellular, composed of intertwined filaments.

**Phylum Myxomycophyta:** Slime molds; about 600 species

**Phylum Eumycophyta:** True fungi; about 81,500 species

# Kingdom Plantae

Organisms in this kingdom are multicellular and carry out photosynthesis in chloroplasts; mostly land dwellers; cell walls contain cellulose; body has distinct tissues; life cycle of alternating sporophyte and gametophyte generations.

**Phylum Chlorophyta:** Green algae; about 7000 species; probable ancestor of modern land plants

**Phylum Phaeophyta:** Brown algae; about 1500 species; includes kelps

**Phylum Rhodophyta:** Red algae; about 4000 species; includes multicellular seaweeds

**Phylum Bryophyta:** Bryophytes; about 15,600 species that lack vascular tissues and true roots, stems, and leaves; includes liverworts and mosses

**Phylum Psilophyta:** Whisk ferns; a few species of seedless plants lacking roots and leaves

**Phylum Sphenophyta:** Horsetails; about 15 species of seedless plants with hollow stems

**Phylum Lycophyta:** Club mosses; about 1000 diverse species of seedless plants with leafy sporophytes

**Phylum Pterophyta:** Ferns; about 12,000 diverse species of seedless plants

**Phylum Cycadophyta:** Cycads; about 100 species of palmlike plants; gymnosperms

**Phylum Ginkgophyta:** Ginkgo; one species only; fan-shaped leaves

**Phylum Gnetophyta:** Seed plants similar to angiosperms; about 70 species

**Phylum Coniferophyta:** Conifers; about 550 species of gymnosperms; most species are evergreens

**Phylum Anthophyta:** Angiosperms; about 235,000 species of plants that produce enclosed seeds; reproductive structures are flowers; mature seeds are enclosed in fruits

# Kingdom Animalia

Organisms in this kingdom are multicellular and obtain food by ingestion; most are motile; reproduction is predominantly sexual.

**Phylum Porifera:** Sponges; about 5000 aquatic, mostly marine

**Phylum Coelenterata:** Coelenterates; about 9000 aquatic species; tentacles armed with stinging cells; includes jellyfish and coral

**Phylum Ctenophora:** Sea walnut and comb jellies; about 90 species; gelatinous marine animals

**Phylum Platyhelminthes:** Flatworms; about 13,000 species; includes tapeworms

**Phylum Nematoda:** Roundworms; about 12,000 parasitic species

**Phylum Acanthocephala:** Spiny-headed worms; about 500 species

**Phylum Rotifera:** Rotifers or "wheel" animals; wormlike or spherical

**Phylum Bryozoa:** "Moss" animals

**Phylum Brachiopoda:** Lamp shells; about 250 species, 30,000 extinct

**Phylum Mollusca:** Mollusks; about 47,000 species of soft-bodied animals; includes snails and clams

**Phylum Annelida:** Segmented worms; about 9000 species; includes earthworms

**Phylum Arthropoda:** Arthopods; at least 1 million species; includes insects, spiders, crustaceans

**Phylum Echinodermata:** Echinoderms; about 6000 marine species; includes starfish, sand dollars, and sea urchins

**Phylum Hemichordata:** Acorn worms; about 80 species

**Phylum Chordata:** Chordates; about 43,000 species that at some stage have gill slits and tail; includes fish, amphibians, reptiles, birds, and mammals

# Glossary

## Pronunciation Key

| Symbol | As In | Phonetic Respelling | | Symbol | As In | Phonetic Respelling |
|--------|-------|---------------------|---|--------|-------|---------------------|
| a | b<u>a</u>t | a (bat) | | ô | d<u>o</u>g | aw (dawg) |
| ā | f<u>a</u>ce | ay (fays) | | oi | f<u>oi</u>l | oy (foyl) |
| ȧ | c<u>a</u>reful | ai (CAIR fuhl) | | ou | m<u>ou</u>ntain | ow (MOWN tuhn) |
| ä | <u>ar</u>gue | ah (AHR gyoo) | | s | <u>s</u>it | s (siht) |
| ch | <u>ch</u>apel | ch (CHAP uhl) | | sh | <u>sh</u>eep | sh (sheep) |
| e | t<u>e</u>st | eh (tehst) | | u | l<u>o</u>ve | uh (luhv) |
| ē | <u>ea</u>t | ee (eet) | | u̇ | p<u>u</u>ll | u (pull) |
| | sk<u>i</u> | ee (skee) | | ü | m<u>u</u>le | oo (myool) |
| ėr | f<u>er</u>n | ur (furn) | | zh | trea<u>s</u>ure | zh (TREHZ uhr) |
| i | b<u>i</u>t | ih (biht) | | ə | med<u>a</u>l | uh (MEHD uhl) |
| ī | r<u>i</u>pe | y (ryp) | | | <u>e</u>ffect | uh (uh FEHKT) |
| | <u>i</u>dea | eye (eye DE uh) | | | ser<u>iou</u>s | uh (SIHR ee uhs) |
| k | <u>c</u>ard | k (kahrd) | | | on<u>io</u>n | uh (UHN yuhn) |
| o | l<u>o</u>ck | ah (lahk) | | | tal<u>e</u>nt | uh (TAL uhnt) |
| ō | <u>o</u>ver | oh (OH vuhr) | | | | |

## A

**abiotic** those components of an ecosystem that are nonliving  (587)

**absorption** movement of nutrient molecules through a membrane  (489)

**acceleration** rate at which the velocity of an object changes  (175)

**acceleration due to gravity** rate at which the velocity of an object changes due to the pull of gravity; on Earth 9.8 m/s²  (181)

**acid** any electrolyte that releases hydrogen ions (H⁺) in solution  (112)

**active continental margin** shoreline located along a boundary where two plates of the earth collide, characterized by high cliffs dropping to small beaches  (457)

**activity** measurement of the rate of nuclear disintegration, made by monitoring of the amount of radiation released  (133)

**adaptations** changes in body parts or in behavior that better enable an organism to survive in its environment  (529)

**air mass** large body of air with uniform temperature and humidity  (442)

**algae** protists that contain chlorophyll and are therefore able to make their own food  (496)

**alkali** (AL kuh ly) **metals** five elements having only one valence electron: lithium, sodium, potassium, rubidium, and cesium; categorized as Family 1 on the periodic table  (96)

**alloy** mixture of two or more metals, or of a metal and a nonmetal  (155)

**alpha particle** particle composed of two protons and two neutrons bound together  (128)

**alternating current** electric current in which the electrons move first in one direction and then in the other  (248)

**ampere** (AM pihr) unit of measure for electric current  (243)

**amplitude** one half the distance from the top of a wave crest to the bottom of a wave trough  (265)

**angiosperms** (AN jee uh spuhrmz) plants that produce seeds in specialized structures called flowers  (547)

**Antarctic Circle** area near the South Pole, latitude 66°32′S  (316)

**anther** on a flower the part of the stamen that produces pollen  (547)

**anticyclone** atmospheric condition characterized by a high-pressure center  (444)

**Arctic Circle** area near the North Pole, latitude 66°32′N  (316)

**area** measure of the surface of an object  (15)

**artificial intelligence** computers that are programmed to interpret information and to draw conclusions from that information  (294)

**assembly language** in computers, machine language instructions grouped into sets  (288)

**asteroid** small planetary body that failed to form into a planet  (339)

**astronomical unit** unit of measurement for distances between solar systems; one unit is the average distance of the earth from the sun—149,597,871 km  (335)

**atmosphere** the layer of gases that surrounds a planet  (419)

**atmospheric pressure** the weight of air; more force is exerted on the earth as the atoms and molecules become more closely packed near sea level  **(420)**

**atom** smallest particle of an element that has the chemical properties of that element  **(87)**

**atomic mass** an element's relative mass, based on the atomic scale; depends on the abundance of each of the element's isotopes  **(90)**

**atomic mass units (amu)** scale of relative mass units, established to express the mass of atoms and subatomic particles  **(90)**

**atomic number** number of protons inside the nucleus of an atom  **(89)**

**aurora** display of light in the night sky that appears when streams of particles from the sun hit the electrically charged particles in the ionosphere, causing those particles to glow in different colors  **(424)**

**average speed** total distance traveled divided by the time it takes to travel that distance  **(174)**

**background radiation** radiation from small amounts of radioactive elements found in the earth and in all living things, as well as cosmic radiation from outer space  **(129)**

**balance** instrument used to measure mass  **(18, 47)**

**barometer** device used to measure air pressure  **(421)**

**barred spiral galaxy** spiral galaxy in which the stars are aligned along a bar crossing the center  **(358)**

**base** any electrolyte that releases hydroxide ions ($OH^-$) in solution  **(112)**

**basic research** work performed to discover scientific principles  **(6)**

**beta particle** a particle, identical to a high-speed electron, with a single negative charge  **(129)**

**Big Bang theory** theory that the universe began in a gigantic explosion about 16.5 billion years ago  **(362)**

**binary fission** method of cell reproduction in which the original cell splits into two cells  **(505)**

**binary system** pair of stars revolving around each other  **(350)**

**biomass** all living matter and its products  **(625)**

**biome** large area of fairly uniform climate and vegetation  **(600)**

**biotic** (by AHT ihk) living components of ecosystems  **(589)**

**biotic potential** population's ability to grow in an environment and to reproduce itself without any limits  **(592)**

**black dwarf** lifeless, lightless cinder, the remains of a dead star  **(352)**

**black hole** collapsed star with enormous gravitational effect on nearby objects  **(354)**

**burster** neutron star that gives off powerful bursts of X rays  **(354)**

**CAD/CAM** computer-aided design and computer-aided manufacturing  **(293)**

**caffeine** stimulant found in many soft drinks, coffee, tea, and chocolate  **(576)**

**calorie** amount of heat needed to raise the temperature of one gram of water one Celsius degree  **(223)**

**cell** basic unit of structure and function in living things  **(481)**

**cell membrane** boundary around the cell controlling movement of material into and out of the cell **(482)**

**cell theory** theory that says cells are the basic units of structure and function in all living things  **(481)**

**cell wall** rigid, nonliving wall around plant cells that supports plants  **(482)**

**Celsius** (SEHL see uhs) scale of temperature measurement in the metric system  **(18, 216)**

**central processing unit (CPU)** actual computing unit, or information processing unit, of a computer  **(286)**

**centripetal** (sehn TRIHP uh tuhl) **force** force that causes an object to move in a circle  **(188)**

**ceramic** substance made from clay  **(160)**

**chain reaction** series of events that occurs when one neutron causes the fission of a single uranium nucleus, releasing two or three neutrons, which in turn cause two or three more uranium nuclei to split  **(138)**

**chemical bond** transferring and sharing of valence electrons between atoms  **(109)**

**chemical equation** equation that describes a chemical reaction  **(116)**

**chemical formula** short way of showing the composition of a compound  **(110)**

**chemical properties** characteristics that are observed or measured when a substance changes its composition  **(68)**

**chemical symbol** a shorthand way to represent an element, consisting of one or two letters, the first always being a capital letter  **(69)**

**chip** electrical unit that contains many transistors  **(26)**

**chlorophyll** (KLAWR uh fihl) green pigment found in plants  **(484)**

**chromosome** body that carries hereditary information from one generation of cells to the next **(506)**

**chromospere** 2500-km-thick layer of low-density gases found above the photosphere of the sun  **(330)**

**circuit** pathway for electric current  **(246)**

**cirrus** (SIHR uhs) **clouds** highest clouds in the troposphere, consisting of ice crystals; appear as fine, white strings  **(440)**

**class** category in the classification system of living things  **(493)**

**climate** average of all the weather conditions of an area over a long period of time  **(449)**

**climax community** stable community that is no longer undergoing succession **(593)**

**cloud** concentration of water droplets **(439)**

**cloud chamber** instrument that shows the tracks left by radiation **(131)**

**coal** solid fossil fuel formed from the remains of plants **(147)**

**cocaine** illegal stimulant that temporarily fills the individual with energy **(576)**

**coefficient** (koh uh FIHSH uhnt) number placed in front of a term in a formula; used to show the amount of a substance in a chemical equation **(117)**

**collision** the movement into each other of two plates carrying continents on their leading edges **(408)**

**colloid** (KAHL oid) clear suspension; light beams are visible in a colloid **(76)**

**comet** small planetary body formed from rock, ice, and metal particles embedded in frozen gases **(342)**

**community** all the living organisms in an ecosystem **(590)**

**complex machine** machine made from a combination of two or more simple machines **(208)**

**composite** combination of two or more different materials **(161)**

**compound** substance that contains two or more elements combined as a result of a chemical change **(79)**

**computer** electronic device that can store and process information **(26, 285)**

**computer network** a system of personal computers linked through telephone wires with other computers **(27)**

**computerized axial tomography (CAT) scanner** diagnostic tool that uses both computer and X-ray technology to map the structure of internal organs **(30)**

**conclusion** judgment formed from the results of an experiment **(10)**

**condensation** process by which water vapor changes into a liquid **(439)**

**conduction** heat transfer through the collision of molecules with one another **(225)**

**conductor** material through which electrical charges move easily **(242)**

**connective tissue** tissue that joins, supports, or protects other types of tissues **(485)**

**constellation** (kahn stuh LAY shuhn) group of stars **(350)**

**consumer** organism that does not make its own food **(597)**

**continental drift** theory stating that the continents have moved, or drifted, from other positions on the earth's surface **(402)**

**continental shelf** underwater shelf of land bordering the continents **(459)**

**continental slope** place where the continental shelf drops off steeply to the ocean floor **(459)**

**control** the part of an experiment that does not change **(9)**

**control rods** movable rods found inside a nuclear reactor that are used to prevent an uncontrolled chain reaction **(139)**

**convection** transfer of heat by currents overturning in liquids and gases **(226, 422)**

**convective** (kuhn VEHK tihv) **layer** layer of the sun that is 105,000 km thick; located above the radiative layer **(330)**

**coordinates** numbers used to locate an event **(54)**

**core** the sun's center, which extends about a fourth of the way to its surface; also the innermost part of the earth, which extends halfway to the earth's surface **(322, 329)**

**Coriolis effect** force that causes moving objects near the earth's surface to be turned from their original paths **(428)**

**corona** (kuh ROH nuh) layer of extremely thin solar gases above the chromosphere of the sun **(331)**

**coulomb** unit of measure for all electric charges, equal to the charge of 6.3 billion billion electrons or protons **(243)**

**covalent** (koh VAY luhnt) **bond** chemical bond formed when atoms share valence electrons **(109)**

**Cro-Magnons** (kroh MAG nuhnz) most direct ancestors of today's humans **(539)**

**crust** the rocky layer above the earth's mantle; composed mostly of igneous rock **(322)**

**crystal** structure in which the atoms are arranged in a regular order **(318)**

**cumulus** (KYOO myuh luhs) **clouds** thick, puffy clouds that look like cotton balls; caused by hot, humid, rising air **(440)**

**curie** unit of measure for radioactivity **(133)**

**current** amount of charge, in coulombs, that passes a particular point in a conductor each second **(243)**

**cyclone** atmospheric condition characterized by a low-pressure center **(444)**

**cytoplasm** (SYT uh plaz uhm) region between the nuclear envelope and cell membrane **(482)**

## D

**data** facts and observations gathered and recorded about a problem **(8)**

**data base management system** computer system used to collect and store information **(292)**

**decibel** unit to measure the intensity, or amplitude, of sound waves **(276)**

**deciduous forest** biome that develops in areas that have short winters and long growing seasons **(603)**

**decomposer** organism that obtains energy and releases nutrients from dead organic material **(598)**

**decomposition reaction** reaction that occurs when a substance is broken down to form two or more products **(120)**

**delta** triangular-shaped deposits of sediments found at the mouths of many rivers  (458)

**density** a measure of the amount of matter in a given volume of a substance  (48)

**desert** biome that receives less than 20 cm of moisture per year, and where temperatures range from 24°C to 32°C  (602)

**dew point** temperature at which condensation takes place; occurs at relative humidity of 100%  (439)

**diffraction** bending of waves around corners or objects  (277)

**digestion** process by which large, complex food particles are broken down into simple ones that an organism can use  (489)

**direct current** electrical charge moving through a circuit in one direction  (248)

**displacement method** measurement of volume determined by calculating the difference between the volume of a liquid alone and the volume of the liquid and a solid together  (18)

**distance** space between two points, measured in units of length, such as meters  (173)

**distillation** (dihs tuh LAY shuhn) process in which a liquid is boiled and the vapors are condensed into separate liquids  (73)

**DNA** nucleic acid formed in the nucleus of the cell  (513)

**doldrums** zone at the equator where there is no wind system  (429)

**domain** group of atoms that are coupled and lined up in the same direction  (256)

**dominant** relating to some factors on chromosomes; factors that cover up, or hide, recessive factors, often keeping them from being expressed  (511)

**Doppler effect** change in pitch caused by the motion of a sound source or of the listener  (279)

**drug** chemical that changes the way a person feels, thinks, or behaves  (574)

## E

**earthquake** violent shaking of the ground, caused by the sudden shifting and breaking of deep rocks  (394)

**ecliptic** (ih KLIHP tihk) plane of revolution around the sun  (335)

**ecological pyramid** relationships between producers and consumers  (599)

**ecology** (ee KAHL uh jee) study of how living and nonliving things interact  (587)

**ecosystem** (EE koh sihs tuhm) group of living and nonliving things that interact with each other over time  (587)

**efficiency** measure of how much of the energy input is available as useful energy output  (207)

**effort force** force exerted on a lever  (203)

**electrolyte** any substance that releases ions when it dissolves  (112)

**electromagnet** iron core inside a solenoid; has a current running through it  (255)

**electromagnetic induction** production of a current when a permanent magnet is moved near a wire  (255)

**electromagnetic wave** wave that can travel through both matter and empty space  (264)

**electromagnetism** (ih lehk troh MAG nuh tihz uhm) force acting on electrically charged particles of matter  (50)

**electron** (ih LEHK trahn) particle that is smaller than an atom and carries a negative electric charge  (88)

**electron cloud** model of the atom in which the electrons orbiting the nucleus can move within a specific region of space around the nucleus  (92)

**electronic devices** machines that use transistors  (26)

**element** substance that cannot be broken down by chemical means into simpler substances  (67)

**ellipse** flattened circle  (315)

**elliptical galaxy** disk-shaped group of stars with little gas or interstellar dust  (358)

**empirical** (ehm PIHR ihk uhl) **formula** chemical formula for an ionic compound  (111)

**endangered** state of a species that has few remaining individuals and is in danger of becoming extinct  (616)

**energy** ability to work  (197)

**engineer** (ehn juh NEER) someone who uses and applies the results of basic research to build new machines, to construct modern buildings and advanced roadways, and to develop new materials  (6)

**entropy** (EN truh pee) measure of disorder in an object or substance  (232)

**environmental resistance** sum of all the limiting factors in a population  (592)

**enzyme** chemical that helps in the digestion of food  (569)

**epicenter** surface of the earth directly above the focus of an earthquake  (394)

**epithelial** (ehp uh THEE lee uhl) **tissue** tissue that covers the body or provides a lining for its parts  (485)

**equator** imaginary line circling the surface of the earth halfway between the two poles  (310)

**equinox** (EE kwuh nahks) time when night and day are equal in length  (315)

**era** large division of geologic time  (373)

**erosion** loosening and movement of soil from one place to another  (612)

**estuary** shallow area where fresh water and salt water mix  (458, 602)

**evaporation** (ih vap oh RAY shuhn) process by which water changes into a gas or vapor at a temperature less than its boiling point  (74, 229, 437)

**evolution** adaptations and changes in living things over time **(374, 529)**

**exchange reaction** reaction in which ions are exchanged; usually occurs when one of the products of a reaction is removed from the solution **(120)**

**exosphere** upper portion of the thermosphere, extending from 650 km above the earth to outer space **(424)**

**experiment** test in which certain conditions are changed **(9)**

**extinct** description of a species that is no longer in existence **(616)**

## F

**family** category of classification for living things **(493)**

**family** in the periodic table, vertical column that contains elements with similar characteristics **(93)**

**faults** deep cracks in the earth's crust **(394)**

**fertilizer** any substance that helps plants grow **(162)**

**film badge** device that detects exposure to radiation **(131)**

**filtration** (fihl TRAY shuhn) technique used to separate the components of a mixture **(73)**

**fission** (FIHSH uhn) splitting of the nucleus of an atom, with the release of two or three neutrons **(138, 622)**

**focal point** one specific spot to which light rays are reflected **(269)**

**focus** point deep below the earth's surface where rocks break during an earthquake **(394)**

**fog** cloud that forms at ground level **(439)**

**food chain** flow of energy through an ecosystem **(598)**

**food web** interaction of plants and animals in food chains **(598)**

**fossil** preserved remains or traces of an organism **(374, 527)**

**fossil fuel** energy source that is formed from the remains of living organisms **(147, 621)**

**frame of reference** background against which motion is observed and measured; any set of points, lines, or planes from which coordinates can be measured **(55, 173)**

**free fall** state in which gravity is the only force acting on a falling object **(180)**

**frequency** number of waves that pass a particular point each second **(265)**

**front** boundary that separates two air masses **(442)**

**fulcrum** support point in machines **(203)**

**fusion** nuclear reaction in which the nuclei of atoms combine **(140, 623)**

## G

**galactic clusters** galaxies that are grouped together **(359)**

**galaxy** group of billions of stars **(357)**

**gamete** (GAM eet) cell involved only in reproduction **(507)**

**gamma rays** release of pure energy from the nucleus of an atom **(129)**

**gas** phase of matter with neither a definite shape nor a definite volume **(45)**

**Geiger** (GY guhr) **counter** instrument that measures radiation by the activity of electrons of argon **(130)**

**genes** factors that are located on the chromosomes; carry traits from generation to generation **(511)**

**genotype** (JEE nuh typ) genes on an individual's chromosomes **(512)**

**genus** (JEE nuhs) category in the classification system of living things **(493)**

**geologic time** time interval from the formation of the earth to the present **(373)**

**geothermal energy** energy from steam that occurs naturally in the earth's hot interior **(624)**

**gonads** organs that produce sex cells **(570)**

**graduate** container used to measure the volume of a liquid **(18)**

**granules** tops of rising columns of hot gases on the sun's surface **(330)**

**grasslands** biome containing prairies **(602)**

**gravitational potential energy** potential energy due to an object's position relative to the ground **(197)**

**gravity** force acting on objects with mass **(50)**

**great circle** any imaginary line that divides the earth in half **(312)**

**greenhouse effect** rise in global temperature due to an increase in carbon dioxide in the atmosphere **(428)**

**ground water** water found beneath the earth's surface **(613)**

**group** in the periodic table, a vertical column that contains elements with similar characteristics **(93)**

**gymnosperm** (JIHM nuh spuhrm) type of seed plant that produces seeds in special structures called *cones* **(546)**

## H

**habitat** place where an organism lives **(591)**

**half-life** time required for half the atoms of a radioactive substance to decay **(133)**

**hallucinogens** (huh LOO suh nuh jehnz) drugs that cause things to appear different from reality **(576)**

**halogen** a member of group, or family, 17, in which each element has seven valence electrons in its outer electron shell **(97)**

**hardware** physical components, or machinery, that perform computer functions **(285)**

**heat** energy that is transferred from one object to another because of a difference in temperature **(51, 223)**

**heat of fusion** amount of heat needed to change one gram of solid into one gram of liquid **(228)**

**heat of vaporization** amount of heat needed to change one gram of a liquid into one gram of gas  **(229)**

**hertz (Hz)** unit for frequency in the metric system  **(265)**

**heterogeneous** (heht uhr uh JEE nee uhs) mixture whose properties are not the same throughout  **(73)**

**high-level languages** languages for computer programs that look like everyday English  **(288)**

**hominids** early ancestors of modern humans  **(537)**

**homogeneous** (hoh muh JEE nee uhs) substance having the same, or uniform, properties throughout  **(68)**

**hormone** chemicals produced in one part of the body but which have an effect on another part of the body  **(572)**

**humidity** moisture in the atmosphere  **(437)**

**humus** (HYOO muhs) organic material  **(612)**

**hurricane** cyclone that forms over the ocean in the tropics  **(446)**

**hybrid** having one dominant gene and one recessive gene for a particular trait  **(512)**

**hydrologic cycle** cycle of evaporation and precipitation  **(441)**

**hypothesis** (hy PAHTH uh sihs) possible explanation of a problem  **(8)**

**ice ages** intervals of time when the earth's temperature drops and ice sheets spread over parts of the earth  **(379)**

**igneous** (IHG nee uhs) **rock** rock formed when magma cools and solidifies  **(320)**

**immune deficiency** condition in which the body loses its ability to fight off invading antigens  **(568)**

**impact crater** depression in a planet or satellite caused by a collision with an asteroid or a meteor  **(335)**

**inbreeding** breeding of two closely related individuals  **(534)**

**inclined plane** sloping surface that connects one level to another  **(205)**

**inertia** tendency of an object to resist any change in motion  **(178)**

**infrared radiation** radiation produced by molecules vibrating at frequencies higher than those of radio waves  **(268)**

**inner planets** planets Mercury, Venus, Earth, and Mars  **(334)**

**input devices** machines with which information is put into a computer  **(285)**

**insoluble** not capable of being dissolved in liquid  **(75)**

**instantaneous speed** distance an object travels at a particular instant  **(175)**

**insulator** substance that is a poor conductor of heat or electricity  **(225, 242)**

**integrated circuit** electrical unit that contains many transistors  **(26)**

**interference** interaction of waves in the same space  **(277)**

**interglacial age** period of time between one ice age and the next, when the ice melts and sea level rises  **(387)**

**internal energy** sum of the internal kinetic and potential energies of a substance  **(228)**

**invertebrate** (ihn VUR tuh briht) animal that has no backbone for support  **(550)**

**ion** (EYE uhn) atom that has lost or gained an electron, thereby becoming an electrically charged particle  **(108)**

**ionic bond** chemical bond between atoms in which atoms lose or gain electrons and become ions  **(110)**

**ionization** (eye uhn ih ZAY shuhn) process of gaining or losing an electron  **(108)**

**ionosphere** (eye AHN uh sfihr) layer of electrically charged particles in the atmosphere that extends from 85 km to 650 km of altitude  **(424)**

**irregular galaxy** galaxy with no particular shape, containing a disordered mass of stars, dust, and gas  **(359)**

**isostasy** (eye SAHS tuh see) a state of balance on the earth's crust that causes the thicker and less-dense material to float above the denser material of the mantle  **(323)**

**isotope** (EYE suh tohp) atoms of the same element that differ in mass due to varying numbers of neutrons  **(90)**

**jet stream** high wind circling both polar areas at 12 to 13 km of altitude  **(430)**

**joule** (jool) in the metric system, the unit of measurement for work  **(195)**

**Kelvin scale** temperature scale that has no negative temperatures  **(217)**

**kilogram** (KIHL uh gram) standard unit of mass in the metric system  **(18)**

**kinetic** (kih NEHT ihk) **energy** energy of motion  **(51, 198)**

**kingdom** largest, most general group in the classification system of living things  **(492)**

**laser** *L*ight *A*mplification by *S*timulated *E*mission of *R*adiation  **(272)**

**latitude** location defined in terms of position north or south of the equator  **(311)**

**lava** magma that reaches the surface of the earth  **(320, 398)**

**law of conservation of charge** principle stating that electric charge cannot be created or destroyed **(239)**

**law of conservation of energy** principle stating that energy can be transformed from one form to another, but energy cannot be created or destroyed **(52, 199)**

**law of conservation of mass** principle stating that although matter can be changed from one form to another, it cannot be created or destroyed **(45, 115)**

**law of conservation of momentum** principle stating that when two or more objects collide, the total momentum of the objects is the same after the collision as it was before the collision **(184)**

**law of definite proportions** principle stating that when two or more elements combine to form a compound, their relative weights are always the same **(81)**

**lens** curved piece of glass or plastic that refracts light to form images **(270)**

**lever** rod or bar that pivots around a *fulcrum* **(203)**

**light-year** distance light travels in one year **(335)**

**limiting factors** factors that limit the growth of a population **(592)**

**liquid** phase of matter that is incompressible, has a definite volume, but has no definite shape **(45)**

**liter** unit of measurement for the volume of liquids **(17)**

**lithosphere** outer layer of the earth, consisting of the asthenosphere and the crust, broken into 13 major plates and several minor ones **(405)**

**longitude** location defined in terms of position east or west of the prime meridian **(311)**

**longitudinal wave** wave in which the particles of the medium move parallel to the direction of wave motion **(264)**

## M

**machine** any tool that helps do work **(203)**

**machine language** commands used to program a computer **(288)**

**macromolecule** (MAK roh MAHL ih kyool) many hundreds of thousands of atoms joined together in one large molecule **(108)**

**magma** (MAG muh) liquid rock inside the earth **(320, 398)**

**magnet** any material that attracts iron **(252)**

**magnetic field** area around a magnet in which the magnet is exerting a force **(253)**

**magnetic pole** area where magnetic attraction is strongest **(252)**

**magnitude** measurement of a star's brightness **(349)**

**mainframe** computer that is big in physical size and in power **(289)**

**mammary glands** in mammals, glands that produce milk to nourish their young **(556)**

**mantle** 2900-km-thick layer of magnesium silicate minerals that surrounds the earth's core **(322)**

**maria** (MAHR ee uh) broad plains found on other planets and on satellites **(337)**

**marijuana** illegal drug **(577)**

**mass** amount of matter that an object contains **(18)**

**mass number** total number of protons and neutrons inside the nucleus of an atom **(89)**

**matter** anything that takes up space and has mass **(45)**

**mean solar day** time it takes the earth to rotate once about its axis; 24 hours **(313)**

**mechanical advantage** measure of how much the use of a machine multiplies the effort force **(206)**

**mechanical wave** wave that travels through different types of matter **(264)**

**meiosis** (my OH sihs) type of cell division that takes place only in reproductive cells, for the purpose of producing gametes **(508)**

**meniscus** curved liquid surface in a graduate **(18)**

**meridian** (muh RIHD ee uhn) imaginary line that runs through the poles and marks the east-west location of a place **(311)**

**mesosphere** layer of atmosphere that extends from 50 km to 85 km above the earth **(423)**

**metallurgy** science of separating a metal from its ore and preparing it for use **(153)**

**metamorphic** (met uh MAWR fihk) **rock** rock changed due to heat and pressure **(321)**

**meteor** burning particles of asteroids and comets, called *shooting stars* **(343)**

**meteoroids** fine mineral grains left over from passing comets or asteroids **(338)**

**meteorology** science dealing with the study of the atmosphere, especially weather and weather forecasting **(447)**

**meter** standard unit of length in the metric system; the distance between two lines marked on a platinum-iridium bar stored in Paris **(13)**

**metric system** system of measurement using decimals **(13)**

**microcomputer** smallest and least-expensive type of computer **(290)**

**microprocessor** CPU, usually contained on a single chip **(287)**

**microwaves** radio waves with the highest frequency and the shortest wavelength **(268)**

**minerals** inorganic substances occurring naturally in the earth **(318, 615)**

**minicomputer** computer that performs less-complex tasks, has less memory, costs less money, and occupies less space than a mainframe **(290)**

**mitosis** (my TOH sihs) process that results in the formation of two daughter cells that are exact copies of the original cell **(507)**

**mixture** two or more elements or substances that keep their separate identities **(72)**

**vertebrate** (VUR tuh briht) animal that has a backbone  **(550)**

**visible light** small part of the electromagnetic spectrum that can be seen by humans  **(268)**

**volcano** vent in the earth's crust through which molten rock, ash, and gases erupt  **(397)**

**volt** unit of measure for the potential difference between two points  **(243)**

**volume** amount of space that an object takes up  **(17)**

**vortex** whirling mass of air that forms a tornado  **(445)**

## W

**watershed** area that receives, retains, and slowly releases precipitation  **(617)**

**waterspout** tornado that develops over water  **(446)**

**watt** unit of measure for power  **(200)**

**wavelength** distance between one wave crest and the next or between any two successive troughs  **(264)**

**weak nuclear force** force found within the particles of the nucleus; involved in breaking apart some nuclei  **(50)**

**weather** state of the atmosphere at a given time and place  **(437)**

**weathering** breakdown of rocks and minerals under natural conditions  **(450)**

**wedge** simple machine made up of one or two slanted faces or inclined planes  **(205)**

**weight** a measure of the force of gravity acting on the mass of an object  **(48)**

**weightless** state of a freely falling object, or state of having no apparent weight  **(181)**

**wellness** highest level of health a person can achieve  **(574)**

**wheel and axle** simple machine made of an axle, which is a rod or a shaft, and an attached wheel  **(205)**

**white dwarf** a small, dim white star produced by the collapse of a red giant  **(352)**

**wind energy** indirect form of solar energy  **(624)**

**word processing** function of programs that create, produce, and store numerous types of documents on a computer  **(293)**

**work** force moving an object over a distance  **(195)**

## X

**X rays** light with the highest known level of energy; can pass through some solid matter  **(269)**

## Z

**zodiac** twelve constellations found along the equator  **(351)**

# Index

Boldface numbers refer to an illustration on that page.

# Credits

The positions of photographs and illustrations are indicated by the following abbreviations: (t) top, (b) bottom, (l) left, (r) right, (c) center.

**Cover:** Richard Henneg and Charles Jackson

**Frontispiece:** Ross Chapple

**Photographs:**
**Page vi**(tl), Bob Daemmrich/Stock Boston; **vi**(cl), The Granger Collection; **vi**(bl), Science Photo Library/Picture Researchers, Inc.; **vi**(br), James H. Carmichael, Jr./Bruce Coleman, Inc.; **vii**(t), E.R. Degginger; **vii**(b), Chemical Design Ltd., Oxford Science Photo/Science Photo Library/ Photo Researchers, Inc.; **vii**(t), Tom Bean/Alaska Photo; **viii**(c), Peter Menzel; **viii**(b), HBJ Photo; **ix**(t), National Optical Astronomy Observatories; **ix**(b), Photri; **x**(tl), M.I. Walker/Photo Researchers, Inc.; **x**(cl), John G. Ross/Photo Researchers, Inc.; **x**(bl), Runk Schoenberger/Grant Heilman; **x**(cb), Bob Gossington/Bruce Coleman, Inc.; **xi**(t), Grant Heilman; **xi**(c), Lowell Georgia/Photo Researchers, Inc.; **xi**(b), Phil Degginger; **xii**(t), Ronald F. Thomas/Taurus Photos, Inc.; **xii**(c), George Holton/Photo Researchers, Inc.; **xii**(b), James D. Wilson/Woodfin Camp & Associates; **xiii**(bl), Picture Group Photo; **xiii**(tr), Ed Reschke/Peter Arnold, Inc.; **xiii**(cr), Ed Reschke/Peter Arnold, Inc.; **xiii**(br), HBJ Photo; **xv**(bl), GECO UK/Science Photo Library/Photo Researchers, Inc.; **xv**(tr), Martha Cooper; **xv**(cr), Charles Harbutt/Archive Pictures, Inc.; **xv**(br), Michael Melford/The Image Bank; **xvi**(tl), Woods Hole Oceanographic Institution/Sygma; **xv**(cl), John W. Granholm, Biomechanics Laboratory, Brigham and Women's Hospital, Boston, Massachusetts; **xvi**(bl), Brad Nelson/University of Utah Medical Center; **xvi**(br), Tom McHugh/Photo Researchers, Inc.; **xviii**(tl), Karen S. Rantzman; **xviii**(lc), HBJ Photo; **xviii**(bl), HBJ Photo/Sam Joosten; **xviii**(r), HBJ Photo; **xviv**(tl), Focus On Sports; **xviv**(bl), Dan McCoy/Rainbow; **xviv**(tr), Phil Huber/Black Star; **xviv**(cr), Bobbi Kingsley/Photo Researchers, Inc.; **xviv**(bl), HBJ Photo/Ed McDonald; **xx**(l), David Parker/Science Photo Library/Photo Researchers, Inc.; **xx**(c), Jules Bucher/Photo Researchers, Inc.; **xx**(tr), David Brownell/The Image Bank; **xx**(br), CNRI/Science Photo Library, **xxi**(t), James D. Wilson/Woodfin Camp & Associates; **xxi**(tl, inset), George Hall/Woodfin Camp & Associates; **xxi**(bl), Laimute Druskis/Taurus Photos, Inc.; **xxi**(tr), William Hubbell/Woodfin Camp & Associates; **xxi**(br), Lawrence Migdale/Photo Researchers, Inc.;

**UNIT 1, Page 1,** Frank Foster; **2,** NASA/Jet Propulsion Laboratory; **4,** Paolo Koch/Photo Researchers, Inc.; **5,** Lucas Film, LTD; **6**(bl), Hank Morgan/Photo Researchers, Inc.; **6**(br), Hank Morgan/Science Source/Photo Researchers, Inc.; **8,** W.Y. Crich/Photo Researchers, Inc.; **10**(bl), James H. Carmichael, Jr./Bruce Coleman, Inc.; **10**(br), Red Catanach/Woods Hole Oceanographic Institution; **11,** Rev. Ronald Royer/Science Photo Library/Photo Researchers, Inc.; **13,** Ferrari North America/Hank Forssberg Advertising; **14**(l), James F. Pribble/Taurus Photos, Inc.; **14**(c), Ken Lax; **14**(r), Ken Lax; **18**(b), Ken Lax; **19**(b), L. Druskis/Taurus Photos, Inc.; **24,** John Madere/The Image Bank; **25**(t), The Bettmann Archive; **25**(b), HBJ Photo; **26(l),** E.R. Degginger/**26**(r), Michael Simpson/FPG; **27(l),** Dan McCoy/Rainbow; **27**(c), J. Barry O'Rourke/The Stock Market; **27**(r), Tom Tracy/The Stock Shop; **28**(tl), Gellner/FPG; **28**(cl), Dick Luria/The Stock Shop; **28**(bl), Eastman Kodak Company; **28**(tr), Phil Huber/Black Star; **28**(br), Bobbi Kingsley/Photo Researchers, Inc.; **29**(l), Paul Shambroom/Science Photo Source/Photo Researchers, Inc.; **29**(tr), Dick Luria/Photo Researchers, Inc.; **29**(br), Louie Psihayos/Contact Press Images; **30,** Science Photo Library/Photo Researchers, Inc.; **31**(tl), Science Photo Library/Photo Researchers, Inc.; **31**(tr), Science Photo Library/Photo Researchers, Inc.; **31**(bl), Montagnier/Institute Pasteur/Science Photo Library/Photo Researchers, Inc.; **31**(br), Phil Hart/Burroughs Wellcome Company; **32**(tl), Russ Kinne/Comstock, Inc.; **32**(bl), The Bettman Archive; **32**(tr), R. Stepney & M Aumer/Science Photo Library/Photo Researchers, Inc.; **32**(br), Hank Morgan/Rainbow; **33**(l), HBJ Photo; **33**(r), NASA; **34**(tl), NASA; **34**(bl), Lawrence Migdale/Photo Researchers, Inc.; **34**(br), Lawrence Migdale/Photo Researchers, Inc.; **35,** David Burnett/Contact & Woodfin Camp & Associates; **37**(l), Larry Lefever/Grant Heilman Photography; **37**(r), Seul/Science Photo Library/Photo Researchers, Inc.; **38,** HBJ Photo; **39,** Lawrence Migdale/Photo Researchers, Inc.; **44,** NASA/Taurus Photos, Inc.; **45,** Barbara Pfeffer/Peter Arnold, Inc.; **46,** HBJ Photo/Earl Kogler; **47,** HBJ Photo/Sam Joosten; **48,** NASA; **49**(l), Walter Hodges/West Light; **49**(r), Bob Daemmrich/Stock Boston; **50,** Leif Skoogfors/Woodfin Camp & Associates; **51**(l), Bob Straus/Woodfin Camp & Associates; **51**(r), Francois Duhamel/Sygma; **52,** HBJ Photo/Ed McDonald; **54,** HBJ Photo; **56**(l), HBJ Photo/Sam Joosten; **56**(r), HBJ Photo/Sam Joosten; **57**(t), The Granger Collection; **57**(b), Lawrence Migdale/Photo Researchers; **62**(t), Courtesy The Fairmount Hotel, San Antonio, Texas; **62**(b), San Antonio, EXPRESS-NEWS; **63**(t), San Antonio EXPRESS-NEWS; **63**(b), Chuck Beckley/San Antonio LIGHT;

**UNIT 2, 64,** Jan Hinsch/Science Photo Library/Photo Researchers, Inc.; **66,** A. Howarth/International Stock Photo; **68**(l), Michael P. Gadomski/Photo Researchers, Inc.; **68**(c), Clyde H. Smith/Peter Arnold, Inc.; **68**(r), HBJ Photo; **69**(l), Bruce M. Wellman/Stock Boston; **69**(r), Charles Marden Fitch/Taurus Photos, Inc.; **70**(tl), E.R. Degginger; **70**(tc), E.R. Degginger; **70**(tr), John Earle/The Stock Market; **72**(l), HBJ Photo/Ed McDonald; **72**(r), HBJ Photo/Ed McDonald; **73**(l), HBJ Photo/Sam Joosten; **73**(r), HBJ Photo/Sam Joosten; **74,** Liane Engelis/Stock Boston; **75,** Serraillier Rapho/Photo Researchers, Inc.; **76,** HBJ Photo/Sam Joosten; **77**(l), E.R. Degginger; **77**(r), E.R. Degginger; **78**(t), A.C. Spark Plug; **78**(b), HBJ Photo/Sam Joosten; **79,** Richard Ellis/Photo Researchers, Inc.; **80**(t), E.R. Degginger; **80**(b), HBJ Photo/Sam Joosten; **81**(b), HBJ Photo/Sam Joosten; **81,** HBJ Photo/Sam Joosten; **82**(l), HBJ Photo; **82**(r), HBJ Photo; **86,** Science Source/Photo Researchers, Inc.; **88,** The Granger Collection; **93,** The Bettmann Archive; **96,** E.R. Degginger; **97**(bl), HBJ Photo; **97**(tr), Jeff Perkell/The Stock Market; **97**(br), HBJ Photo/Sam Joosten; **99**(bl), A.W. Ambler/Photo Researchers, Inc.; **99**(bc), E.R. Degginger/Bruce Coleman, Inc.; **99**(tr), Tom McHugh/Photo Researchers, Inc.; **99**(cr), Lenore Weber/Taurus Photos, Inc.; **99**(br), Tom McHugh/Photo Researchers, Inc.; **100**(tl), E.R. Degginger; **100**(tr), Pictor/DPI; **101,** Laimute Druskis/Taurus Photos, Inc.; **106,** Lawrence Hughes/The Image Bank; **110,** Stacy Pick/Stock Boston; **111,** The Bettman Archive, Inc.; **112,** C. Vioujard/Gamma; **116,** Ivan Massar/Black Star; **119,** Steve Szabo/WASHINGTON POST/Woodfin Camp & Associates; **120,** E.R. Degginger; **121,** Glyn Cloyd/Taurus Photos, Inc.; **126,** Walter Dickenman/Sandia National Laboratories; **127,** Mary Evans, Picture Library/Photo Researchers, Inc.; **129,** Joseph Nettis/Photo Researchers, Inc.; **130,** HBJ Photo; **131,** John Giannicchi/Science Source; **132,** CNRI/Science Photo Library; **134**(bl), Science Photo Library/Photo Researchers, Inc.; **134**(br), Fermi Laboratory/Peter Arnold, Inc.; **136,** The Granger Collection; **137,** STERN/Black Star; **139**(r), Craig Hammell/The Stock Market; **140**(inset), Science Photo Library/Photo Researchers, Inc.; **140**(b), Lawrence Livermore Laboratory/Science Source/Photo Researchers, Inc.; **141,** Mark Godfrey/Archive Pictures, Inc.; **146,** Alan Zenreich; **147,** Shell Photo Service; **148,** Thomas B. Hollyman/Photo Researchers, Inc.; **150**(bl), Chemical Design Ltd., Oxford Science Photo/Science Photo Library/Photo Researchers, Inc.; **150**(br), E.R. Degginger; **151,** Yoav/Phototake/NYC; **152**(tl), Ira Wyman/Sygma; **152**(tr), Ira Wyman/Sygma; **153,** Paolo Koch/Photo Researchers, Inc.; **154,** Dick Luria/The Stock Shop; **155**(bl), E.R. Degginger; **155**(tr), E.R. Degginger; **156,** Bob Evans/Peter Arnold, Inc.; **158,** Art Resource; **159**(bl), Courtesy of AT&T; **159**(br), Bell Laboratories; **160**(tl), Art Resource; **160**(br), Garrett Turbine Engine Company; **161,** HBJ Photo; **162,** Paolo Koch/Photo Researchers, Inc.; **163,** Peter Vadnai/The Stock Market; **164,** HBJ Photo/Ed McDonald; **168**(t), Brad Nelson/University of Utah Medical Center; **168**(b), Dan McCoy/Rainbow; **169**(t), Fred McConnaughey/Photo Researchers, Inc.; **169**(bl), John W. Granholm, Biomechanics Laboratory, Brigham and Women's Hospital, Boston, Massachusetts; **169**(br), Alexander Tsiaras/Medichrome;

**UNIT 3, 170–171,** Steve Elmore; **172,**Camerique; **174,** Russ Kinne/Comstock; **175,** Camerique; **177**(both), HBJ Photo; **178**(l), HBJ Photo; **178**(tr, br), General Motors Corporation; **179**(t inset), Robert Alexander/Photo Researchers, Inc; **179**(b), Jerry Cooke/Photo Researchers, Inc.; **180,** Guy Sauvage/Photo Researchers, Inc.; **181,** NASA; **183,** HBJ Photo/Sam Joosten; **185**(l), HBJ Photo; **185**(r), Focus on Sports; **186,** NASA; **187,** Dickie Westray/Taurus Photos, Inc.; **188**(l), McNeill/Miller/H. Armstrong Roberts; **188**(r), PSSC Physics; **189,** Larry Smith/H. Armstrong Roberts; **194,** Rand McNally; **196,** Co Rentmeester/The Image Bank; **197,** Peter Hendrie/The Image Bank; **198**(l), Focus On Sports; **198**(r), Focus On Sports; **199,** Howard Edgerton/MIT; **200,** HBJ Photo; **201,** Robert J. Witkowski/Shostal; **203,** HBJ Photo; **204**(b), Margaret McCarthy/Peter Arnold, Inc.; **205**(tl), HBJ Photo; **205**(tr), HBJ Photo/Sam Joosten; **205**(b), Douglas Faulkner/Photo Researchers, Inc.; **206,** HBJ Photo; **207**(r), HBJ Photo/Sam Joosten; **208,** J. Kevin Fitzsimons; **209,** John Lawlor/The Stock Market; **214,** NASA/Science Source/Photo Researchers, Inc.; **217**(l), LLNL/Science Source/Photo Researchers, Inc.; **217**(r) all, E.R. Degginger; **218,** Yoav Levy/Phototake; **219,** Peter Southwick/Stock Boston; **220,** HBJ Photo/David Phillips; **221,** Frank Siteman/Taurus Photos, Inc.; **222,** HBJ Photo/Sam Joosten; **224,** HBJ Photo/David Phillips; **225,** Ronald F. Thomas/Taurus Photos, Inc.; **226**(tl), E.R. Degginger; **226**(tc), Jim Brandenburg/Bruce Coleman, Inc.; **226**(tr), David Brownell/The Image Bank; **226**(b), HBJ Photo; **227,** Karen S. Rantzman; **229**(all), HBJ Photo/Sam Joosten; **231**(l), HBJ Photo/Sam Joosten; **231**(r), HBJ Photo/Sam Joosten; **232,** Tom Bean/Alaska Photo; **233,** Charles Harbutt/Archive Pictures, Inc.; **238,** Dan McCoy/Rainbow; **242,** Erich Hartmann/Magnum Photos; **246,** Grapes Michaud/Photo Researchers, Inc.; **248,** HBJ Photo/Sam Joosten; **249,** Skip Barron/Comstock; **250,** Jules Bucher/Photo Researchers, Inc.; **252**(t), Russ Kinne/Comstock; **252**(b), HBJ Photo/Sam Joosten; **253,** Graig Davis/Sygma; **254**(b), HBJ Photo; **255**(l), Tom Tracy/The Image Bank; **255**(tr), Michael Melford/The Image Bank; **255**(br), Larry Voigt/Photo Researchers, Inc.; **257,** HBJ Photo; **262,** Chuck O'Rear/Westlight; **263,** Dennis Stock/Magnum Photos; **266,** NASA; **268**(l) both, S. Stammers/Science Photo Library/Photo Researchers, Inc.; **268**(r), Gabe Palmer; **269**(t), E.R. Degginger; **270**(l), Herb Snitzer/Stock Boston; **270**(r), HBJ Photo/David Phillips; **271**(both), David Parker/Science Photo Library/Photo Researchers, Inc.; **272,** David Parker/Science Photo Library/Photo Researchers, Inc.; **273**(tl), Di Giacomo/Masini/The Image Bank; **273**(tc), Royal Greenwich Observatory/Science Photo Library/Photo Researchers, Inc.; **273**(tr), Shelly Katz/Black Star; **273**(br), Larry Mulvehill/Photo Researchers, Inc.; **274**(t), David R. Frazier/Photo Researchers, Inc.; **274**(b), Chad Ehlers/International Stock Photo; **275,** Fundamental Photographs; **276,** Peter Vadnai/The Stock Market; **278**(both), HBJ Photo/Sam Joosten; **279,** Martha Cooper; **284,** Walter Bibikow/The Image Bank; **285**(t inset), Bill Gallery/Stock Boston; **285**(b), NASA; **286**(bl), James Israel/Shostal;

592(bl), Michael Fogden/Bruce Coleman, Inc.; 593(l), Wendell Metzen/Bruce Coleman, Inc.; 593(r), Judi Buie/Bruce Coleman, Inc.; 598(l), M. Stouffer/Animals Animals; 598(r), B.G. Murray, Jr./Animals Animals; 602, Ronald F. Thomas/Taurus Photos, Inc.; 603(cl), Jim Brandenberg/Woodfin Camp & Associates; 603(tr), Ronald F. Thomas/Taurus Photos, Inc.; 603(br), S.J. Krasemann/Photo Researchers, Inc.; 604(t inset), Wendy Neefus/Earth Scenes; 604(t), George Holton/Photo Researchers, Inc.; 604(lb), Joe Bilbas/Photo Researchers, Inc.; 605, Raymond A. Mendez; 610, E.R. Degginger; 611, David R. Frazier/Photo Researchers, Inc.; 612(l), George Hall/Woodfin Camp & Associates; 612(r), George Holton/Photo Researchers, Inc.; 613(t), Larry Miller/Photo Researchers, Inc.; 613(b), Ted Spiegel/Black Starr; 615, Reynolds Metal Company; 616, Townsend P. Dickinson/Photo Researchers, Inc.; 617, James M. McCann/Photo Researchers, Inc.; 618, Menschenfreund/Taurus Photos, Inc.; 619, Bob Evans/Peter Arnold, Inc.; 622(l), Brignolo/The Image Bank; 622(r), E.R. Degginger; 623, William Hubbell/Woodfin Camp & Associates; 624, James D. Wilson/Woodfin Camp & Associates; 625, Abigail Heyman/Archive Pictures, Inc.; 626, HBJ Photo/Sam Joosten; 630(t), Fred Ward/Black Star; 630(bl), Dr. Michael Recht; 630(br), Earth Satellite Corporation/Science Photo Library/Photo Researchers, Inc.; 631(t), Fred Ward/Black Star; 631(b), Photri; 632–633, Lionel Freedman.

From *Biology* Copyright © 1986 by Harcourt Brace Jovanovich, Inc. Reprinted by permission of Harcourt Brace Jovanovich, Inc.

From *Essentials of Health* Copyright © 1986 by Harcourt Brace Jovanovich, Inc. Reprinted by permission of Harcourt Brace Jovanovich, Inc.

**Illustrations:**
**Michael Adams** 3
**Susan Blubaugh** 15, 17
**Beverly Brenner** 396, 397, 405, 428
**Len Ebert** 277(b)
**GCI** 17, 18, 19, 271, 291, 592
**Robert Frank** 373, 378, 493, 594, 599(t), 599(m)
**Les Gray** 9(t, l, and r)
**Wendy Griswald-Smith** 510, 511, 547, 558
**JAK Graphics** 62(tl), 70, 107, 109, 110, 113, 115, 117, 149, 196, 202, 204, 207, 210, 215, 223, 228, 230, 311(l)
**Joe LeMonnier** 4, 53, 89–90, 91(l), 92, 94–95, 128, 133, 135, 138, 139(r), 175(t), 190, 226, 240, 241, 244, 246, 247(m), 247(b), 251, 254, 256(tl), 256(b), 258, 264, 265, 267, 269, 277(t), 286, 310, 311(r), 312, 313, 314, 315, 316, 317, 318, 319, 321, 322, 324, 331, 333, 334, 335, 338, 344, 356, 361, 363, 379, 386, 394, 403, 404, 407(t), 407(b), 422, 423, 425, 426, 427, 429(t), 429(b), 430, 440, 441, 442, 443, 444, 448, 449, 452, 459, 465, 467, 470, 512(m), 512(tl, bl), 513, 514, 518, 522, 575, 620, 621
**Ed Lipinski** 278, 280, 366, 371, 384, 408, 410, 432, 472
**Tom Powers** 349–350
**Fiona Reid** 420, 491, 555(r), 595, 596, 597, 601
**Glenn Shofield** 352, 355, 414
**Catherine Twomey** 482, 484, 487, 532, 540, 566(tl), 566(tr), 571, 572

A 7
B 8
C 9
D 0
E 1
F 2
G 3
H 4
I 5
J 6

A 7
B 8
C 9
D 0
E 1
F 2
G 3
H 4
I 5
J 6